CHALLENGE: A PROGRAM FOR THE MATHEMATICALLY TALENTED

GRADES 3-6

VOL. 4

Teacher's Edition

Vincent Haag, Franklin and Marshall College
Burt Kaufman, Broward County Public Schools
Edward Martin, Broward County Public Schools
Gerald Rising, State University of New York at Buffalo

Addison-Wesley Publishing Company

Menlo Park, California • Reading, Massachusetts
Don Mills, Ontario • Wokingham, England • Amsterdam
Sydney • Singapore • Tokyo • Madrid • Bogotá
Santiago • San Juan

Acknowledgments and Dedication

The lineage of the central ideas of this series may be traced to the *Elementary Mathematics* texts developed by the Comprehensive School Mathematics Program (CSMP), a project with which this author team was associated. While we and many others contributed to CSMP, all who know that project would agree that its central ideas about elementary school mathematics curriculum as well as the development of those ideas into creative classroom activities are directly attributable to Frédérique and Georges Papy.

To Georges and Frédérique, respected colleagues who led the way, we therefore dedicate these books.

This book is published by the Addison-Wesley Innovative Division.

Design: Signature Design Associates

Addison-Wesley Publishing Company
Menlo Park, California • Reading, Massachusetts
Don Mills, Ontario • Wokingham, England • Amsterdam
Sydney • Singapore • Tokyo • Madrid • Bogotá
Santiago • San Juan

ISBN-0-201-20170-4
ABCDEFGHIJKL-WR-89876

C O N T E N T S

To the Teacher

Welcome to the continuation of an exciting intellectual and pedagogical experience. Based on our own classroom use of the activities in this series, we believe that with their help you can broaden the mathematical horizons of bright children and in the process extend your own view of what such students (and you) can do.

In this program you play the central role. Our aim, as minority partners in your enterprise, is to continue providing you with the strongest possible support. The experiences we describe in this series are quite different from yet highly supportive of those your students are encountering in their regular mathematics program. As you have found, they include novel situations, games, detective stories, and puzzles involving calculators, all of which are designed to induce logical thinking, strategic reasoning, estimation, mental arithmetic, and—we believe most importantly—genuine problem solving. No matter how careful our descriptions, however, you are ultimately the one who must interpret these materials intelligently, with compassion for and dedication to your students. Only you can know them as individuals.

We remind you that the activities we provide in this series are aimed at students who are in the upper 5 to 10 percent in ability in their age group who are highly motivated. Some of you are working with a more select group of students, perhaps a very few chosen from a large school district in a community that places high value on educational achievement. In such a case you may have found that you can move somewhat more rapidly through this program once you and your students have become acquainted with the style and intentions of the activities. Equally, others of you could well be working with a group of students some of whom fall below your expectations. With such a class you are more likely to have found constraints than freedom, and you probably adapted carefully to the needs of unusually bright students while easing your pace somewhat for the benefit of your weaker students.

The following comments might be useful if this is your first experience with the series.

Preparation for Teachers New to the Program

The best preparation for teaching Volume 4 of this series is, of course teaching Volume 1, Volume 2, or Volume 3. Observing Volume 1, 2, or 3 instruction would also help. You may find yourself teaching Volume 4 to students who studied Volumes 2 and 3 with other teachers. If you take your task seriously and prepare adequately for this instruction, you should have little difficulty. You will find that the lesson dialogs will provide strong support for your teaching until you become more secure with the materials and can become less tied to the specifics of the dialogs.

There are certain tasks you should undertake before you present the first lesson to your class. Familiarize yourself with the basic pedagogical tools of the program by carefully studying selected introductory activities from Volume 1 and then browsing through Volumes 2 and 3. The following are the topics together with activities in Volume 1 that will give you necessary background.

Topic	Activity Number in Volume 1
Minicomputer	1, 2, 6, 9, 10, 14, 43, 44, 46, 49
Negative numbers	11, 12, 13
Arrow diagrams	47, 48
Multiples and divisors	19, 20
Detective stories	5
String diagrams	4, 7
Minicomputer Golf	64
Minicomputer Tug-of-War	24

You may wish to explore the given series of activities immediately before you teach a lesson on that topic.

The above review we have suggested will give you a *general* understanding of teaching devices you will be using. You will find that your students will know still more than you at the outset. We urge you to be open with them about this. A statement like the following will help you gain the support of your students: "You all know that M . . . is not available to continue teaching this program. The content is new to me. Although I have studied it carefully, I will need to rely on each of you to share with me and your classmates your understanding of what you have studied."

Selection of the Students

If you are involved in the selection process, we urge you to gather all available information about the pool of students from which classes are to be drawn. Look at students' scores on ability and achievement tests, but also be alert to the recommendations of teachers and counselors who have previously worked with the students. Screening by testing may be necessary in some communities in order to provide an objective basis for decisions about participation. If this is the case, you should recognize the arbitrariness of such a selection process and seek to make it as accurate as possible. We urge you to carry out any such testing in the spring, when students have settled down to their academic endeavors; testing during the first week of school can lead to serious selection errors.

Recognizing these selection problems, what is desired? Most importantly, you want students who have demonstrated their ability to learn and to use mathematical ideas. This usually includes but is not the same as the ability to compute with skill and accuracy. Suitable students will probably have achieved well in the regular school mathematics program. Beyond this you want students who show interest in mathematics and general ability to respond to school programs. Having said that, we recognize that good teachers should sometimes take risks. You or your colleagues may, for example, identify a child who shows some evidence of talent even though test scores may not bear this out. Such a student may be bored or "turned off" by regular school instruction and testing. You may wish to take a chance by including such a child. Particularly in communities where some children come from intellectually impoverished homes, a willingness to take such risks is often richly rewarded.

Once students have been selected for a special class (and especially after this selection has been communicated to parents), you may find it diffucult to guide them out of your program even if it later becomes apparent that the program is not suited to them. For this reason we recommend that you make it clear at the time of selection what will be expected of students in the program. We have found the key expectation to be that students do the assigned work with reasonable care and accuracy. If you and your school administrators communicate such a requirement clearly at the outset, you will find it much easier to handle those few cases in which it becomes clear that a student is out of place in the program.

Organization of the Program

Volumes 1 and 2 of this series are designed for use with gifted third-grade students in a supplementary instructional program, and Volumes 3 and 4 for gifted fourth-grade students who have completed Volumes 1 and 2. However, gifted students who miss the opportunity offered by this program while they are in third grade can nevertheless derive considerable benefit from starting work on Volumes 1 and 2 in fourth or fifth grade.
activities per session. A second option is to teach four half-hour sessions per week, using one activity per session. Other options include altering the rate at which the activities are taught. For example, you might teach only two activities per week, in which case you would complete one rather than two volumes per year.

The contents of this series have been arranged in a spiral fashion, so that by teaching the activities in the order in which they appear in the guides, you will repeatedly be reviewing and extending ideas that have been encountered earlier in the program. One consequence of this system is that you need feel no compulsion to rush through the last few activities of a volume in order to complete it by the end of the school year. We suggest that you simply pick up in September where you left off in June.

Because of the greater ability of its intended audience, we have found that this content may be taught in a "pull-out" format, in which the students study with their regular mathematics class for three days each week and participate separately in this program during the other two. Students with whom we have worked had no difficulty keeping abreast of their less able classmates when following this schedule. Alternatively, the program may be taught as a supplement to the full regular course. It is important to note, however, that under no circumstances should these materials be considered a substitute for the regular school program.

Use in the Classroom

You will find the detailed descriptions of the activities to be particularly useful when you teach this content for the first time. They tell you what materials are needed and what worksheets are appropriate. In many cases, examples of possible teacher-student dialogs based on our classroom tests are also provided. Of course, we urge you to modify and extend these conversations as you become increasingly comfortable with the ideas of the program yourself; in the meantime, the detailed descriptions will provide you with a good basis for your teaching.

The activities in this series are designed for full-group participation, usually followed by independent or small-group work on the worksheets. The L-worksheets are associated directly with specific activities and should be used in this way. The A-worksheets may be used with those students whose competence and speed of working on the L-worksheets indicate they need an additional challenge.

The H-worksheets (together with any A- and L-worksheets not covered in class) are designed for homework. We find that gifted children and their parents expect this kind of out-of-class work. You are urged to correct and return all completed worksheets. Some of you may want to involve your students in this process. We have found that this participation can lead to a better standard of work on the part of the students. Some of them are even more concerned about impressing their peers than they are about impressing you! Keys to the worksheets are provided in a separate section at the end of this guide.

Unlike the A- and L-worksheets, which are associated with specific activities, the H-worksheets provide continuity by ranging over the content of the program, thereby keeping earlier concepts alive. We recommend that a normal homework assignment consist of one or two worksheets per activity.

Some Teaching Suggestions

You will be pleased with the way your students respond to these challenging materials. Try to include all the students in your group activities. One of the many ways to do this is to ask follow-up questions such as, "Is that right, Susan?" or "What do you think, Donny?" Use such questions after both correct and incorrect answers.

One very important outcome of the use of worksheets should be that the students learn to follow directions. When you assign the first few you may wish to ask students to read the simple directions out loud and then check for understanding. The need for reading aloud should diminish as the students become accustomed to the format.

You will probably wish to encourage neatness as well as accuracy and completeness. Use your judgment here, because you want students to correct false starts, which may mean crossing out part of their work. On the other hand, where sloppy work prevents students from solving problems, you will wish to be more severe.

Able students such as these often have a history of being rewarded for any response they give, be it right or wrong. (Wrong answers are often considered cute or funny.) Such unhelpful reinforcement can create serious problems for such students and for you in teaching them. Early in your work with these materials you may find some students who are content with giving you any answer just for the glory of being the first to respond. We urge you to deal with such answers directly but sympathetically. One way to do this is to ask, "Why do you think that?" Very often, thinking about a problem will lead directly to the correct answer. Now you can say, "Remember, everyone, that we're after the correct answer, not the fastest answer. Think before you say anything." Some students will need similar guidance about thoughtlessly dashing off their answers to the worksheets.

Methods Used by the Program

In our view, the strength of these materials lies in the teaching devices they use: strings, arrows, the Papy Minicomputer, detective stories, and so on. These devices may best be described as pedagogical languages in that they break down communication barriers. In so doing, they make additional creative and stimulating problems accessible to your students, thus improving their chances of realizing their full potential. To prove this to yourself, pick one of the worksheets at random and try to communicate the same problems unambiguously without using such pedagogical languages. You will invariably find that the same kinds of questions become at best wordy and cumbersome.

There is an important principle here. When we teach, we should ask ourselves not only, "Are the students able to perform?" but also, "Do the students understand the task?" When tasks are well-defined in language the students understand, good performance is much more likely.

ACTIVITY 1
String Pictures 1

Materials Needed
Teacher: Colored chalk
Students: Paper and colored pencils

Draw the following string picture on the board:

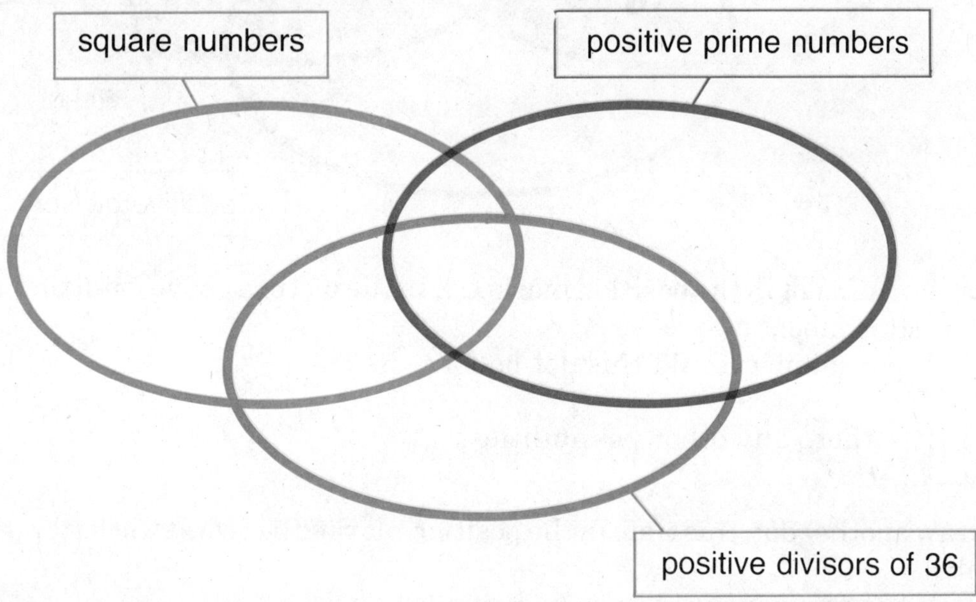

T: Who can tell me some numbers that belong in the blue string?
S: *4, 9, 16.*
Accept any square number: 1, 4, 9, 16, 25, 36, 49, 64, 81, 100, 121, ... Some students, to show off, will give large numbers such as 1,369. If this happens you can continue as follows:
T: What number must you multiply by itself to get 1,369?
S: *37.*
T: Will someone with a calculator check that?
S: *37 × 37 is 1,369.*
T: Very good.
T: Now can you tell me some numbers that belong in the red string?
S: *7, 13.*
Accept any prime number: 2, 3, 5, 7, 11, 13, 17, ...
T: A prime between 30 and 40?
S: *31.*
T: Another?
S: *37.*

1

T: Now I'd like some numbers that belong in the green string.
S: *4, 9.*
Accept any divisor of 36, that is, any of the nine numbers: 1, 2, 3, 4, 6, 9, 12, 18, 36.
T: Where does the number 49 belong?
Let a student come to the board and draw and label a dot for 49. In a similar fashion, ask students to place dots for 9, 5, and 50.

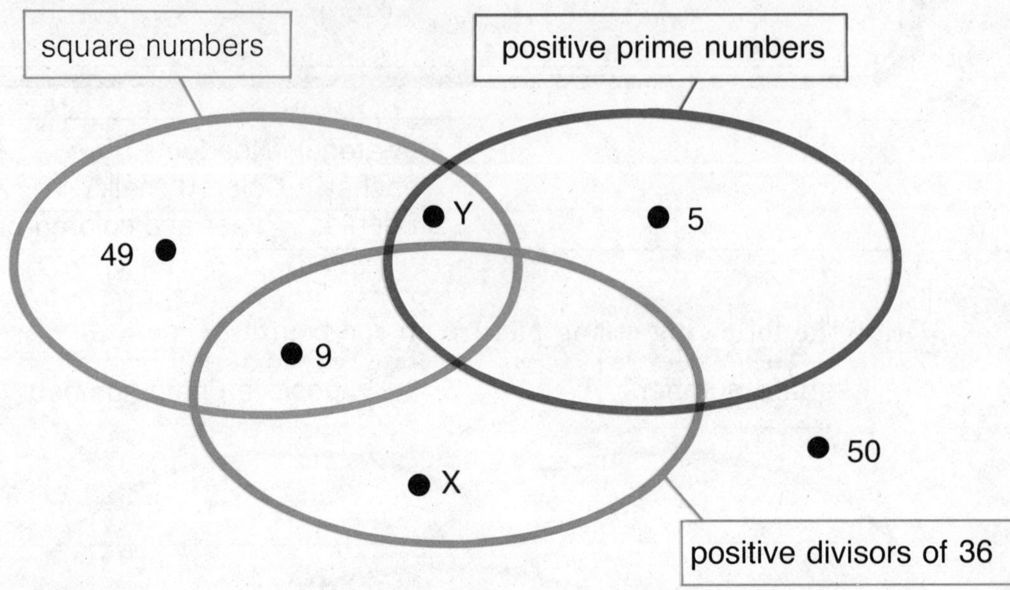

Draw a new dot in the position marked X in the picture above, omitting the letter label.
T: What number could this dot be for?
S: *6.*
T: Are there any other possibilities?
S: *12, 18.*

Draw another dot, this time in the position marked Y. (Omit the letter label.)
T: What number could this dot be for?
In fact, the region that includes Y is empty, although students will often make wild suggestions to avoid not being able to answer the question. If they do, ask them to convince you by checking all three strings. For example:
S: *1.*
T: Does 1 belong in the blue string?
S: *Yes, because 1 is 1 times 1.*
T: Does 1 belong in the green string?
S: *Yes, because 1 is a positive divisor of 36.*
T: Does 1 belong in the red string?
S: *No, because 1 is* not *a prime.*
T: Where should *1* be placed?
S: *In the same region as 9.*
Point to dot Y again.
T: Now can anyone give me a number for this dot?
Students will soon agree that there are no dots in this region. Let one of them erase the dot and hatch the empty region, as shown below. If

the student does not hatch the entire region, ask another volunteer to give assistance.

T: Is there a way of drawing the strings so that we don't have to use hatching?

While students work on this task, label the original picture like this:

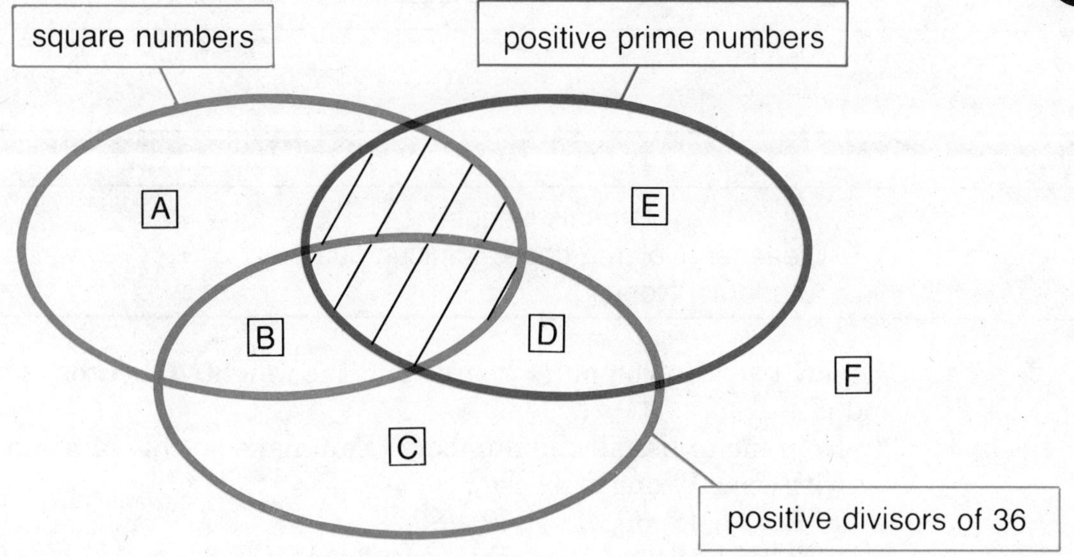

Students should suggest a picture something like this:

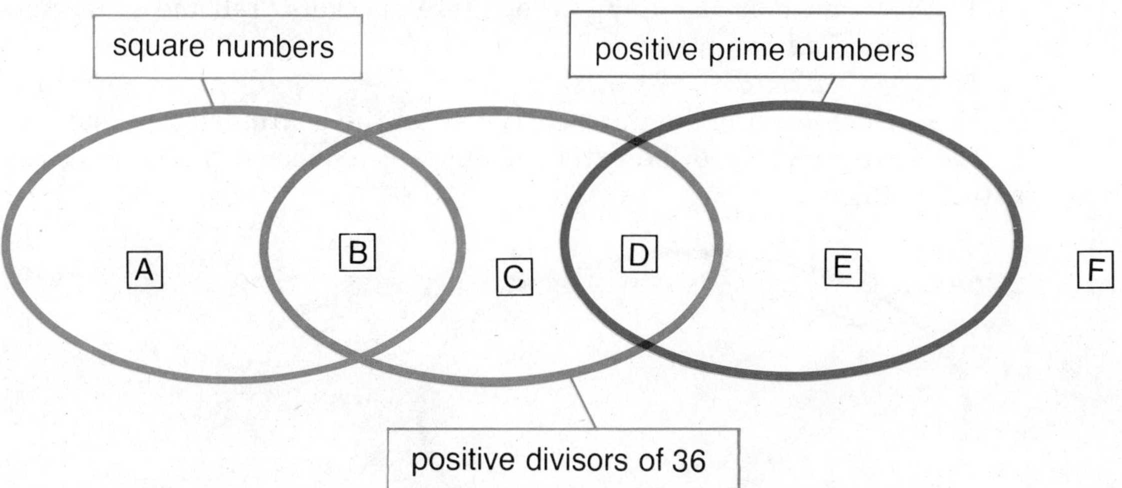

Let volunteers label the six regions as shown, to agree with the labels in the original picture.

Resources Available
For out-of-class use: Any H-worksheet up through H3

ACTIVITY 2
String Pictures 2

Materials Needed
Teacher: Colored chalk, Minicomputer kit
Students: None

Display two Minicomputer boards and the weighted checkers 2, 3, 4, 5, and 6.

T: Help me to list all the numbers I can make on this Minicomputer with exactly one 6-checker.

S: *6, 12, 24, 48, 60, 120, 240, 480.*

T: What if I allowed more than two boards?

S: *Then you could also make 600, 2,400, ... and so on.*

Point to the weighted checkers displayed on the board.

T: Now you may use any one of these checkers. Tell me some new numbers I can make.

S: *16, 30, 32, 200, ...*

Draw the following diagram fairly low on the board, leaving room for the string picture to be extended upward as shown in the diagram after this one.

Can be shown on a 2-board Minicomputer using exactly one of the 2−, 3−, 4−, 5−, or 6− checkers.

T: Tell me some numbers that belong in the green string.

A complete list of all the possibilities is as follows:

2 3 4 5 6 8 10 12 16 20 24 30 32 40
48 50 60 80 100 120 160 200 240 400 480

T: Now tell me some numbers that do *not* belong in this string. Accept any number apart from those listed above. Extend your picture to include the following:

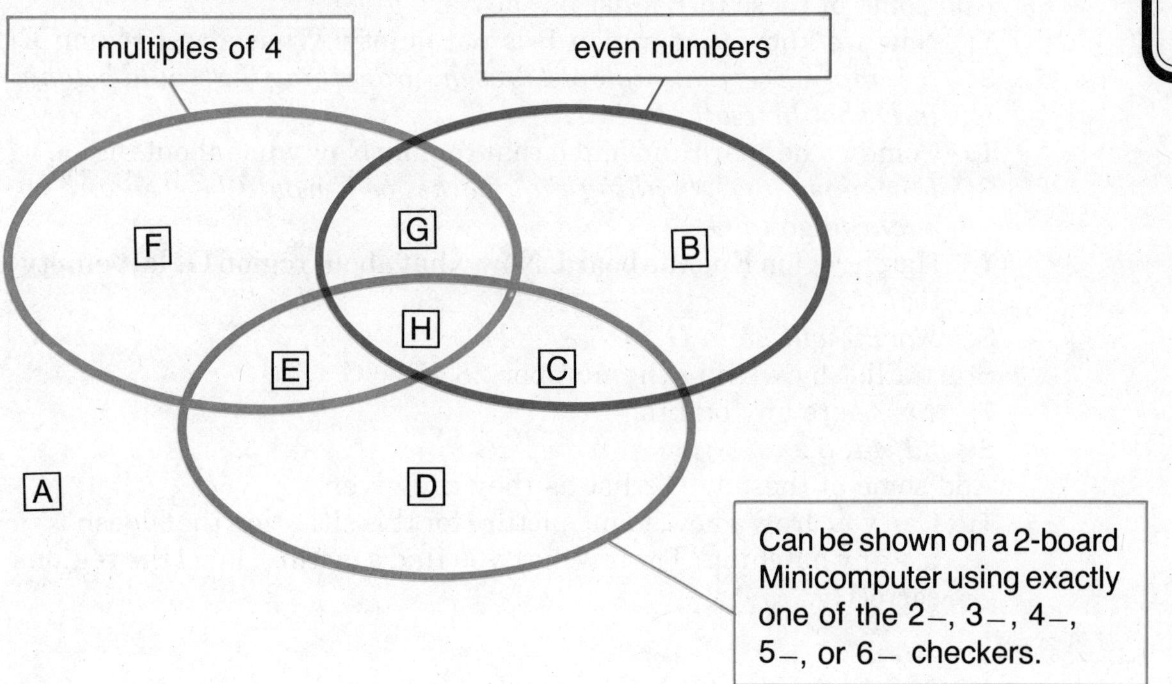

Write this list beside your string picture:

A
B
C
D
E
F
G
H

T: Help me write the first few positive numbers next to the letter for the region where they belong. Start with 1. Where does it go?

S: *A.*

Start a list on the board by writing the number 1 after A.
Similarly: 2 ⟶ C, 3 ⟶ D, 4 ⟶ H, 5 ⟶ D, ...
By the time you reach 10 your list should look like this:

A: 1, 7, 9
B:
C: 2, 6, 10
D: 3, 5
E:
F:
G:
H: 4, 8

T: Four of the regions are still empty. Can we find any numbers that belong in them? How about region B?

S: *14 belongs in B.*

Start a list after B by writing the number 14.

T: Are there any others?

S: *18, 22, 26, 34, ...*

Add some of these to B's list as they are given.

T: Now we know that region B is not empty. What about region E?

S: *It's empty. Every multiple of 4 is even, so anything that could belong in E should really be in H.*

T: Come to the board and hatch that region. Now what about region F?

S: *F is empty, too. Anything that works for F would be even and so ought to go in G.*

T: Hatch region F on the board. Now what about region G? Is it empty too?

S: *No. 28 will go in G.*

Start a list by writing the number 28 after G.

T: Are there any others?

S: *36, 44, 52, ...*

Add some of these to G's list as they are given.

T: Can you draw a new string picture for this situation that doesn't use any hatching? Try it. When you find a picture, label the regions correctly.

The results should be as follows:

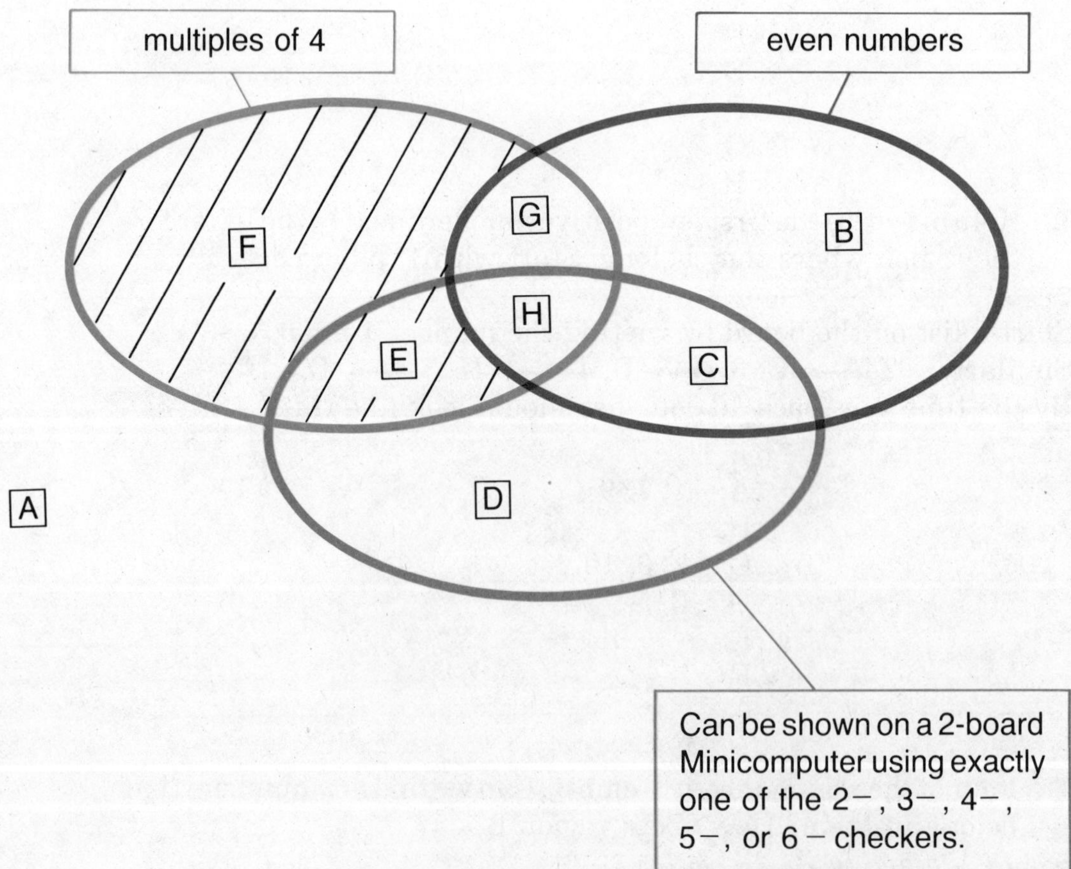

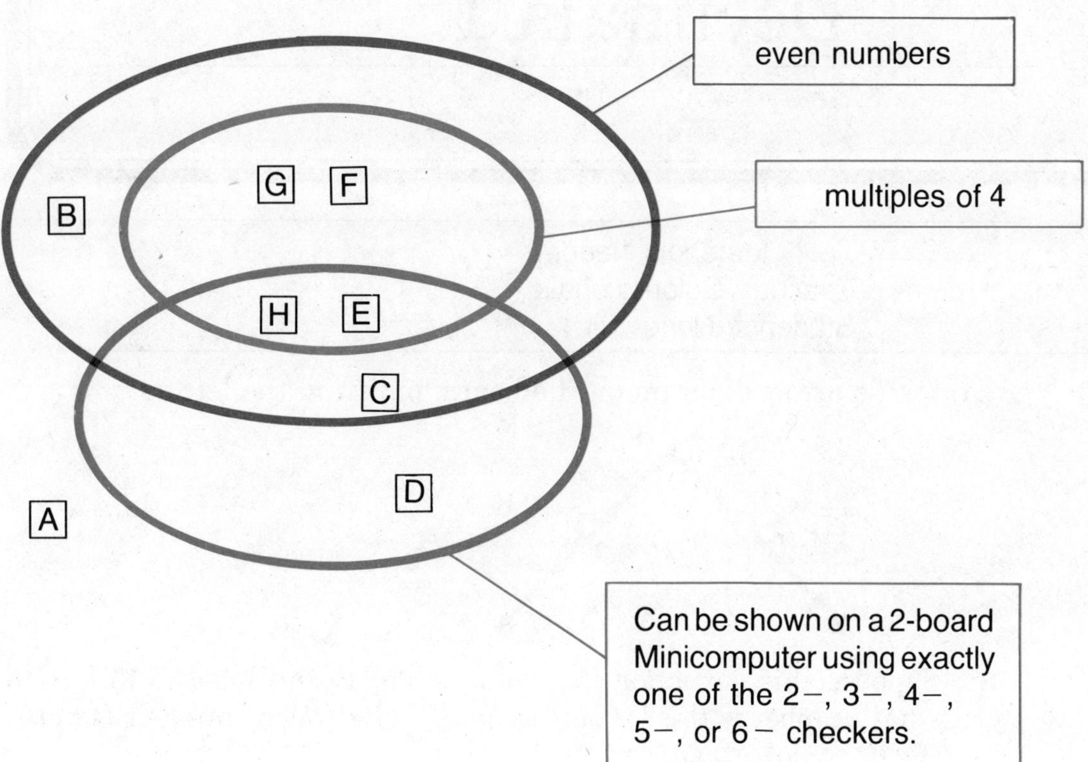

Resources Available

For out-of-class use: Any H-worksheet up through H3

ACTIVITY 3
Decimals 1

Materials Needed
Teacher: Colored chalk
Students: None

Draw this arrow diagram on the board, omitting the letters.

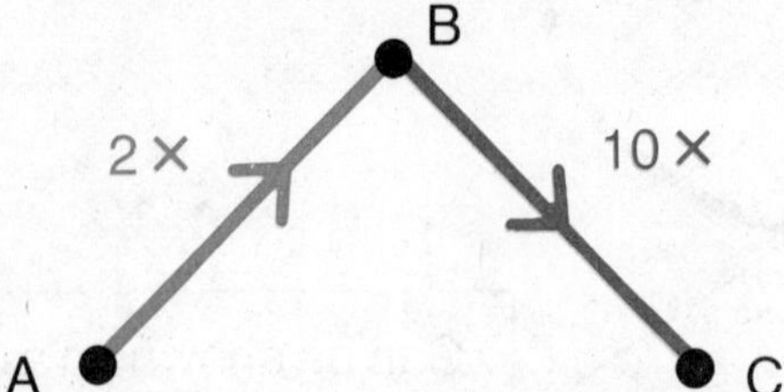

T: Suppose this dot is for 15. (Point to dot B and label it **15**.) Then what number is this? (Point to dot C.) (150) What number is here? (Point to dot A.) (7.5)

Erase the numerical labels, choose another label (say, 6.5) for dot B, and again ask for the numbers at dots C and A. Repeat this, using numbers at dot B that you feel will challenge but not frustrate the students. Below are some suggestions, with the boxes containing the desired student responses.

A	B	C
3.25	6.5	65
20	40	400
3.5	7	70
1.75	3.5	35
17.5	35	350

Draw a green arrow on the diagram, as follows:

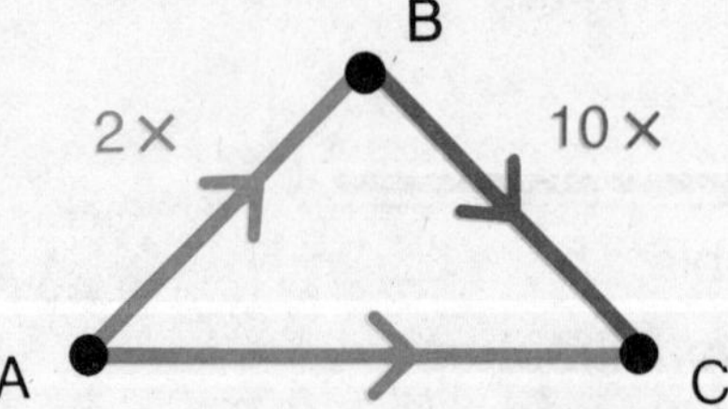

T: What should the green arrow be for? (20 ×)

3

Label the green arrow **20 ×**. Then draw two new arrows, as follows:

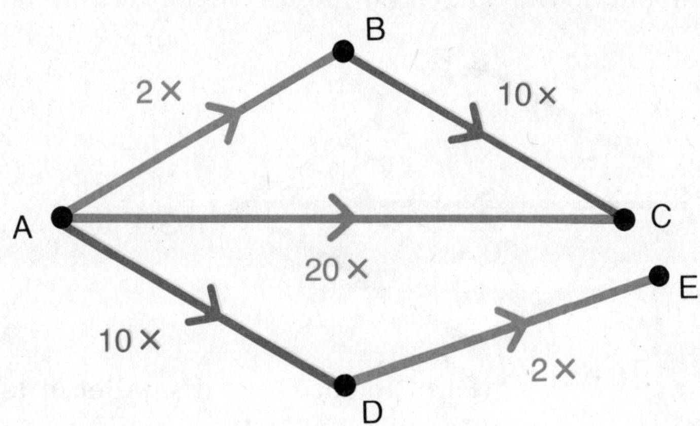

S: *That's not right! The new 2 × arrow should end at the same dot (pointing to dot C) as the first 10 × arrow.*

T: Why?

S: *10 × followed by 2 × is the same as 2 × followed by 10 ×. They're both 20 ×—the green arrow.*

If no student makes this observation, or if it is made without explanation, ask leading questions to establish that no matter what number is at dot A, the number at dot C will always be the same as the number at dot E. Then correct the diagram as follows:

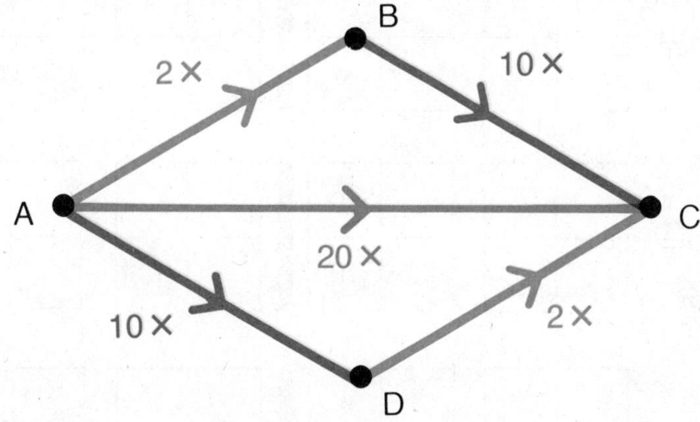

T: Suppose the number here is 82. (Point to dot C.) Then what is this number? (Point to dot A.) (4.1)

Repeat this activity, using a number at any dot that will challenge but not create too difficult a calculation, and in each case ask for the other numbers. For example:

A	B	D	C
4.1	8.2	41	82
0.18	0.36	1.8	3.6
5.15	10.3	51.5	103
0.45	0.9	4.5	9
0.68	1.36	6.8	13.6

3

If students have difficulties with some of these calculations, such as the third problem above, you could handle the situation as follows:

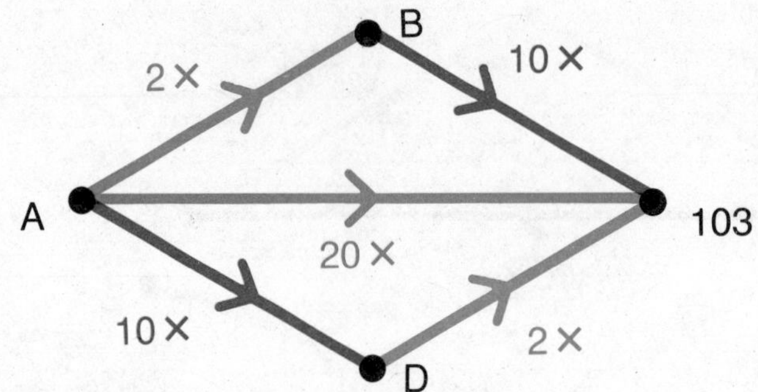

T: What number is this? (Point to dot D.) Is it smaller or larger than 103? (smaller)
S: *It's half of 103. That's about 51.*
T: Yes. Half of 102 is 51. What's one-half of 1? (0.5)
So what's one-half of 103? (51.5)
Now what number goes here? (Point to dot A.)
S: *One-tenth of 51.5. That's 5.15.*

If some do not see that one-tenth of 51.5 is 5.15, use the Minicomputer:

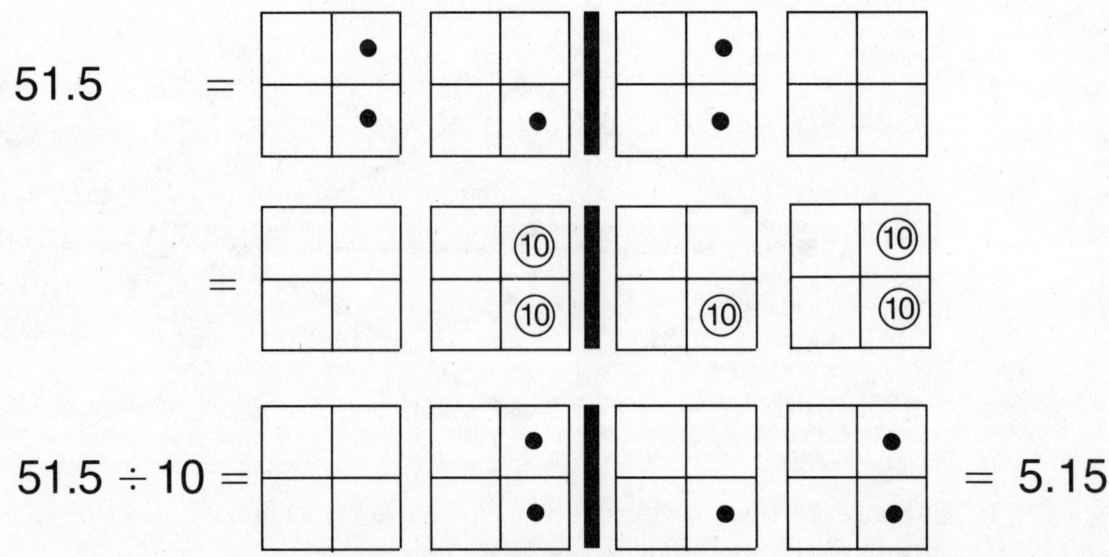

Students enjoy challenging one another. Let several of them come to the board and label one dot while the rest of the class decides what numbers are at the other dots. To avoid having this problem lead to unwelcome frustration, tell the students that the first dot to be labeled must be for a whole number between certain limits—say 1 and 100.

Resources Available

For out-of-class use: Any H-worksheet up through H6

ACTIVITY 4
Decimals 2

Materials Needed
Teacher: Colored chalk
Students: Colored pencils

Draw this picture on the board:

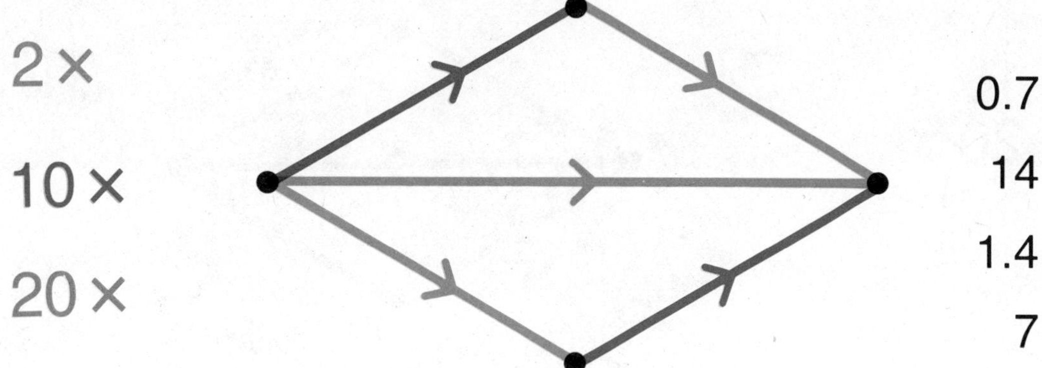

Point to the list of numbers.

T: Use these numbers to label the dots.

Let students come to the board, label dots, and explain their choices.

The completed picture should look like this:

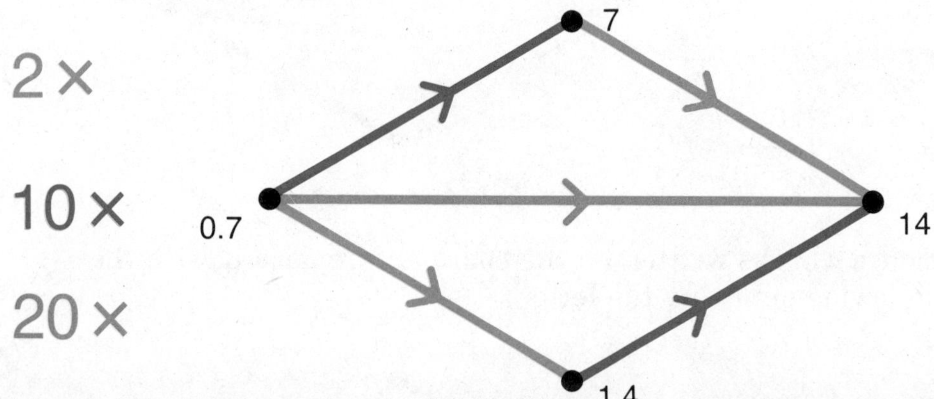

T: Now, see if you can use this arrow diagram to help you solve these problems.

As you say this, begin writing these problems on the board:

$14 \div 10 =$
$7 \div 10 =$
$1.4 \div 2 =$
$14 \div 20 =$

4

When a student volunteers to solve the first problem, have him or her come to the board to trace along an appropriate return arrow.
S: *14 ÷ 10 = 1.4 (tracing the ÷10 arrow).*

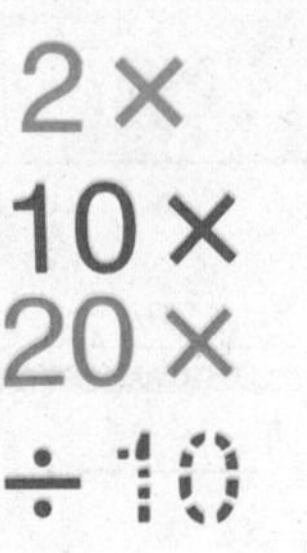

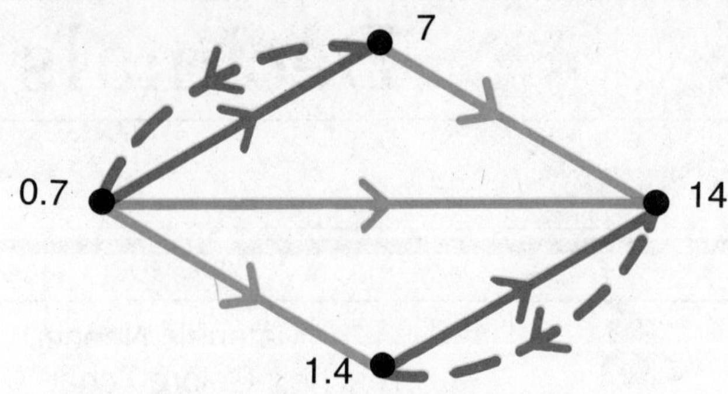

Similarly, for the other problems:
7 ÷ 10 = 0.7 (tracing the ÷10 arrow)
1.4 ÷ 2 = 0.7 (tracing the ÷2 arrow)

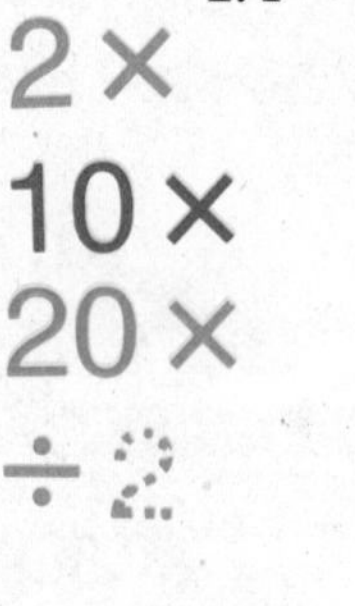

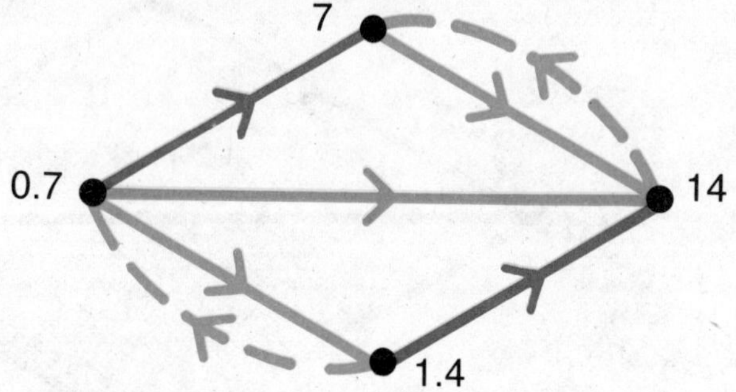

1.4 ÷ 2 = 0.7 (tracing the ÷2 arrow)

2×
10×
20×
÷20

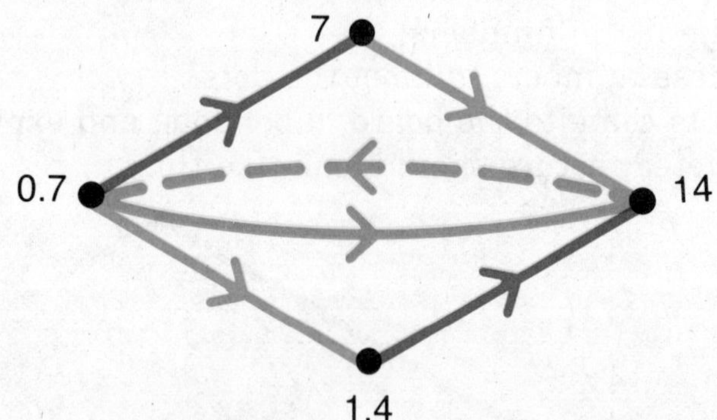

Erase what is written on the board and replace it with the following, omitting the letters.

3×
10×

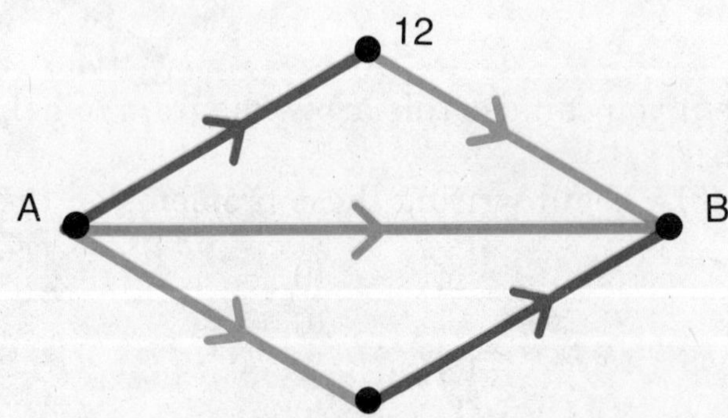

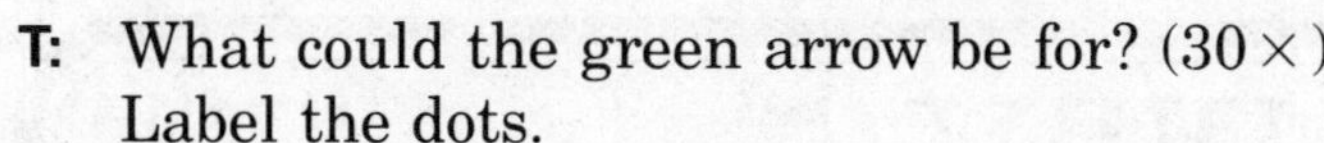

T: What could the green arrow be for? (30 ×)
Label the dots.

Make sure those who volunteer answers explain their reasons for the labels they write. For example, dot A is for 1.2 because 12 ÷ 10 = 1.2. (Trace the arrow for ÷ 10.) The completed figure will be:

3 ×
10 ×
30 ×

1.2 12 36 3.6

Erase the labels for the dots.

T: Now let's use this arrow diagram to help us solve these problems.

Write these problems on the board:

24 ÷ 3 =	33 ÷ 10 =
8 ÷ 10 =	3.3 ÷ 3 =
24 ÷ 30 =	33 ÷ 30 =

As before, make sure each volunteer explains his or her answer by referring to the return arrow that is being used.

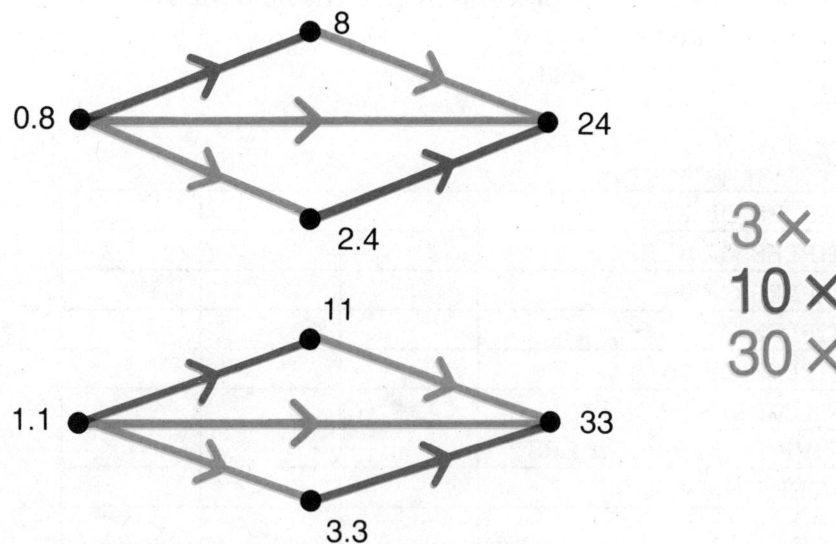

Resources Available

For class use: Worksheets L1 and L2

For out-of-class use: Any H-worksheet up through H6

ACTIVITY 5
Numerical String
Game Analysis 1

Materials Needed

Teacher: Numerical String Game kit, colored chalk

Students: String Game Analysis Sheets (a supply of these is at the back of the workbook), colored pencils

Ask the students to work individually on Worksheet L3. Check the solutions as students finish the worksheet and raise their hands. If a student has identified both strings correctly, let him or her continue with Worksheet L4. If either string is incorrect, say that the solution is incorrect and tell the student to continue working on it. Allow about 15 minutes for this part of the activity.

After most of the students have finished Worksheet L3 or have given up trying, discuss the solution with the class. The following is one possible outline for such a discussion.

1. As a result of the placement of $\hat{1}$, the board analysis poster should look like this:

	Red	Blue	
MULTIPLES OF 2		X	
MULTIPLES OF 3		X	
MULTIPLES OF 4		X	
MULTIPLES OF 5		X	
MULTIPLES OF 10		X	
ODD NUMBERS	X		
POSITIVE PRIME NUMBERS		X	
GREATER THAN 50		X	
LESS THAN 50	X		
GREATER THAN $\hat{10}$	X		
LESS THAN $\hat{10}$		X	
POSITIVE DIVISORS OF 12		X	
POSITIVE DIVISORS OF 18		X	
POSITIVE DIVISORS OF 20		X	
POSITIVE DIVISORS OF 24		X	
POSITIVE DIVISORS OF 27		X	

5

2. As a result of the placement of 6, the board analysis poster should look like this:

	Red	Blue	
MULTIPLES OF 2		X	
MULTIPLES OF 3		X	
MULTIPLES OF 4	X	X	
MULTIPLES OF 5	X	X	
MULTIPLES OF 10	X	X	
ODD NUMBERS	X	✓	
POSITIVE PRIME NUMBERS	X	X	
GREATER THAN 50	X	X	
LESS THAN 50	X	X	
GREATER THAN 1̂0	X	X	
LESS THAN 1̂0	X	X	
POSITIVE DIVISORS OF 12		X	
POSITIVE DIVISORS OF 18		X	
POSITIVE DIVISORS OF 20	X	X	
POSITIVE DIVISORS OF 24		X	
POSITIVE DIVISORS OF 27	X	X	

(The blue string is determined.)

3. The fact that there are exactly three numbers in the intersection of the two strings implies that the red string cannot be:
   a. Multiples of 2—because there are no multiples of 2 that are odd.
   b. Multiples of 3—because there are more than three odd multiples of 3 (for example, 9, 27, 45, 105, and so on).
   c. Positive divisors of 12—because there are only two odd positive divisors of 12, namely, 1 and 3.
   d. Positive divisors of 24—because there are only two odd positive divisors of 24, namely, 1 and 3.

   So the red string is for the positive divisors of 18.

Let the students work for a few more minutes on Worksheet L4 before they discuss its solution. Check individual solutions as in the case of Worksheet L3, and stop the class for a discussion of the solution when you feel the students are ready. In outline, the discussion of the solution might go as follows:

1. As a result of the placement of 0, the board analysis poster should look like this:

	Red	Blue	
MULTIPLES OF 2		X	
MULTIPLES OF 3		X	
MULTIPLES OF 4		X	
MULTIPLES OF 5		X	
MULTIPLES OF 10		X	
ODD NUMBERS	X		
POSITIVE PRIME NUMBERS	X		
GREATER THAN 50	X		
LESS THAN 50		X	
GREATER THAN $\widehat{10}$		X	
LESS THAN $\widehat{10}$	X		
POSITIVE DIVISORS OF 12	X		
POSITIVE DIVISORS OF 18	X		
POSITIVE DIVISORS OF 20	X		
POSITIVE DIVISORS OF 24	X		
POSITIVE DIVISORS OF 27	X		

2. Because $\widehat{10}$ is not in the region indicated, it is not in the red string at all. This is so because for $\widehat{10}$ to be in the red string it must be in the intersection and hence also in the blue string. But $\widehat{10}$ is not odd, is not a positive prime number, is not greater than 50, is not less than $\widehat{10}$, and is not a positive divisor of anything, because it is not positive. Because $\widehat{10}$ is not in the red string, the board analysis poster should now look like this:

	Red	Blue	
MULTIPLES OF 2	X	X	
MULTIPLES OF 3		X	
MULTIPLES OF 4		X	
MULTIPLES OF 5	X	X	
MULTIPLES OF 10	X	X	
ODD NUMBERS	X		
POSITIVE PRIME NUMBERS	X		
GREATER THAN 50	X		
LESS THAN 50	X	X	
GREATER THAN $\widehat{10}$		X	
LESS THAN $\widehat{10}$	X		
POSITIVE DIVISORS OF 12	X		
POSITIVE DIVISORS OF 18	X		
POSITIVE DIVISORS OF 20	X		
POSITIVE DIVISORS OF 24	X		
POSITIVE DIVISORS OF 27	X		

3. Because 3 is not in the intersection, 3 is not in the blue string (because of the hatching). Similarly for 4. So the board analysis poster should now look like this:

5

	Red	Blue	
MULTIPLES OF 2	X	X	
MULTIPLES OF 3		X	
MULTIPLES OF 4		X	
MULTIPLES OF 5	X	X	
MULTIPLES OF 10	X	X	
ODD NUMBERS	X	X	
POSITIVE PRIME NUMBERS	X	X	
GREATER THAN 50	X		
LESS THAN 50	X	X	
GREATER THAN $\widehat{10}$		X	
LESS THAN $\widehat{10}$	X		
POSITIVE DIVISORS OF 12	X	X	
POSITIVE DIVISORS OF 18	X	X	
POSITIVE DIVISORS OF 20	X	X	
POSITIVE DIVISORS OF 24	X	X	
POSITIVE DIVISORS OF 27	X	X	

4. The red string cannot be for multiples of 3, because if it were and also the blue string were for:
    a. The numbers greater than 50, then it would be impossible to locate 100, for example.
    b. The numbers less than $\widehat{10}$, then it would be impossible to locate $\widehat{32}$, for example.

   So MULTIPLES OF 3 can be crossed off in the Red column.
5. A similar analysis shows that the red string cannot be for the multiples of 4, so it is for the numbers greater than $\widehat{10}$.
6. The blue string cannot be for the numbers less than $\widehat{10}$ because it would then be impossible to locate $\widehat{80}$, for example. ($\widehat{80}$ would have to be in the blue string because it is less than $\widehat{10}$, and not in the red string because it is not greater than $\widehat{10}$. But the region inside the blue string and outside the red string is empty.) So we can conclude that the blue string is for the numbers greater than 50.

For class use: Worksheets L3 and L4
For out-of-class use: Any H-worksheet up through H9

ACTIVITY 6
String Game
(Analysis Version) 1

Materials Needed

Teacher: Numerical String Game kit, colored chalk

Students: String Game Analysis Sheets (a supply of these is at the back of the workbook), colored pencils

In this activity we introduce the analysis version of the String Game. This version may be played with two or three strings; however, for this introductory activity, we consider only two-string games. The game is played as follows.

Divide the class into two teams, Team A and Team B. Prepare your board for the String Game as you would to play the usual version. Begin by giving several starting clues. Such a clue can indicate the region of the picture where a particular number belongs or a region where it does not belong, or it can indicate how many numbers belong in a particular region. Ask the class to consider collectively the 16 possible labels for each string (listed on Numerical String Game Poster 1) and to decide which of them the strings cannot be for.

Explain to the class how to play the game after the initial analysis.

Play: During a team's turn, a member selects a game piece and places it in the string picture. If the game piece is correctly placed, say yes and let the piece remain in the picture. If the game piece is incorrectly placed, record the play with a crossed-out numeral in the picture and return the piece to the collection of unplayed pieces. Let the entire class analyze the situation. Although only the team whose turn it is can score, anyone can help with the analysis after a play.

Score: A team gains five points each time a member's play eliminates at least one-fourth (computed to the nearest whole number) of the remaining possible labels for the strings. The team gains an additional two points for each possibility eliminated over the number required to score. If fewer than the required number are eliminated, there is no score.

Alternating teams, select students or ask for volunteers to make plays. Before a team makes a play, decide what is the smallest number of possibilities that must be eliminated for the team to score. After each play, compute and record the score.

The class can help you with the scoring. Continue until the strings are determined. The team with the highest score wins.

Play the analysis version of the String Game with your class. Two games are suggested here. String labels, appropriate starting clues, lists showing which labels are eliminated by the starting clues, and a crib sheet for each game are given.

Game 1: Starting Clues

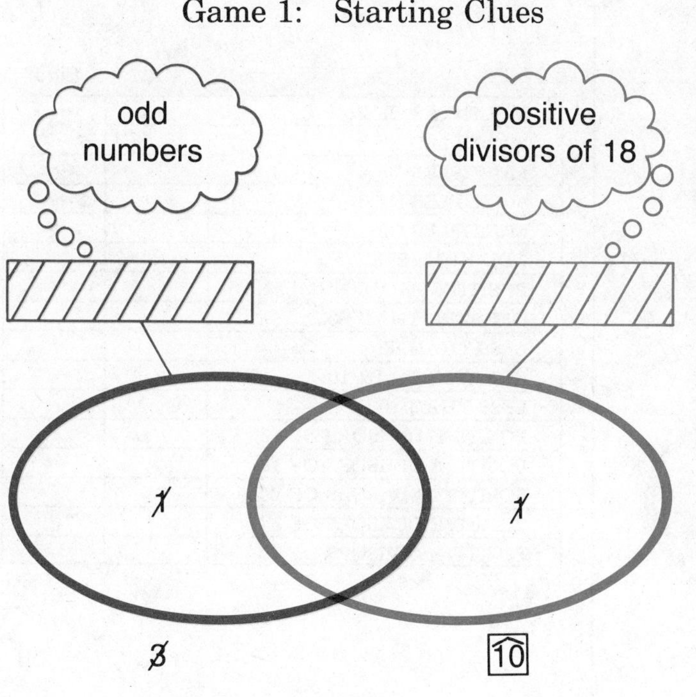

	Red	Blue
MULTIPLES OF 2	X	X
MULTIPLES OF 3		
MULTIPLES OF 4		
MULTIPLES OF 5	X	X
MULTIPLES OF 10	X	X
ODD NUMBERS		
POSITIVE PRIME NUMBERS		
GREATER THAN 50		
LESS THAN 50	X	X
GREATER THAN $\hat{10}$		
LESS THAN $\hat{10}$		
POSITIVE DIVISORS OF 12		
POSITIVE DIVISORS OF 18		
POSITIVE DIVISORS OF 20		
POSITIVE DIVISORS OF 24		
POSITIVE DIVISORS OF 27		

Correct Placement of Pieces

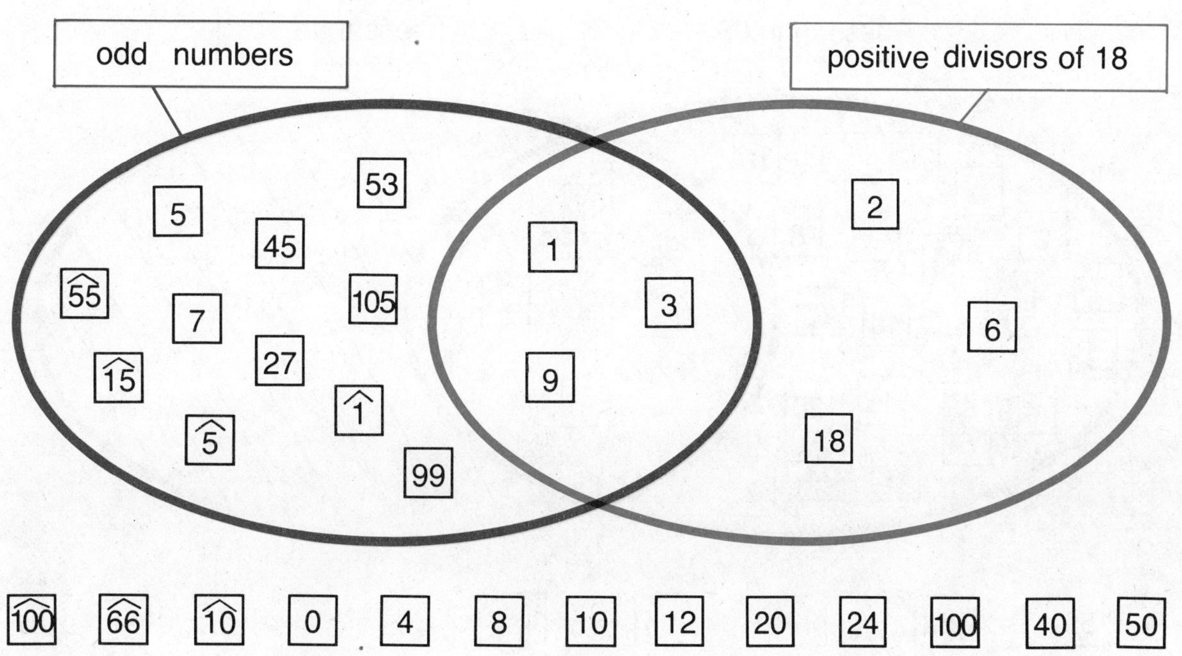

6

Game 2: Starting Clues

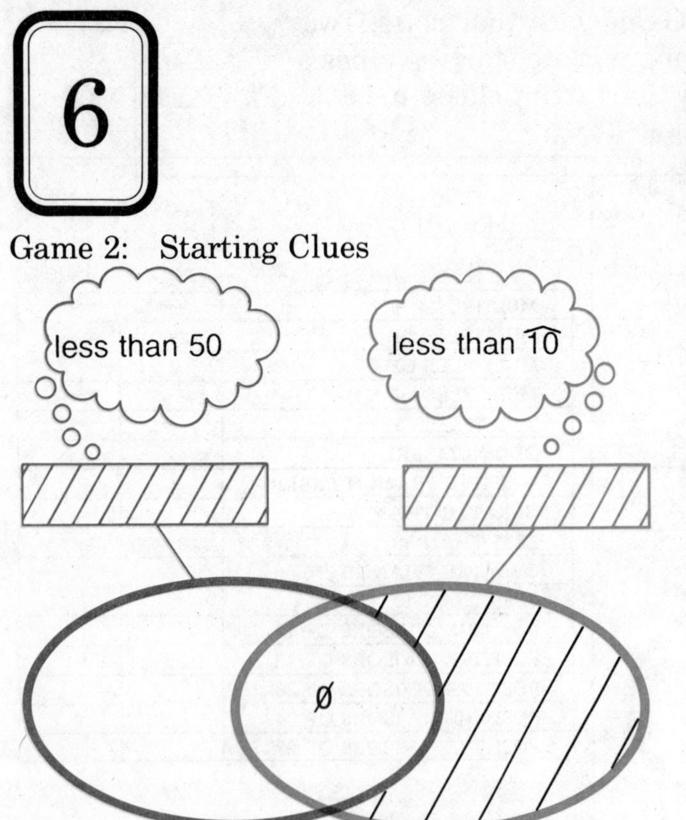

	Red	Blue
MULTIPLES OF 2		X
MULTIPLES OF 3		X
MULTIPLES OF 4		X
MULTIPLES OF 5		X
MULTIPLES OF 10		X
ODD NUMBERS		
POSITIVE PRIME NUMBERS		
GREATER THAN 50		
LESS THAN 50		X
GREATER THAN $\widehat{10}$		X
LESS THAN $\widehat{10}$		
POSITIVE DIVISORS OF 12		
POSITIVE DIVISORS OF 18		
POSITIVE DIVISORS OF 20		
POSITIVE DIVISORS OF 24		
POSITIVE DIVISORS OF 27		

Correct Placement of Pieces

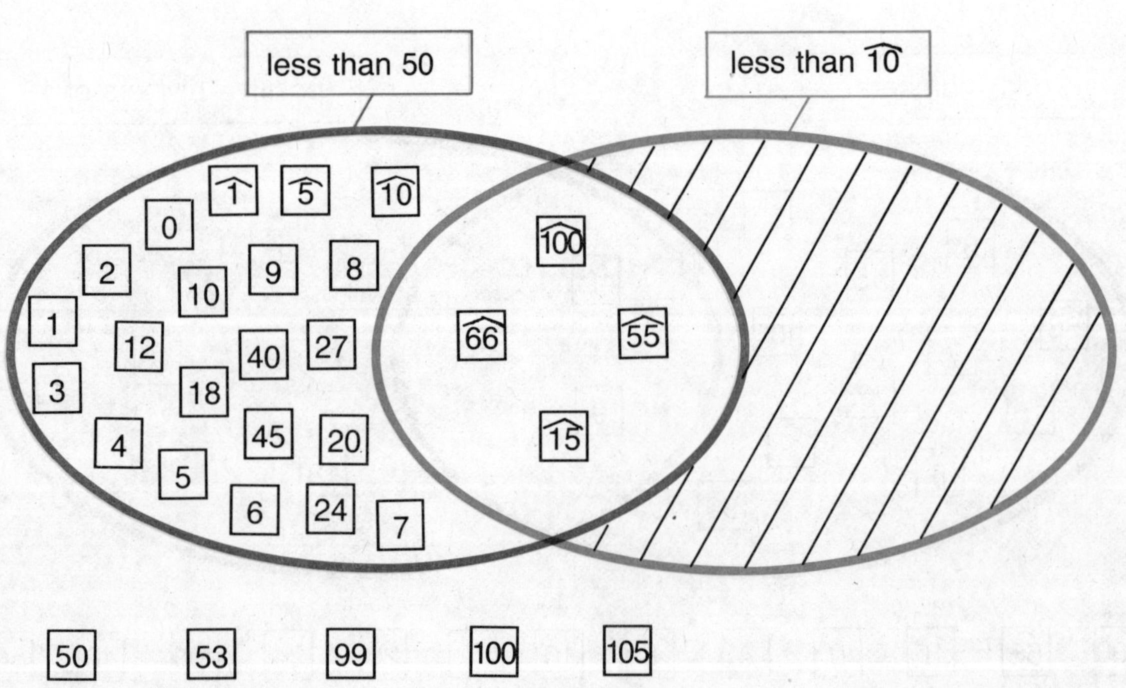

The following is an example of how game 1 might proceed.

6

	Red	Blue
MULTIPLES OF 2	X	X
MULTIPLES OF 3		
MULTIPLES OF 4		
MULTIPLES OF 5	X	X
MULTIPLES OF 10	X	X
ODD NUMBERS		
POSITIVE PRIME NUMBERS		
GREATER THAN 50		
LESS THAN 50	X	X
GREATER THAN 10		
LESS THAN 10		
POSITIVE DIVISORS OF 12		
POSITIVE DIVISORS OF 18		
POSITIVE DIVISORS OF 20		
POSITIVE DIVISORS OF 24		
POSITIVE DIVISORS OF 27		

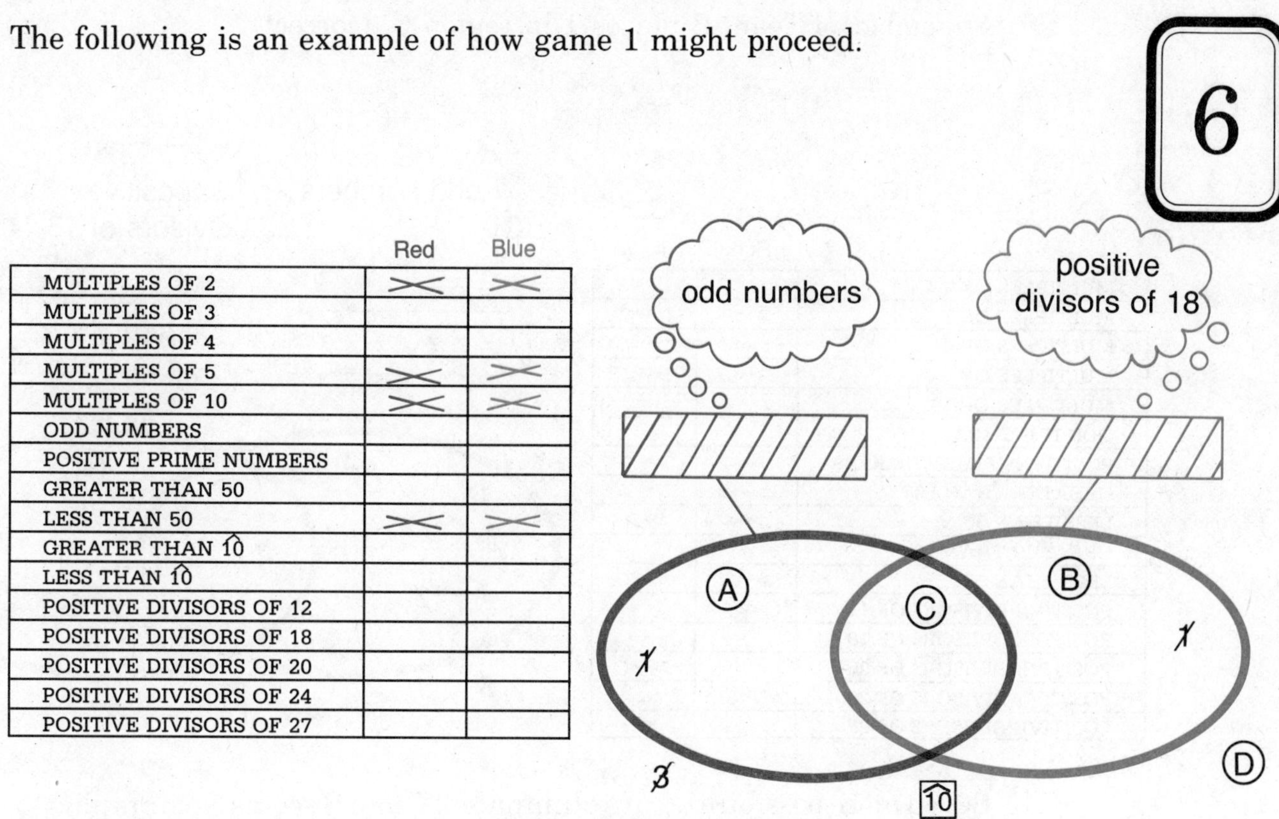

Twenty-four labels remain as possibilities for the strings. One-fourth of 24 is 6. Team A needs to eliminate at least six of the remaining possible labels to score.

A member of Team A places 3 in region A. (incorrect)

	Red	Blue
MULTIPLES OF 2	X	X
MULTIPLES OF 3		
MULTIPLES OF 4		X
MULTIPLES OF 5	X	X
MULTIPLES OF 10	X	X
ODD NUMBERS		
POSITIVE PRIME NUMBERS		
GREATER THAN 50		X
LESS THAN 50	X	X
GREATER THAN 10		
LESS THAN 10		X
POSITIVE DIVISORS OF 12		
POSITIVE DIVISORS OF 18		
POSITIVE DIVISORS OF 20		X
POSITIVE DIVISORS OF 24		
POSITIVE DIVISORS OF 27		

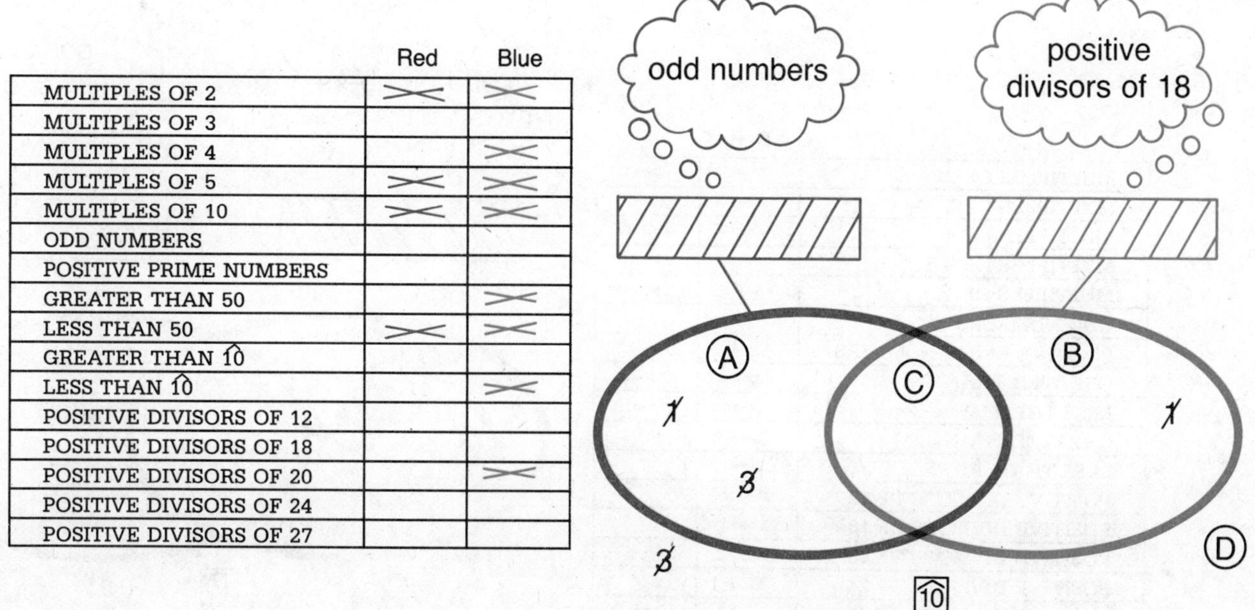

Only four more possibilities are eliminated. Team A does not score. Twenty labels remain as possibilities for the strings. One-fourth of 20 is 5. Team B needs to eliminate at least five of the remaining possible labels to score.

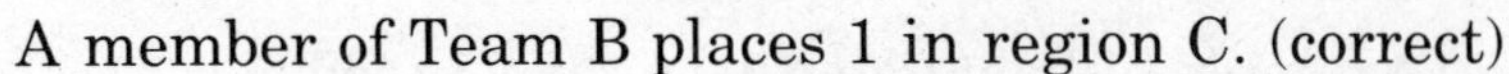
A member of Team B places 1 in region C. (correct)

	Red	Blue
MULTIPLES OF 2	X	X
MULTIPLES OF 3	X	X
MULTIPLES OF 4	X	X
MULTIPLES OF 5	X	X
MULTIPLES OF 10	X	X
ODD NUMBERS		
POSITIVE PRIME NUMBERS	X	X
GREATER THAN 50	X	X
LESS THAN 50	X	X
GREATER THAN 10		
LESS THAN 10	X	X
POSITIVE DIVISORS OF 12		
POSITIVE DIVISORS OF 18		
POSITIVE DIVISORS OF 20		X
POSITIVE DIVISORS OF 24		
POSITIVE DIVISORS OF 27		

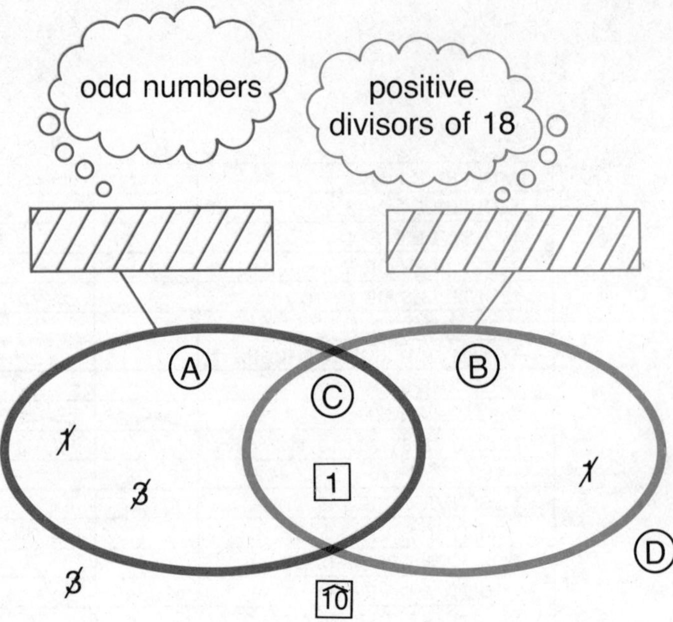

Seven more possibilities are eliminated. Team B scores 5 points plus 4 bonus points. Thirteen labels remain. One-fourth of 13 is 3 (to the nearest whole number). Team A needs to eliminate at least three of the remaining possible labels to score.

A member of Team A places 2 in region B. (correct)

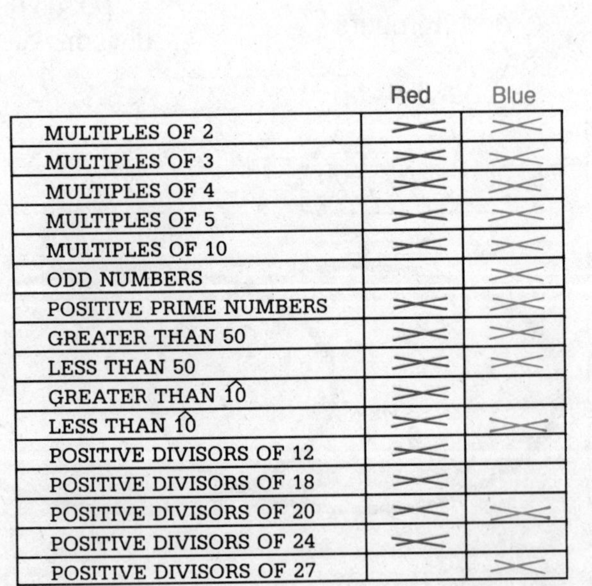

	Red	Blue
MULTIPLES OF 2	X	X
MULTIPLES OF 3	X	X
MULTIPLES OF 4	X	X
MULTIPLES OF 5	X	X
MULTIPLES OF 10	X	X
ODD NUMBERS		X
POSITIVE PRIME NUMBERS	X	X
GREATER THAN 50	X	X
LESS THAN 50	X	X
GREATER THAN 10	X	
LESS THAN 10	X	X
POSITIVE DIVISORS OF 12	X	
POSITIVE DIVISORS OF 18	X	
POSITIVE DIVISORS OF 20	X	X
POSITIVE DIVISORS OF 24	X	
POSITIVE DIVISORS OF 27		X

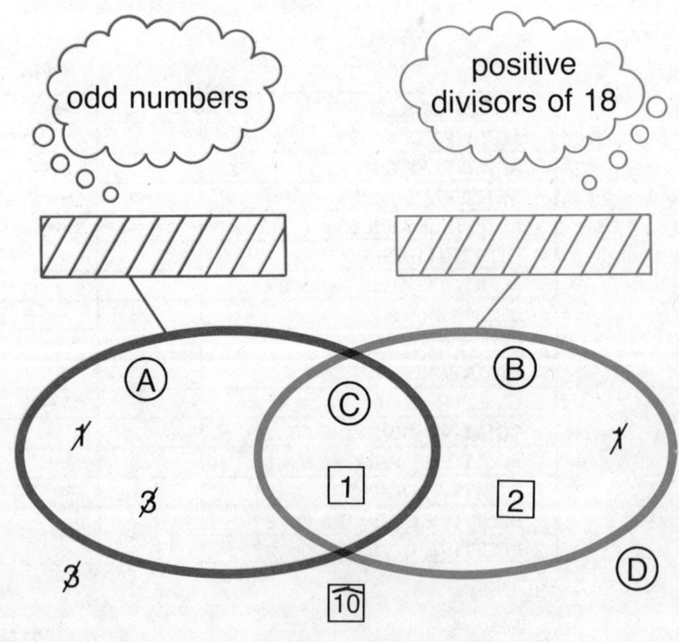

Seven more possibilities are eliminated. Team A scores 5 points plus 8 bonus points. Six labels remain. One-fourth of 6 is 2 (to the nearest whole number). Team B needs to eliminate at least two of the remaining labels to score.

A member of Team B places 9 in region A. (incorrect)

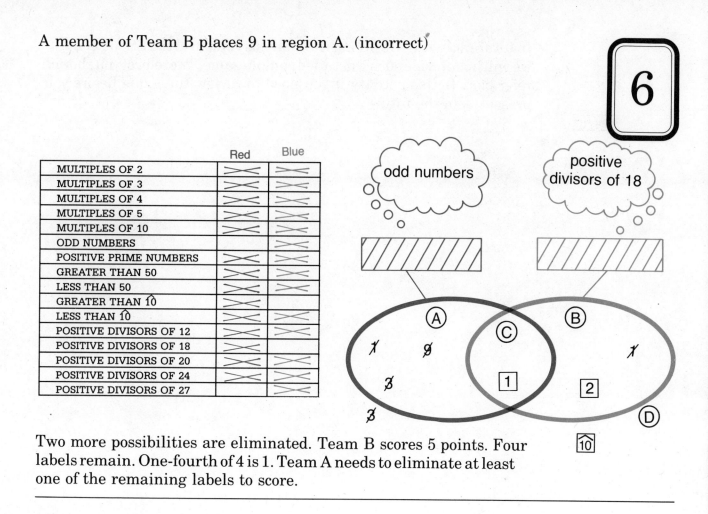

6

	Red	Blue
MULTIPLES OF 2	X	X
MULTIPLES OF 3	X	X
MULTIPLES OF 4	X	X
MULTIPLES OF 5	X	X
MULTIPLES OF 10	X	X
ODD NUMBERS		X
POSITIVE PRIME NUMBERS	X	X
GREATER THAN 50	X	X
LESS THAN 50	X	X
GREATER THAN 10	X	
LESS THAN 10	X	X
POSITIVE DIVISORS OF 12	X	X
POSITIVE DIVISORS OF 18	X	
POSITIVE DIVISORS OF 20	X	X
POSITIVE DIVISORS OF 24	X	X
POSITIVE DIVISORS OF 27		X

odd numbers

positive divisors of 18

A B C D

1 9 3 1 3

1 2 10

Two more possibilities are eliminated. Team B scores 5 points. Four labels remain. One-fourth of 4 is 1. Team A needs to eliminate at least one of the remaining labels to score.

A member of team A places 5 in region A. (correct)

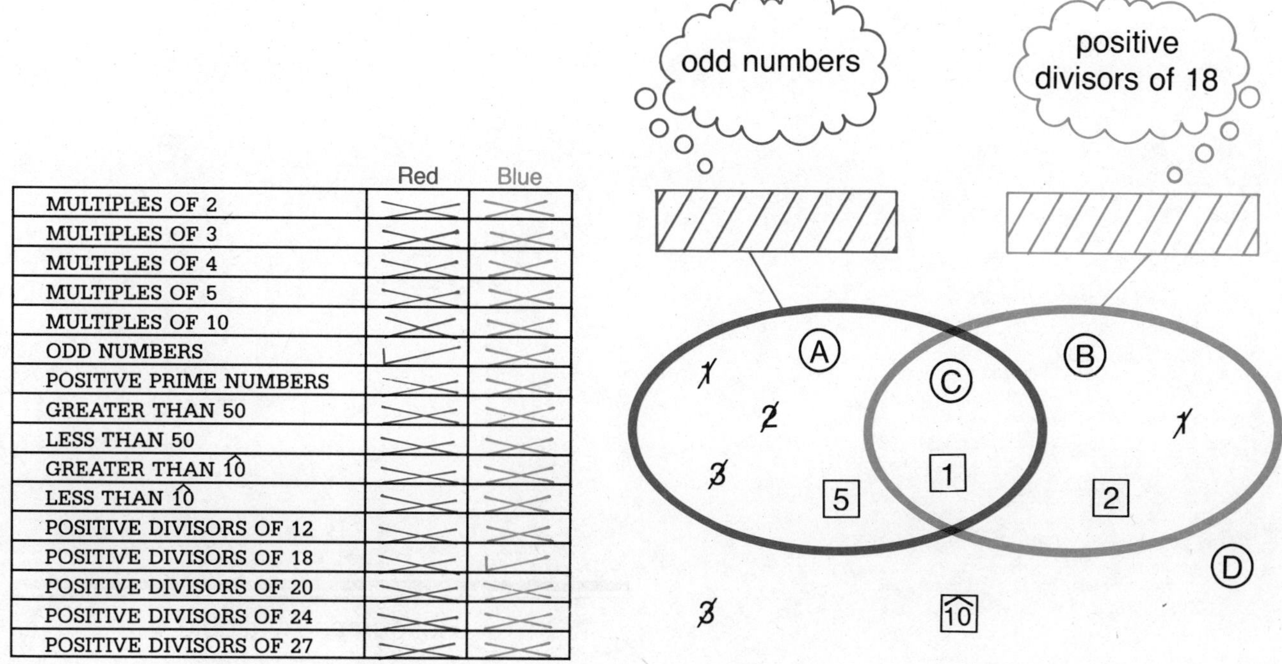

	Red	Blue
MULTIPLES OF 2	X	X
MULTIPLES OF 3	X	X
MULTIPLES OF 4	X	X
MULTIPLES OF 5	X	X
MULTIPLES OF 10	X	X
ODD NUMBERS	✓	X
POSITIVE PRIME NUMBERS	X	X
GREATER THAN 50	X	X
LESS THAN 50	X	X
GREATER THAN 10	X	X
LESS THAN 10	X	X
POSITIVE DIVISORS OF 12	X	X
POSITIVE DIVISORS OF 18	X	✓
POSITIVE DIVISORS OF 20	X	X
POSITIVE DIVISORS OF 24	X	X
POSITIVE DIVISORS OF 27	X	X

Two more possibilities are eliminated. Team A scores 5 points plus 2 bonus points. The strings are determined. Team A wins 20 to 14.

6

In future activities involving the analysis version of the String Game we will not provide such a detailed sample game. Therefore, you should refer back to this activity if you need to review the game before you present it in the future.

Resources Available

For class use: Worksheets L5 and L6

For out-of-class use: Any H-worksheet up through H9

ACTIVITY 7
Composition 1

Materials Needed
Teacher: Colored chalk
Students: None

Draw the following on the board:

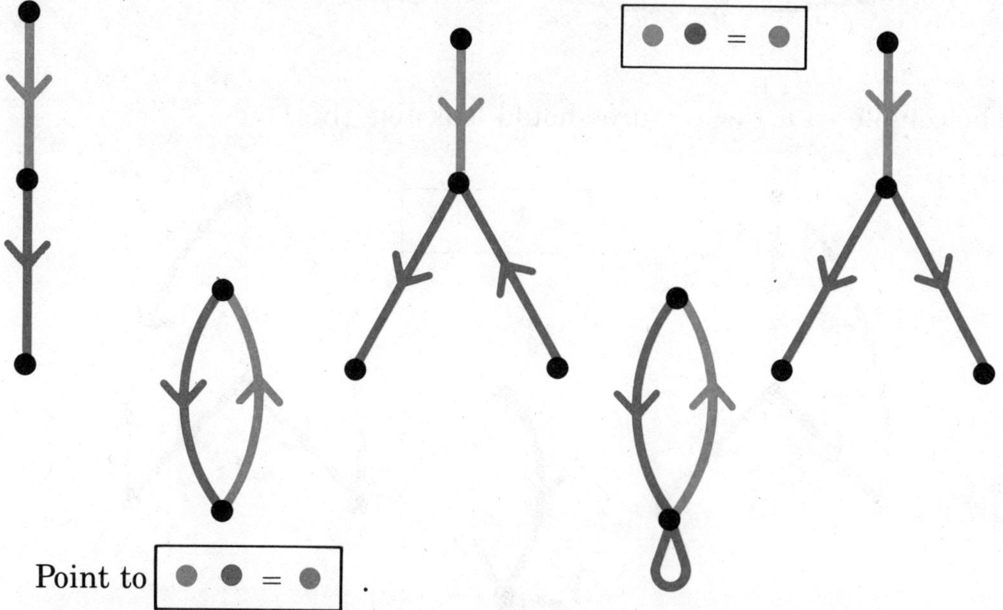

Point to [● ● = ●].

T: This key means that a blue arrow (point to the blue arrow at the upper left) followed by a red arrow (point to the red arrow following) gives us a green arrow.

Draw the resulting green arrow as follows:

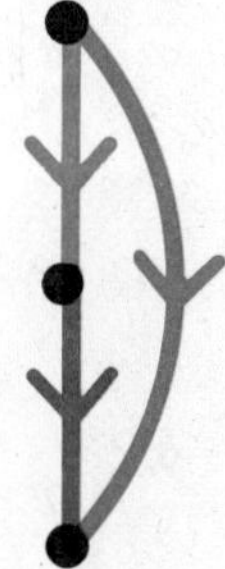

T: Can anyone see any other green arrows we can draw?

Let volunteers draw green arrows at the board. If anyone has difficulty, encourage him or her to use both hands as he or she traces along a blue-red arrow path like this:

S: *Blue . . .*

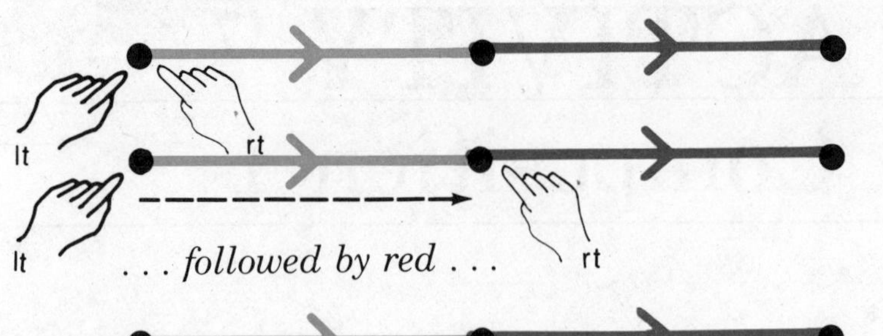

. . . *followed by red* . . .

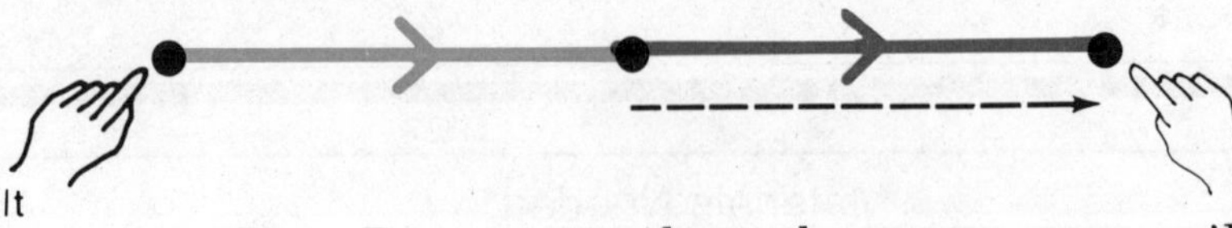

T: Stop. Do you see where the green arrow will begin and end?
S: *Yes.*

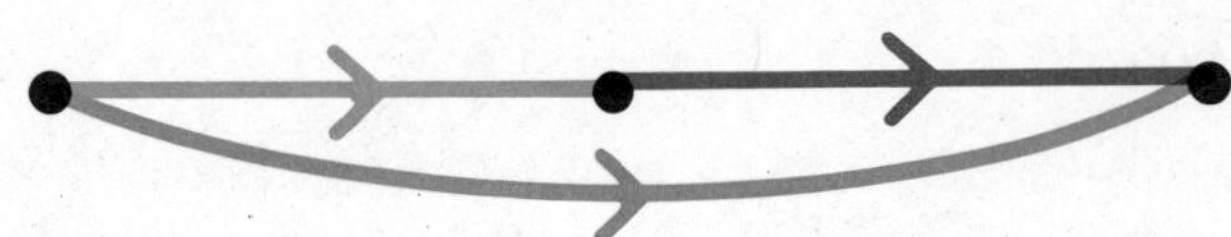

The completed arrow picture should look like this:

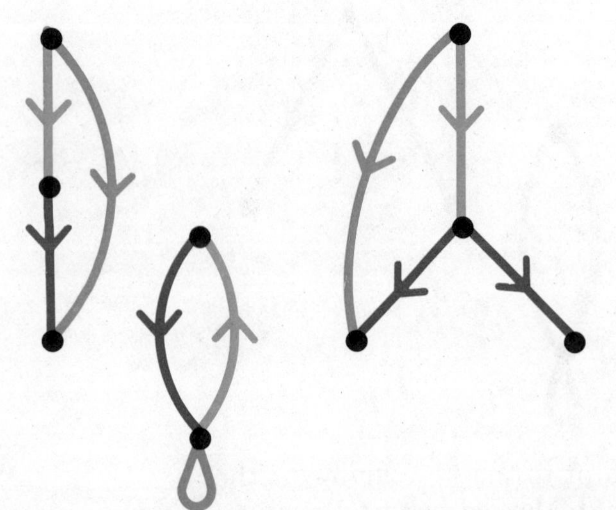

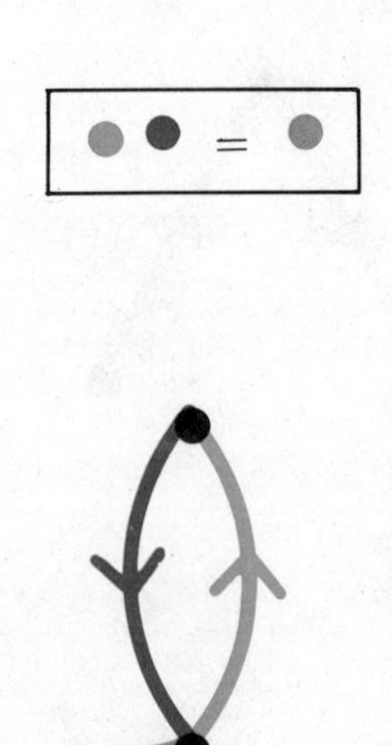

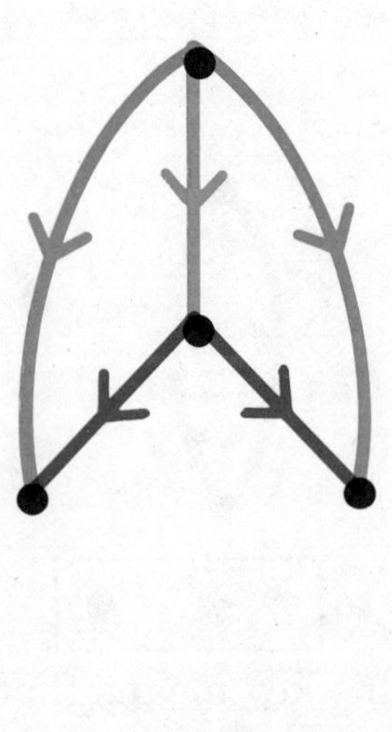

Draw a new picture on the board:

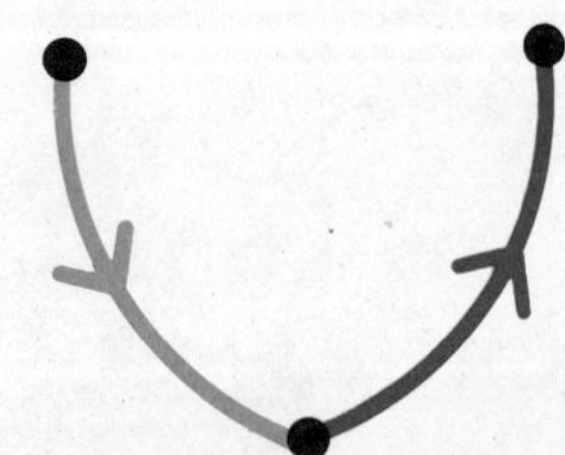

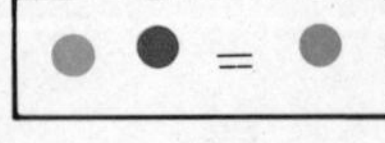

T: Can you draw a green arrow?
S: *Yes.*

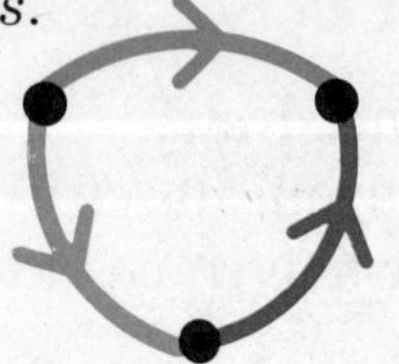

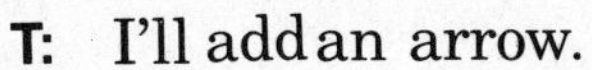

T: I'll addan arrow.

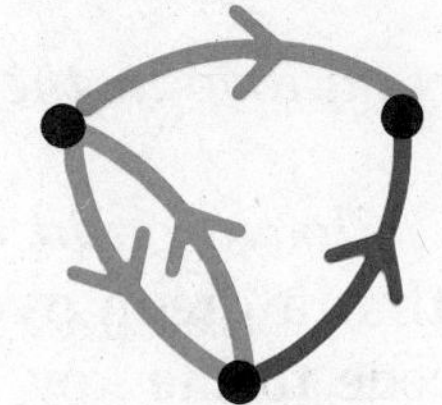

Any more green arrows?
S: *No.*

T: I'll add another arrow.

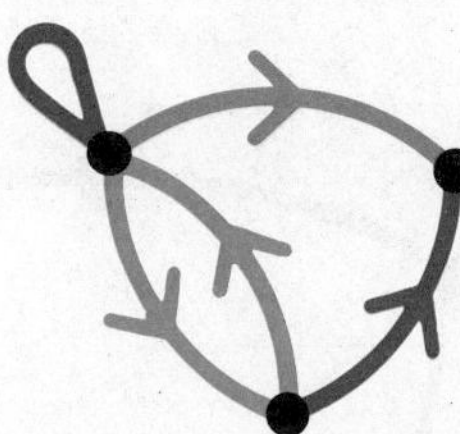

Any more green arrows?
S: *Yes.*

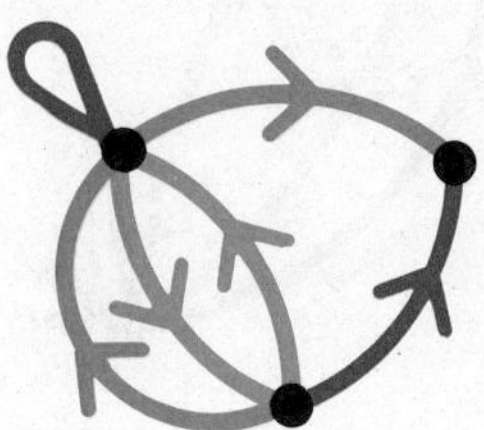

T: Here is another red.

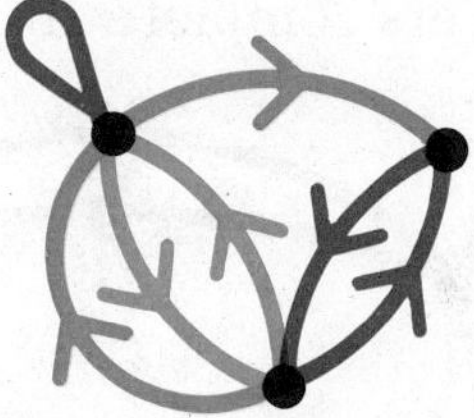

Any more green arrows now?
S: *No.*
T: One more blue.

Is there another green?
S: *Yes.*

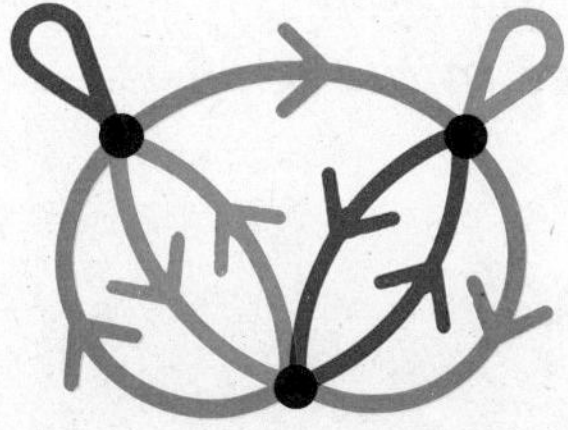

T: What do you notice about the green arrows?
Several answers may be given here that, although correct (such as, "They go clockwise"), do not contribute to the goal of this exercise. Accept any correct response, but wait for the following:

S: *They form a loop in the same direction.*
or
S: *You can follow around and get back to the same point.*
T: We call that a green **cycle.**
Add a new code to the key as follows:

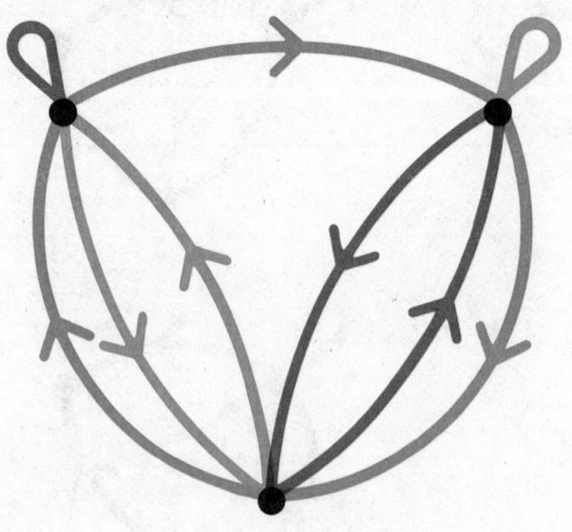

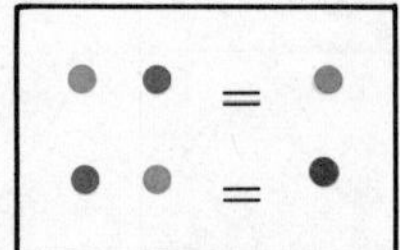

T: Do we get any more arrows now?
Let volunteers complete the diagram as follows:

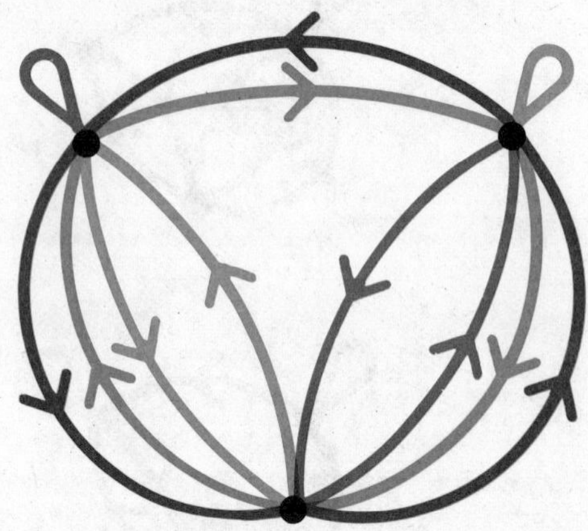

T: What did we get?
S: *A purple cycle.*
S: *It goes in the opposite direction to the green cycle.*

Resources Available
For class use: Worksheets L7 and L8
For out-of-class use: Any H-worksheet up through H12

ACTIVITY 8
Composition 2

Materials Needed
Teacher: Colored chalk
Students: Paper and colored pencils

Draw the following on the board:

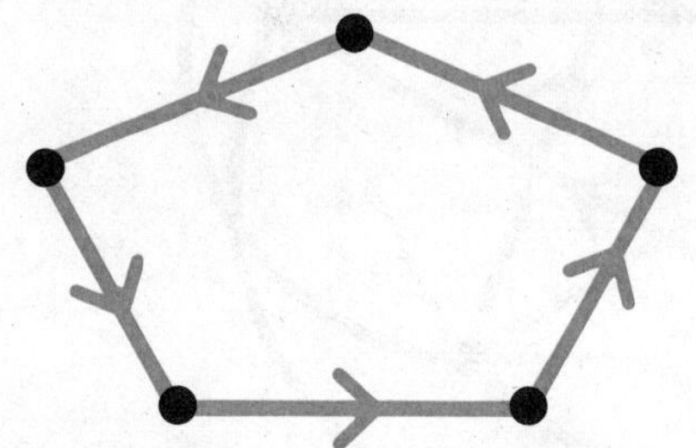

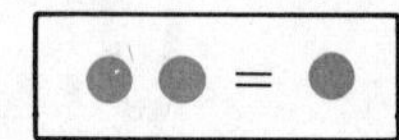

T: How would you describe this arrow picture?
S: *It's a blue cycle.*
T: What do you think the key means?
S: *Two blues make a green.*

There is no need to belabor the point and insist on precisely accurate answers to this stage. However, if students seem to need it, you could draw a separate picture in order to make the development more explicit.

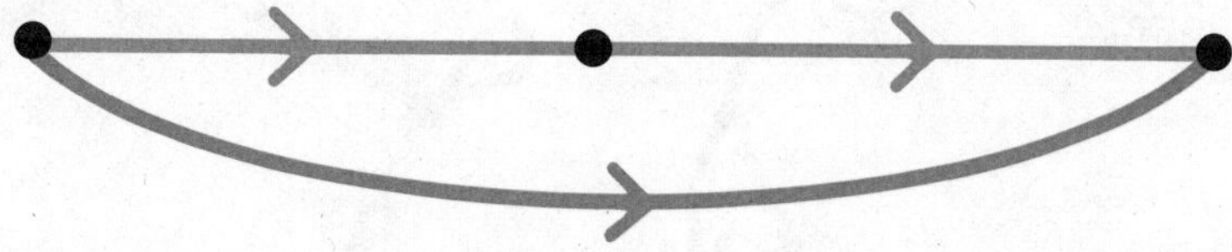

T: I'd like you to copy the blue cycle onto your papers and then draw the missing green arrows.

Give the class sufficient time to complete their drawings. As students finish, send them to the board one at a time to add one green arrow each to the arrow picture.

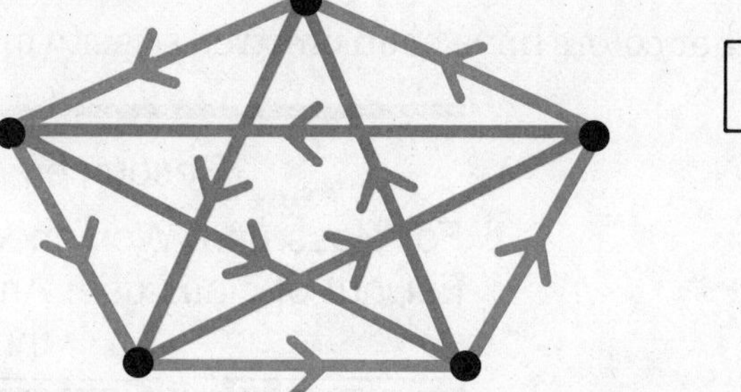

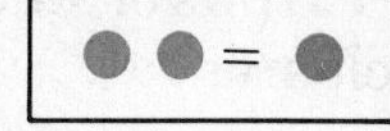

Note to the Teacher

The arrows need not be in exactly the same positions as those in our solutions, but they must connect the same pairs of dots.

T: Now let's look at another pattern.
Add the following to the key:

●●● = ●

T: Draw the missing purple arrows on your picture.
Again give the students time to work, and let volunteers complete the picture at the board.

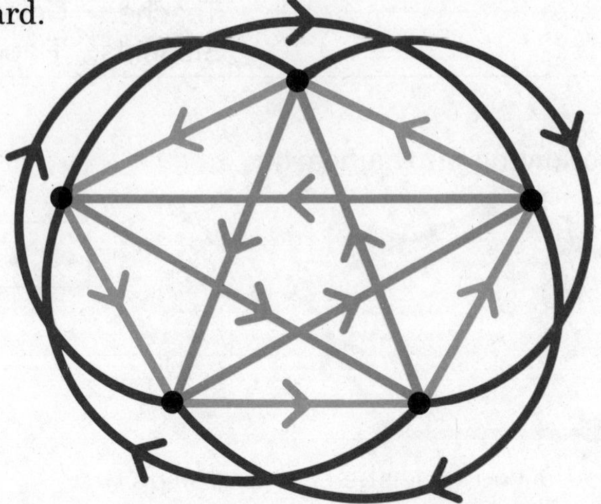

T: How are the green and purple arrows related?
S: *They go between the same dots but in opposite directions.*
In a similar way, continue to ask about the composition of four and five consecutive blue arrows. The answers are as follows:

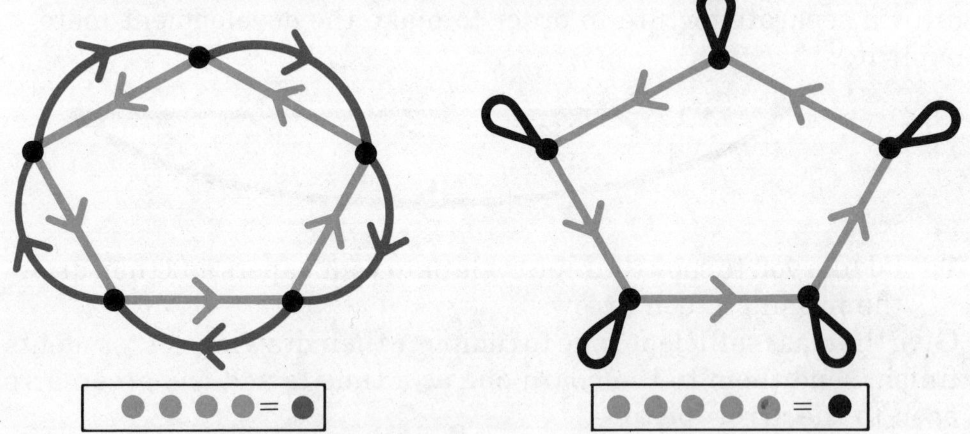

(Arrows of other colors have been omitted so as to make the patterns clearer.)

Resources Available

For class use: Worksheets L9 and L10
For out-of-class use: Any H-worksheet up through H12

ACTIVITY 9
Fractional Multipliers 1

Materials Needed
Teacher: Colored chalk
Students: Colored pencils

Draw this arrow picture on the board:

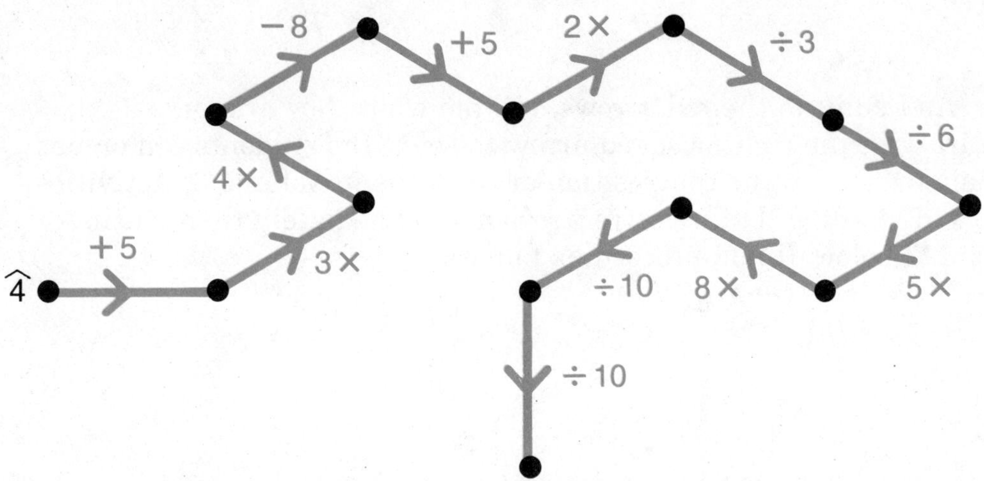

T: As I point to the dots on this arrow road, tell me what numbers they are for.

Encourage students to calculate the answers quickly in their heads. You may wish to go along the road several times, so don't actually label the dots. The correct answers are as follows:

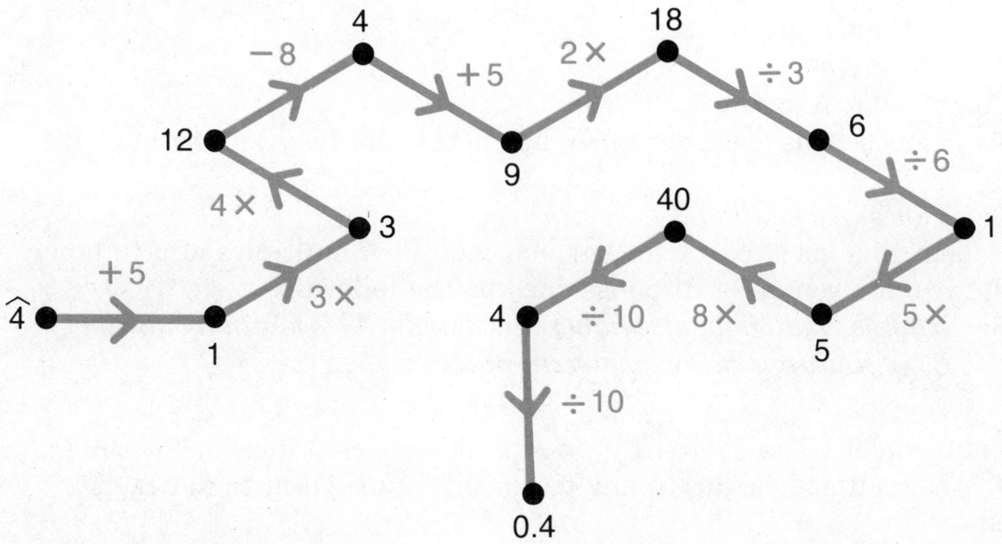

9

Now erase $\hat{4}$ and add the following red arrows to your picture:

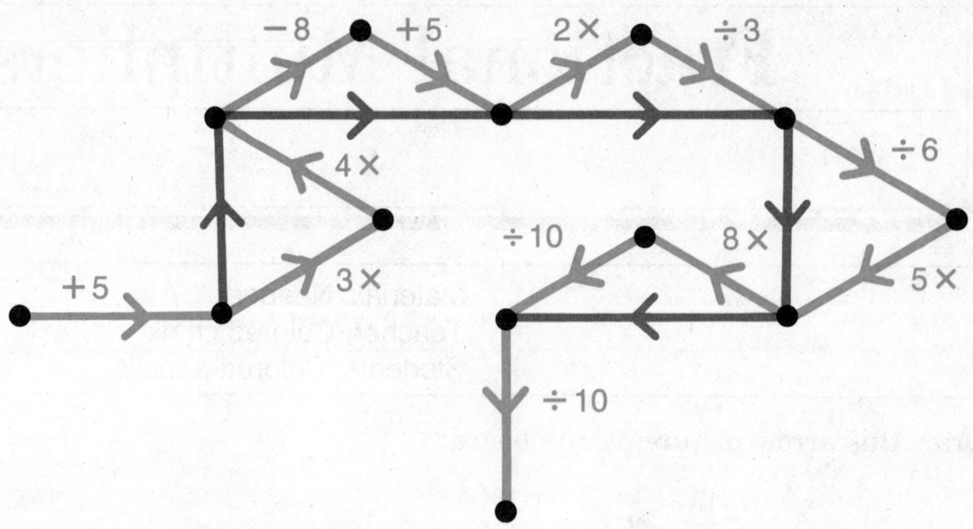

T: As I point to the red arrows, tell me what they are for.
Start with the rightmost red arrow to see if the students remember their work with the composition of relations in Volume 3, Activities 33 and 34. If you obtain a correct response immediately, then continue from ■ below. If not, proceed as follows:

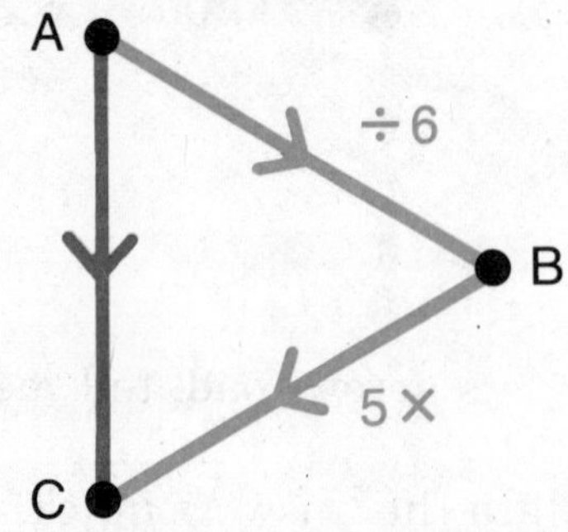

Point to dot A.
T: Suppose this dot is for 12. What is this dot for? (Point to dot B.)
S: *2.*
T: 2 is how much of 12?
S: *One-sixth.*
Point to dot A again.
T: Suppose this dot is for 30. What is this dot for? (Point to dot B.)
S: *5.*
S: *That's one-sixth of 30.*
Repeat this questioning for various choices of multiples of 6 to label dot A until you get a response such as the following:
S: *It doesn't matter what number this dot (dot A) is for; that one (dot B) will always be for one-sixth of it.*

Point to dot C.
T: This number is how many times this one? (Point to dot B.)
S: *5.*

T: And this number (point to dot B) is one-sixth of this one (point to dot A). How much of this number (point to dot A) is this one (point to dot C)?

S: *Five-sixths.*

T: So what is this arrow for? (Trace along the red arrow from dot A to dot C.)

S: $\frac{5}{6}\times$.

Ask the students to identify the red arrows several times, not always in the order in which they appear on the diagram. Here are the answers:

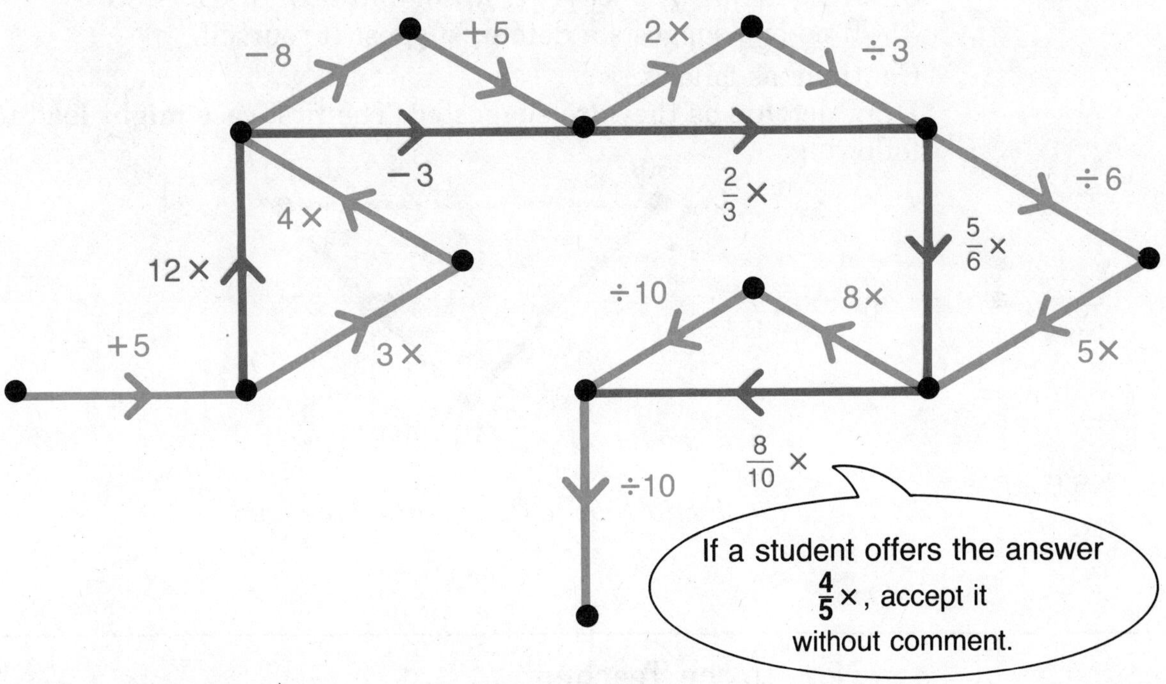

Let the students start work on Worksheet L11 while you draw the following new arrow diagram on the board:

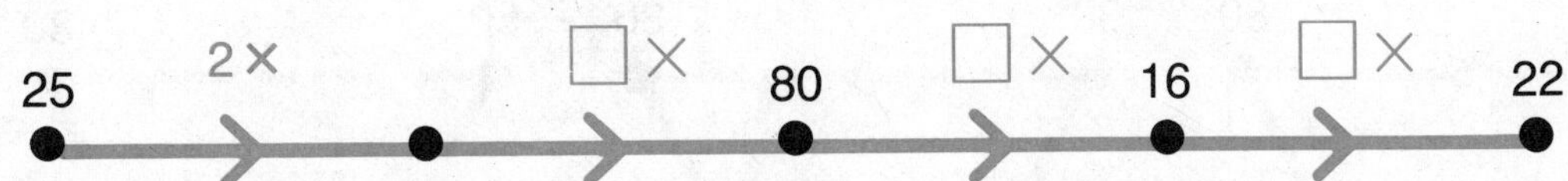

T: Stop work for a moment, please. You'll have time to finish the worksheet later. For now I want you to help me complete this arrow picture.

S: *The next dot is for 50.*

T: *Now we must get to 80. If addition were allowed, what could this arrow (the second blue one) be for?*

S: *+30.*

T: But we have to multiply. Any suggestions?

At this point, the students may respond in various ways.

1. A correct answer may be offered immediately.

S: $\frac{8}{5}\times$

T: Can you explain how you get that using a detour like this? (Point to the $\div 6$, $5\times$, $\frac{5}{6}\times$ triangle in the earlier arrow picture.)

2. A student may suggest that a detour might prove useful.

S: *We could try dividing and then multiplying, as we did in the first arrow picture.*

T: What should we divide by?

S: *We'll have to get to a number that's easy to multiply up to 80.*

S: *If we divide by 5 we'll get to 10, and then $8 \times 10 = 80$.*

3. If no one suggests a detour, suggest it yourself.

Continue as follows:

Draw detours as they are suggested. The first case might lead to the following:

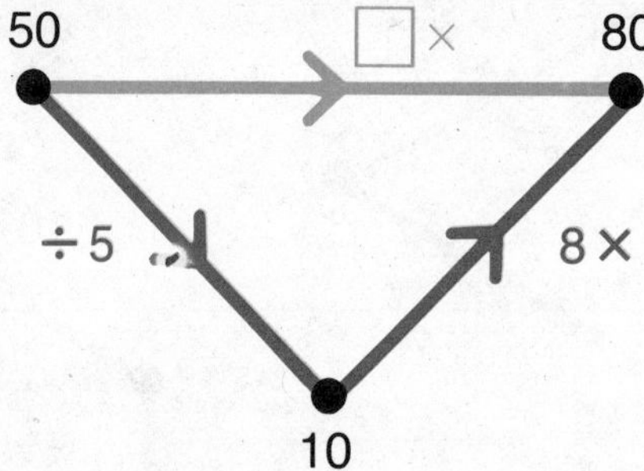

T: *So what should I write in the little blue box?*

S: $\frac{8}{5}$.

Note to the Teacher

The strategy is to divide so that the goal dot is a multiple of the detour dot. Of course, there is often a great number of possibilities (dividing by the starting number will always work, but don't mention this unless a student makes the suggestion), and alternative detours should be encouraged. Here are some:

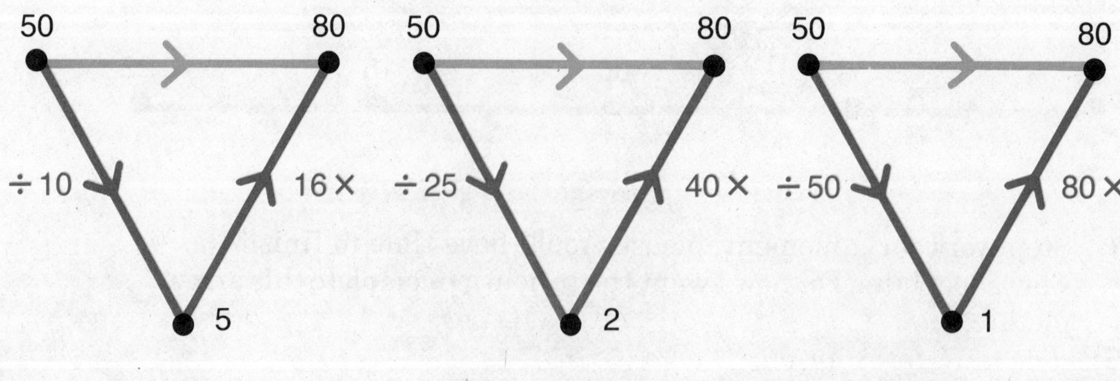

These lead to: $\frac{16}{10}\times$ $\frac{40}{25}\times$ $\frac{80}{50}\times$

Encourage the students to develop similar detours to complete the arrow diagram. One possible completion of the picture is as follows: 9

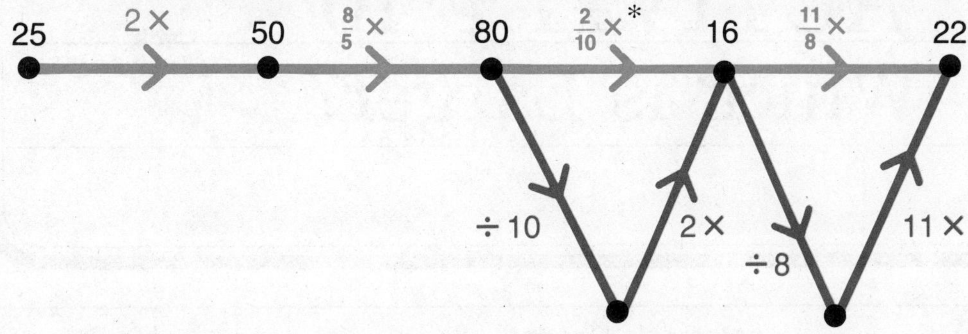

*Note: Another answer, without a detour, is $\frac{1}{5}\times$.

In the time that remains, students can complete Worksheet L11 and start Worksheet L12.

Resources Available

For class use: Worksheets L11 and L12

For out-of-class use: Any H-worksheet up through H15

ACTIVITY 10
Which is Larger?

Materials Needed
Teacher: Colored chalk
Students: Paper and colored pencils

Draw this arrow diagram on the board, omitting the letters.

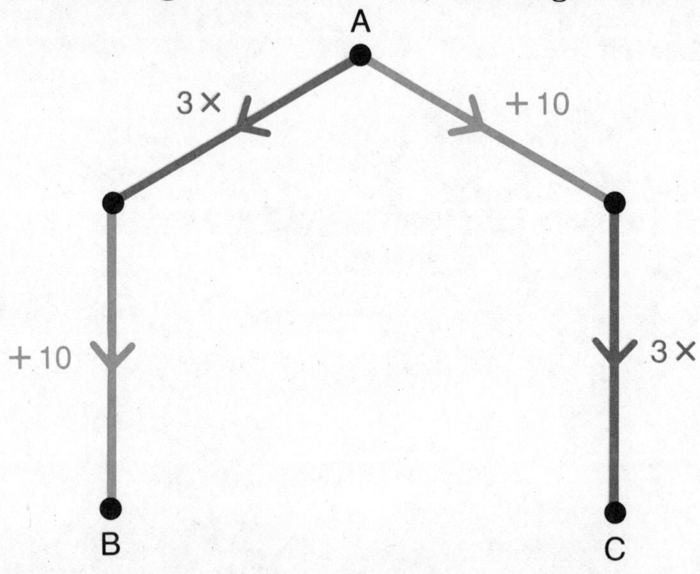

T: The dots in this diagram are for positive numbers.
Point to dots B and C.
T: Which of these numbers is larger?
S: *The one on the right.*
T: Why do you say that?
S: *I started with 2 at the top; then the bottom left dot is for 16 and the bottom right dot is for 36.*
T: Is this also true if you start with 8 here? (Point to dot A.)
S: *Yes. Then you get 34 at the left and 54 at the right.*
Suggest other numbers for dot A. Here are some possibilities:

A	B	C
8	34	54
13	49	69
0.5	11.5	31.5
1.2	13.6	33.6

Be sure to adjust the difficulty of the required calculations according to the computational ability of your class. Then invite students to decide what they think will be the difference between the bottom two numbers *no matter what starting number* is used at the top dot.

S: *The bottom left-hand number will be 10 plus 3 times the starting number, but the bottom right-hand number will be 3 times the sum of 10 and the starting; that's 30 plus 3 times the starting number. So the right-hand number is 20 more than the left-hand number.*

If no student responds in this way, help the class to make the analysis by starting at dot A with, say, 3.3 and following the computations on the arrow diagram as follows:

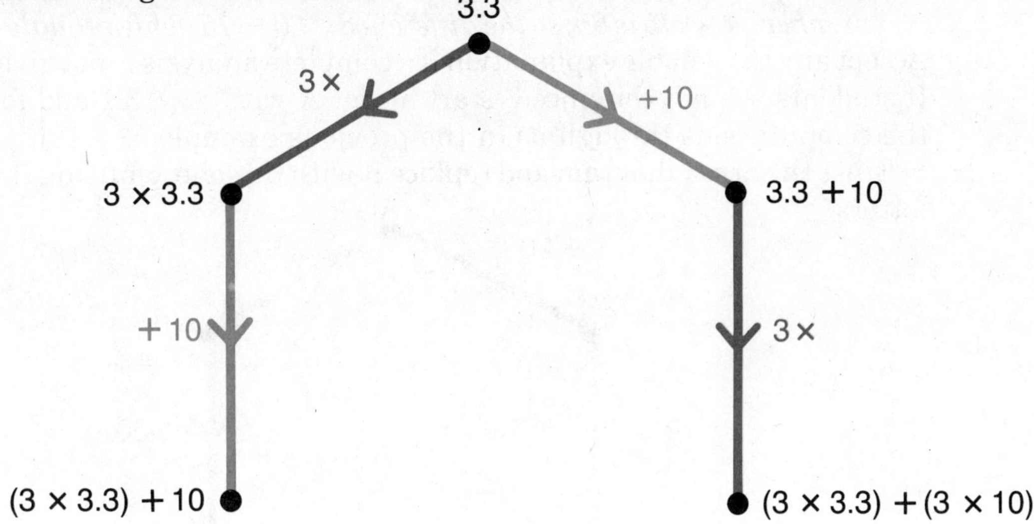

The difference is $(3 \times 10) - 10 = 20$.

Erase the diagram and replace it with this one, omitting the letters.

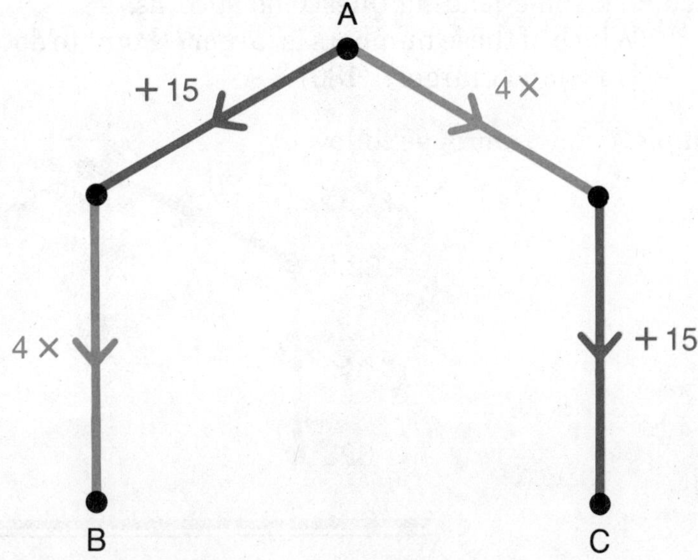

T: Again the dots are for positive numbers.

Point to dots B and C.

T: Which of these numbers is larger?

S: *The one on the left.*

T: Why do you think that?

S: *You multiply a bigger number by 4 on the left than you do on the right.*

Accept any such answer, even though incomplete.

T: How much larger is this number (point to dot B) than this (point to dot C)?

S: *45 larger.*

T: How did you work that out?

S: *The bottom right-hand number is 15 plus 4 times the starting number, and the bottom left-hand number is 4 times the sum of 15 and the starting number; that's 4 times 15 plus 4 times the starting number. 4 × (15 is 60, so the difference is 60 − 15, which equals 45.)*

Accept any reasonable explanation if a complete analysis is not given. If students are not convinced, start at dot A with, say, 3.1 and follow the computations through as in the previous example.

Erase the arrow diagram and replace it with this one, omitting the letters.

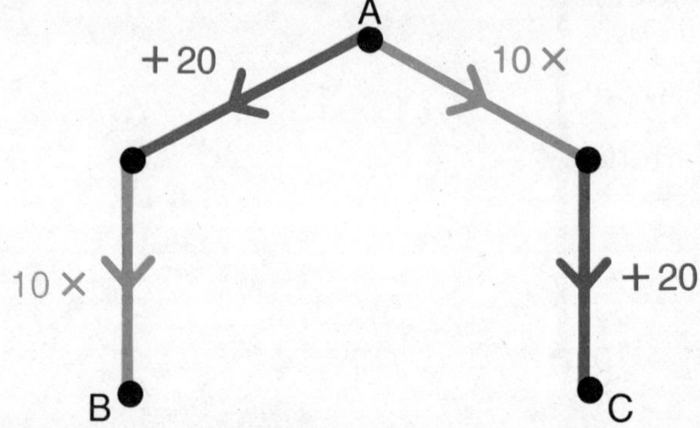

T: Once again, all the dots are for positive numbers. The largest number in the picture is 325. Copy the figure onto your papers and label the dots.

Let the students work on the problem independently for a few minutes. If needed, ask some leading questions such as:

> Which of these numbers is larger? (Point to dots B and C.)
> How much larger? (180)

The complete diagram is as follows:

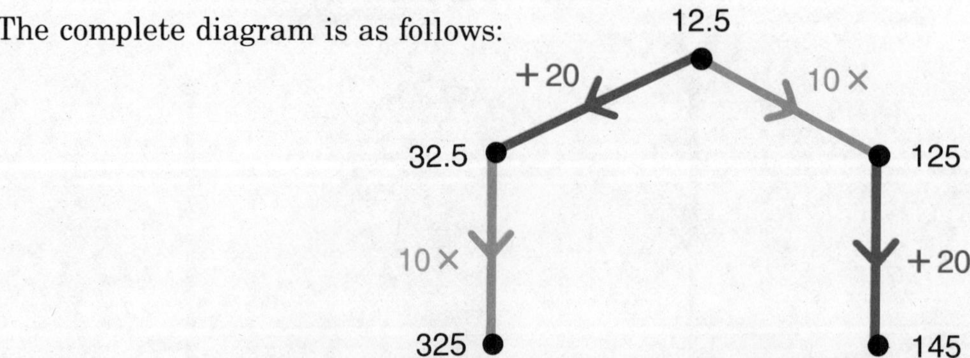

Resources Available

For class use: Worksheets L13 and L14

For out-of-class use: Any H-worksheet up through H15

ACTIVITY 11
Composition 3

Materials Needed
Teacher: Colored chalk
Students: None

Draw the following large arrow picture and composition code on the board:

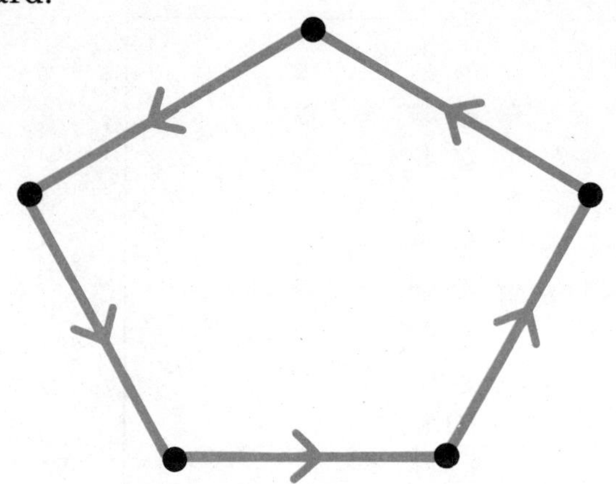

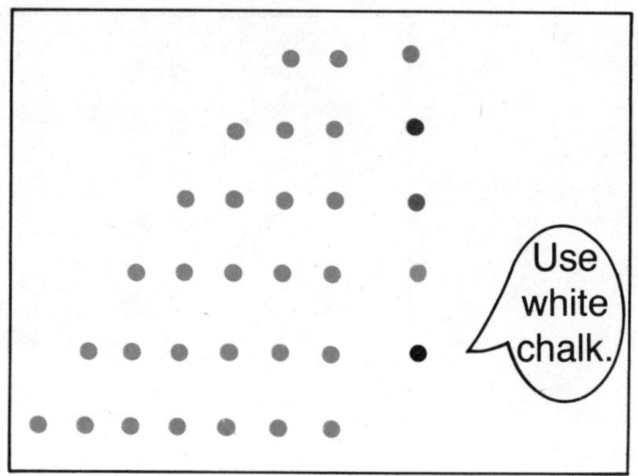

Briefly review the meaning of the code beside the arrow picture:

Blue followed by blue gives a green arrow; three blue arrows following one another give a purple arrow; and so on.

T: Who would like to draw the green arrows in the arrow picture?

Let a volunteer (assisted by others, if necessary) draw the green arrows on the board. Similarly, let volunteers draw the purple, red, and orange arrows. At this stage the digram should look like this:

Very good. Now, what about the white arrows? Can anyone suggest how to draw a white arrow?

You may receive incorrect responses at this point, partly because the diagram is becoming crowded and partly because students will not think systematically. As soon as you get a correct answer . . .

S: *The white is the same as the blue.*

. . . ask the student to demonstrate it by pointing at any beginning point with both hands and tracing along the chain of six blue arrows with the right hand.

T: What about seven blue dots? What color should I use?

S: *Green.*

If a wrong answer is given, ask the student to trace along a chain of seven blue arrows.

T: I'm getting tired of drawing these long strings of blue dots, so I'm going to use a kind of shorthand.

Add to the composition code as follows:

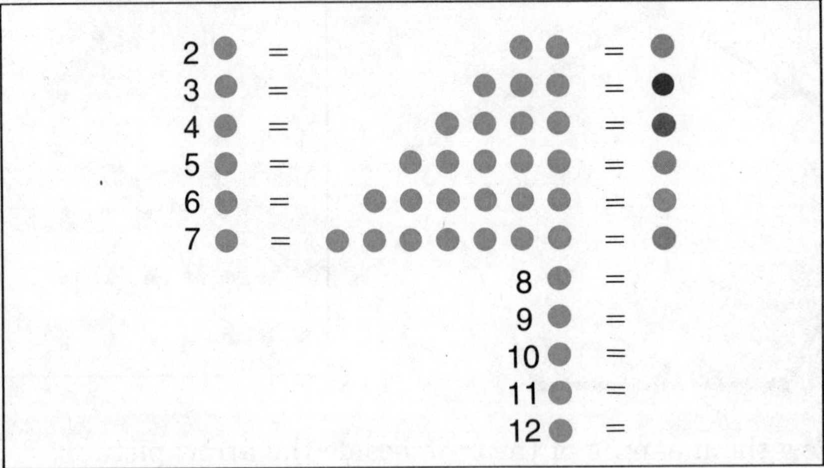

Point to **8** •

T: What color should I use for this?

S: *Purple.*

Let the student draw an appropriately colored dot in the code.

Point to **9** •

T: And this?

S: *Red.*

T: Can anyone explain what is going on?
S: *Five blue dots is once around, and we're starting over.*
In the same way, obtain the following:

10 ● = ●
11 ● = ●
12 ● = ●

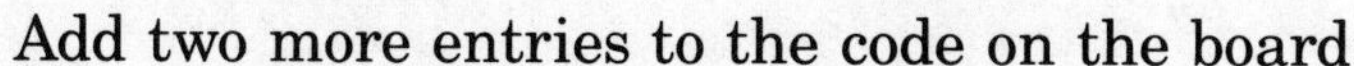

Add two more entries to the code on the board:

32 ● =
103 ● =

Point to **32**●.
T: What color is this?
S: *Green, because it is six times around and two more.*
Point to **103**●.
S: *Purple.*

Resources Available

For class use: Worksheets L15 and L16
For out-of-class use: Any H-worksheet up through H18

ACTIVITY 12
Composition 4

Materials Needed
Teacher: Colored chalk
Students: Colored pencils

Draw these four arrow pictures on the board:

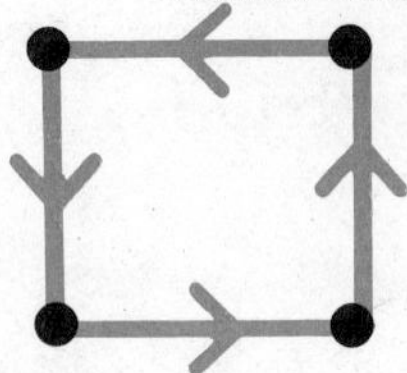
•

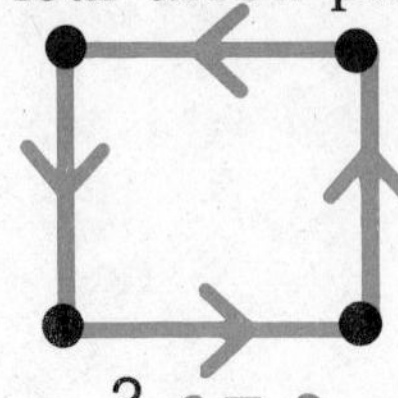
2 • = •

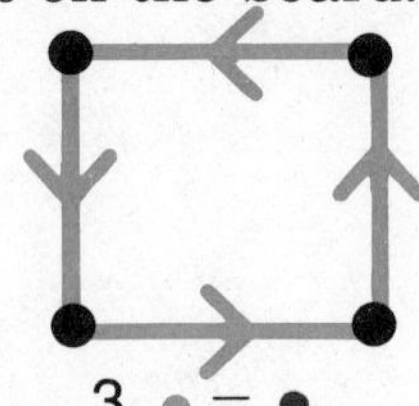
3 • = •

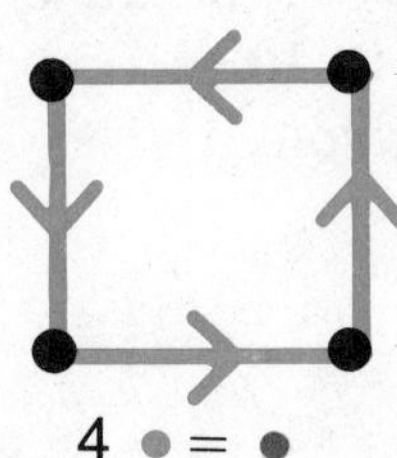
4 • = •

Call on students to add arrows to the diagrams until they look like this:

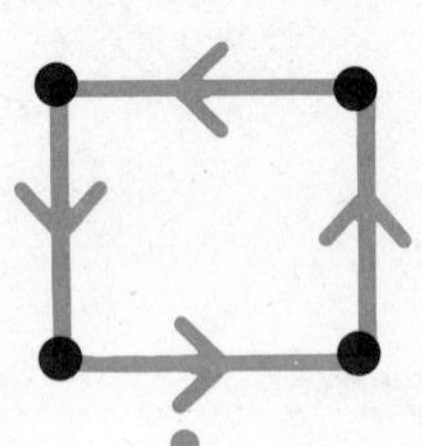
•

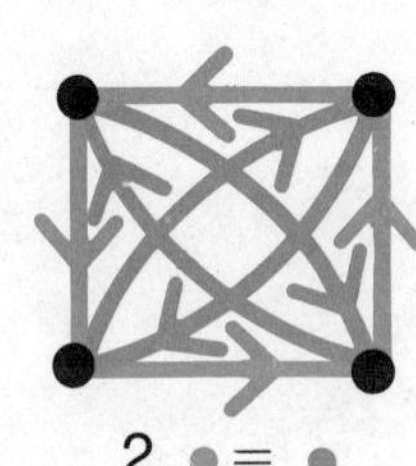
2 • = •

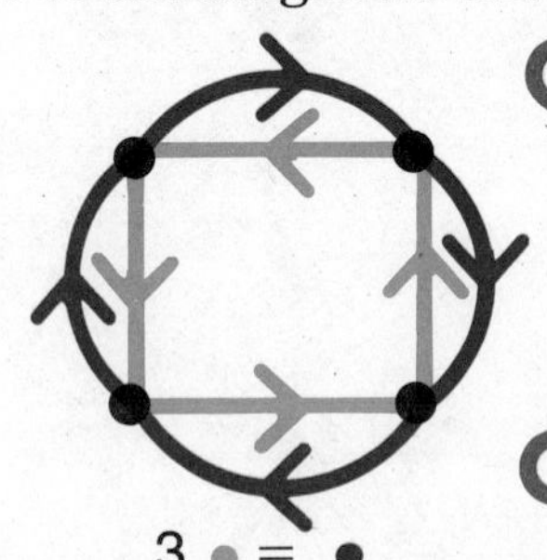
3 • = •

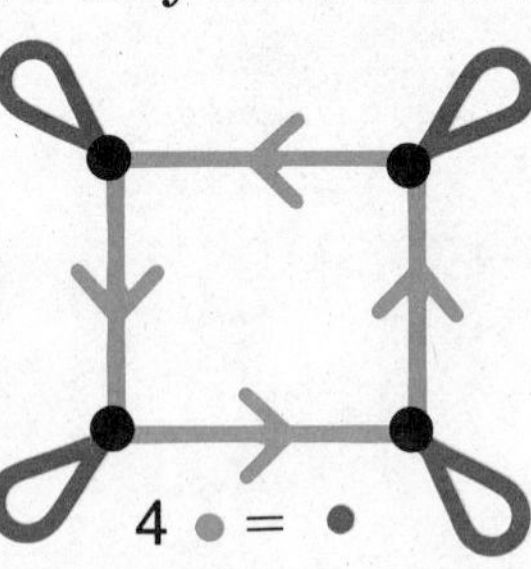
4 • = •

Point to the leftmost diagram.

T: A little while ago, I told you that an arrow picture like this is called a **cycle.** Can you see any other cycles?

S: *There is a purple cycle.*

T: Any others?

Students may answer no to this question. If so, ask, "What about green?"

S: *There are* **two** *green cycles.*

T: And red?

S: *There are four red cycles.*

T: Turn to Worksheet L17 and try to count some other cycles.

Resources Available
For class use: Worksheets L17 and L18, and for those who finish early, Worksheets A1–4
For out-of-class use: Any H-worksheet up through H18

ACTIVITIES 13 and 14
Probability 1

Materials Needed
Teacher: Two Minicomputer checkers (one red and one blue), chalk
Students: None

T: I have two Minicomputer checkers in my hands, one red and one blue. I'll hold them behind my back and shake them. Then I'll put one in each hand. Now I'll hold out my right hand. (Do this as you describe it.)

What is the probability that the red checker is in my right hand? (Keep your right hand closed, and keep your left hand still behind you.)

You will most likely get responses such as 1 in 2, one-half, 1 chance in 2.

T: What is the probability that it is blue? (The same: 1 in 2, one-half.)

We can show this by drawing a probability tree.

Draw the following diagram on the board:

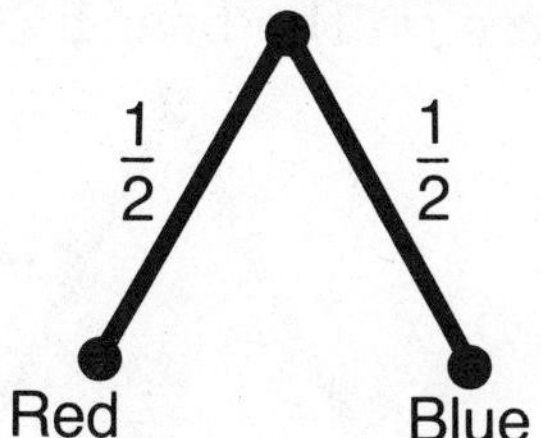

T: How could I use these checkers to select one of two people to get a prize?

S: *Call one of them Red and the other Blue. Then the one whose checker is in your hand wins.*

T: Is this fair?

S: *Yes. Each one has the same chance of winning.*

T: Could we select the person by flipping a coin?

S: *Yes. You could call one person Heads and the other Tails.*

T: What is the probability that the coin will come up heads? (one-half, 1 in 2) tails? (the same) Is this a fair way of selecting one of two people to get the prize? (yes)

Draw another probability tree on the board:

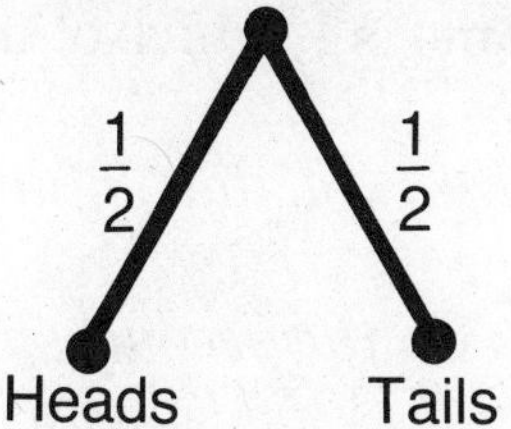

13
14

Then draw this spinner:

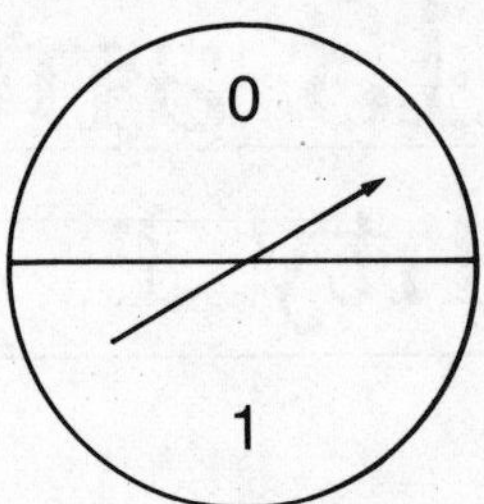

T: You have used spinners in games. What is the probability that the arrow of this spinner will stop on 0? (one-half, 1 in 2) On 1? (the same) Could we use this spinner to give the prize to one of two people?

S: *Yes. Call one person 0 and the other 1.*

Draw this new probability tree on the board:

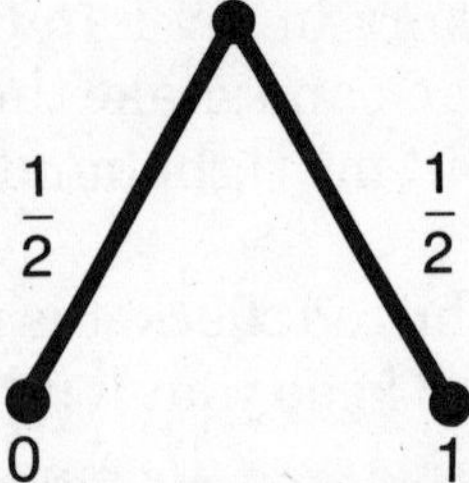

T: What do you think would happen if I spun the spinner 100 times?

S: *You would get about fifty-fifty.*

T: Explain that, please.

S: *About 50 times you would get 0 and about 50 times you would get 1.*

Draw this spinner and this tree on the board:

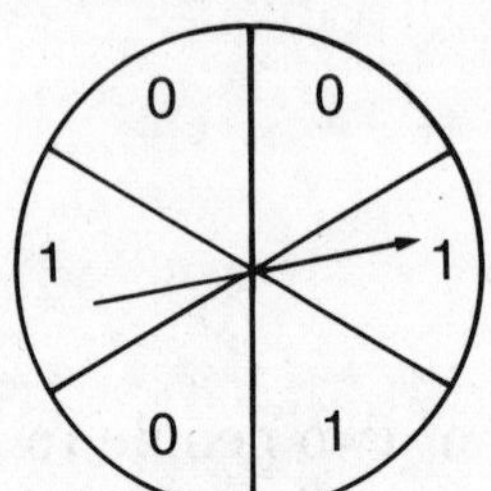

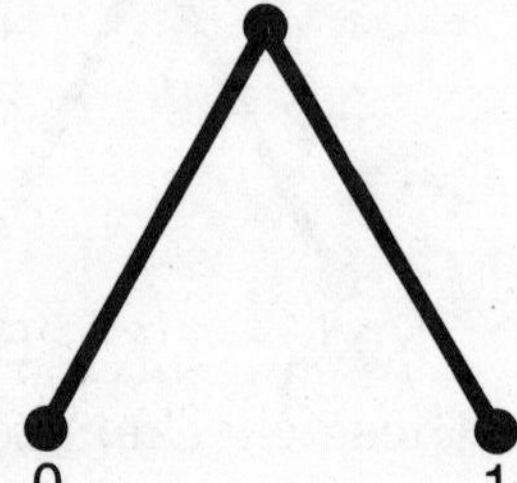

T: If you spin this spinner, what is the probability that the arrow will stop on 0? (3 in 6, three-sixths) On 1? (the same: 3 in 6, three-sixths)

You now have these diagrams on the board:

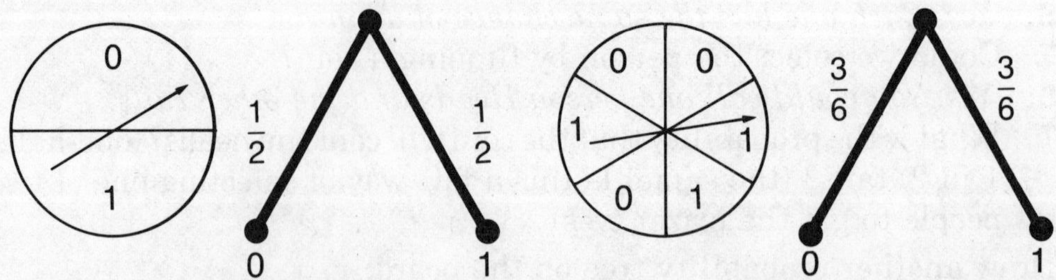

T: If you win a prize when the outcome is 1, which of these two spinners would you choose to spin?

S: *The second, because there are three 1s on that spinner and only one on the first.*

S: *But there are three 1s out of six on the second spinner.*

S: *They are the same; 3 chances in 6 is the same as 1 chance in 2.*

Record this observation on the board: $\frac{1}{2} = \frac{3}{6}$. 13 14

Then draw another spinner and tree:

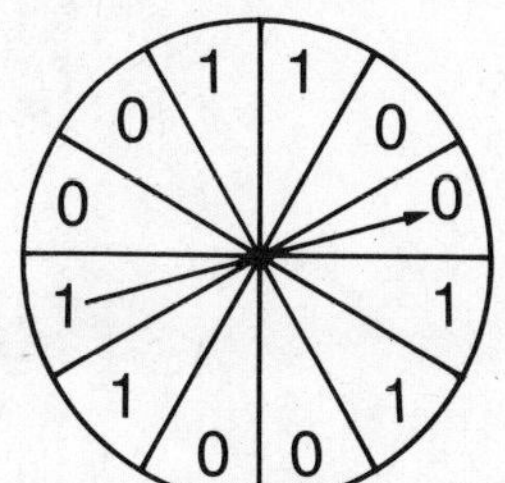

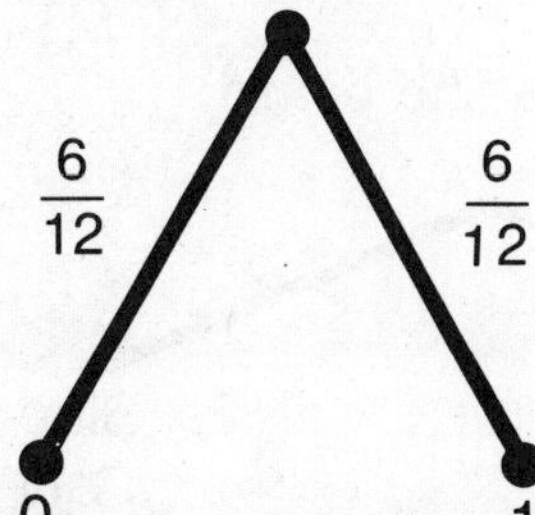

Repeat your questions, obtaining $\frac{1}{2} = \frac{3}{6} = \frac{6}{12}$. Invite students to draw (or describe) other 0/1-spinners giving equal possibilities for 0 and 1. For each drawing or description, include the corresponding probability tree and add the information to the list of equalities, obtaining, for example:

$$\frac{1}{2} = \frac{3}{6} = \frac{6}{12} = \frac{30}{60} = \frac{60}{120} = \frac{120}{240} = \frac{3{,}000{,}000}{6{,}000{,}000} = \ldots$$

Erase from the board all the preceding work.

T: So far we have found a number of fair ways to select one of two people to get a prize. We can use the red and blue checkers, flip a coin, or use a fair 0/1-spinner. But suppose there were four people (called A, B, C, and D) and only one prize. How could we give the prize to one of them?

Students will most likely suggest a spinner such as this:

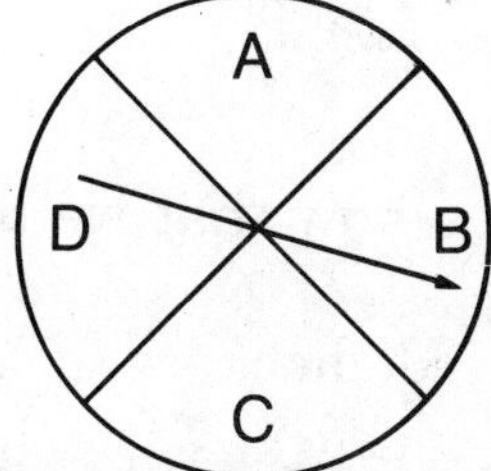

T: Good idea. But suppose that all we have are one red and one blue checker.

Let the students discuss this. They might need some help in deciding to separate the people into two groups of two and then use the checkers twice, first to select one group and then to select one person from that group to get the prize.

It is good practice to let four students illustrate the decision process, such as students A and B in one group and C and D in the other.

(From here on, the "$\frac{1}{2}$" labels in the diagrams are omitted.)

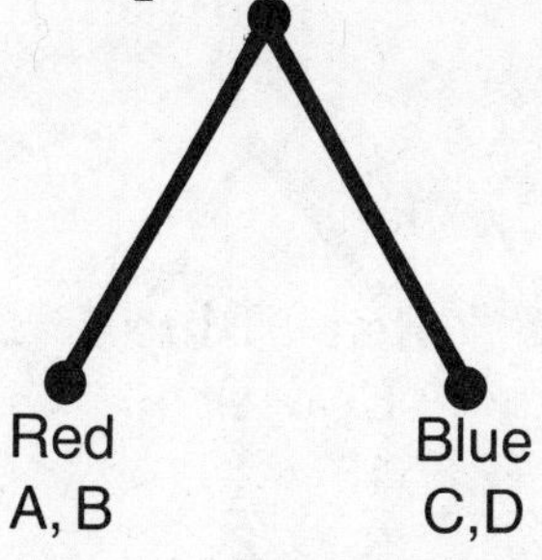

13
14

T: If the outcome is Red, we choose A and B. If it is Blue, we choose C and D. Then what should we do next?

S: *Use the checkers again to choose either between A and B or between C and D.*

Draw the following on the board:

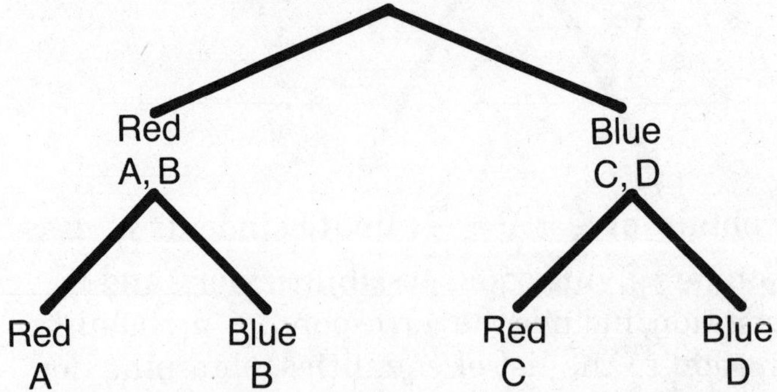

T: Is this fair?

S: *Yes. Each one has one chance in four.*

T: We can use a code for deciding who gets the prize. Let's start with B.

Direct your question to the student designated B.

T: B, how must the checkers be selected so that you get the prize?

S: *First there must be a red checker and the second time a blue.*

T: So your code is Red Blue.

Ask each of the other three students to annouce his or her code while you write them on the board.

A: Red Red
B: Red Blue
C: Blue Red
D: Blue Blue

T: We don't need the probability tree now that we have the code.

Erase the tree, leaving only the code.

T: How would we use the blue and red checkers to select one person among eight to get the prize?

The class should have no difficulty deciding on the following tree diagram:

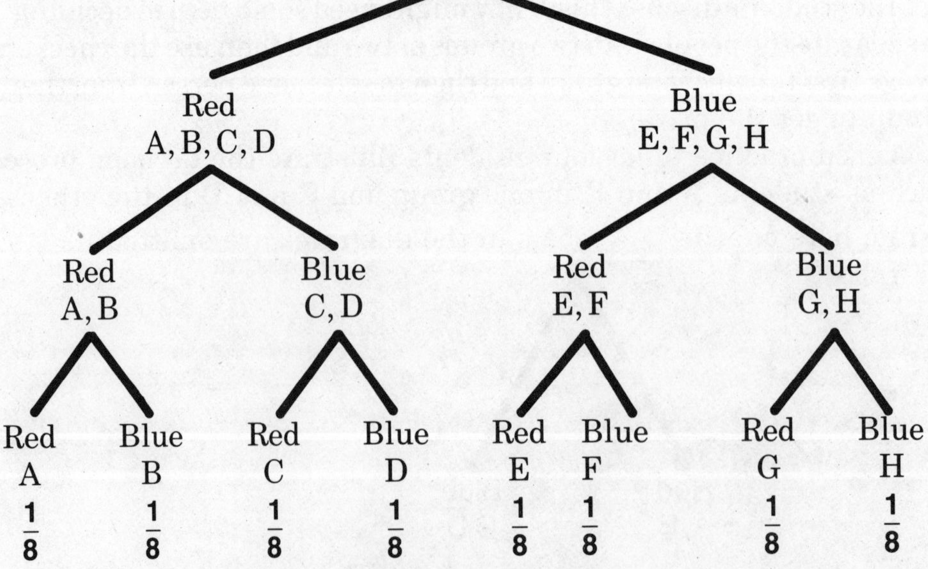

and on the code for each of the eight people:

A: R R R
B: R R B
C: R B R
D: R B B
E: B R R
F: B R B
G: B B R
H: B B B

Then when it is established that each person has one chance in eight of getting the prize, actually perform the experiment of selecting one of the two checkers. For purposes of this description, suppose the outcome is Blue.

T: The first stage is Blue. Now who can still get the prize? (E, F, G, or H)

Perform the experiment again; suppose the outcome is Red.

T: The second stage is Red. Now who can still get the prize? (E or F)

Again select a checker. Suppose the outcome is Red.

T: The third stage is Red. Who gets the prize? (E)

Erase the probability tree.

T: With two stages there are four possibilities. With three stages there are eight. If we have four stages (that is, if we choose a checker four times, one after another), how many possibilities will there be? (16) With five stages? (32)

Illustrate the first of these answers with a tree diagram:

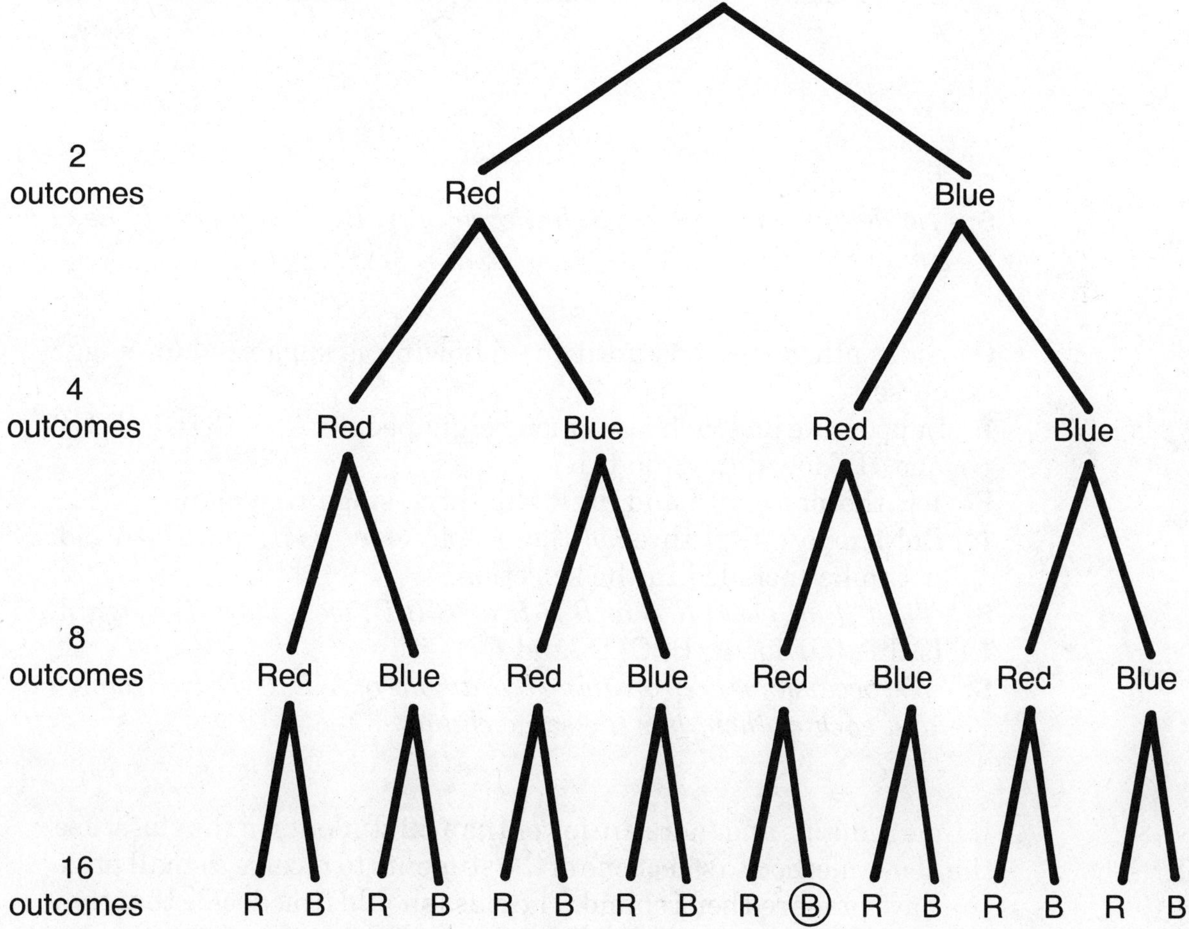

Select a student and give him or her a code. (For example, John is B R R B.) Then ask him to locate the end of his path in the tree (circled in the diagram above).

13
14

T: Suppose there are only five people and we want to use the checker to select one of the five to get the prize. How can we do this fairly?
S: *Use the checkers twice to pick one person out of A, B, C, and D. Then use the checkers again to choose between the winner and E.*

Draw a tree to show this suggestion:

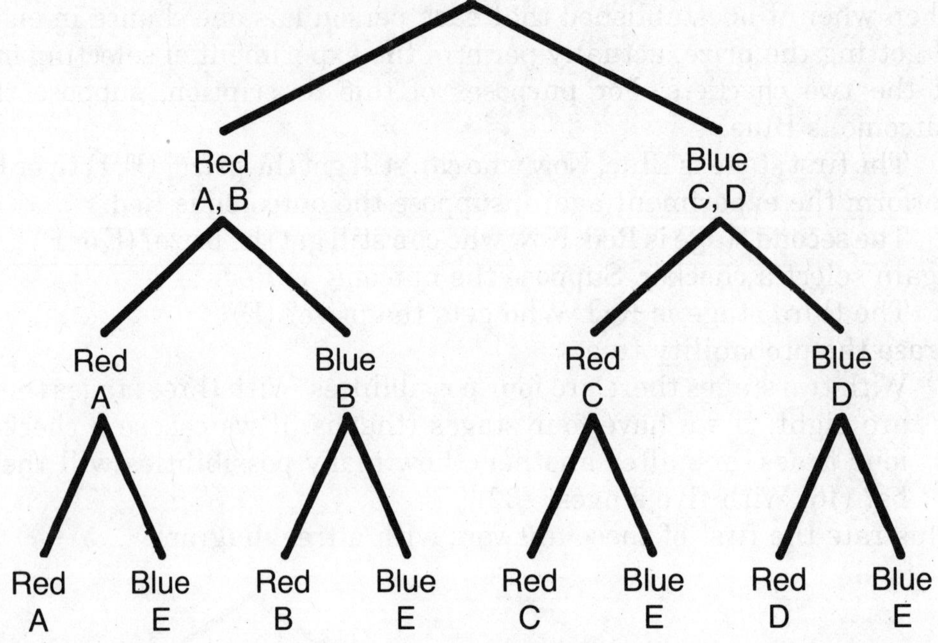

T: Is this fair?
S: *No. E has 4 chances in 8, but each of A, B, C, and D only has one chance in 8.*

Consider other methods until the following is suggested (or suggest it yourself).

T: Suppose we had to choose among eight people: A, B, C, D, E, F, G, and H. How did we do this?

Review the procedure and draw the three-stage tree again.

T: But suppose that three of the people—say, F, G, and H—decided not to be included in the selection.
S: *Then if we get B R B or B B R or B B B, we'll start over again.*
T: Is this fair for A, B, C, D, and E?
S: *Yes, because we keep on doing it until one of A, B, C, D, or E wins, and each of them has the same chance.*

If time remains and there are fewer than 32 students in the class, use the above method to select one of the students to receive a small prize you have prepared beforehand. The class should first decide that they must use the checkers:

Three times if there are at least 5 and at most 8 students.
Four times if there are at least 9 and at most 16 students.
Five times if there are at least 17 and at most 32 students.

For example, if there are 23 students in the class, give each one a five-letter code name from this list:

RRRRR   RBRRR   BRRRR
RRRRB   RBRRB   BRRRB
RRRBR   RBRBR   BRRBR
RRRBB   RBRBB   BRRBB
RRBRR   RBBRR   BRBRR
RRBRB   RBBRB   BRBRB
RRBBR   RBBBR   BRBBR
RRBBB   RBBBB

Then select a checker five times. If necessary, repeat this exercise until one of the listed code names is selected.

Resources Available

For out-of-class use: Any H-worksheet up through H21

ACTIVITIES 15 and 16
Guess My Rule: Exponents

Materials Needed
Teacher: Chalk
Students: Paper and pencils

Write the following on the board:

$$2 * 3 = 8$$
$$3 * 2 = 9$$
$$3 * 1 = 3$$
$$1 * 3 = 1$$
$$5 * 2 = \square$$

T: I have a secret rule for *, and I've given you four clues to help you discover what that rule is. See if you can guess my rule. Which number do you think goes in the box? If you think you know the answer, write it on you papers.

Note to the Teacher

The secret rule * in this activity is given by: $a * b = a^b$; that is $a * b$ is a to the power b. Thus, $2 * 3 = 2^3 = 2 \times 2 \times 2 = 8$ and the number in the box is 25 because $5 * 2 = 5^2 = 5 \times 5 = 25$.

This is for your information only. Do not divulge the rule to your students until they guess it.

Walk around the room checking the students' papers. Acknowledge aloud any correct answers and mention incorrect ones explicitly. For example, "Yes that's correct" or "No, 10 is not correct." Let a student who guesses correctly tell the class that the answer is 25, but ask him or her not to give away the rule. If no one guesses correctly, write 25 in the box yourself. Proceed similarly with these problems. (The answers given in the boxes are for your information only.)

$7 * 2 = \boxed{49}$	$4 * 2 = \boxed{16}$
$10 * 2 = \boxed{100}$	$9 * 2 = \boxed{81}$
$8 * 2 = \boxed{64}$	$11 * 2 = \boxed{121}$
$1 * 2 = \boxed{1}$	

T: Who can explain what happens with * 2?

S: *7 * 2 = 49 because 7 × 7 = 49, 10 * 2 = 100 because 10 × 10 = 100, and so on.*

S: *You always get square numbers when you use * 2.*

T: Good. Let's try some with * *3*.

Write these problems on the board (omitting the answers), and follow a similar procedure to the one above:

$$5 * 3 = \boxed{125}$$
$$3 * 3 = \boxed{27}$$
$$4 * 3 = \boxed{64}$$

T: Who can explain * 3?

S: *Just multiply the first number by itself three times. For example, 5*3* is 5 × 5 × 5, which is 125.

Accept any reasonable explanation.

T: Before someone explains what the rule* is in general, here are a few more problems so that everyone can try once more to guess the rule.

Write these equations on the board, omitting the answers, and proceed as above:

$$2 * 4 = \boxed{16}$$
$$3 * 4 = \boxed{81}$$
$$10 * 3 = \boxed{1{,}000}$$
$$1 * 10 = \boxed{1}$$
$$10 * 1 = \boxed{10}$$
$$2 * 10 = \boxed{1{,}024}$$

T: Who can explain the rule?

S: *You multiply the first number by itself as many times as the second number tells you to. For example, 2*4 means multiply 2 by itself four times; 2 × 2 × 2 × 2 = 16.*

Accept any reasonable explanations your students offer. Because this is a rather difficult idea to verbalize, students might prefer to explain the rule at the board by writing the appropriate multiplication problem. For example:

$$2 * 4 = \boxed{16} = 2 \times 2 \times 2 \times 2$$
$$3 * 4 = \boxed{81} = 3 \times 3 \times 3 \times 3$$
$$10 * 3 = \boxed{1{,}000} = 10 \times 10 \times 10$$
$$1 * 10 = \boxed{1} = 1 \times 1 \times 1 \times 1 \times 1 \times 1 \times 1 \times 1 \times 1 \times 1$$
$$10 * 1 = \boxed{10} = 10$$
$$2 * 10 = \boxed{1{,}024} = 2 \times 2 \times 2 \times 2 \times 2 \times 2 \times 2 \times 2 \times 2 \times 2$$

T: As you can see, writing out such lengthy multiplication calculations can sometimes be tiring and unpleasant. Fortunately, there is a shorthand notation that lets us cut down on the amount of writing.

Write the following equation on the board as you read it aloud:

$$16 = 2 \times 2 \times 2 \times 2 = 2^4$$

T: For $2 \times 2 \times 2 \times 2$ we write 2^4 and read this symbol as "two to the fourth power" or "two to the power four." Copy these problems and fill in the boxes.

Write these problems on the board, omitting the answers:

$$2^5 = \boxed{32}$$
$$3^3 = \boxed{27}$$
$$2^7 = \boxed{128}$$
$$4^3 = \boxed{64}$$
$$12^2 = \boxed{144}$$
$$0^{11} = \boxed{0}$$
$$1^{26} = \boxed{1}$$

Check through the problems collectively. Encourage students who have difficulty with this notation to begin by writing out the associated multiplication calculation.

Erase everything you have written on the board. Then replace it with $\mathbf{2^5 \times 2^3}$.

T: What number is $2^5 \times 2^3$?

Allow a few minutes for the students to work on this problem.

S: *256.*

T: How did you get 256?

S: *$2^5 = 32$, $2^3 = 8$, and $32 \times 8 = 256$.*

Complete the calculation on the board and extend it as follows:

$$2^5 \times 2^3 = 256 = 2^{\square}$$

T: What number goes in the box?

S: *8.*

T: Please explain.

S: *$2^5 = 2 \times 2 \times 2 \times 2 \times 2$ and $2^3 = 2 \times 2 \times 2$,*
so $2^5 \times 2^3 = 2 \times 2 \times 2 \times 2 \times 2 \times 2 \times 2 \times 2 = 2^8$.

Complete the calculation on the board and add the following problem:

$$2^5 \times 2^3 = 256 = 2^8$$
$$3^2 \times 3^3 = \underline{\qquad} = 3^{\square}$$

S: *$3^2 \times 3^3 = 243 = 3^5$, because $3^2 \times 3^3 = 3 \times 3 \times 3 \times 3 \times 3 = 243$.*

15
16

T: Do you notice anything interesting about these problems?
S: *$2^5 \times 2^3 = 2^{5+3} = 2^8$.*
$3^2 \times 3^3 = 3^{2+3} = 3^5$.
T: Try these.

Write the following on the board:

$$5^4 \times 5^7 = 5^{\square}$$
$$6^3 \times 6^{12} = 6^{\square}$$
$$19^1 \times 19^6 = 19^{\square}$$

S: *$5^4 \times 5^7 = 5^{11}$.*
$6^3 \times 6^{12} = 6^{15}$.
$19^1 \times 19^6 = 19^7$.

Write on the board: **$2^{\square} = 64$.**

T: What number goes in the box?
S: *6, because $2^6 = 2 \times 2 \times 2 \times 2 \times 2 \times 2 = 64$.*

Continue on the board:

$$2^6 = 64$$
$$2^{\square} = 127$$

S: *Nothing works because 2 to any (positive whole number) power is even, and 127 is odd.*

S: *I know another reason why there is no solution. $2^6 = 64$, so $2^7 = 2^6 \times 2^1 = 64 \times 2 = 128$. So 127 is too small.*

Write these problems on the board:

$2^{\square} = 512$		$(3 \times 4)^2 = \square$
$6^3 = \square$		$2^3 \times 3^2 = \square$
$7^3 = \square$		$2^3 \times 5^2 = \square$
$\square^3 = 125$		$2^3 \times 5^3 = \square$
$5^{\square} = 610$		$(2 \times 5)^3 = \square$
$\square^{\square} = 27$		$(2 \times 5)^6 = 10^{\square}$
$\square^{\triangle} = 256$		$2^6 \times 5^6 = 10^{\square}$
$2^2 \times 3^2 = \square$		$4^3 = 2^{\square}$
$(2 \times 3)^2 = \square$		$9^2 = 3^{\square}$
$3^2 \times 4^2 = \square$		

Let the students work individually on these problems. Observe the class at work, giving assistance to those who need it. Remind students that for a problem such as $\square^{\square} = 27$, the same shapes indicate that the same number must go in both boxes. On the other hand, for a problem such as $\square^{\triangle} = 81$, the different shapes indicate that the numbers in the square and triangle *might* be different. However, it is possible to write the same number in $\square$ and $\triangle$ if there is one that works.

When most of the students have finished, check through the problems collectively.

15
16

The answers are as follows:

$2^9 = 512$
$6^3 = 216$
$7^3 = 343$
$5^3 = 125$
$5^{\square} = 610$ (there is no whole-number solution.)
$3^3 = 27$

These are the only three solutions.
$16^2 = 256$
$4^4 = 256$
$2^8 = 256$

$2^2 \times 3^2 = 36$
$(2 \times 3)^2 = 36$
$3^2 \times 4^2 = 144$
$(3 \times 4)^2 = 144$
$2^3 \times 3^2 = 72$
$2^3 \times 5^2 = 200$
$2^3 \times 5^3 = 1{,}000$
$(2 \times 5)^3 = 1{,}000$
$(2 \times 5)^6 = 10^6$
$2^6 \times 5^6 = 10^6$
$4^3 = 2^6$
$9^2 = 3^4$

Resources Available

For out-of-class use: Any H-worksheet up through H24

ACTIVITY 17
Decimals 3

Materials Needed
Teacher: Colored chalk
Students: Paper and pencils

Draw this number line on the board:

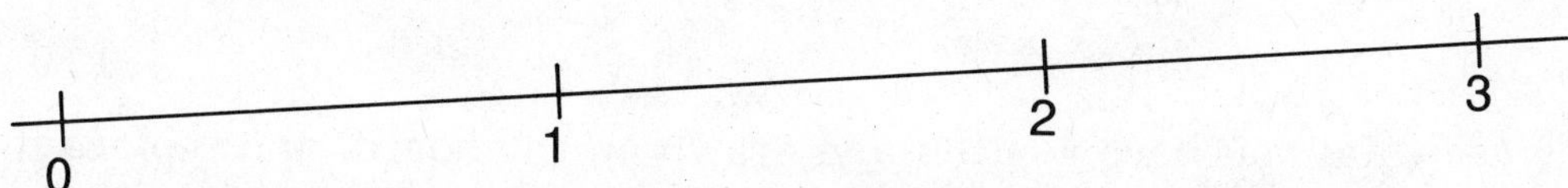

T: Can anyone mark $\frac{1}{5}$ on this number line?

Let students come to the board and point to places where they think $\frac{1}{5}$ should be located. As you discuss each location, try to bring out the idea of breaking up the segment from 0 to 1 into five equal parts. When this has been done reasonably accurately, ask students also to mark points that break up each of the segments from 1 to 2 and from 2 to 3 into five equal parts. Then ask students to draw and label dots for $\frac{1}{5}$, $\frac{4}{5}$, $1\frac{3}{5}$, and $2\frac{2}{5}$. If necessary, help students count from 0: $\frac{1}{5}$ (mark it with a dot), $\frac{2}{5}$, $\frac{3}{5}$, $\frac{4}{5}$ (mark it). Then 1, $1\frac{1}{5}$, $1\frac{2}{5}$, $1\frac{3}{5}$ (mark it), and so on, as shown below:

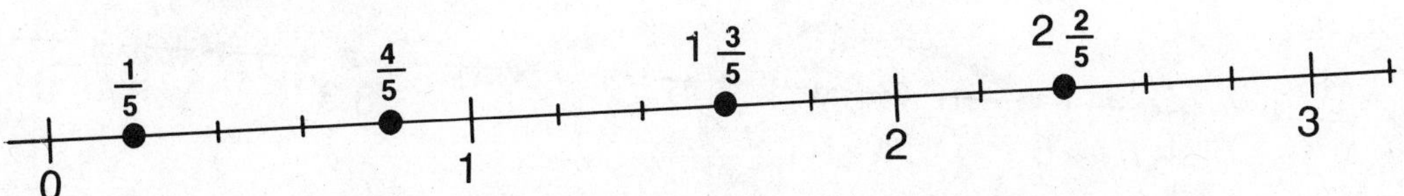

Now mark the midpoints of each of the new small intervals.

T: We have now broken up the segment from 0 to 1 into how many equal parts? (10)

Draw a dot at the mark between 0 and $\frac{1}{5}$.

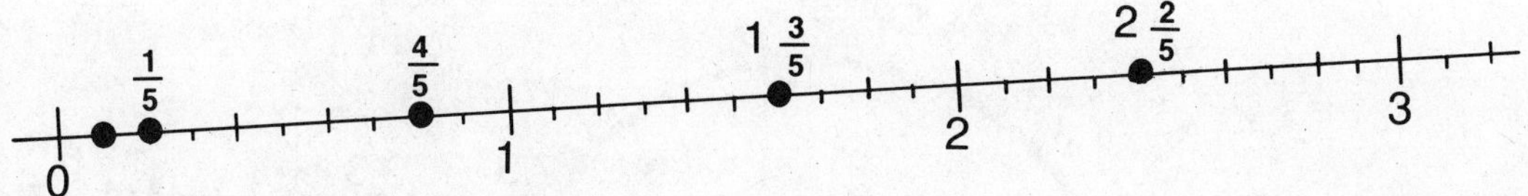

T: What is the number for this dot? ($\frac{1}{10}$)

What is another name for $\frac{1}{5}$? ($\frac{2}{10}$) Why ?

S: *I counted. The dot for* $\frac{1}{5}$ *is at* $\frac{2}{10}$.

17

T: Do you know a decimal name for $\frac{1}{5}$?

S: *0.2, because "zero point two" means "two-tenths."*

Write the equation $\frac{1}{5} = \frac{2}{10} = \mathbf{0.2}$ below the number line.

Similarly, let students give various names for $\frac{8}{5}$:

$$\frac{8}{5} = 1\frac{3}{5} = \frac{16}{10} = 1.6.$$

If necessary, you can provide assistance by suggesting that students count fifths and tenths from 0. Next, ask a student to draw and label a dot for 0.9 on this number line to suggest a fractional name for 0.9. $\left(\frac{9}{10}\right)$ Continue locating several other numbers between 0 and 3 on this number line.

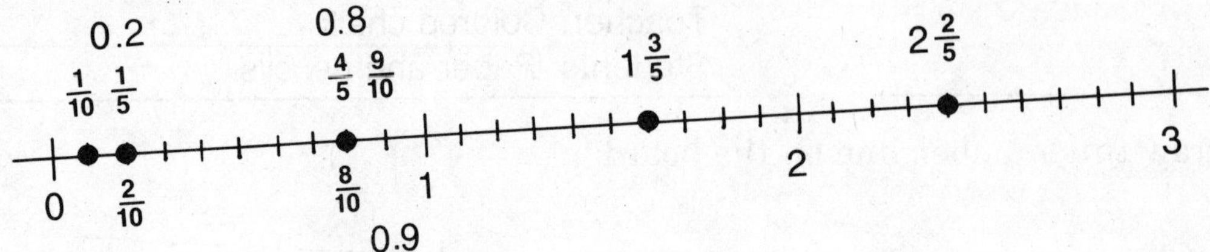

Erase what you have written and drawn on the board, and replace it with this new portion of the number line.

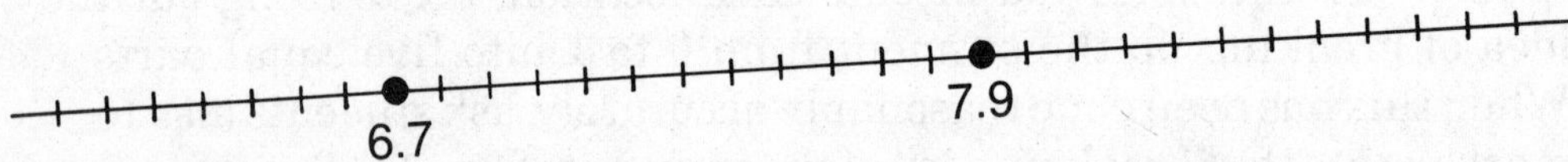

T: Can anyone mark 7 on this part of the number line?

Proceed similarly for 6.4, 8.3, and 7.4.

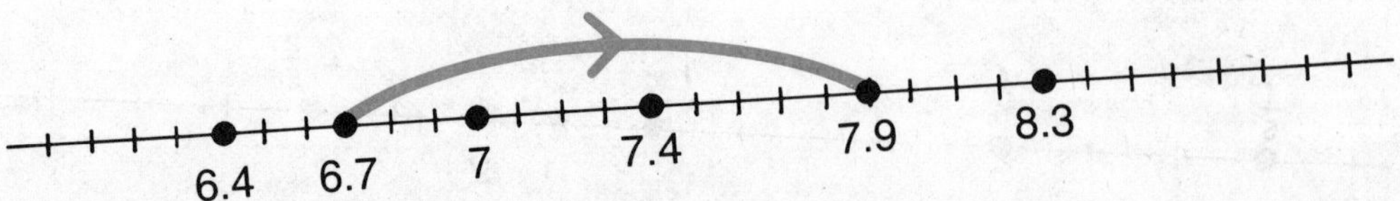

T: What could the blue arrow be for? (+1.2)
Let's check that: 6.7 + 1.2 = 7.9.
What could the return arrow be for? (−1.2)

Draw the return arrow in red, and draw a green arrow as shown below.

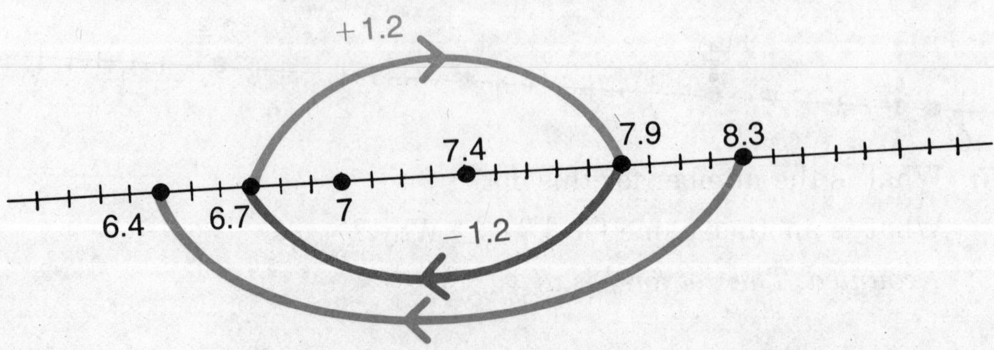

17

T: What could the green arrow be for? (−1.9)
Check this: 8.3 − 1.9 = 6.4.

If your students appear to need practice, you can ask them to perform a number of simple additions and subtractions that can be illustrated on the portion of the number line on the board. For example:

$$6.5 + 2.1 = \square$$
$$8.4 - 1.3 = \square$$
$$6.3 + 1.8 = \square$$
$$8.5 - 1.6 = \square$$

End the lesson with this detective story.

T: Bic is a secret number. Here's the first clue.

Clue 1:

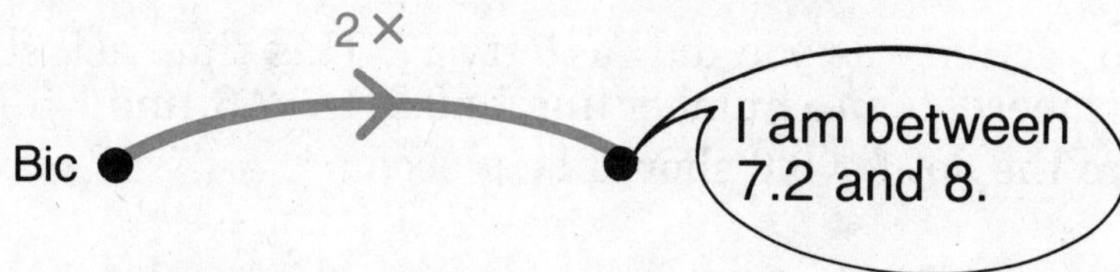

T: What could Bic be? Write some possibilities on your papers.
Among the numbers students might write are 3.65, 3.7, 3.8, 3.85, 3.9, and 3.95. If there is time, locate some of these numbers on the number line.

T: Here's the second clue.
Clue 2: Bic may be shown on this Minicomputer using only three regular checkers.

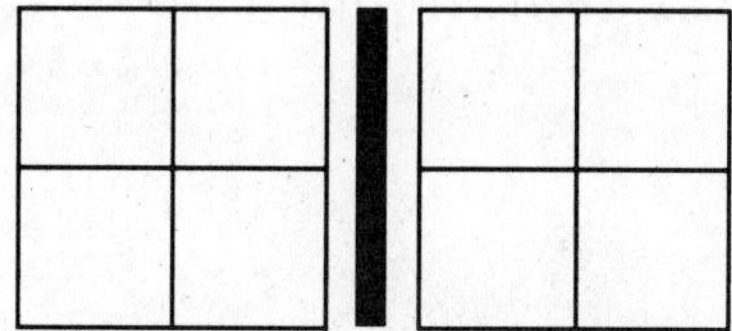

S: *Bic is 3.8.*

Resources Available

For out-of-class use: Any H-worksheet up through H27

ACTIVITY 18
Decimals 4

Materials Needed
Teacher: Colored chalk
Students: Colored pencils

Begin this activity as you did Activity 17. This time ask students to draw and label dots on a number line for 0.3, 1.7, 2.3, and $1\frac{2}{5}$. Then ask where the dot for $\widehat{0.6}$ should be placed.

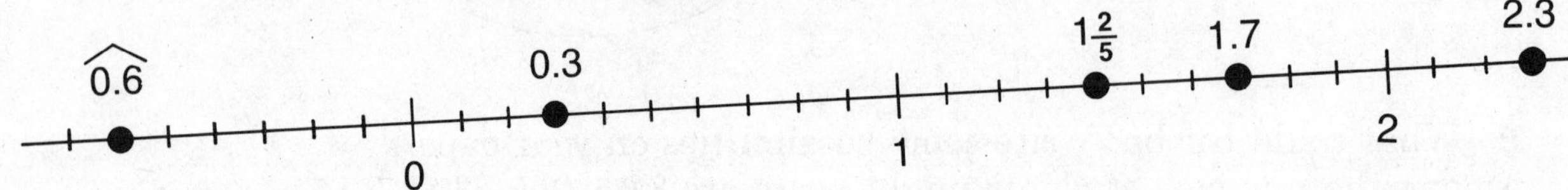

T: Between which two whole numbers is $2\frac{1}{5}$? (between 2 and 3)

T: Can anyone draw and label the dot for $2\frac{1}{5}$ on the number line?

Let a student do this.

T: What is a decimal name for $2\frac{1}{5}$? (2.2)

Include this information on your number line. Then draw a red arrow as indicated.

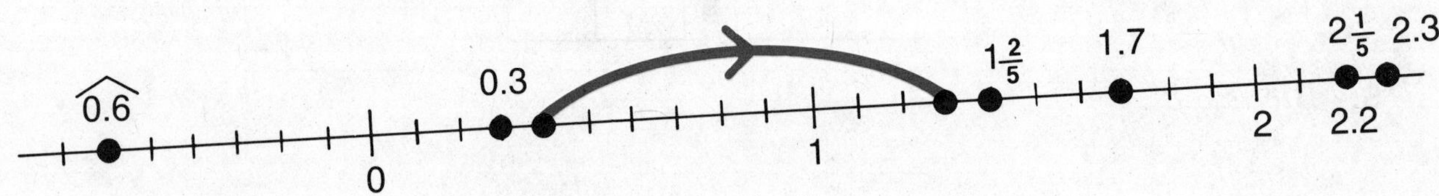

T: What could this red arrow be for?
S: *+9.*
T: Let's check that. What is the number at the starting dot? (0.4) Then $0.4 + 9 = 9.4$. Is 9.4 the number at the ending dot of the red arrow?
S: *No, it ends at 1.3.*
S: *So the red arrow is for +0.9.*
T: Let's check: $0.4 + 0.9 = 1.3$. Good. What could this blue arrow be for?

Draw a blue arrow as shown in the next diagram, but don't draw the green arrow until it is referred to later.

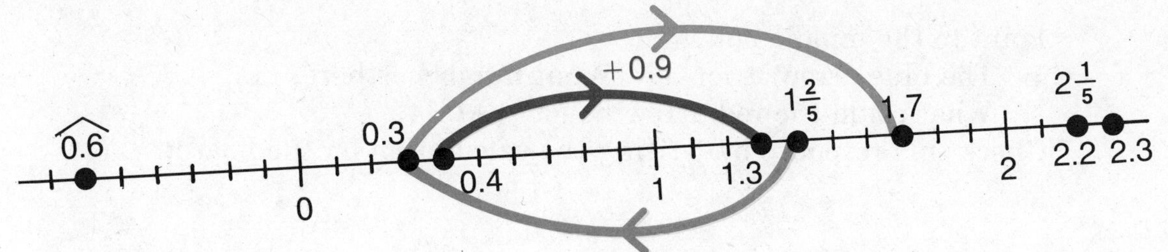

18

S: *+0.14.*

Write on the board:

$$\begin{array}{r} 0.30 \\ +\ 0.14 \\ \hline 0.44 \end{array}$$

S: *It should be bigger than 0.14.*

S: *1.4.*

T: That's right. 0.3 + 1.4 = 1.7.
What could the green arrow be for? First, what is a decimal name for $1\frac{2}{5}$? (1.4)

S: *The green arrow could be for −1.1, because 1.4 − 1.1 = 0.3.*

T: Will someone please draw an arrow for 3×? Use any color that is not yet in the picture.

S: *We can draw a 3× arrow from 0.1 to 0.3.*

Let the student draw this arrow, shown below in orange.

T: Can anyone draw a 3× arrow starting at 0.7?

S: *It ends at 2.1.*

T: How about a 3× arrow ending at 1.8?

S: *It starts at 0.6.*

T: Ending at 0?

S: *It's a loop at 0.*

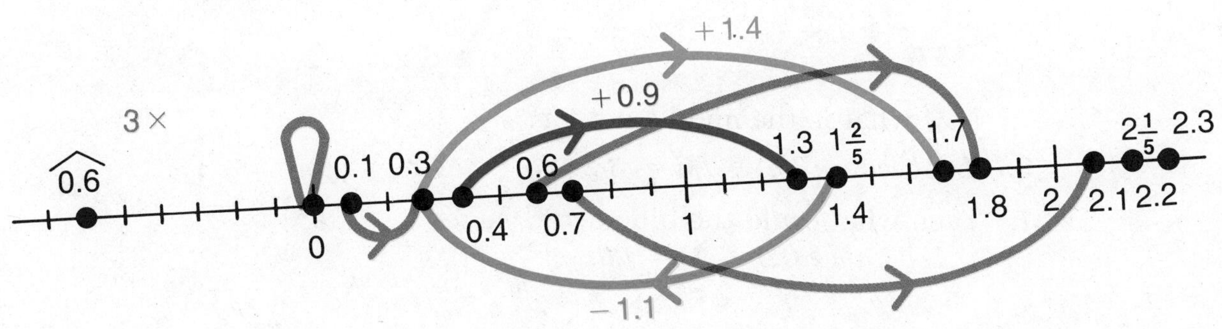

Erase what you have drawn and written on the board, and replace it with this diagram:

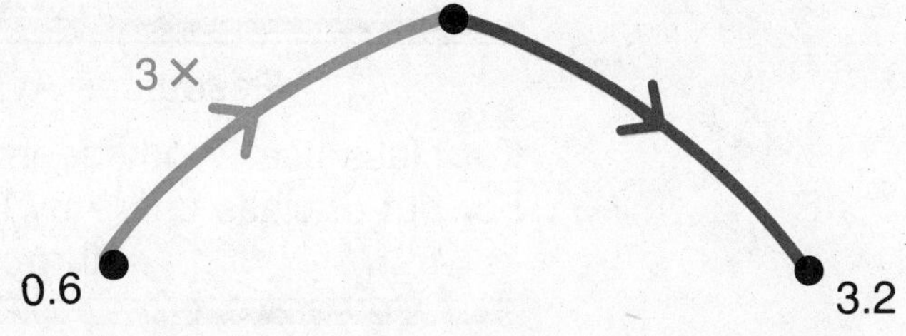

18

Point to the middle dot.

T: The blue arrow is for 3×. What number is here? (1.8)
What could the red arrow be for? (+0.14)

Check this response by writing the calculation on the board:

$$\begin{array}{r} 1.80 \\ +\ 0.14 \\ \hline 1.94 \end{array}$$

S: *That's not big enough. The red arrow could be for* +1.4.

Check once again, showing the response to be correct.
Change the label so that the blue arrow is now for 6×.

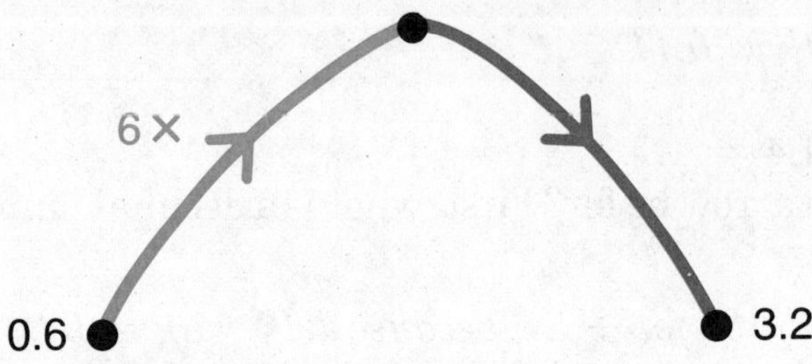

T: Now what is the middle dot for? (3.6)
So what could the red arrow be for?

S: *−0.4, because 3.6 − 0.4 = 3.2.*

Change the labels once again so that the red arrow is for 2×.

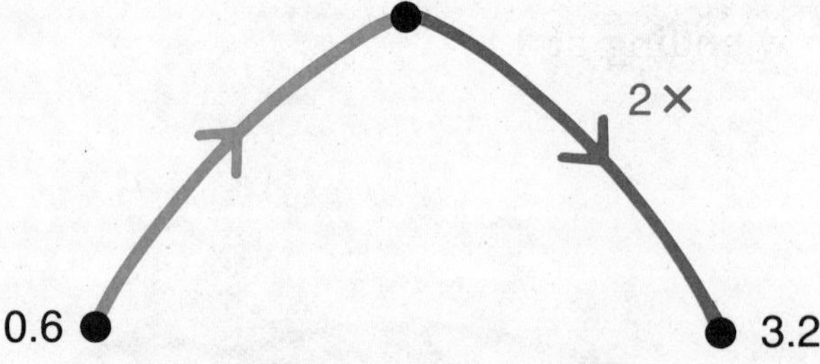

T: Now what is the middle dot for?

S: *1.6, because 1.6 + 1.6 = 3.2. So* $\frac{1}{2}$ × *3.2 = 1.6.*

T: Then what could the blue arrow be for?

S: *+1, because 0.6 + 1 = 1.6.*

Resources Available

For class use: Worksheets L19 and L20
For out-of-class use: Any H-worksheet up through H27

ACTIVITIES 19 and 20
Weighted Checkers 1

Materials Needed
Teacher: Minicomputer kit, chalk
Students: None

Note to the Teacher

You may wish to conduct the following exercise as a game between two teams. If so, divide the class into two teams and alternate between the teams in calling on students to come to the board to solve the problems presented. If a solution is correct, award that team one point. If the solution is incorrect, call on someone from the other team to solve the same problem. If it is answered correctly, award that team one point. Continue alternating teams until the problem is finally solved.

If you choose not to use a game format, simply call on students to come to the board one by one to answer questions.

In either format, no student should get a second chance (unless the teams have unequal numbers of students) until everyone has had a first opportunity. In the game format, a reasonable time limit should be established. We suggest one minute for the first student trying a given problem and 30 seconds for others doing the same problem.

Display on the board the complete set of weighted checkers, both regular and negative. Also display three Minicomputer boards. Pick up the $\hat{3}$-checker.

T: If I put this negative weighted checker on the 4-square, what number would be on the Minicomputer? ($\widehat{12}$) Why?

S: *The $\hat{3}$-checker is like three negative checkers.*

T: That's right. A 3-checker is like three regular checkers, and a $\hat{3}$-checker is like three negative checkers. So $\hat{3}$ on the 4-square is $\hat{4} + \hat{4} + \hat{4} = \widehat{12}$.

After each of the following problems has been solved, change the configuration of checkers in preparation for the next problem.

T: In each of these problems someone has taken away *exactly one* weighted checker. Our job is to put it back.

19
20

(1)

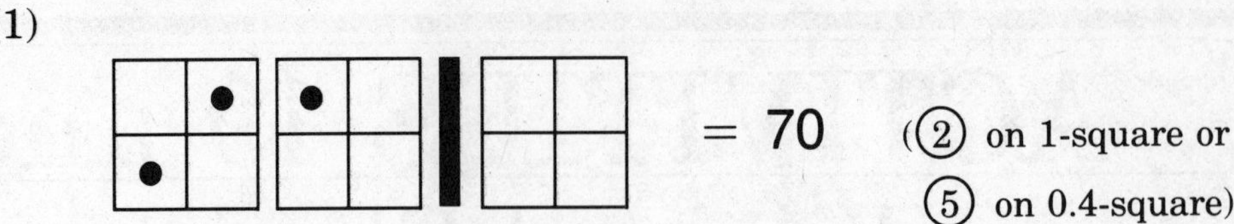

= 70 (② on 1-square or ⑤ on 0.4-square)

(2)

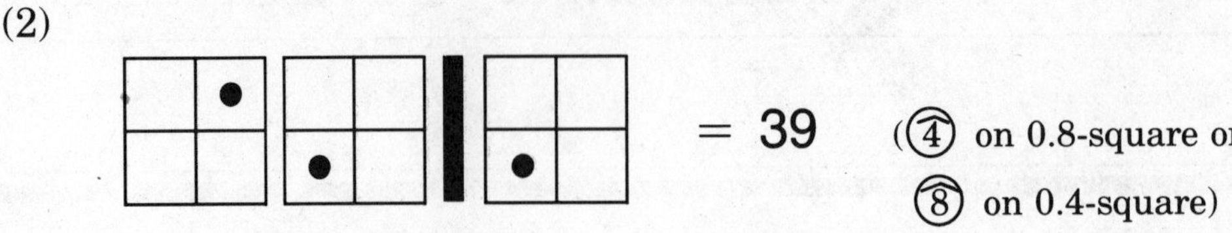

= 39 ($\hat{4}$ on 0.8-square or $\hat{8}$ on 0.4-square)

(3)

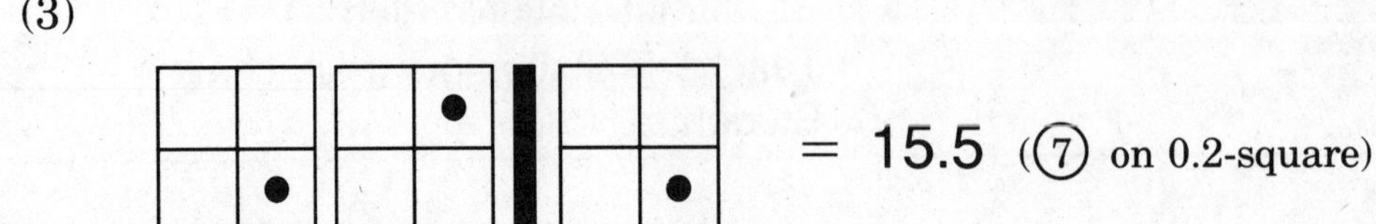

= 15.5 (⑦ on 0.2-square)

(4)

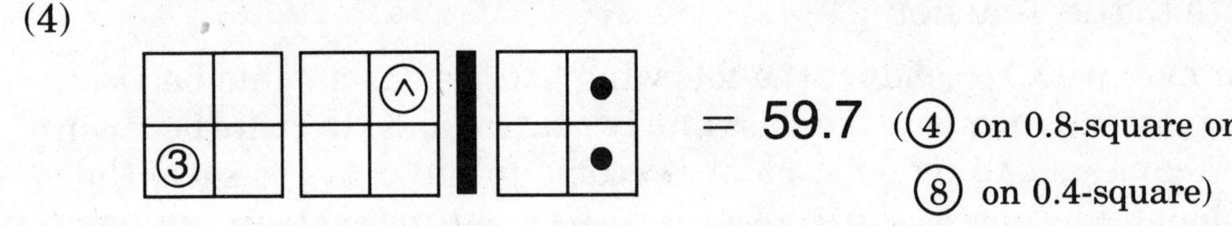

= 59.7 (④ on 0.8-square or ⑧ on 0.4-square)

(5)

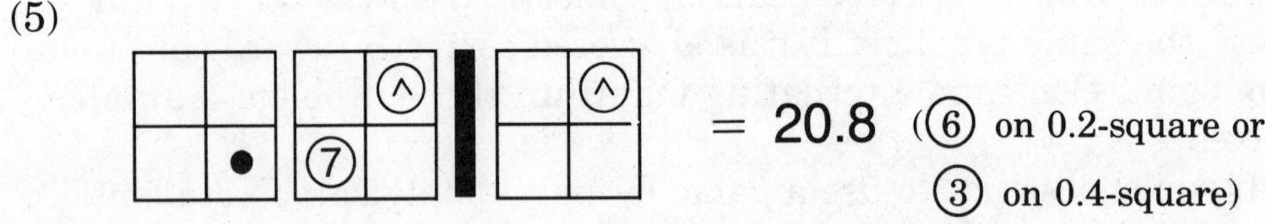

= 20.8 (⑥ on 0.2-square or ③ on 0.4-square)

(6)

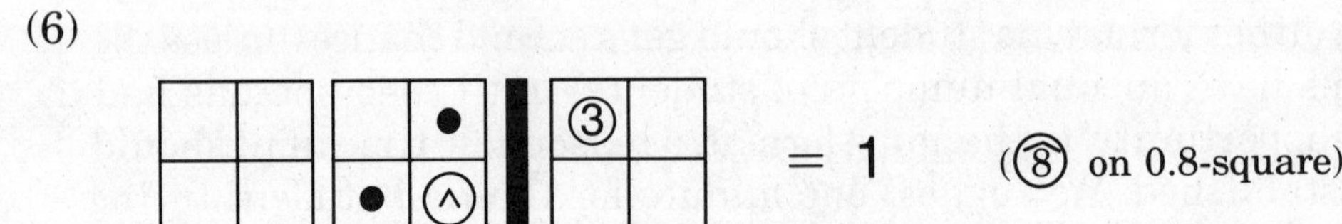

= 1 ($\hat{8}$ on 0.8-square)

(7)

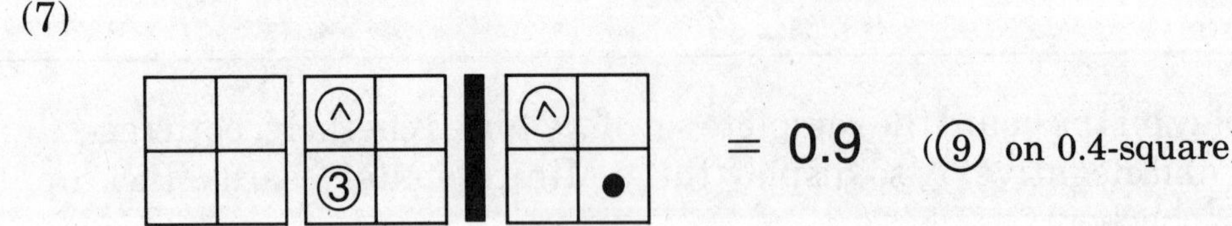

= 0.9 (⑨ on 0.4-square)

Continue with the following problems if students are interested and you have the time. (If you are using the game format, continue the scoring rather than beginning again.)

Display two Minicomputer boards, a regular checker, a negative checker, a 7-checker, and a $\hat{3}$-checker.

T: I'm going to ask you to show certain types of numbers on the Minicomputer. For each problem some checkers will already be on the Minicomputer. You will have to add to them exactly one regular checker or one negative checker or one 7-checker or one $\hat{3}$-checker and get the type of number I ask for. Sometimes there will be more than one way to solve the problem. We'll go on playing until all solutions of the problem have been found. I will tell you in advance how many solutions there are, and while you're waiting for your turn you should be trying to find other solutions. Finally, to get a point for a correct solution you have to complete the blank correctly.

(1) A number between 13.4 and 18.2:

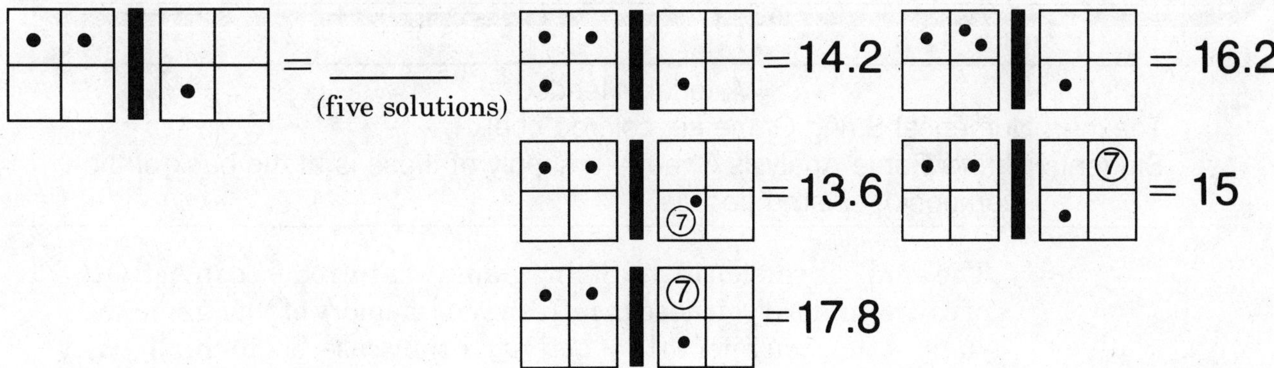

(2) A whole number:

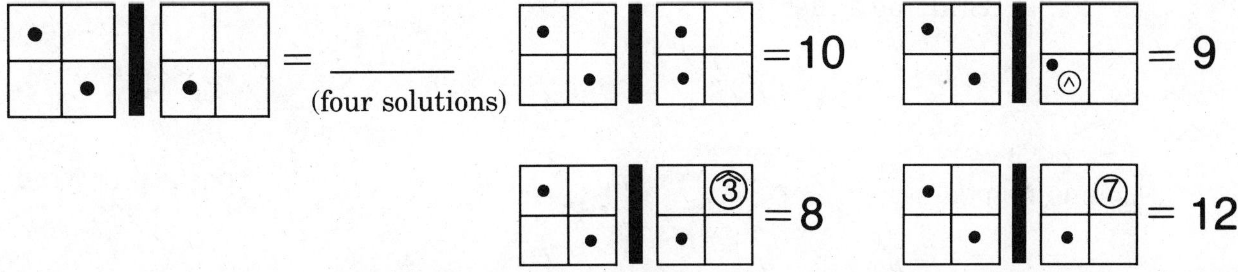

(3) One-half of a positive multiple of 5:

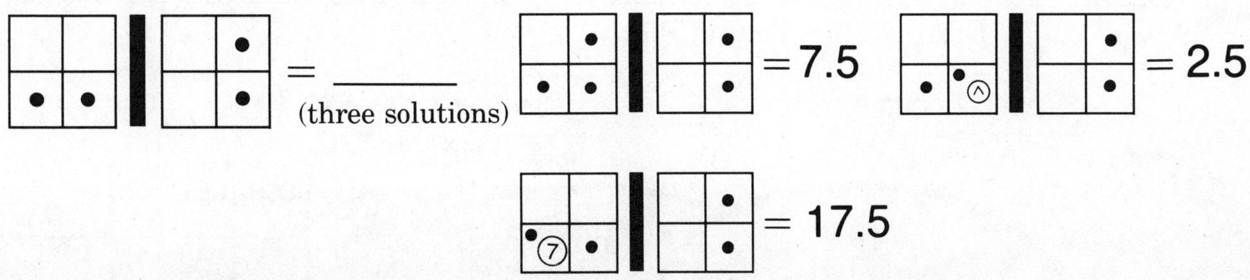

Resources Available

For class use: Worksheets L21 and L22

For out-of-class use: Any H-worksheet up through H30

ACTIVITY 21
String Game (Analysis Version) 2

Materials Needed

Teacher: Numerical String Game kit, colored chalk

Students: String Game Analysis Sheets (a supply of these is at the back of the workbook), colored pencils

The analysis version of the String Game was introduced in Activity 6 of this volume. If you need to refresh your memory of this game we suggest that you refer to that activity. In any case, begin this activity by reminding your class of the playing rules.

Play the analysis version of the String Game with your class. A possible game is outlined below.

Starting Clues

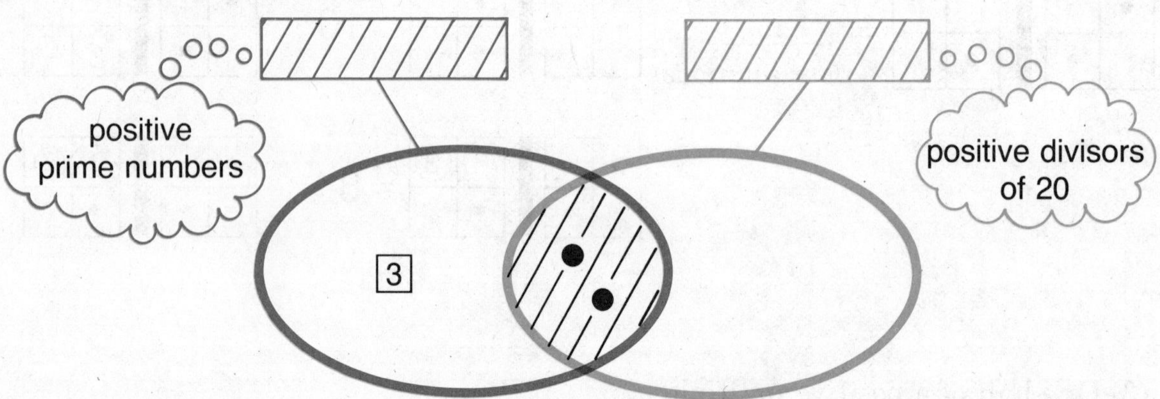

Correct Placement of Pieces

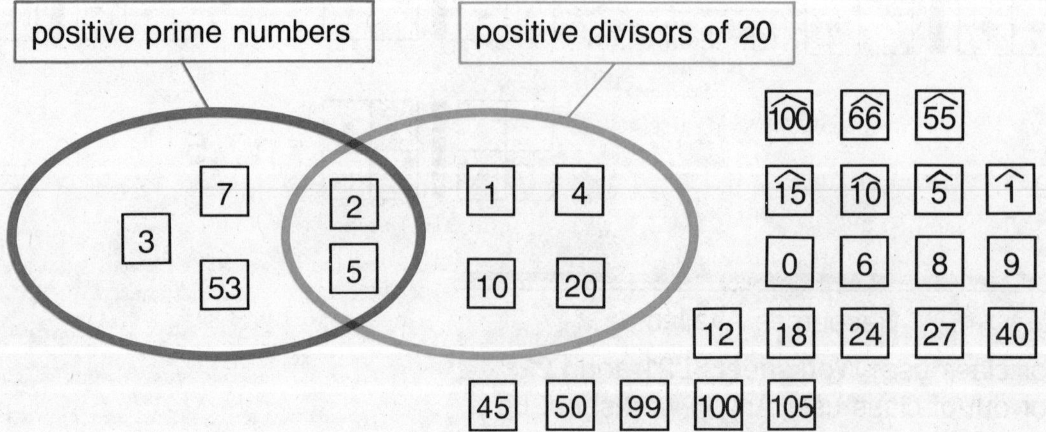

To analyze the starting situation, your students will probably begin by considering the placement of [3], which will lead to the following eliminations.

	Red	Blue	
MULTIPLES OF 2	X		
MULTIPLES OF 3		X	
MULTIPLES OF 4	X		
MULTIPLES OF 5	X		
MULTIPLES OF 10	X		
ODD NUMBERS		X	
POSITIVE PRIME NUMBERS		X	
GREATER THAN 50	X		
LESS THAN 50		X	
GREATER THAN 10		X	
LESS THAN 10	X		
POSITIVE DIVISORS OF 12		X	
POSITIVE DIVISORS OF 18		X	
POSITIVE DIVISORS OF 20	X		
POSITIVE DIVISORS OF 24		X	
POSITIVE DIVISORS OF 27		X	

For each of the remaining possibilities for the blue string, your students should next check that there is at least one of the remaining possibilities for the red string with which it could be matched in order to give exactly two numbers in the intersection. If there is not, then the possibility under consideration may be crossed off the Blue list. This type of argument results in the following eliminations.

	Red	Blue	
MULTIPLES OF 2	X	X	
MULTIPLES OF 3		X	
MULTIPLES OF 4	X		
MULTIPLES OF 5	X	X	
MULTIPLES OF 10	X	X	
ODD NUMBERS		X	
POSITIVE PRIME NUMBERS		X	
GREATER THAN 50	X	X	
LESS THAN 50		X	
GREATER THAN 10		X	
LESS THAN 10	X	X	
POSITIVE DIVISORS OF 12		X	
POSITIVE DIVISORS OF 18		X	
POSITIVE DIVISORS OF 20	X		
POSITIVE DIVISORS OF 24		X	
POSITIVE DIVISORS OF 27		X	

For each of the remaining possibilities for the red string, the students should check that there is at least one of the remaining possibilities for the blue string with which it could be matched in order to give exactly two numbers in the intersection. If there is not, then the possibility under consideration may be crossed off the Red list. This type of argument results in the following eliminations.

	Red	Blue	
MULTIPLES OF 2	X	X	
MULTIPLES OF 3	X	X	
MULTIPLES OF 4	X		
MULTIPLES OF 5	X	X	
MULTIPLES OF 10	X	X	
ODD NUMBERS		X	
POSITIVE PRIME NUMBERS		X	
GREATER THAN 50	X	X	
LESS THAN 50	X	X	
GREATER THAN 10	X	X	
LESS THAN 10	X	X	
POSITIVE DIVISORS OF 12		X	
POSITIVE DIVISORS OF 18		X	
POSITIVE DIVISORS OF 20	X		
POSITIVE DIVISORS OF 24	X	X	
POSITIVE DIVISORS OF 27	X	X	

Do not be concerned if your class does not reduce the possibilities for the two strings to this extent. Whatever reduction students manage to achieve forms the starting point for the playing of the game, as explained in Activity 6.

Resources Available

For class use: Worksheets L23 and L24

For out-of-class use: Any H-worksheet up through H33

ACTIVITY 22
Numerical String Game (High-Speed Version) 1

Materials Needed
Teacher: Numerical String Game kit, colored chalk
Students: String Game Analysis Sheets (a supply of these is at the back of the workbook), colored pencils

In this activity we describe a new version of the String Game designed for the more experienced students who often prefer a quicker-moving game in which each player has more influence on the outcome than in earlier versions. For reasons that will shortly become apparent, we call this version of the game the High-Speed String Game.

Divide your class into four teams of as nearly equal numbers and average ability as possible. These four teams take turns to play and are represented by each of their members in turn. On his or her turn, each player plays as in previous versions of the game (with the exception that all unplayed number pieces are available to all four teams). After playing one or two pieces (depending on whether the first piece has been placed correctly) and before sitting down and making way for the next player, a player may indicate that he or she wishes to announce what is written on the hidden string labels. As soon as this announcement is made, the current round of the game is over. If the player identifies *both* strings correctly, the team he or she represents is awarded two points. If the identification of either string is incorrect, each of the other three teams is awarded one point.

In either case, commence a new round of the game with new starting clues and the next scheduled player. Continue playing rounds in this fashion until one team has won three points. That team is declared the winner.

Encourage the students to use their String Game analysis sheets while playing this version of the game.

The following list suggests starting positions for String Games. Feel free to choose from among these suggestions. It is difficult to predict how many of these starting positions you will need for a given activity involving the high-speed version of the game. Refer to this list in future activities and use any that have not been used previously. If and when you run out, you will need to create some starting positions of your own.

22

1.

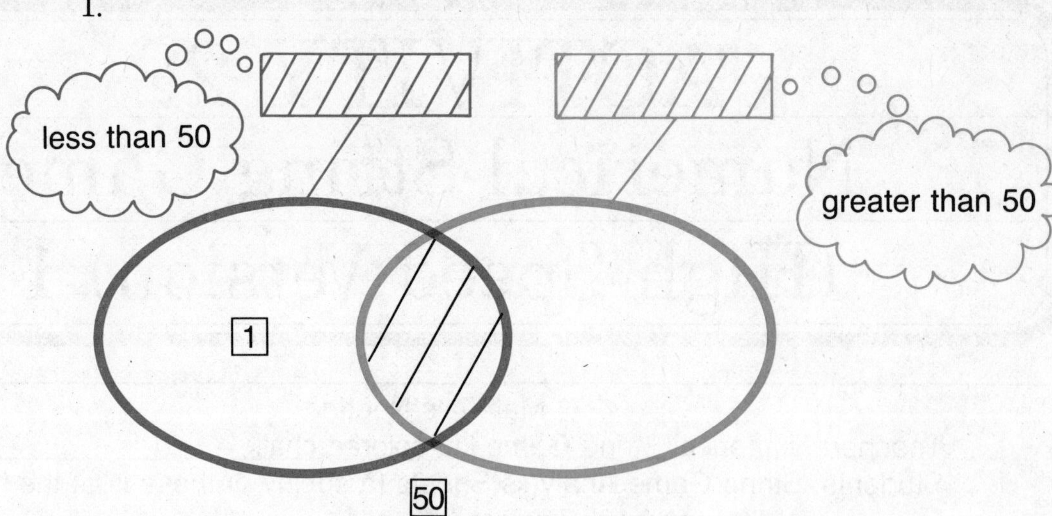
less than 50
greater than 50
1
50

2.

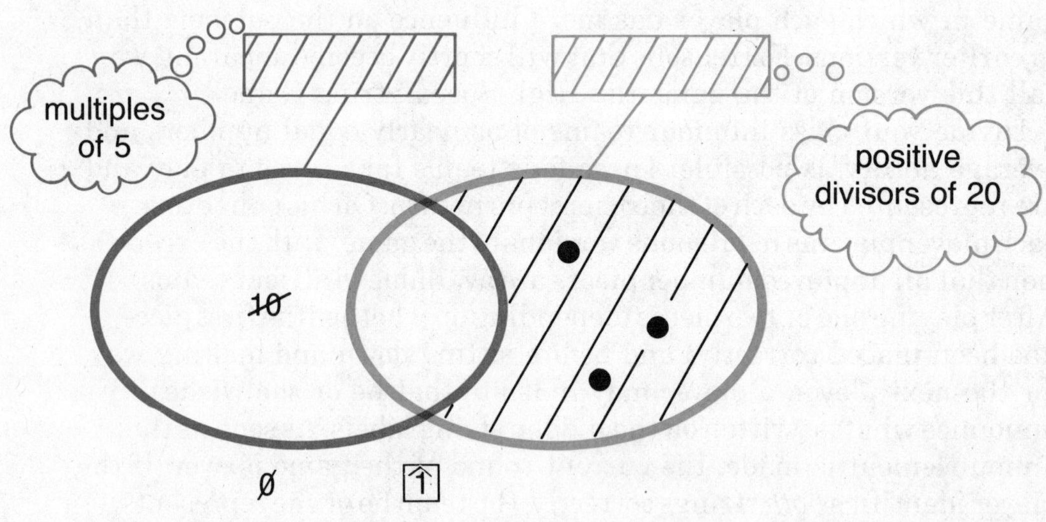
multiples of 5
positive divisors of 20
10
1

3.

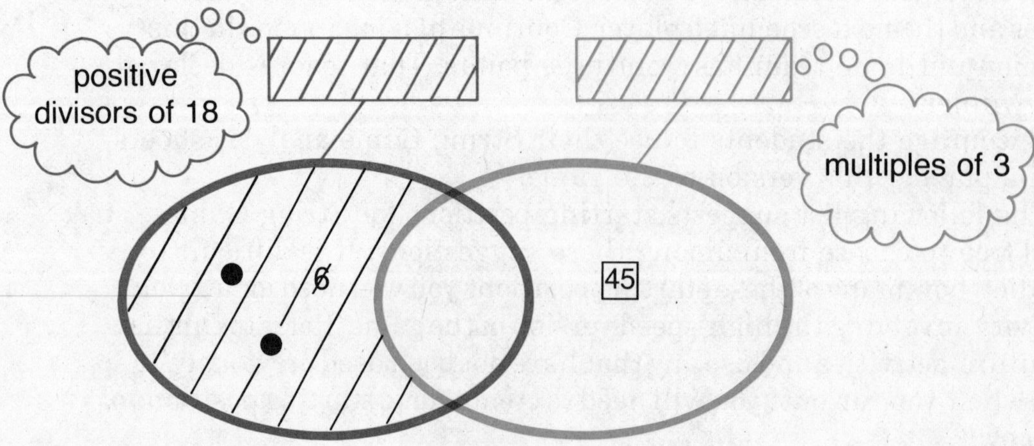
positive divisors of 18
multiples of 3
6
45

22

4.

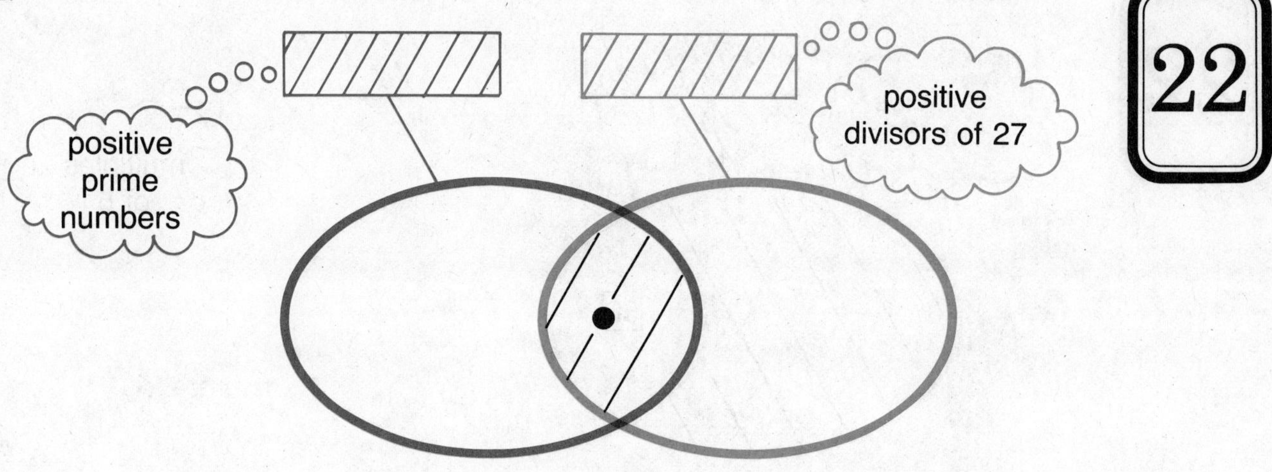
positive
prime
numbers
positive
divisors of 27

5.

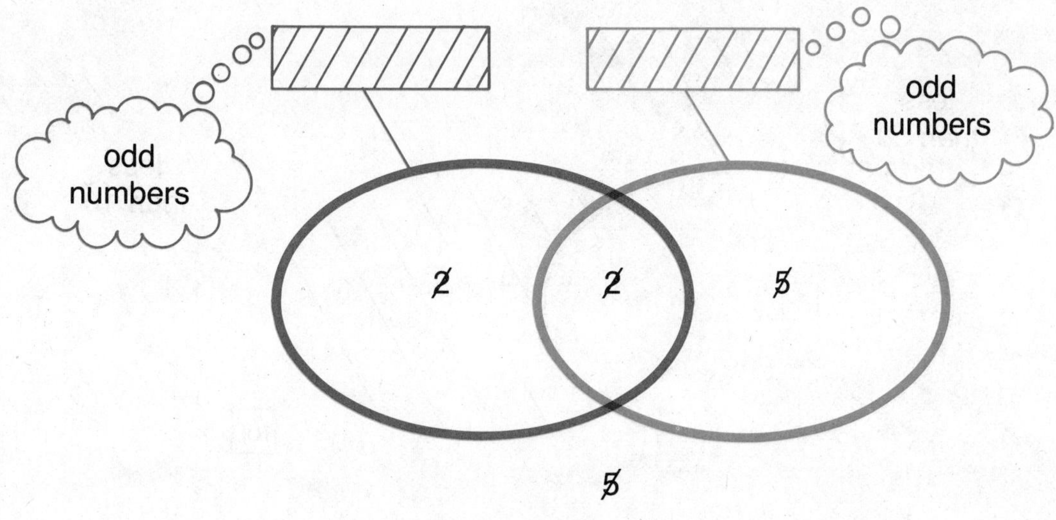
odd
numbers
odd
numbers

6.

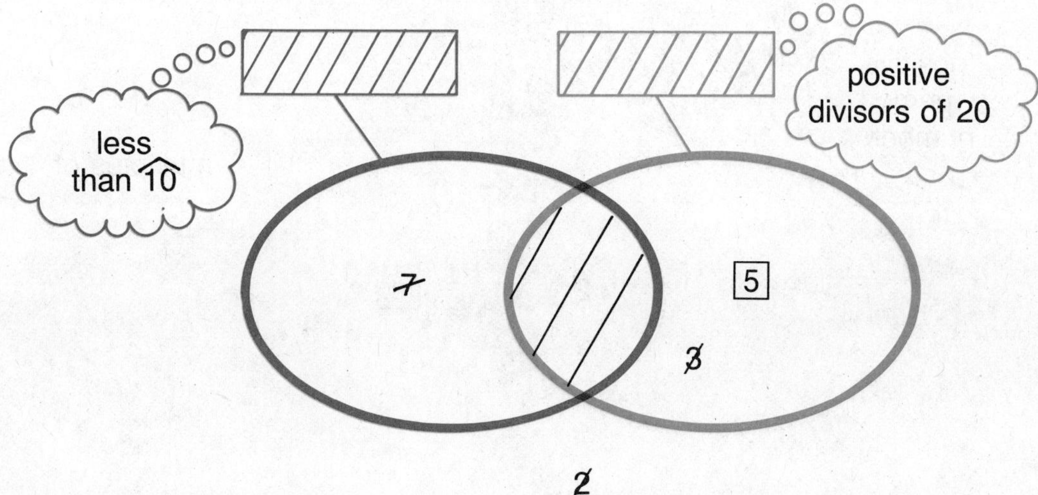
less
than 10
positive
divisors of 20
5

22

7.

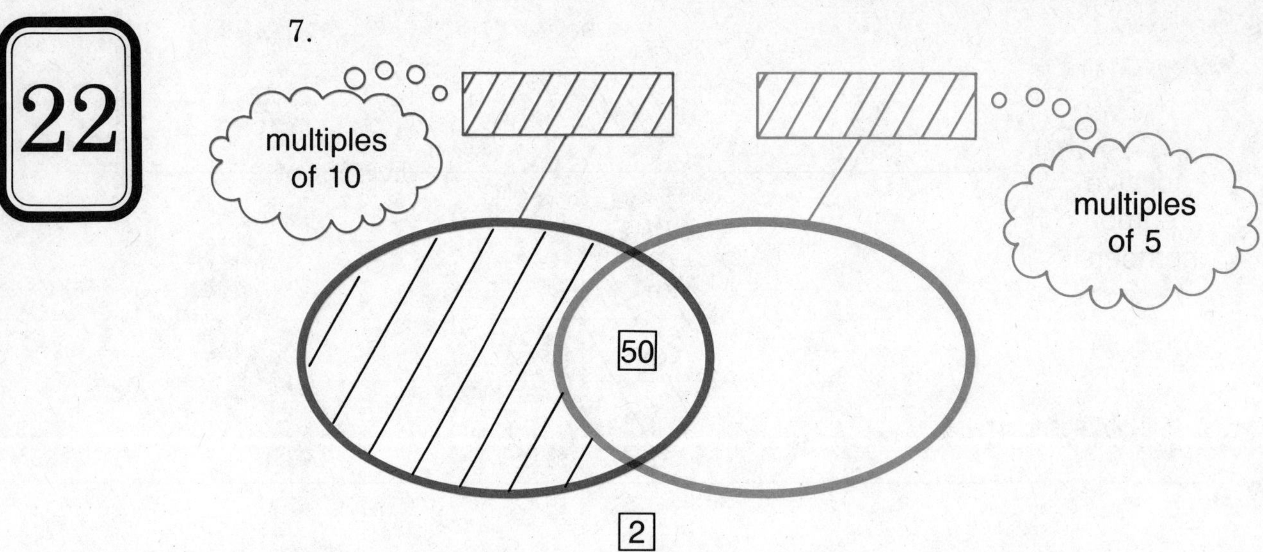
multiples of 10
multiples of 5
50
2

8.

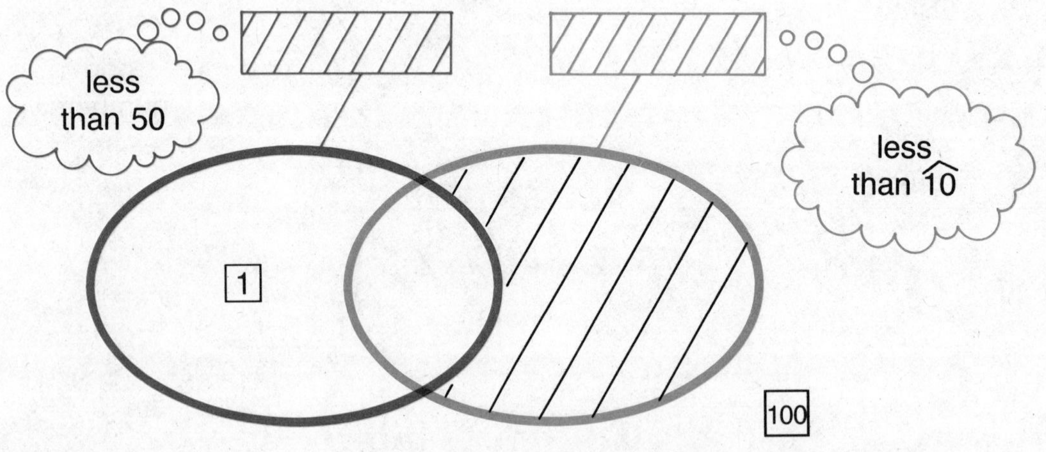
less than 50
less than $\widehat{10}$
1
100

9.

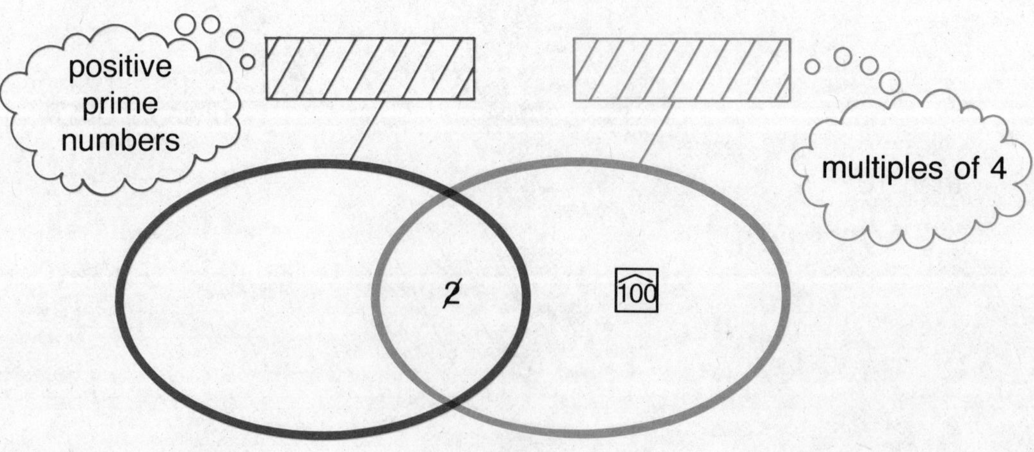
positive prime numbers
multiples of 4
2
$\widehat{100}$

2

10.

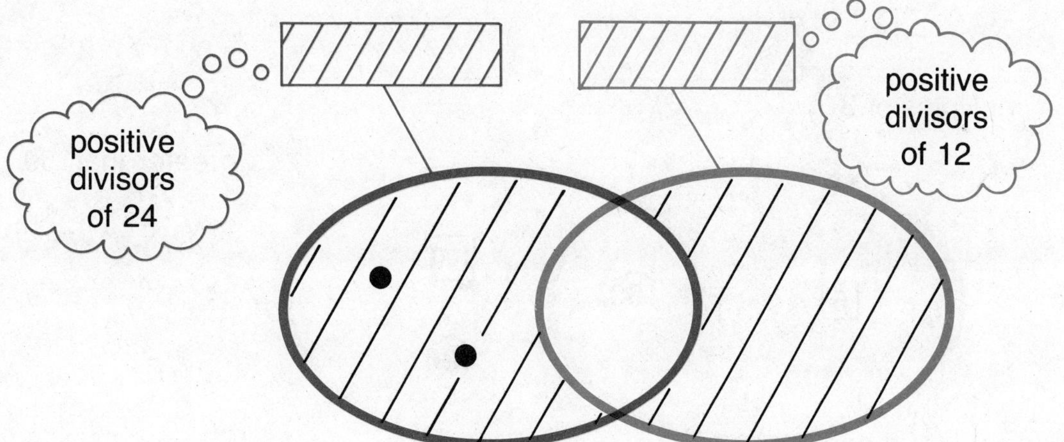
positive divisors of 24
positive divisors of 12

22

11.

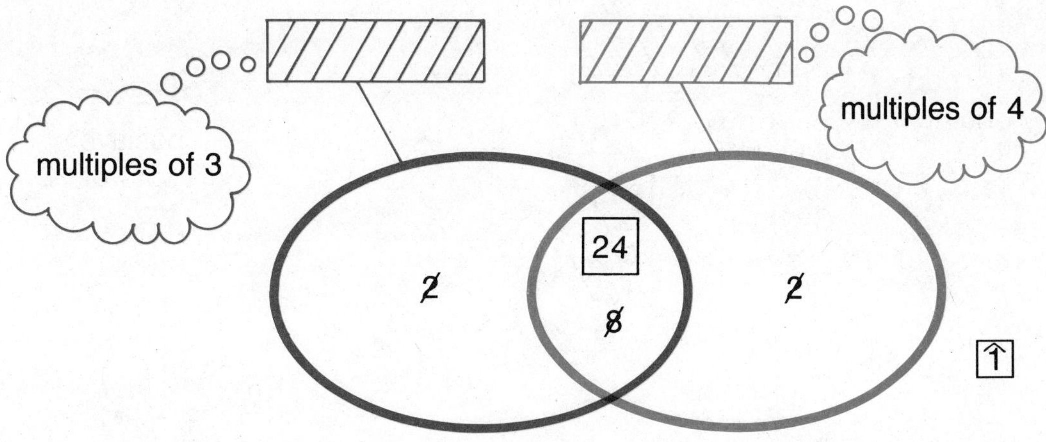
multiples of 3
multiples of 4
24

12.

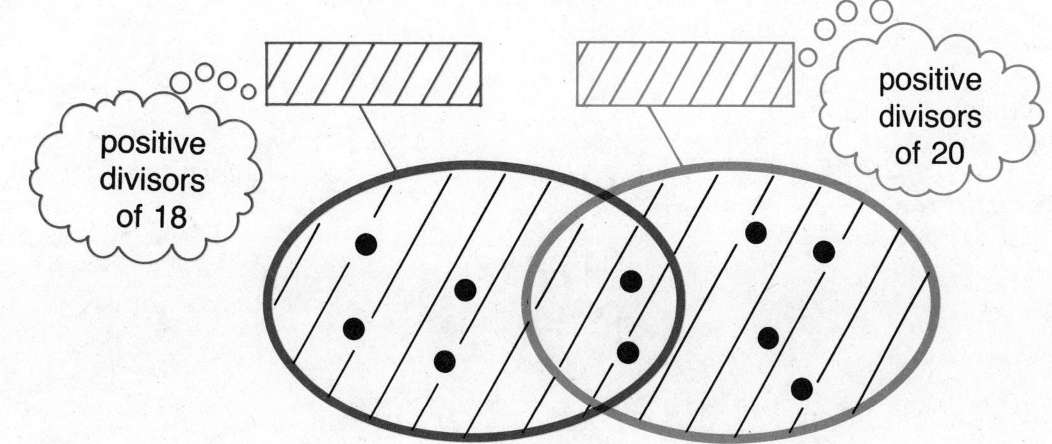
positive divisors of 18
positive divisors of 20

22

13.

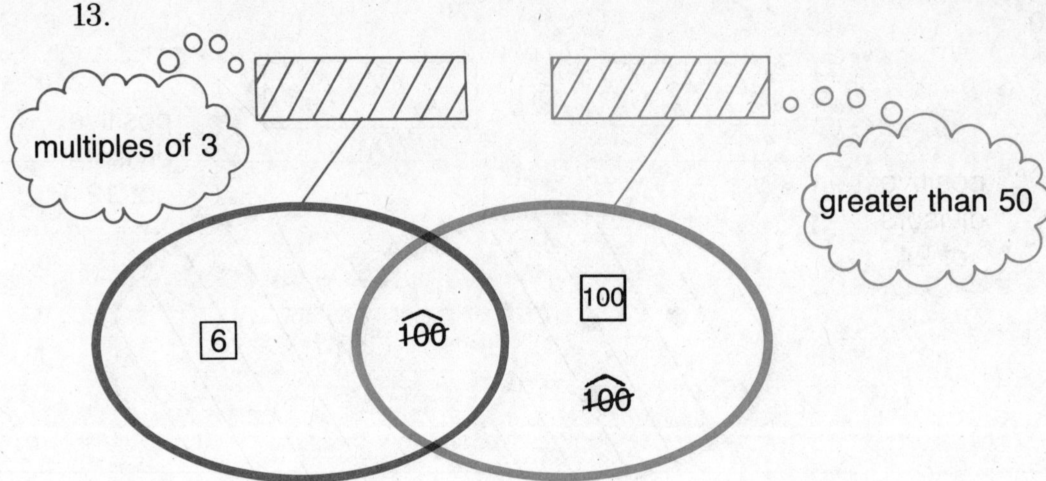

multiples of 3
greater than 50
6
100
100
100

14.

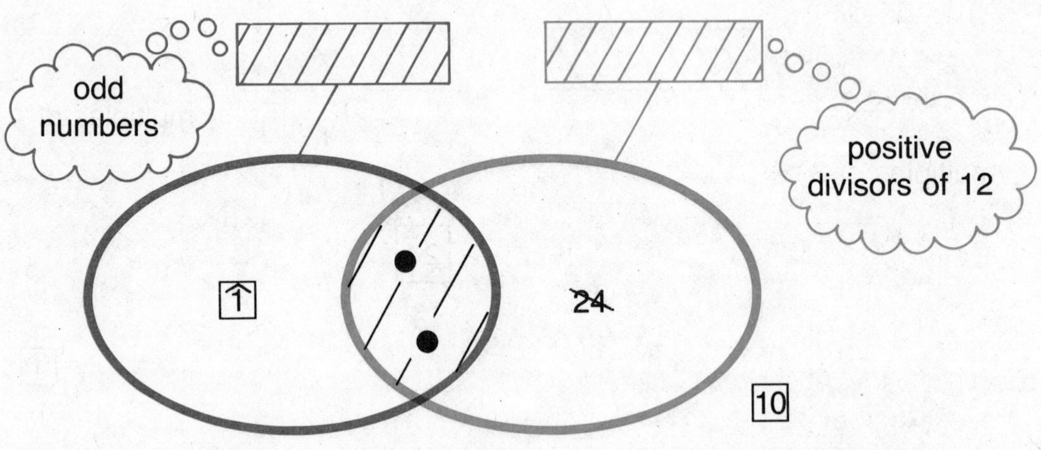

odd numbers
positive divisors of 12
1
24
10

15.

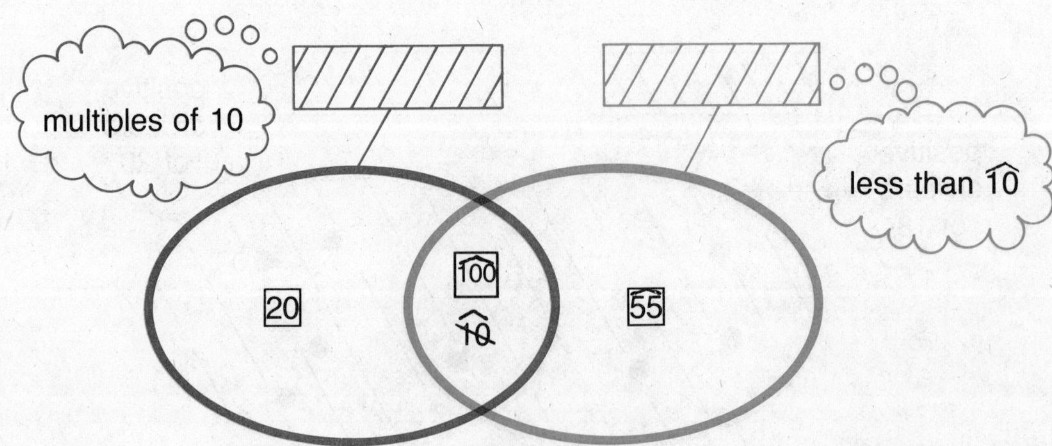

multiples of 10
less than 10
20
100
10
55

22

16.

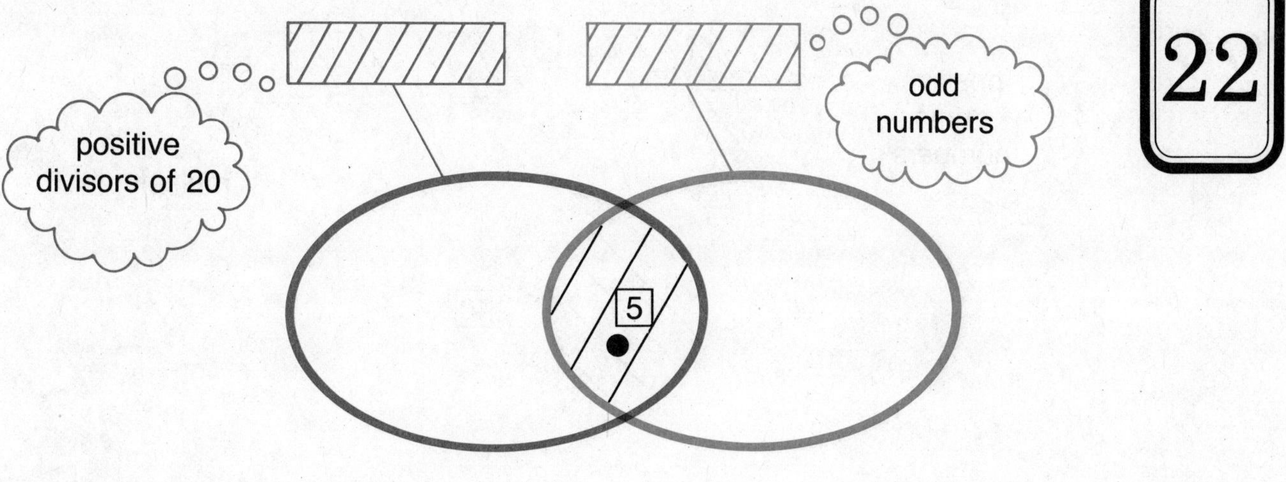
positive
divisors of 20
odd
numbers
5

17.

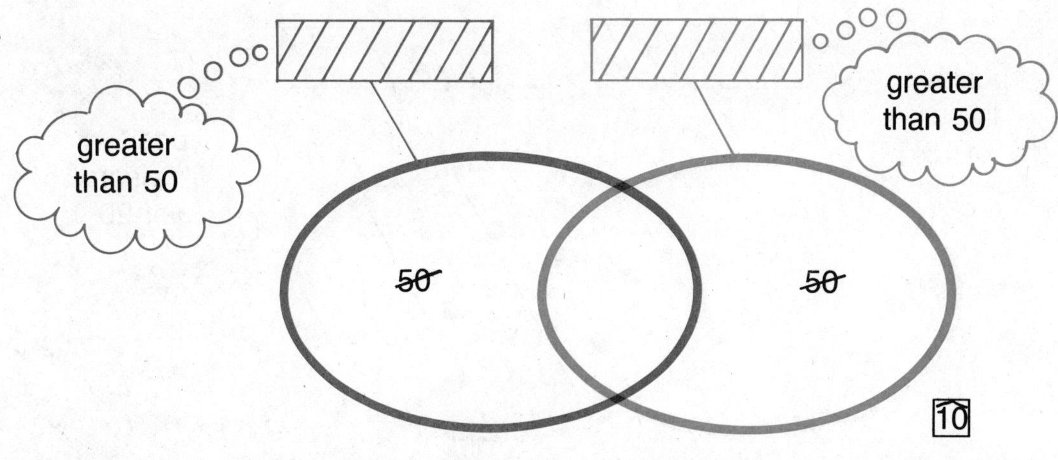
greater
than 50
greater
than 50
50
50
10

18.

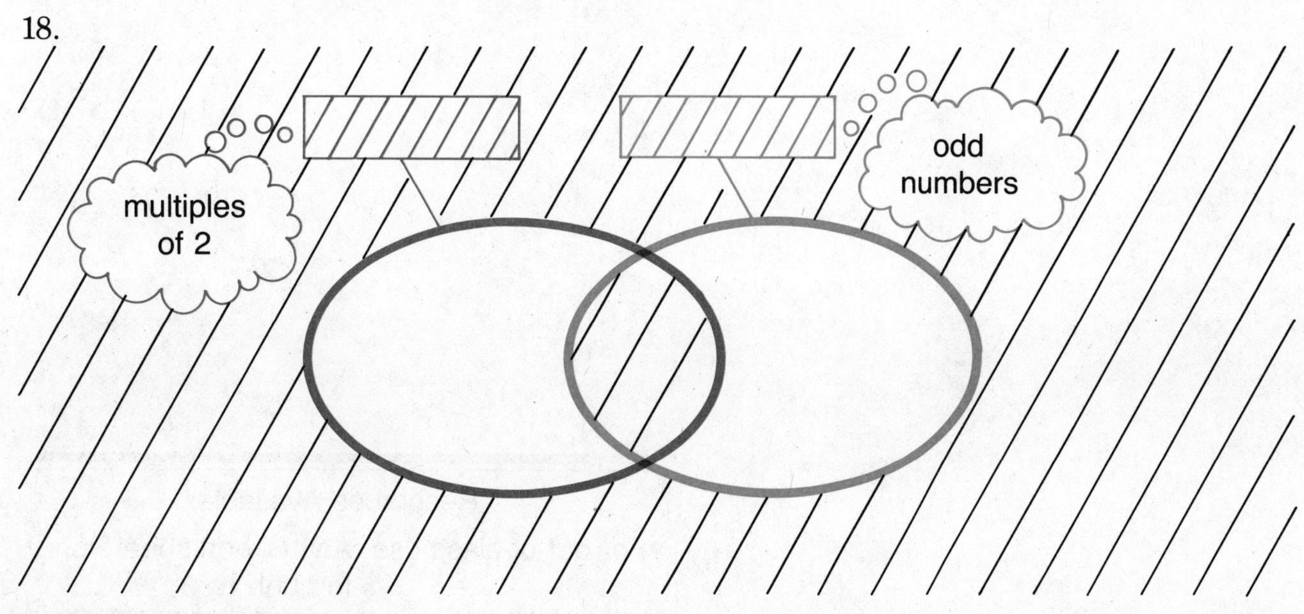
multiples
of 2
odd
numbers

19.

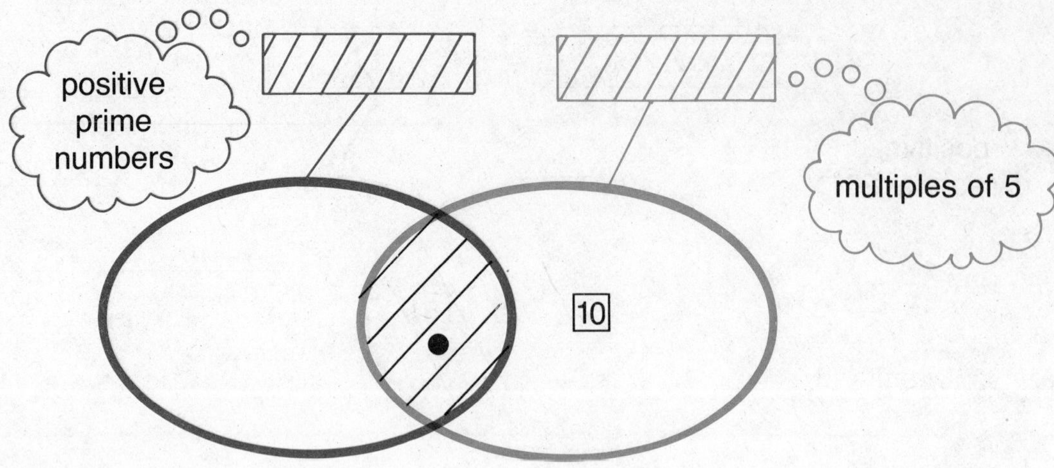

20.

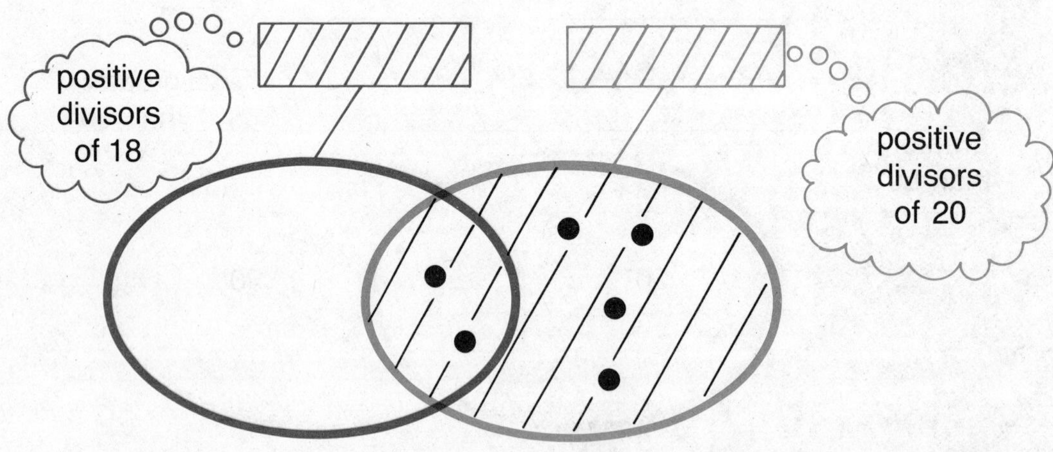

Resources Available

For out-of-class use: Any H-worksheet up through H33

ACTIVITY 23
Composition 5

Materials Needed
Teacher: Colored chalk, Poster 1, colored felt-tip pens or crayons
Students: None

Display Poster 1 from the Volume 4 poster packet.

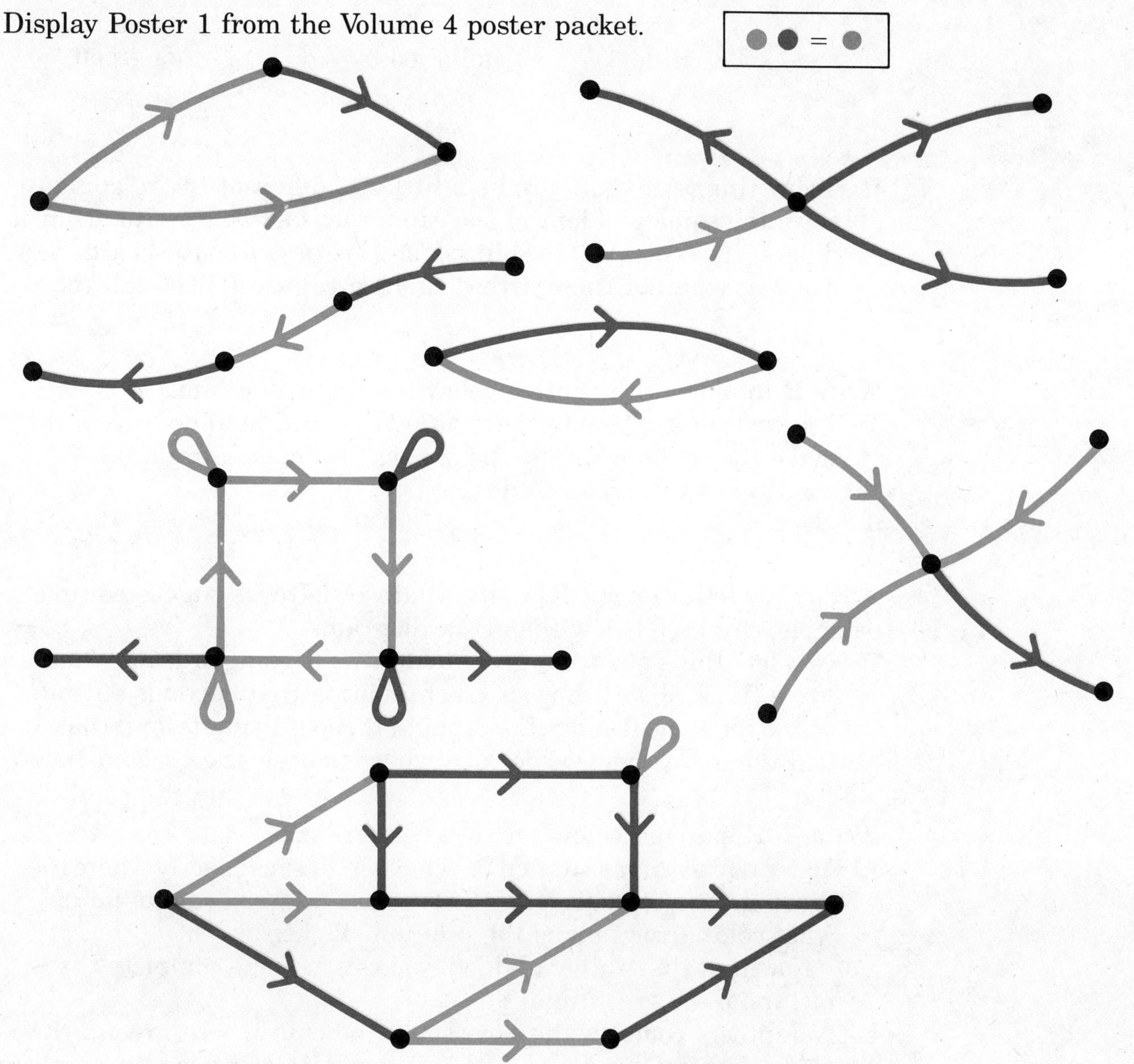

T: We've solved several problems like this before. We have some blue arrows and some red arrows, and we have to draw some green arrows. What is the rule for drawing the green arrows?

S: *Whenever you have a blue arrow followed by a red arrow you can draw a green arrow from the beginning of the blue arrow to the end of the red arrow.*
T: Very good.

Point to the boxed-in code ● ● = ●. Using the finger-tracing method from Activity 7, explain how the green arrow drawn in the top left of the diagram exemplifies the rule.

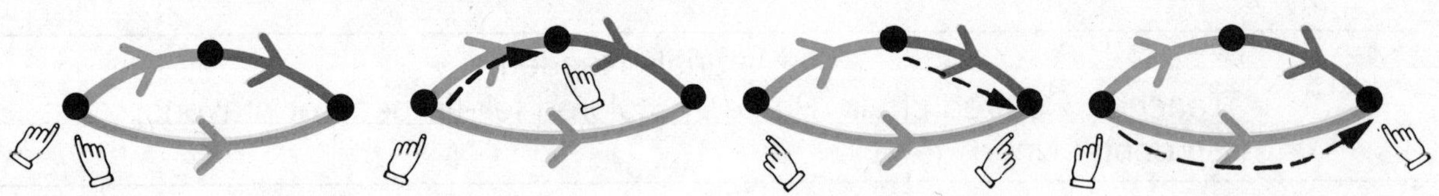

Blue . . . followed by red . . . is green.

T: Today things are going to be a little bit different. We're going to solve the same problem in the same way, but we'll write about it differently. Look at all the blue arrows I've drawn on the board. We say that together these arrows make a **relation.** Let's call the R.

Write **R** in blue on the poster below the arrow diagram.
T: I've written it in blue to remind us that it's the blue arrows that make the relation R. The red arrows also make a relation. What shall we call the red relation?
S: *S.*

Accept any letter except R. Write whatever letter is suggested (in our example, S) in red below the arrow diagram.
T: Now let's think about the green arrows we're going to draw. When we've finished we'll have a green relation that depends entirely on the relations R and S. So we ought to choose a name for it that will remind us how we decided where to draw the green arrows.

Write **R∘S** in green below the arrow diagram.
T: You can read this as "R then S." That way, it says exactly where the green arrows come from. I've written it in green to remind us what color arrows make the relation "R then S."

Now that that's all explained, you can help me complete the picture of the green relation.

Let volunteers come to the board and indicate where green arrows should be drawn. Draw those that are correct. Do not mention it unless a student makes an error, but watch out for students treating red arrows as if they belong to the relation R. (Such confusion may result from the word *red* starting with the letter R.)

The complete picture is as follows:

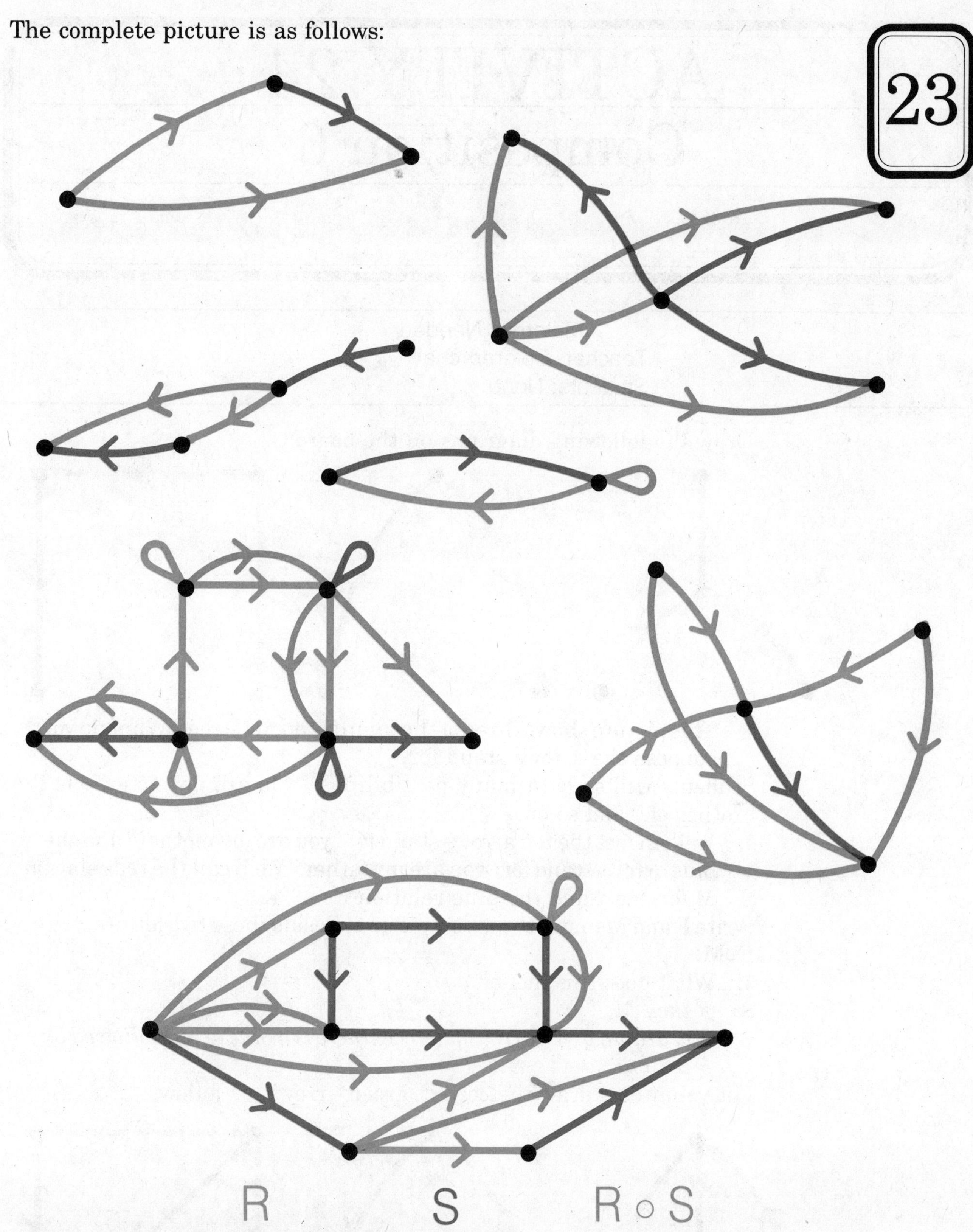

Resources Available

For class use: Worksheets L25 and L26

For out-of-class use: Any H-worksheet up through H36

ACTIVITY 24
Composition 6

Materials Needed
Teacher: Colored chalk
Students: None

Draw the following diagrams on the board:

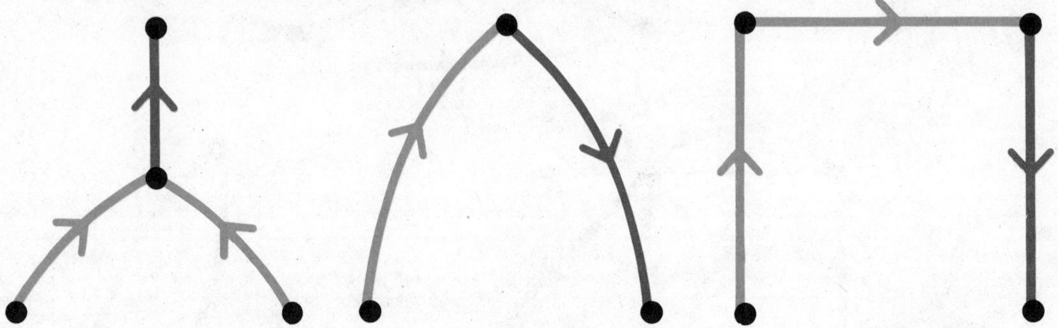

T: This picture shows three of the families on my street. What do you suppose the arrows stand for?

Students will suggest many possibilities: "you are my sister," "is the brother of," and so on.

T: Well, in fact the red arrows stand for "you are my mother" and the blue arrows stand for "you are my father." We'll call the red relation M for short and the blue relation F.

Write **F** and **M** under the arrow picture. Beside these two letters write **F∘M.**

T: What does this mean?

S: *F then M.*

S: *You draw a green arrow wherever there is a blue arrow followed by a red one.*

Let volunteers draw the correct green arrows, as follows:

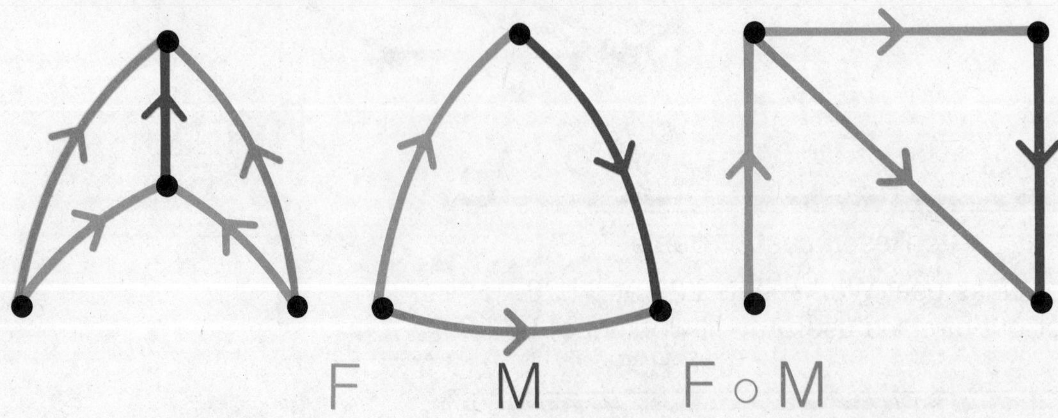

T: Now let's find out what these green arrows mean.

Refer to the central family picture. Use your index finger to trace along arrows as you mention them.

T: The blue arrow stands for "you are my father" and the red arrow stands for "you are my mother." What does the green arrow stand for?

If students are confused, label the dots as follows:

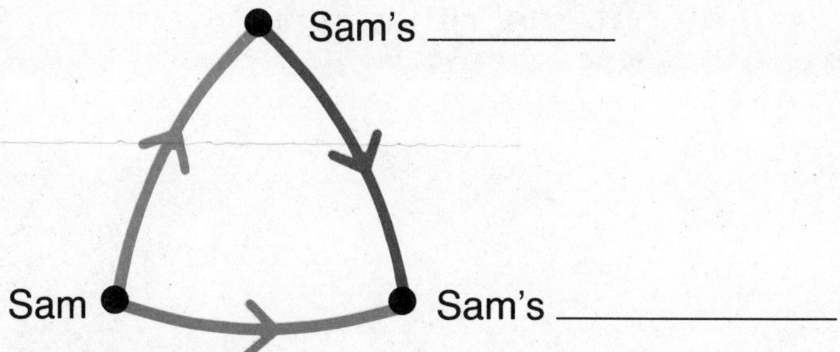

Students should suggest "father" and "grandmother" (respectively) for the upper and lower blanks.

S: *The green arrow stands for "you are my grandmother."*

T: Good. But there are two kinds of grandmothers, you know. This one is Sam's father's mother. What other kind of grandmother would Sam have?

S: *His mother's mother.*

Write on the board:

father's mother = paternal grandmother

mother's mother = maternal grandmother

T: Which is the green arrow?

S: *Paternal grandmother.*

T: While we're at it, what are these?

Write on the board:

$M \circ F$

$M \circ M$

$F \circ F$

Let students draw the relevant arrow pictures on the board:

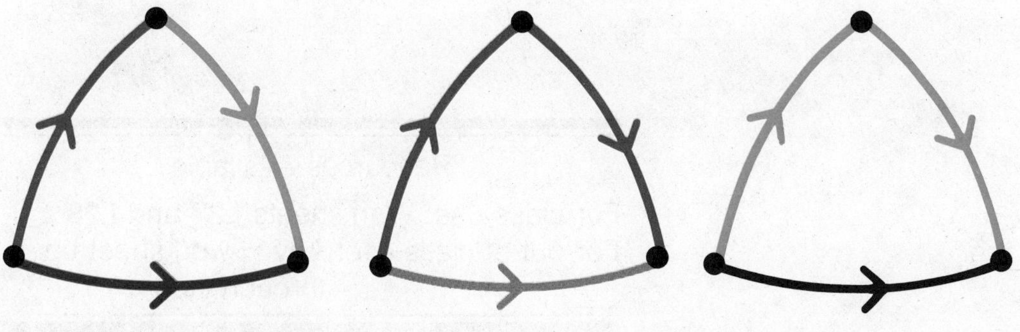

The class should then be able to provide the following answers:

M ∘ F maternal grandfather

M ∘ M maternal grandmother

F ∘ F paternal grandfather

Resources Available

For class use: Worksheets L27 and L28

For out-of-class use: Any H-worksheet up through H36

ACTIVITY 25
Calculator Sentences 1

Materials Needed
Teacher: Colored chalk
Students: None (a calculator is *not* necessary)

Write the following on the board:

T: These stand for calculator keys. Let's assume that the calculator does operations as they are punched in. What would the display show if you pressed these keys?
S: *140.*
If a student answers "59," remind him or her that you are using a calculator that works things out from left to right.
T: Let's draw an arrow picture for this calculator sentence. How shall we start?
S: *Draw a dot and label it* ***9.***
T: And then?
S: *Draw a* $+5$ *arrow.*
Draw the following diagram on the board:

S: *And then a* $\times 10$ *arrow.*
Complete the arrow picture:

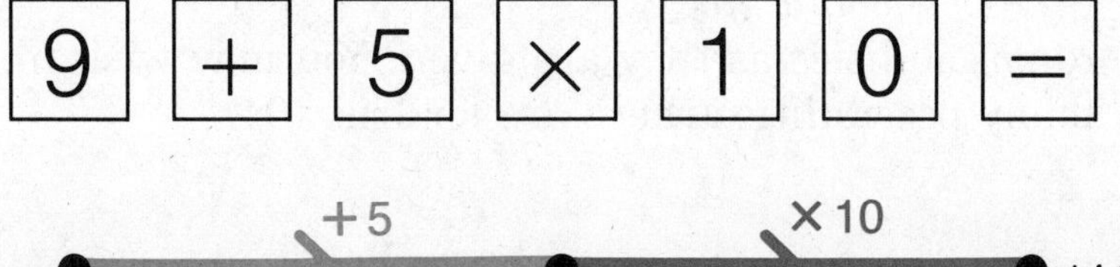

T: Now I'm going to change the calculator sentence.
Erase the operation signs and add the name Daisy at the end.

T: Each blank square stands for one of the operation keys [+], [−], [×], [÷]. Both blanks could stand for the same thing. Here's the first thing we have found out.
Write the following on the board:

Operations		Daisy
+	×	140

T: Who would like to come to the board and add to my list?
After four or five volunteers have added to the list, ask:
T: How many possibilities do you think there are for Daisy?
Accept all the students' estimates, then return to letting volunteers add to the list on the board.

In fact there are 16 possibilities, as follows:

+	+	24	−	+	14	×	+	55	÷	+	11.8
+	−	4	−	−	$\widehat{6}$	×	−	35	÷	−	$\widehat{8.2}$
+	×	140	−	×	40	×	×	450	÷	×	18
+	÷	1.4	−	÷	0.4	×	÷	4.5	÷	÷	0.18

There is no need to force the issue if all of these are not found by the students. If you wish, you could challenge the class by telling them how many possibilities they have *not* discovered. The students can then be encouraged to search for the remaining possibilities in their own time.

Erase everything you have written and drawn on the board. Then write this new calculator sentence on the board:

T: This time we have three blank squares, which means we are working with three operations. Help me to list some of the possibilities for Iris.
S: +, +, + *would give 33.*
S: −, −, − *would give 3.*
Record possibilities as they are given. You may wish to ask students how many possibilities there are for Iris. (64)

Resources Available
For class use: Worksheets L29 and L30
For out-of-class use: Any H-worksheet up through H39

ACTIVITY 26

Calculator Sentences 2

Materials Needed
Teacher: Colored chalk
Students: Paper and pencils

Write the following on the board:

5	0		5		2		1	0	=	Rose

Operations   Rose

T: Each blank square stands for one of the operation keys [+], [−], [×], [÷]. But today the rule is changed in an important way. All three blanks have to stand for a *different* key. Which of these is not allowed today?

Start this list on the board:

÷	−	+	18
+	×	+	120

S: *The second, because there are two plus signs.*

T: Copy the calculator sentence onto your paper and work out some of the possibilities for Rose. Be sure you obey the no-repeats rule.

Check on student progress. Ask volunteers to record some of their answers on the board after they have had sufficient time to work. Here is the complete list (but you should *not* require that all the answers be found at this point).

+	−	×	530	−	+	×	470	×	+	−	242	÷	+	−	2
+	−	÷	5.3	−	+	÷	4.7	×	+	÷	25.2	÷	+	×	120
+	×	−	100	−	×	+	100	×	−	+	258	÷	×	+	30
+	×	÷	11	−	×	÷	9	×	−	÷	24.8	÷	×	−	10
+	÷	−	17.5	−	÷	+	32.5	×	÷	+	135	÷	−	+	18
+	÷	×	275	−	÷	×	225	×	÷	−	115	÷	−	×	80

T: In the last activity, when each blank was allowed to stand for any of the four operation keys, how many ways were there of filling in the three boxes?

S: *64. For each of the four ways of filling in the first box there are four ways of filling in the second, so there are 16 ways of filling in the first two boxes. For each of these 16 ways there are four ways to fill in the last box; that's 64 ways in all.*

T: Now let's see how many ways there are when we allow no repetitions. Guess how many ways there are, and write your guess on your papers. Think for a moment or two before you write anything. Once you have made up your mind, fold your paper so that your answer is hidden,and exchange papers with another student.

Draw the following tree diagram below the calculator sentence:

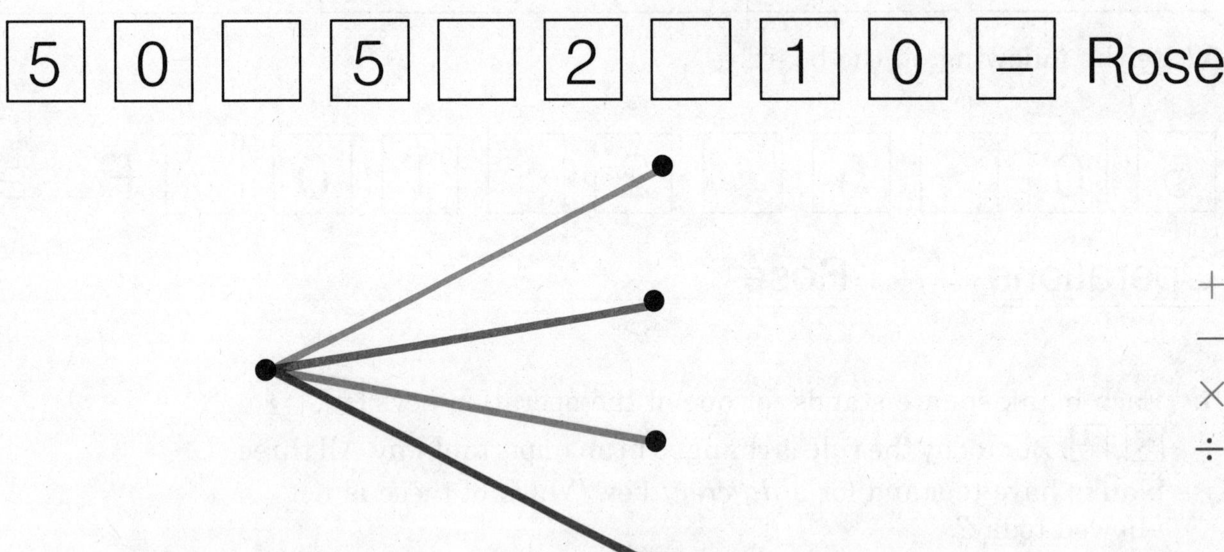

T: My drawing shows the four possible signs I could choose for the first blank. Let's suppose I choose "times" for the first blank. What sign could I choose for the second?

S: *"Plus," "minus," or "divided by."*

Add to your diagram as follows:

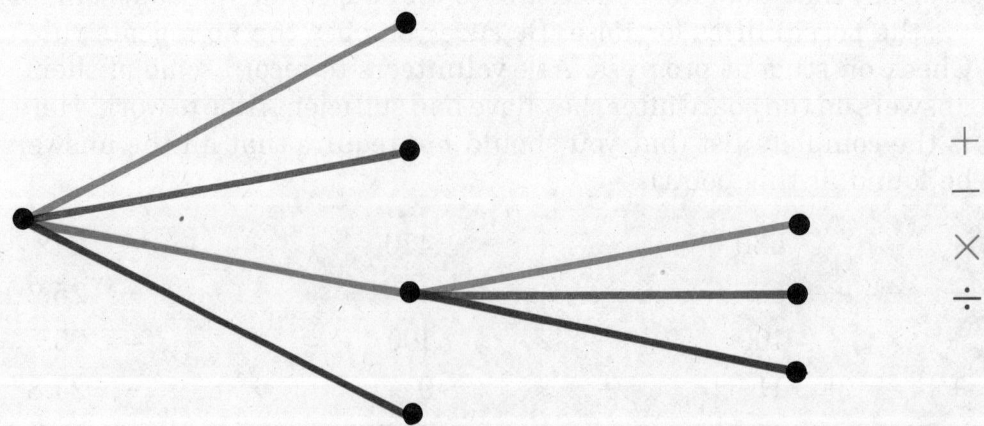

With the help of the class, complete the 12 branches at the second stage. The diagram should look like this:

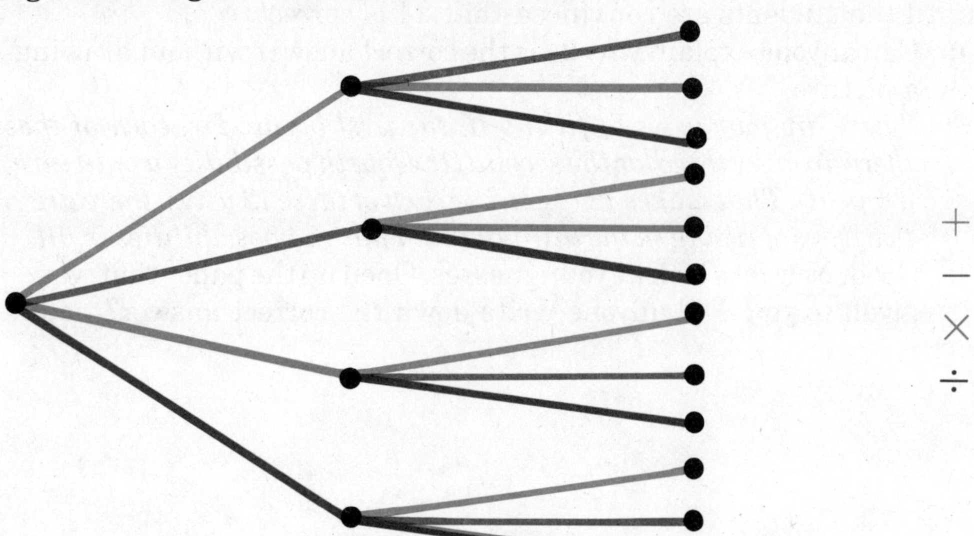

T: Show me the path that stands for "minus" in the first blank and "divided by" in the second.

S: *Red-purple.*

T: After "minus," and "divided by," what choices do I have for the third blank?

S: *"Plus" or "times."*

Add to the picture once again:

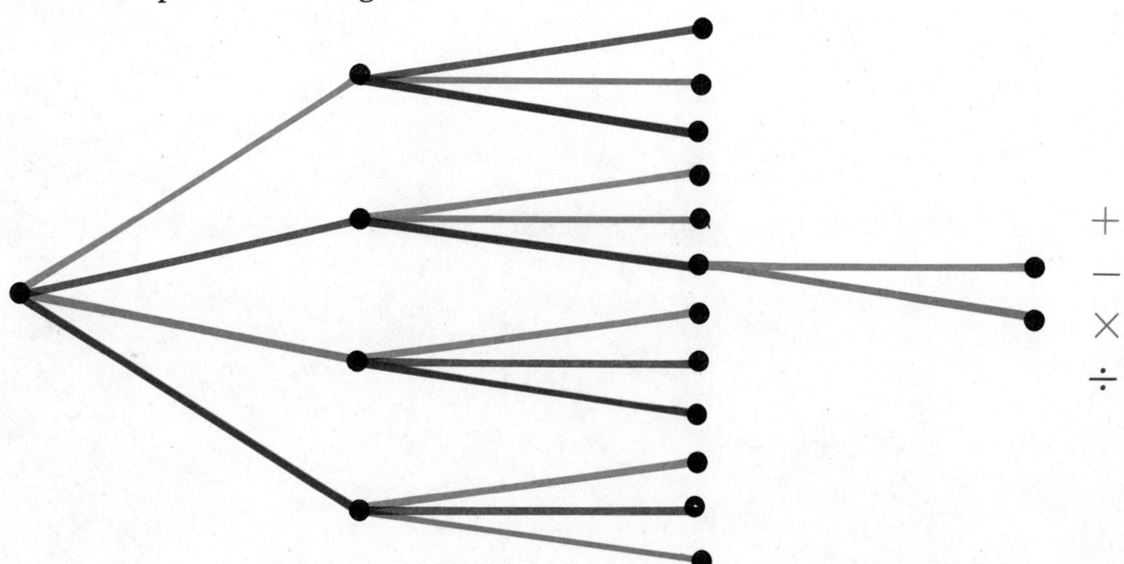

T: Can anyone tell me how many possibilities there are going to be for Rose?

S: *24.*

T: Let's check that by finding some more paths. Which path stands for "times," "plus"?

S: *Green-blue.*

T: What choices does that leave for the third blank?

S: *Red for "minus" or purple for "divided by."*

Continue to draw in a few more pairs of branches at the third stage until the students are convinced that 24 is correct.

T: Can anyone explain why 24 is the correct answer without drawing a picture?

S: *There are four ways of filling in the first blank. For each of these, there are only three for the second (the fourth possibility would give a repeat). That makes 12 ways. For each of these 12 ways, there are two ways of filling in the third blank. That's 24 possibilities in all.*

T: Good. Now let's look at your guesses. Open up the paper that was given to you. Did anyone write down the correct answer?

Resources Available

For out-of-class use: Any H-worksheet up through H39

ACTIVITY 27
Decimals 5

Materials Needed
Teacher: Colored chalk
Students: Colored pencils

T: I am going to draw an arrow road, and I want you to help me label the dots and arrows.
Draw the following on the board:

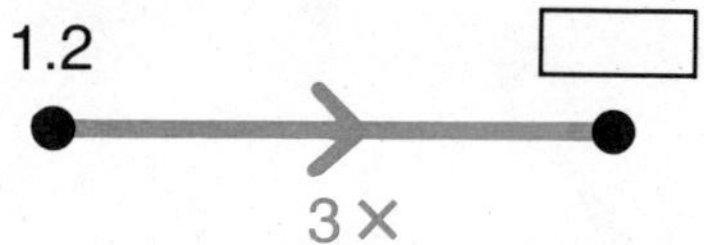

T: What number is the ending dot for? (3.6)
Label the dot and continue the arrow road:

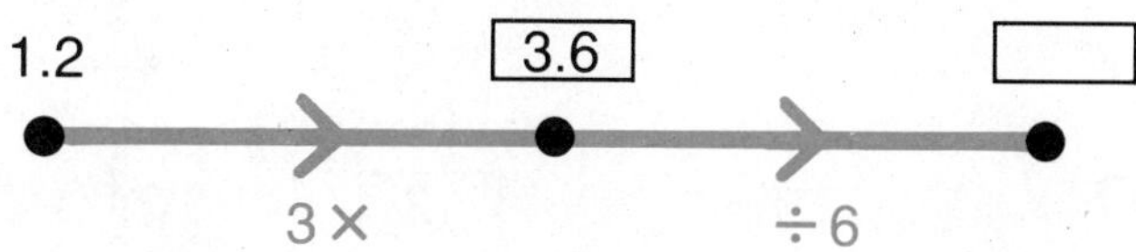

T: What number is the ending dot for? (0.6)
Label the dot and continue:

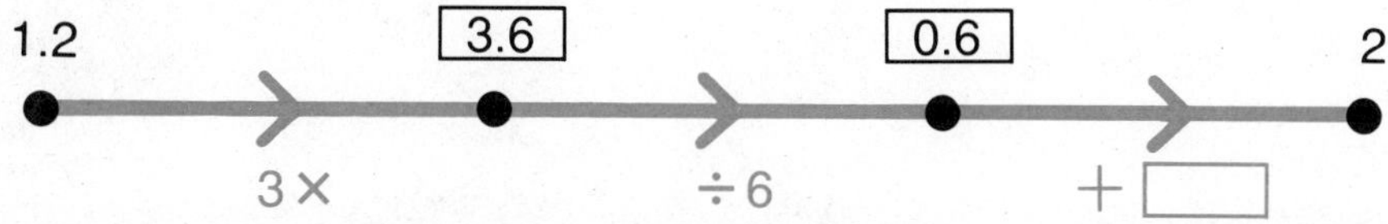

T: What could this arrow be for? (+1.4)
Continue the arrow road, one arrow at a time, as long as there is student interest and involvement. The following drawing is one possible road you might use. The numbers in boxes are to be determined by the class.

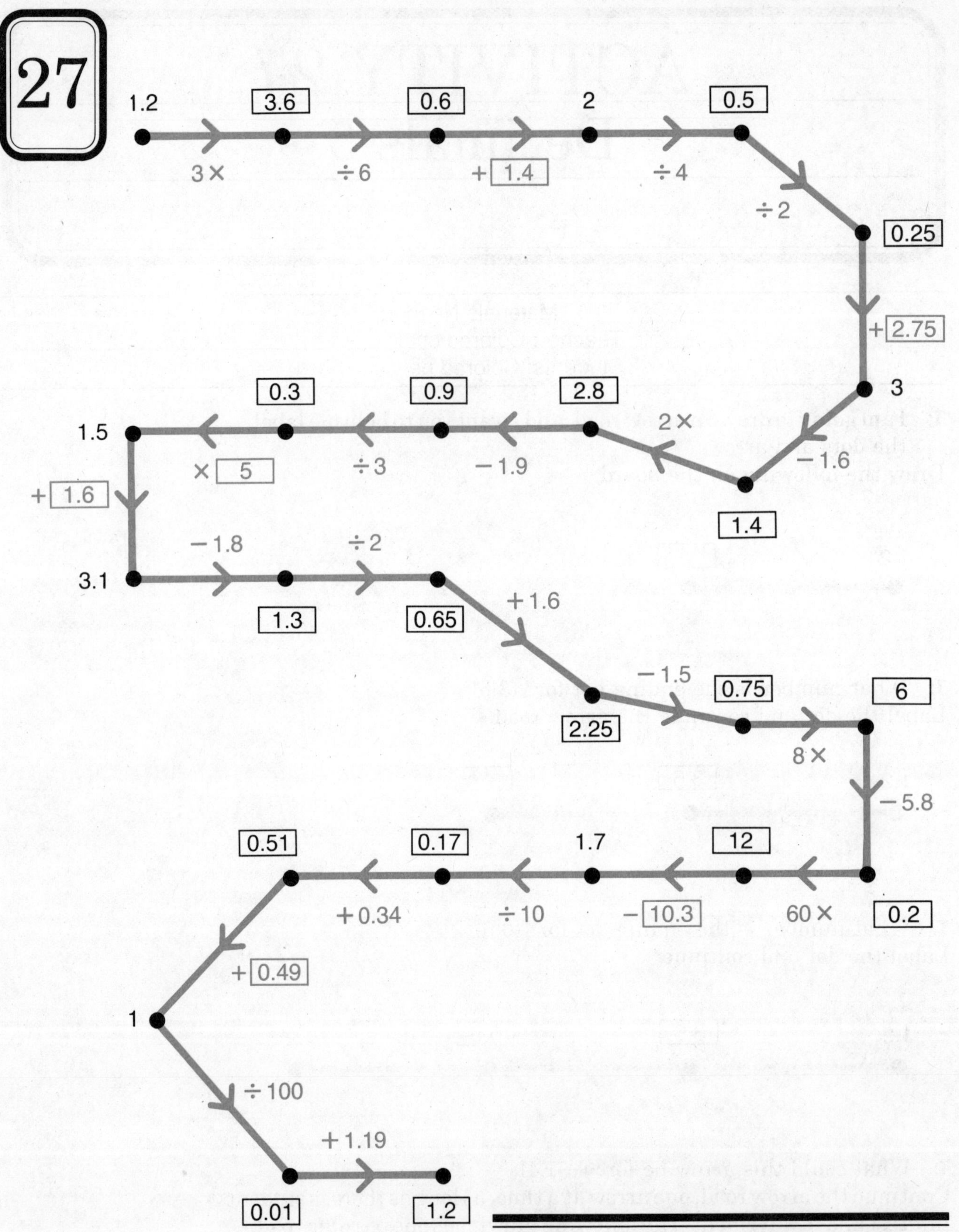

Resources Available

For class use: Worksheets L31 and L32

For out-of-class use: Any H-worksheet up through H42

ACTIVITY 28
Decimals 6

Materials Needed
Teacher: Colored chalk
Students: Paper and colored pencils

Here are three problems for the class to solve individually or in small groups. Each involves finding a red-blue arrow road from one number to another. Challenge students to find shortest roads. When a student finds a solution, invite him or her to write the number of arrows in that solution on the board beside the problem. Encourage the class to reduce the number, if possible.

Problem 1: Build a red-blue arrow from 1 to 11.
Try to use as few arrows as possible.

+0.5

1 ● ● 11

2 ×

(A road with five arrows is the shortest.)

Problem 2: Build a red-blue arrow road from 15 to 1.
Try to use as few arrows as possible.

÷3

15 ● ● 1

+0.4

(A shortest road has seven arrows.)

Problem 3: Build a red-blue arrow road from 0.1 to 7.5.
Try to use as few arrows as possible.

3 ×

0.1 ● ● 7.5

−0.2

(A shortest road has five arrows.)

When most of the students have found a solution to problem 1, discuss the problem with the whole class.

T: Most of you have found a solution to problem 1. Let's try to find a way to get as short a road as possible. Start at 11 and work backward. What arrow should we use that ends at 11?

S: *A blue arrow.*

Draw it:

+0.5

1

11

2×

T: What number is the starting dot of the blue arrow for? (5.5)

Label the dot and continue working backward:

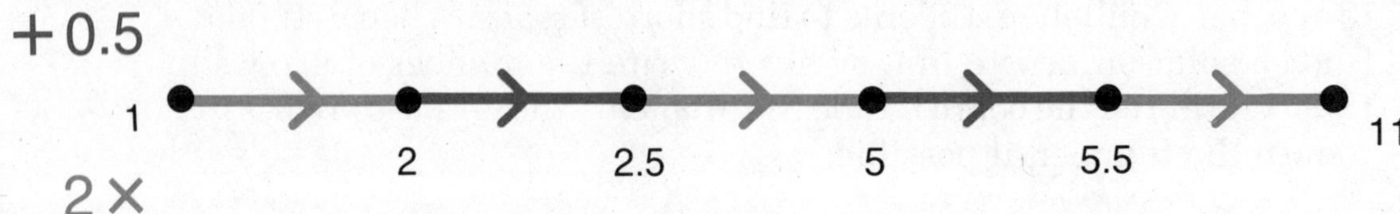

A solution to problem 2:

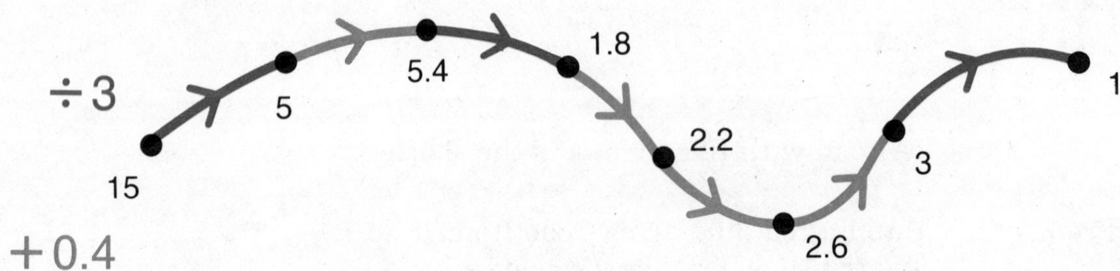

A solution to problem 3:

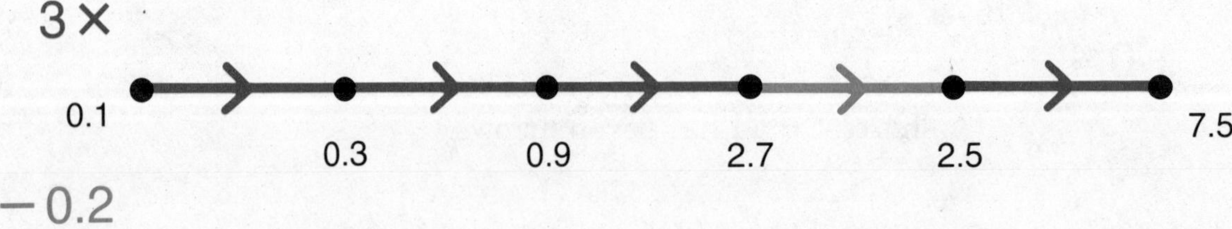

Resources Available

For out-of-class use: Any H-worksheet up through H42

ACTIVITY 29
Probability 2

Materials Needed
Teacher: Colored chalk, three red and three blue Minicomputer checkers
Students: Colored pencils

Show the class that you are holding in your hands two red and two blue Minicomputer checkers. Then put your hands behind your back and shake the checkers. Transfer two of them to your right hand and bring your right hand forward, still closed so that the class cannot see what is in it.

T: I have two checkers in my right hand. How many of them could be red checkers?

S: *None, one, or two.*

T: We say, "The *outcome* could be zero, one or two red checkers."

Open your right hand and reveal what outcome has occurred. Do this several times, at least until each possible outcome has occurred at least once.

T: What is the probability of getting no red checkers in this experiment?

S: *There are three outcomes: zero, one or two. So the probability is one chance in three.*

T: How can we decide whether that is correct?

S: *Do it lots of times. Do it 60 times and see if we get no reds 20 times.*

T: All right, but would we really be sure even if 20 out of 60 times we got no reds? Let's try to do it by thinking.

Draw this diagram on the board:

T: Here is a picture of the four checkers: two Rs for "red," two Bs for blue." Someone please draw a blue cord between two checkers to show a way to get no red checkers.
S: *That's the same as two blues.*
Let a student draw a blue cord. (There is only one possibility.)

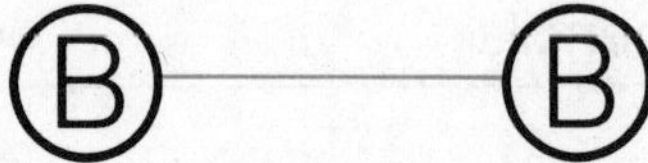

T: Are there any other blue cords that we could draw? (no) Someone please draw a green cord to show a way to get one red checker.
S: *That's one red and one blue.*
Let a student draw a green cord. (There are four possibilities.)

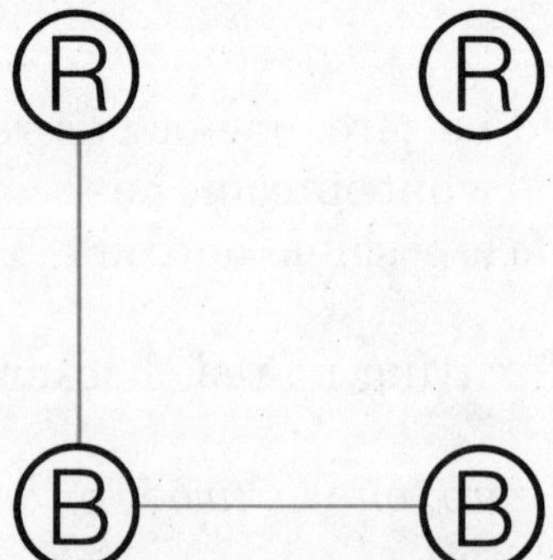

Invite students to draw other green cords until it is agreed they have all been drawn.

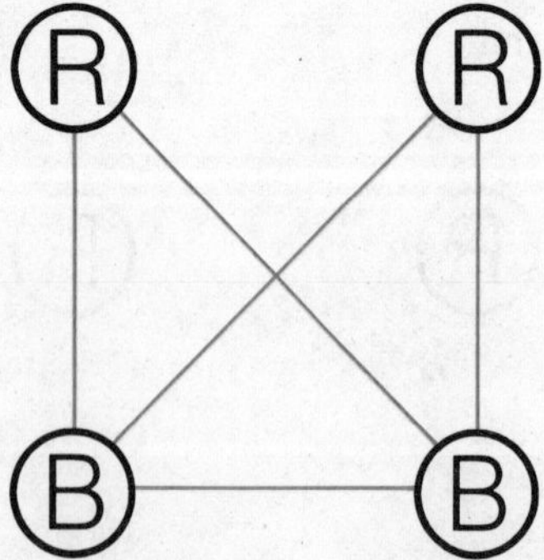

29

T: Now, someone please draw a red cord to show a way to get two red checkers.

Let a student draw the only possible red cord:

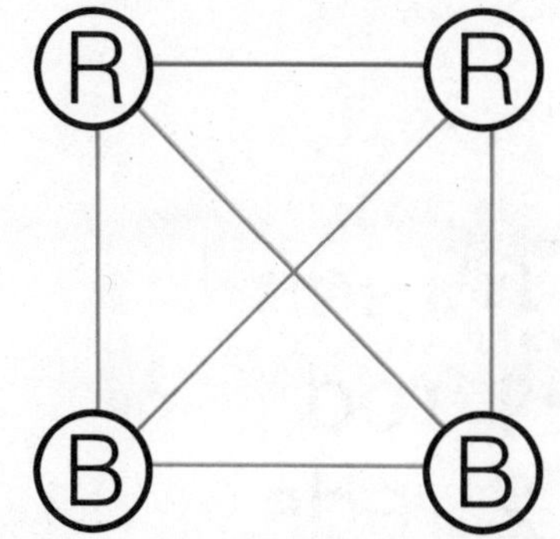

0 reds

1 red

2 reds

T: How many cords did we draw altogether? (6)
How many of them were blue? (1)
How many were green? (4)
How many were red? (1)
So what is the probability of getting no red checkers? (one chance in six, or $\frac{1}{6}$)
What is the probability of getting one red checker? (four chances in six, or $\frac{4}{6}$)
What is the probability of getting two red checkers? (one chance in six, or $\frac{1}{6}$)

Draw a probability tree for the experiment:

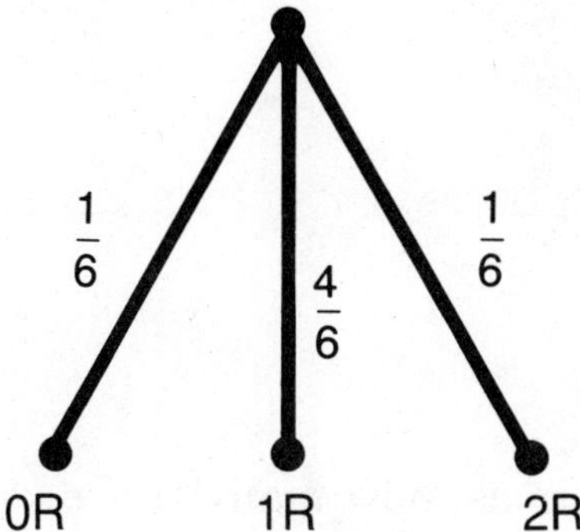

T: If we do this experiment 60 times, do you still think we will get no reds 20 times?

S: *No. We should get no reds about 10 times, about once every six times.*

S: *And we should get one red about 40 times and two reds about 10 times.*

T: Let's do the same kind of experiment, but this time we will pick two checkers out of three red and three blue checkers.

29

Repeat all the above procedures, leading to the diagram and probability tree below (which should be drawn alongside the first diagram and tree).

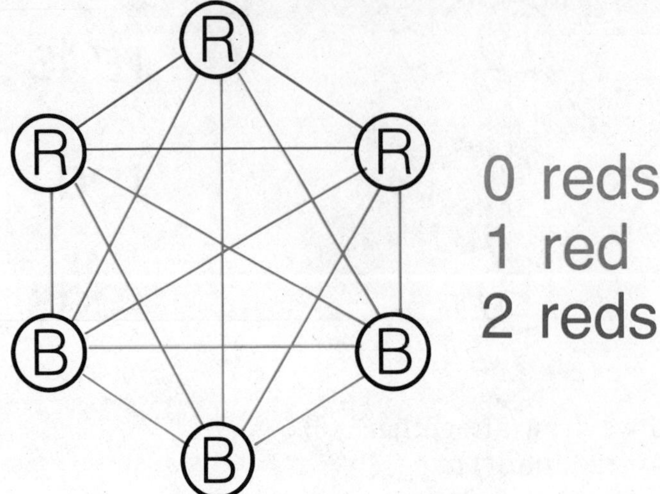

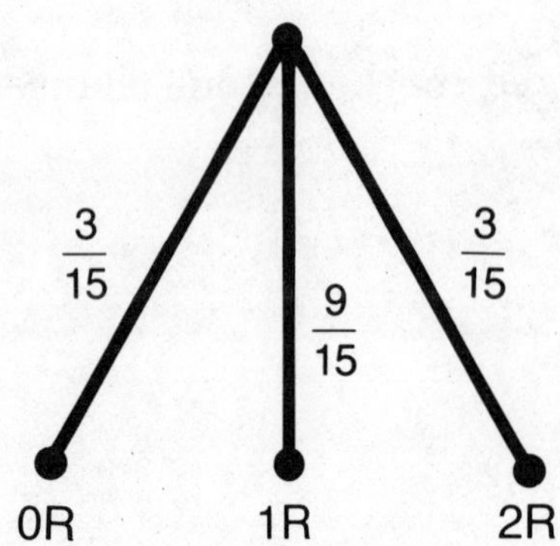

T: If we did this experiment 150 times, how many times would we get one red?

S: *About 90 times.*

S: *And we would get no reds about 30 times; the same for two reds.*

Resources Available

For class use: Worksheets L33 and L34

For out-of-class use: Any H-worksheet up through H45

ACTIVITY 30
Binary Abacus

Materials Needed
Teacher: Minicomputer checkers (both regular and negative)
Students: None

If your chalkboard is metallic so it will hold your magnetized checkers, draw this picture on the board:

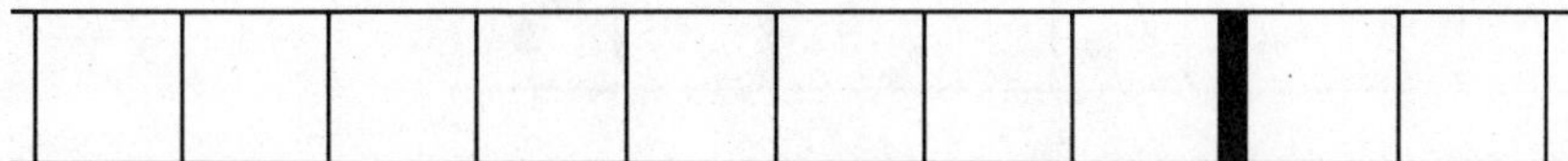

Note to the Teacher

If your chalkboard is not metallic, cover the lower squares of your Minicomputer boards so that only the top row of squares appears, as in the diagram above.

This activity is a review and extension of Activities 21, 22, and 27 in Volume 3.

T: Do you remember the binary abacus? What is this number?
Place two checkers as shown below:

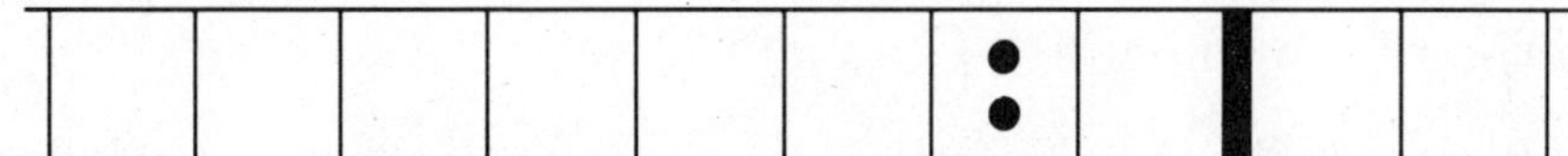

S: *It's 4; 2 + 2.*
Help students to recall the rule of the binary abacus:

> Two checkers on a square show the same number as one checker on the next square to the left.

30

Also help them recall the values of the squares:

128 64 32 16 8 4 2 1 0.5 0.25

Then present a number of review problems, such as these:

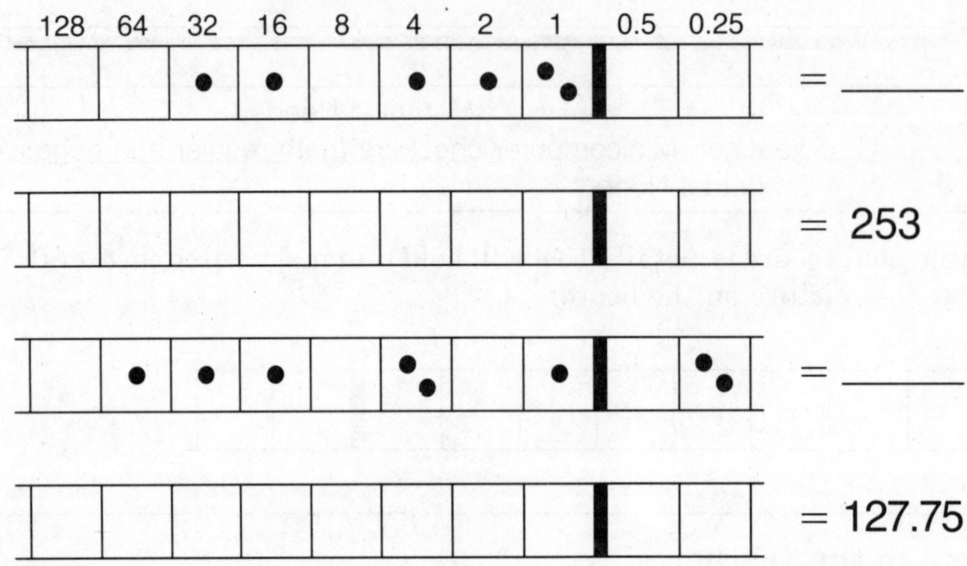

If further review is needed, pose additional problems of the above type. Then remove the checkers from the binary abacus and place a negative checker and a regular checker as follows:

128 64 32 16 8 4 2 1 0.5 0.25

T: What is this number?
S: *12.*
S: *No. It's* $8 + \hat{4}$. *That's 4.*
T: And what is this number?

Place checkers as shown below:

128 64 32 16 8 4 2 1 0.5 0.25

Accept any answers without comment, and let the students come to a decision among themselves on the correct answer. Some might prefer direct addition:

$$32 + \widehat{16} + 8 + 8 + 4 + \widehat{2} + 1 + 0.5 + \widehat{0.25} = 35.25$$

Others might prefer to make the robot moves $8 + 8 = 16$, $4 = 2 + 2$, and $0.5 = 0.25 + 0.25$ to obtain the configuration:

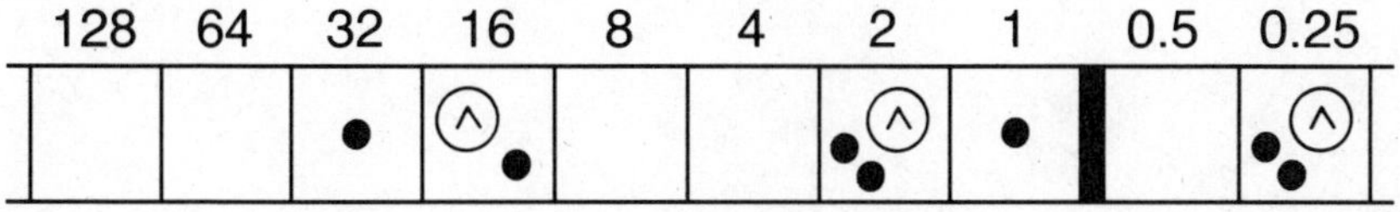

128	64	32	16	8	4	2	1	0.5	0.25
		•	(^) •			• • (^)	•		• • (^)

Upon "cancellation," the configuration is:

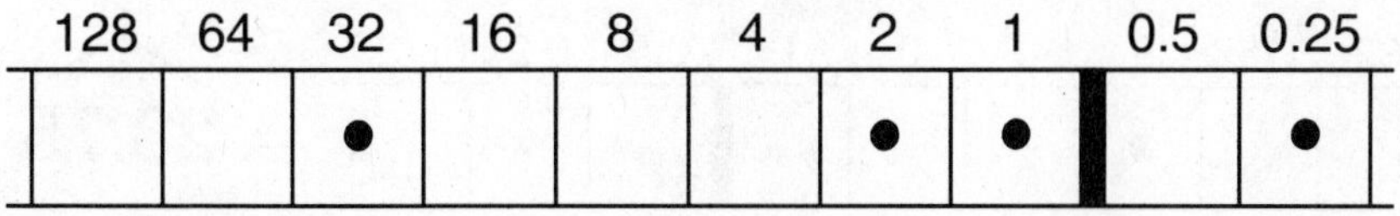

128	64	32	16	8	4	2	1	0.5	0.25	
		•				•	•		•	= 35.25

Continue with this kind of activity in which random configurations of negative and regular checkers on the binary abacus are displayed and the associated number identified. Then pose the following question (or a similar one).

T: Show 31 on the binary abacus, using regular or negative checkers or both.
What is the smallest number of checkers we need?

S: *Two: a regular checker on 32 and a negative checker on 1.*

T: Good. How many checkers do we need to show 7.75?

S: *Four. Put a regular checker on 8 and a negative checker on 1. That makes 7. Then put regular checkers on 0.5 and 0.25.*

S: *I know how to do it with only two checkers. Put a regular checker on 8 and a negative checker on 0.25.* ($8 + \widehat{0.25} = 7.75$)

If this answer is not given by anyone in the class, either give the hint that 7.75 can be shown with just two checkers and assign the problem as homework or give the solution yourself. Then pose other problems, such as these:

1. What is the smallest number of checkers needed to show 51.5 on the binary abacus?
(answer: four checkers)

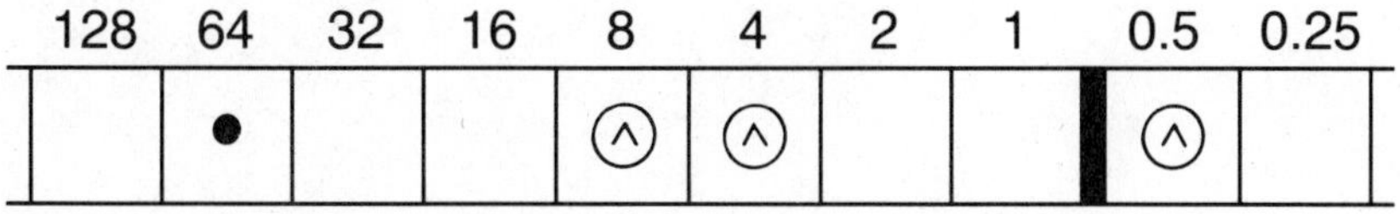

128	64	32	16	8	4	2	1	0.5	0.25	
	•			(^)	(^)			(^)		= 51.5

or

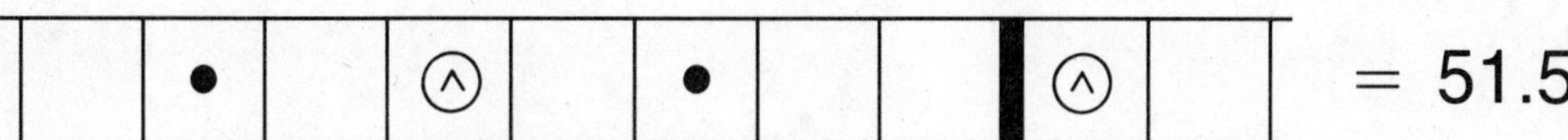

or

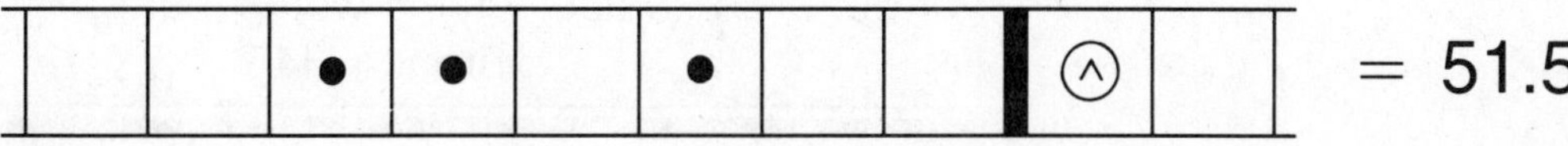

30

2. What is the smallest number of checkers needed to show $\widehat{23.75}$ on the binary abacus?
   (answer: three checkers)

128	64	32	16	8	4	2	1	0.5	0.25	0.125	
		(^)		•					•		$= \widehat{23.75}$

or

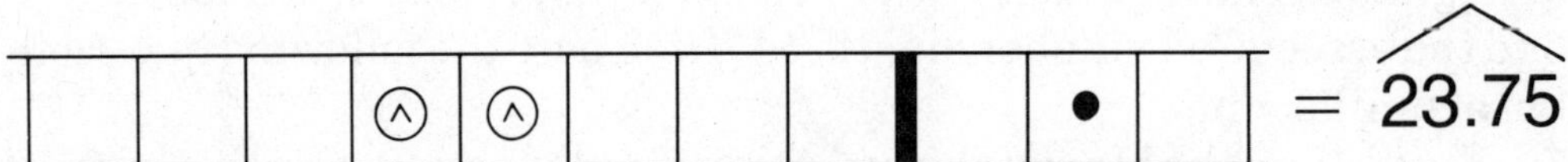

3. What is the smallest number of checkers needed to show 31.375 on the binary abacus?
   (answer: four checkers)

128	64	32	16	8	4	2	1	0.5	0.25	0.125	
		•					(^)	•		(^)	= 31.375

Resources Available

For out-of-class use: Any H-worksheet up through H45

ACTIVITIES 31 and 32

Guess My Rule

Addition Modulo 10

Materials Needed
Teacher: Chalk
Students: Paper and pencils

Write the following on the board:

$$4 * 8 = 2$$
$$8 * 7 = 5$$
$$9 * 5 = 4$$
$$2 * 3 = 5$$
$$6 * 9 = \square$$

T: I have a secret rule for $*$, and I've given you four clues to help you discover what that rule is. See if you can guess my rule. Which number do you think I should write in the box? If you think you know the answer, write it on your paper.

Note to the Teacher

The secret rule in this activity is given by:

$a * b$ = the ones' digit of $(a+b)$.

For example, $9 * 5 = 4$, since $9 + 5 = 14$ and the ones' digit of 14 is 4. Do not divulge the rule to your students until they guess it.

Walk around the room observing the students' work. Acknowledge aloud any correct answers, and mention incorrect ones explicitly. For example, "Yes, that's correct" or "No, the number is not 6." Let a student who guesses correctly tell the class that the answer is 5, but ask him or her not to give away the rule. If no one guesses correctly, write **5** in the box yourself.

Proceed similarly with the following problems. (The answers given in the boxes are for your information only.)

$$6 * 16 = \boxed{2}$$
$$13 * 19 = \boxed{2}$$
$$25 * 35 = \boxed{0}$$
$$14 * 65 = \boxed{9}$$
$$128 * 246 = \boxed{4}$$

T: Who can explain the rule?
S: *You just add the numbers and take the last number.**
Engage the whole class in checking that this rule works for all the calculations written on the board.
T: This rule is used quite a lot in mathematics, so we usually give it a special name that is never used for any other rule. Instead of writing $\mathbf{8 * 7 = 5}$ we write $\mathbf{8 +_{10} 7 = 5}$, and we read this as "eight plus seven modulo 10 equals five." Here's a calculation written in our new notation. Who can read it?
Write on the board: $\mathbf{32 +_{10} 15 = 7}$.
S: *32 plus 15 modulo 10 equals 7.*
T: Now each of you write a calculation on your paper using the new notation. Be careful to make the 10 very small, and write it below and to the right of the plus sign.
Call on a few students to read the calculation they have just written. If any of the calculations are read incorrectly or have incorrect answers, ask another student to correct the errors.

Write the following problems on the board and ask the students to copy and complete them. (For your information only, answers are provided in the boxes.)

$$3 +_{10} 15 = \boxed{8}$$
$$64 +_{10} 92 = \boxed{6}$$
$$(4 +_{10} 7) +_{10} 9 = \boxed{0}$$
$$4 +_{10} (7 +_{10} 9) = \boxed{0}$$
$$15 +_{10} (36 +_{10} 88) = \boxed{9}$$
$$(15 +_{10} 36) +_{10} 88 = \boxed{9}$$

*That is, the last digit.

Note to the Teacher

These last four problems should convince the students that for this operation the two possible placements of parentheses in a modulo-10 sum of three numbers yield the same result. From here on, therefore, we omit the parentheses.

$$103 +_{10} 56 = \boxed{9}$$
$$56 +_{10} 103 = \boxed{9}$$
$$7 +_{10} 7 +_{10} 7 = \boxed{1}$$
$$8 +_{10} 7 +_{10} 6 = \boxed{1}$$
$$9 +_{10} 9 +_{10} 9 +_{10} 9 = \boxed{6}$$

$$\boxed{4} +_{10} 3 = 7$$

(Any whole number with 4 as its last digit is a possible answer.)

$$\boxed{7} +_{10} 5 = 2$$

(Any whole number with 7 as its last digit is a possible answer.)

$$5 +_{10} \boxed{8} +_{10} 4 = 7$$

(Any whole number with 8 as its last digit is a possible answer.)

$$1 +_{10} 2 +_{10} 3 +_{10} 4 +_{10} 5 +_{10} 6 +_{10} 7 +_{10} 8 +_{10} 9 = \boxed{5}$$

After the students have worked individually for several minutes, let a number of them write their answers on the board. For the last four problems discuss the solutions with the whole class. Here is one way such a discussion might proceed:

Point to $\square +_{10} 3 = 7$.

T: Let's discuss this problem. Susan wrote 4 in the box. Is she correct?

S: *Yes.* $4 +_{10} 3 = 7$ *because* $4 + 3 = 7$*, and there's only one digit, which is 7.*

T: Does anyone have a different answer?

S: *No. There can only be one answer.*

S: *I have another one: 14. It works because* $14 + 3 = 17$*, and the ones' digit is 7.*

S: *There are lots of answers: 24, 34, 44, 54, and so on.*

S: *They all end in 4.*

S: *The next two problems also have lots of answers—7, 17, 27, 37, 47, and so on, for the first one. Any number ending in 7 could go in the box.*

S: *And for the next one, any number ending in 8 works.*

T: How did you do this big calculation, Josh?

Josh: *Well,* $1 +_{10} 2 = 3$ *and* $3 +_{10} 3 = 6$ *and* $6 +_{10} 4 = 0$ *and* $0 +_{10} 5 = 5$ *and* $5 +_{10} 6 = 1$ *and* $1 +_{10} 7 = 8$ *and* $8 +_{10} 6 = 6$ *and* $6 +_{10} 9 = 5$.

S: *I did it another way, I added all the numbers together and got 45. So the answer is 5.*

T: Both of those methods are good and give the correct result. But I'd like to show you a quicker way to do this calculation by looking at the problem in a clever way.

Write on the board:

$$1 +_{10} 2 +_{10} 3 +_{10} 4 +_{10} 5 +_{10} 6 +_{10} 7 +_{10} 8 +_{10} 9$$

T: What is $1 +_{10} 9$?

S: *0.*

T: Do you see other numbers we could pair to get 0 in this calculation?

S: *2 and 8, 3 and 7, 4 and 6.*

Indicate these pairings on the board:

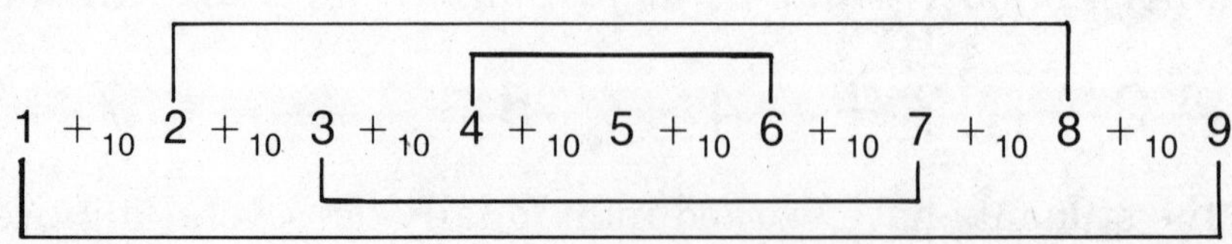

T: What is $(1 +_{10} 9) +_{10} (2 +_{10} 8) +_{10} (3 +_{10} 7) +_{10} (4 +_{10} 6)$?

S: $0 +_{10} 0 +_{10} 0 +_{10} 0 = 0$.

T: So what is the result of the calculation?

S: *5, because* $0 +_{10} 5 = 5$.

Write on the board:

$$\square +_{10} \square = 4$$

T: Remember that you have to write the same number in both boxes. Who can give me a solution to this problem?

S: *2.*

S: *12.*

S: *22, 32, 42, and so on.*

T: Are these the only possible solutions?

S: *Any whole number that ends in 2 is a solution, and there is no other whole number that works.*

S: *I have a different solution: 7.*
T: What is $7 +_{10} 7$?
S: *4.*
S: *But then 27, 37, 47, and so on also work. We can use any whole number that ends in 7.*
T: Are there any other whole numbers that work?
S: *No.*
T: Can you convince me that you're correct?
S: *Well,* $0 +_{10} 0 = 0$; $1 +_{10} 1 = 2$; $3 +_{10} 3 = 6$; $4 +_{10} 4 = 8$; $5 +_{10} 5 = 0$; $6 +_{10} 6 = 2$; $8 +_{10} 8 = 6$; *and* $9 +_{10} 9 = 8$. *Because only the last digits of numbers matter when you're adding modulo 10, you can't get 4 unless the ones' digit is 2 or 7.*

Write on the board:

$$\square +_{10} \square = 1$$

S: *Impossible.*
T: Explain.
S: *If you add a number to itself in the usual way, you always get an even number. That means the last digit is 0, 2, 4, 6, or 8—never 1.*

Write the following problems on the board, and ask the students to copy and complete them:

$$\square +_{10} 4 +_{10} \square = 6$$

(answer: 1, 11, 21, 31, . . . 6, 16, 26, 36, . . .)

$$\square +_{10} \square +_{10} \square = 7$$

(answer: 9, 19, 29, 39, . . .)

$$\square +_{10} 35 +_{10} \square = 1$$

(answer: 3, 13, 23, 33, . . . 8, 18, 28, 38, . . .)

$$\square +_{10} 2 +_{10} \square +_{10} 7 +_{10} \square = 1$$

(answer: 4, 14, 24, 34, . . .)

Before the lesson is over, ask several students to write their answers on the board.

Resources Available

For out-of-class use: Any H-worksheet up through H48

ACTIVITY 33
Functions 1

Materials Needed
Teacher: Colored chalk
Students: Paper and colored pencils

Draw about 15 dots on the board, distributed randomly like this:

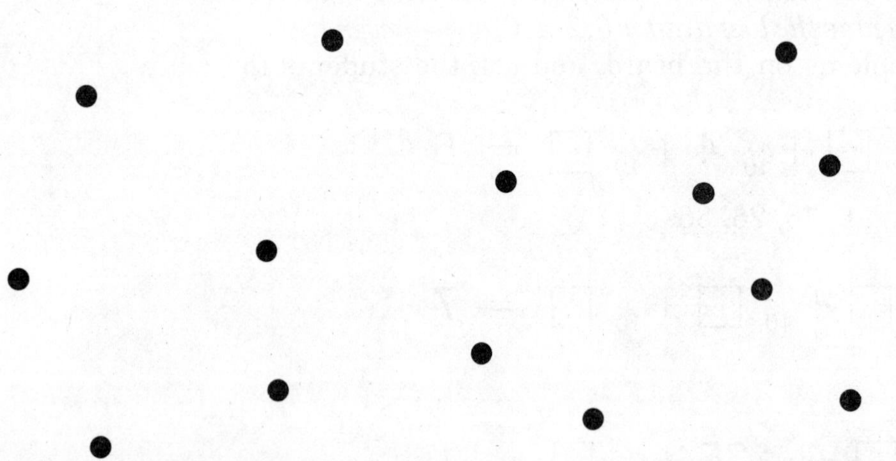

T: We're going to make up a relation using these dots. We'll call it F and we'll draw it using red arrows.

In a corner of the area where you have drawn the dots, write **F** in red.

T: The relation F has to obey one strict rule.

Write on the board:

Rule At most one red arrow starts at each dot.

T: What does "at most one" mean?
S: *Zero or one.*
T: How many red arrows does F have at the moment?
S: *None.*
T: Does F obey our rule?
S: *Yes.*

T: Let's add some arrows to it.
Let one volunteer at a time add a red arrow wherever he or she wishes. After each addition ask whether F still obeys the rule. Be on the watch for the following configuration, which is wrong.

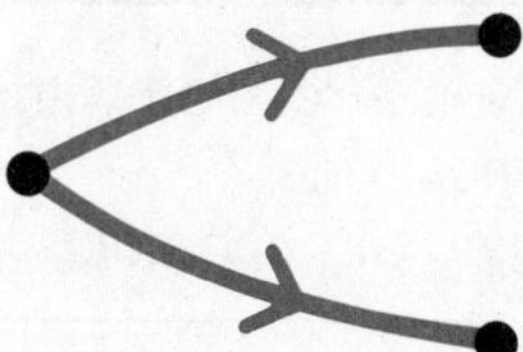

If such an error occurs, draw a blue box around the starting dot:

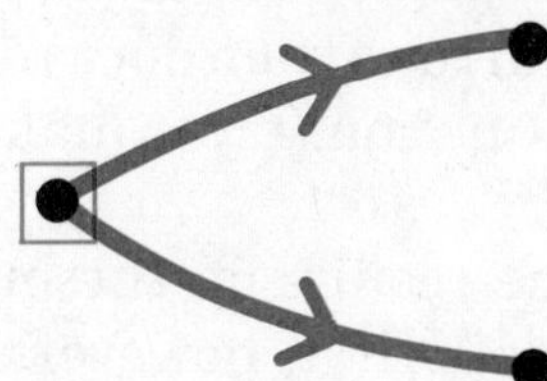

Refer to it as a guilty dot.

If students do not include such examples, you may wish to draw two arrows that end at the same point:

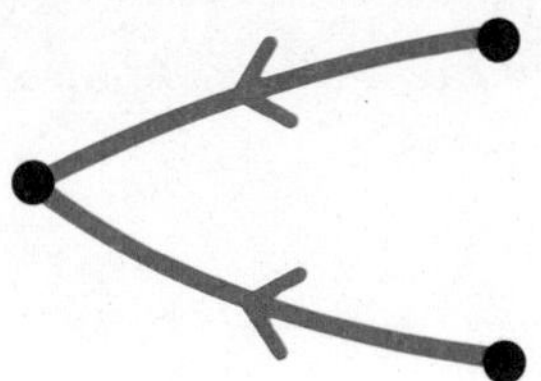

T: Is this allowed?
S: *Yes.*
Here is one possible arrow picture for F:

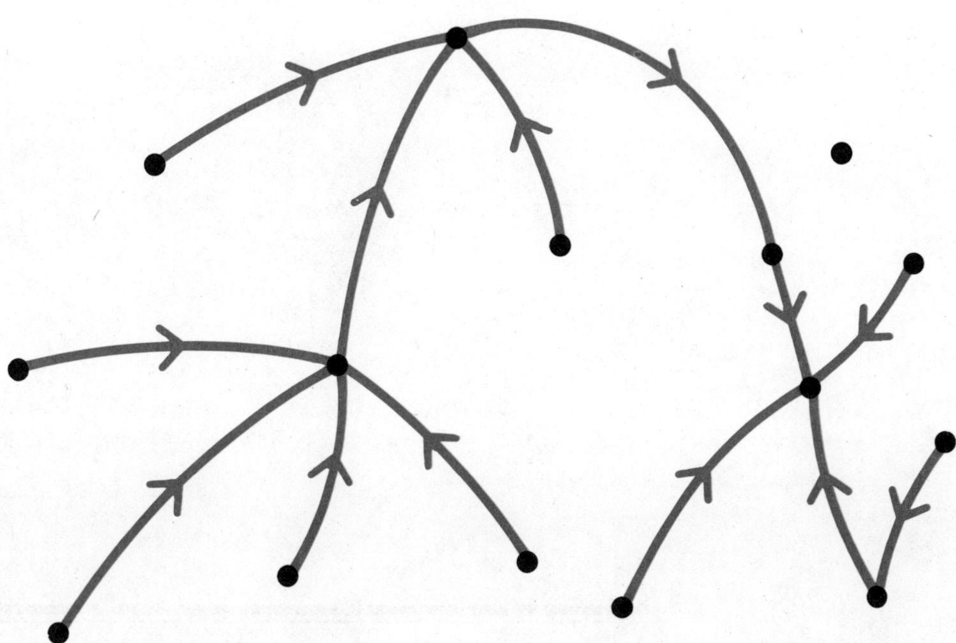

(Note: It is not necessary for every dot to be the starting point of one or more arrows.)

T: A relation like F that obeys our rule and therefore has no guilty dots is called a **function.** Here's a reminder for you:
Write on the board:

> A FUNCTION is a relation with
> at most one
> arrow starting at each dot.

T: Everyone take a blank sheet of paper and draw at least 12 dots. Then choose one color and draw arrows from dot to dot so that you end up with a relation that is a function. Try to make the diagram look as pretty as you can.
You may wish to diplay some of the results on the bulletin board. Be sure to check carefully for guilty dots first, however.

Resources Available

For out-of-class use: Any H-worksheet up through H51

ACTIVITY 34
Functions 2

Materials Needed
Teacher: Colored chalk
Students: Colored pencils

T: Can you help me write a description of a function on the board?
With the help of the class, write the following reminder on the board:

> A FUNCTION is a relation with
> at most one
> arrow starting at each dot.

T: Here are some relations. Which of them are functions?

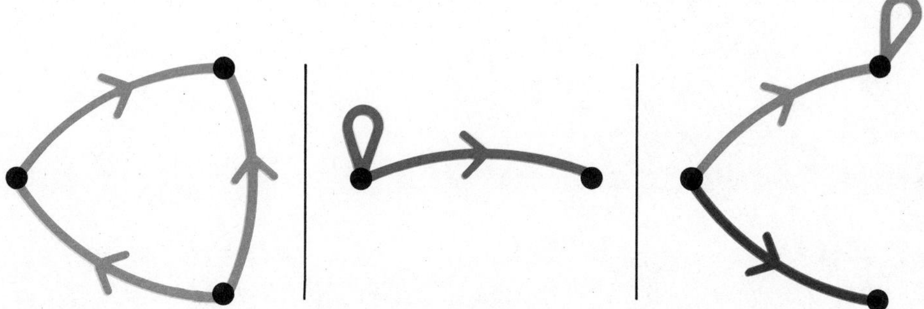

Students who give the relations only a superficial glance may well think that none of them is a function. The correct answer, however, is:
S: *Green and purple.*
Have students put boxes around the guilty dots.

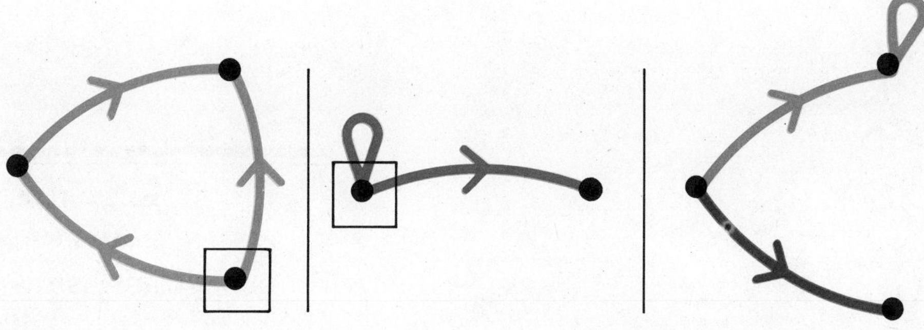

34

If the subject has not already come to light during the discussion of the above guilty dots, point to the starting dot of the purple arrow.

T: Why isn't this dot guilty?

S: *There are two arrows that start there, but they come from different functions.*

S: *There is only one green arrow and only one purple arrow starting at this dot.*

T: Is the relation "you are my father" a function?

S: *Yes.*

T: Why?

S: *Because you only have one father.*

T: How about "you are my sister"?

S: *No, because you can have more than one sister.*

T: Are any of you guilty?

Let the students discuss this point and identify those with two or more sisters.

T: How about "you are my grandmother"?

S: *No, because you have two grandmothers.*

T: Can you add a word so that we get a function?

S: *"You are my maternal grandmother."*

S: *"You are my paternal grandmother."*

Resources Available

For class use: Worksheets L35 and L36
For out-of-class use: Any H-worksheet up through H51

ACTIVITIES 35 and 36
Multiplication Modulo 10

Materials Needed
Teacher: Chalk
Students: Paper and pencils

Write the following on the board: $3 \times_{10} 4 = \square$.

T: What number do you think I should write in the box?

S: *2, because 3 × 4 = 12 and the ones' digit of 12 is 2.*

T: Very good. Now copy these problems and complete them on your papers.

Write the following problems on the board. (For your information only, answers are provided in the boxes.)

$$4 \times_{10} 6 = \boxed{4}$$
$$3 \times_{10} 9 = \boxed{7}$$
$$2 \times_{10} 3 = \boxed{6}$$
$$5 \times_{10} 4 = \boxed{0}$$
$$8 \times_{10} 8 = \boxed{4}$$
$$12 \times_{10} 16 = \boxed{2}$$
$$53 \times_{10} 15 = \boxed{5}$$
$$\boxed{6} \times_{10} 3 = 8$$

(other possibilities: 16, 26, 36, . . .)

$$\boxed{2} \times_{10} 2 = 4$$

(other possibilities: 12, 22, 32, . . . 7, 17, 27, . . .)

$$4 \times_{10} \boxed{1} = 4$$

(other possibilities: 11, 21, 32, . . . 6, 16, 26, . . .)

$$18 \times_{10} \boxed{4} = 2$$

(other possibilities: 14, 24, 34, . . . 9, 19, 29, . . .)

35
36

$$(2 \times_{10} 3) +_{10} (4 \times_{10} 3) = \boxed{8}$$
$$(2 +_{10} 4) \times_{10} 3 = \boxed{8}$$
$$5 \times_{10} (3 \times_{10} 8) = \boxed{5}$$
$$(5 \times_{10} 3) +_{10} (5 \times_{10} 8) = \boxed{5}$$
$$(3 \times_{10} \boxed{6}) +_{10} 3 = 1$$

(other possibilities: 16, 26, 36, . . .)

$$7 \times_{10} (\boxed{2} +_{10} 3) = 5$$

(other possibilities: 12, 22, 32, . . .)

After the students have worked individually for several minutes, let a number of them write their answers on the board. Ask for explanations for the more difficult problems. For several problems (particularly those with more than one solution), ask the students to explain how they are sure they have found all the solutions.

Write the following problems on the board, one after the other, pausing after each problem to allow the students to provide the answer:

$$2 \times_{10} 2 = \boxed{4}$$
$$2 \times_{10} 2 \times_{10} 2 = \boxed{8}$$
$$2 \times_{10} 2 \times_{10} 2 \times_{10} 2 = \boxed{6}$$
$$2 \times_{10} 2 \times_{10} 2 \times_{10} 2 \times_{10} 2 = \boxed{2}$$

T: It gets tiring writing all those 2s and $\times_{10}$s, so we'll use a shorthand way of writing. Instead of $2 \times_{10} 2$ we write 2^2 and read it "two to the second power, modulo 10."

Write this information on the board: $2 \times_{10} 2 = 2^2 = 4$.

T: For $2 \times_{10} 2 \times_{10} 2$ we write 2^3 and read it "two to the third power, modulo 10."

Write this information on the board: $2 \times_{10} 2 \times_{10} 2 = 2^3 = 8$.

T: Now I'll rewrite the calculations on the board in this new notation.

Write on the board:

$$2^1 = 2$$
$$2^2 = 4$$
$$2^3 = 8$$
$$2^4 = 6$$
$$2^5 =$$

35
36

T: What number is 2^5?
S: *2, because* $6 \times_{10} 2 = 2$.

Continue in this way for the following calculations:

$$2^6 = \boxed{4}$$
$$2^7 = \boxed{8}$$
$$2^8 = \boxed{6}$$
$$2^9 = \boxed{2}$$
$$2^{10} = \boxed{4}$$
$$2^{11} = \boxed{8}$$
$$2^{12} = \boxed{6}$$

T: How are you getting the answers so fast?
S: *There's a pattern: they just repeat in order 2, 4, 8, 6; 2, 4, 8, 6; and so on.*

You may find it helpful to highlight this pattern by organizing the calculations on the board in groups of four.

$2^1 = 2$	$2^5 = 2$	$2^9 = 2$
$2^2 = 4$	$2^6 = 4$	$2^{10} = 4$
$2^3 = 8$	$2^7 = 8$	$2^{11} = 8$
$2^4 = 6$	$2^8 = 6$	$2^{12} = 6$

T: Be careful, because now I'm going to skip around. What number is 2^{14}?
S: *4.*

Write the calculation on the board and continue with other problems. For each problem, allow a minute for all the students to think about the solution.

$$2^{14} = 4$$
$$2^{18} = \boxed{4}$$
$$2^{21} = \boxed{2}$$
$$2^{23} = \boxed{8}$$
$$2^{28} = \boxed{6}$$
$$2^{40} = \boxed{6}$$

Some students may make guesses. For example, for the big jump to 2^{40} you might get several incorrect answers before the correct one.

T: What number is 2^{40}?

S: *2.*

T: No.

S: *8.*

T: No.

S: *4.*

T: No.

S: *It has to be 6; there's no other choice!*

T: You're right. But was it necessary to guess or was there a way to be sure it was 6 from the beginning?

S: *I was sure it was 6, because 40 is a multiple of 4 and whenever the power is a multiple of 4, 2 to that power is 6.*

Accept any reasonable explanation, but do not force the students to be too explicit. The explanation above is very sophisticated, and you should not expect it for any but the best students.

If students seem to be catching on to the pattern, continue with the following problems:

$$2^{41} = \boxed{2}$$
$$2^{50} = \boxed{4}$$
$$2^{53} = \boxed{2}$$
$$2^{100} = \boxed{6}$$
$$2^{105} = \boxed{2}$$
$$2^{1,001} = \boxed{2}$$

Note to the Teacher

A quick way to find 2^n (modulo 10) is as follows:

Divide n by 4 and consider the remainder.
If the remainder is 0, then $2^n = 6$.
If the remainder is 1, then $2^n = 2$.
If the remainder is 2, then $2^n = 4$.
If the remainder is 3, then $2^n = 8$.

Do not expect the students to discover this pattern exactly, but encourage them to continue searching for a pattern. If some students suggest this pattern, praise their good thinking and let the others continue thinking about it.

Resources Available

For class use: Worksheets L37 and L38
For out-of-class use: Any H-worksheet up through H54

ACTIVITIES 37 and 38
Rational Numbers
On the Number Line

Materials Needed

Teacher: Colored chalk, a variety of objects of different lengths (for example, an eraser, various pencils, pieces of chalk, a paperclip) or a pair of chalkboard compasses

Students: Paper and pencils

Write **YETI** at the top of the board and draw this part of the number line. (Space the numerals about 30 to 40 cm apart.)

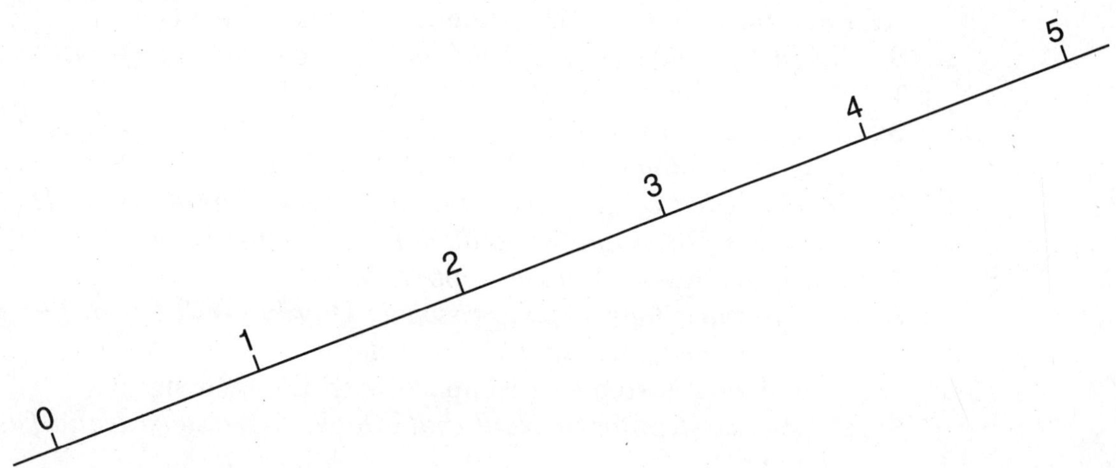

T: Have you ever heard of the Yeti?
S: *No.*
T: The Yeti is sometimes also called "the Abominable Snowman."

Let the students discuss the legend of the Abominable Snowman.

T: According to the legend, the Yeti is a primitive creature living in the Himalaya mountains around Mount Everest. It has not yet been proven that the Snowman actually exists, but many people believe that it does.

One morning some explorers discovered a line of footprints in the snow. The footprints were very large and very far apart. The explorers were sure they were the tracks of the Abominable Snowman.

Pretend that the marks on the number line I have drawn represent the Snowman's tracks.

The explorers were fascinated by the footprints. They started walking from one of the footprints (labeled **0** in our picture). Each explorer made sure that every step he or she took was the same length and made a note of when he or she landed exactly on one of the Snowman's footprints (at the places labeled **1, 2, 3,** . . . in our picture). Provide a selection of objects of different lengths; for example, an eraser, various pencils, pieces of chalk, and a paperclip. Invite students to choose one of the objects to simulate a step size and then to "step off" with the object or length of their choice, each time starting at 0 and trying to land on 1. A convenient alternative to providing a selection of objects would be to provide a pair of chalkboard compasses. The advantage of this tool is that any reasonable step size can be chosen by opening the compasses suitably.

Draw this table on the board:

Explorer	A	B	C	D	E	F	G	H	J
Number of Steps to Reach 1	4	12	6	2	5	10	9	3	99

T: According to this chart, which explorer took the longest steps?
Allow a short time for the students to study the chart.
S: *D took the longest steps. D only needed two steps to go from 0 to 1.*
T: Which explorer took the shortest steps?
S: *J; J needed 99 steps to reach 1.*
T: Who took longer steps, H or E?
S: *H; H needed three steps to reach 1 while E needed five. H's steps must have been longer because H took fewer steps.*
T: Good. Who took shorter steps, A or D?
S: *A; A needed four steps to reach 1; D only needed two. The more steps you need, the shorter your step.*
T: How does A's step size compare with D's step size?
S: *A took two steps for each one that D took. So A's steps are half as long as D's.*
Ask the students to compare several other step sizes. Then continue as follows:

T: Let's think about explorer D. D took *two* steps to go from 0 to 1. Who can point to the place where D's first step landed?
Invite a volunteer to locate D's first step.

S: *D's first step landed in the middle between 0 and 1.*
T: How could we label this point?
S: $\frac{1}{2}$.
Do this.
T: The 1 (point to the numerator of the fraction) tells us that this is the first step and the 2 (point to the denominator of the fraction) tells us that D needed two steps to go from 0 to 1.
Who can tell me where D's second step landed?
S: *At 1.*
T: How could we label this point to show that D's second step landed here?
S: $\frac{2}{2}$.
Do this.

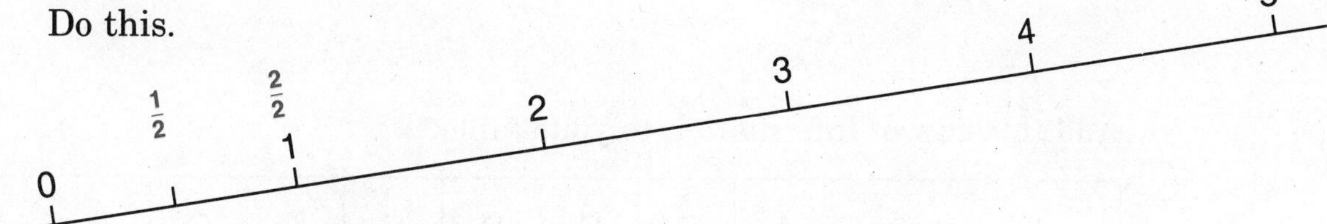

Continue to label points for D's third, fourth, and seventh steps.

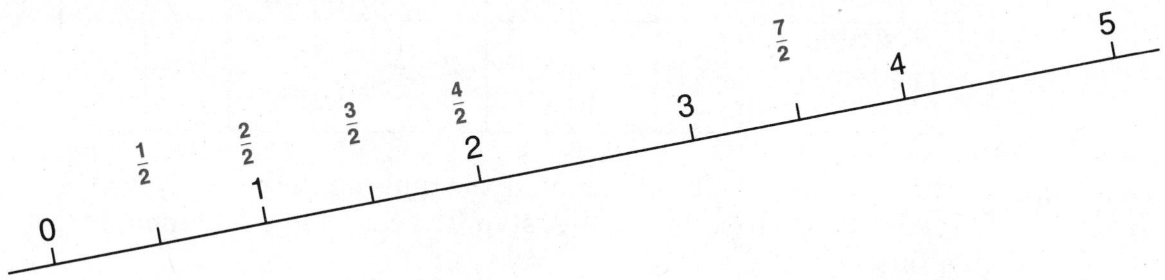

T: Now let's look at A. A took four steps to go from 0 to 1. Who can point to the place where A's first step landed?
Invite a volunteer to locate A's first step.

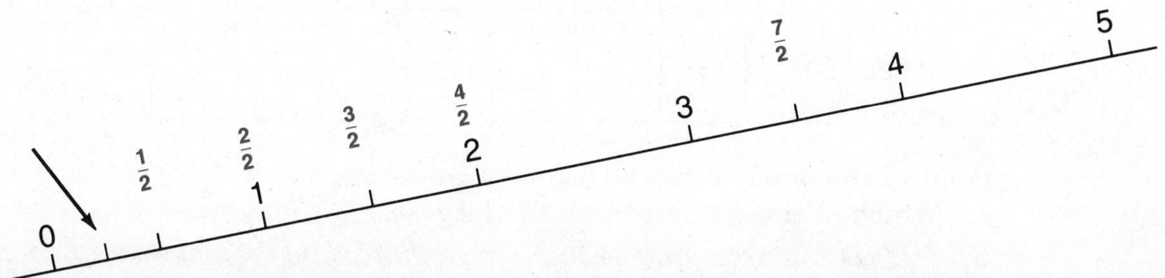

For the benefit of those students who have difficulty locating A's first step, lead the discussion as follows:
T: Who took longer steps, A or D?
S: *D; D only took two steps while A took four.*
T: How many steps did A take for *each* step that D took?
S: *A took two steps for each step D took.*

T: So, where did A's first step land?
S: *In the middle, between 0 and $\frac{1}{2}$.*
T: How would we label this point?
S: $\frac{1}{4}$.
Continue by asking students to label points for A's second, third, fourth, eighth, and tenth steps.

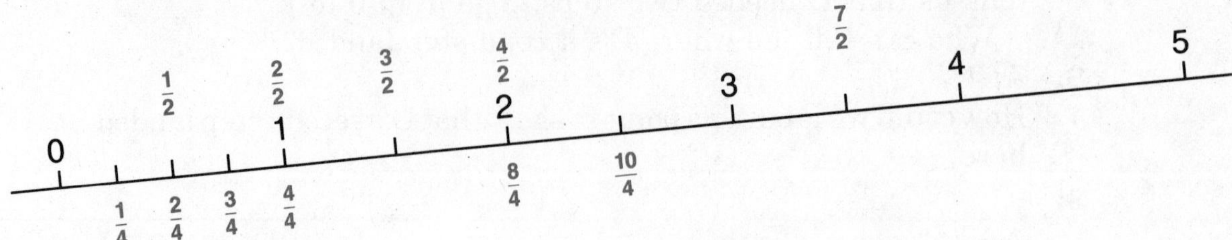

Add this row of information to your table:

Explorer	A	B	C	D	E	F	G	H	J
Number of Steps to Reach 1	4	12	6	2	5	10	9	3	99
First Step Landed on (Step Size)	$\frac{1}{4}$			$\frac{1}{2}$					

Invite students to help you complete the table on the board by writing a fraction for each explorer's first step. The completed table should look like this:

Explorer	A	B	C	D	E	F	G	H	J
Number of Steps to Reach 1	4	12	6	2	5	10	9	3	99
First Step Landed on (Step Size)	$\frac{1}{4}$	$\frac{1}{12}$	$\frac{1}{6}$	$\frac{1}{2}$	$\frac{1}{5}$	$\frac{1}{10}$	$\frac{1}{9}$	$\frac{1}{3}$	$\frac{1}{99}$

Point to the newly completed row of fractions.
T: Which of these numbers is the largest?
S: *$\frac{1}{2}$. It's D's step size, and we just agreed that D had the longest step.*
Write $\frac{1}{2}$ on the board.
T: Which is the smallest?
S: *$\frac{1}{99}$.*
Write $\frac{1}{99}$ on the board far to the right of $\frac{1}{2}$.

$$\frac{1}{2} \qquad\qquad > \qquad\qquad \frac{1}{99}$$

37
38

T: On your papers write the numbers $\frac{1}{4}, \frac{1}{12}, \ldots, \frac{1}{99}$ in order from largest to smallest.

Let the students work independently on this problem. As the class finishes the work, ask students to list on the board the fractions from largest to smallest.

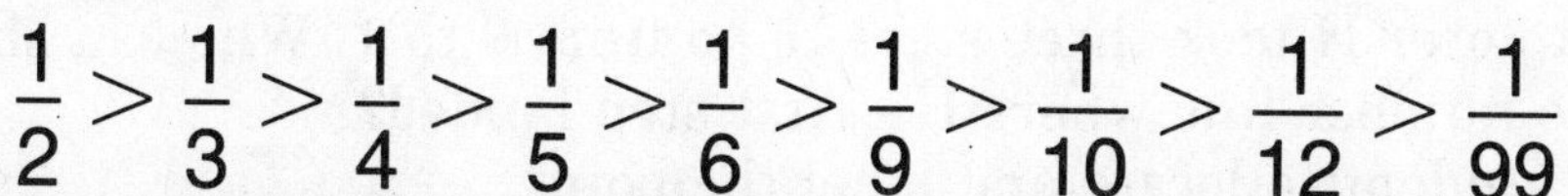

$$\frac{1}{2} > \frac{1}{3} > \frac{1}{4} > \frac{1}{5} > \frac{1}{6} > \frac{1}{9} > \frac{1}{10} > \frac{1}{12} > \frac{1}{99}$$

T: Look at the table again. How many steps did A take to go from 0 to 1? (four) How many steps did A take to reach $\frac{1}{2}$?

S: *Two steps.*

Write this information on the board, indicating that you are recording the results of the foregoing discussion: $\frac{1}{2} = \frac{2}{4}$.

T: Look at the table. Which other explorers landed on $\frac{1}{2}$, and how many steps did they each take?

S: *B landed on $\frac{1}{2}$ after taking six steps.*

Include this information on the board:

$$\frac{1}{2} = \frac{2}{4} = \frac{6}{12}$$

S: *F landed on $\frac{1}{2}$ after taking five steps.*

S: *C landed on $\frac{1}{2}$ after taking three steps.*

$$\frac{1}{2} = \frac{2}{4} = \frac{6}{12} = \frac{5}{10} = \frac{3}{6}$$

Use the number line to settle any disputes. For example, to show that $\frac{1}{2}$ has no "thirds name," invite a student to trace the path of explorer H, who takes three steps to go from 0 to 1.

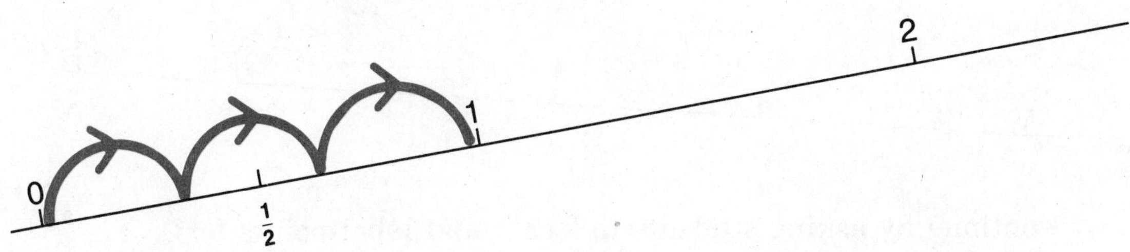

T: What are some other names for $\frac{1}{2}$ that are not suggested by the table?

Let the students suggest many other names for $\frac{1}{2}$:

$$\frac{1}{2} = \frac{2}{4} = \frac{6}{12} = \frac{5}{10} = \frac{3}{6} = \frac{10}{20} = \frac{50}{100} = \frac{200}{400}$$

37
38

T: Do you notice anything interesting about the names for $\frac{1}{2}$?
S: *The bottom number is always twice the top number.*
S: *The bottom number is always even.*
Accept any reasonable comment.

T: Explorer H took three steps to go from 0 to 1. Who can show on the number line where H's first step landed?
Ask a student to locate and label the point.

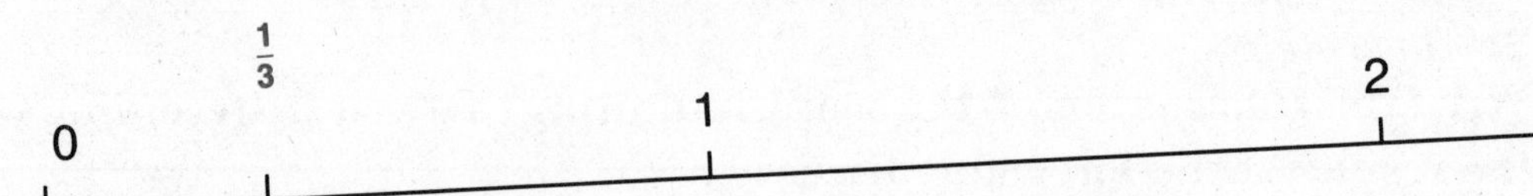

Continue in this manner by asking the students to locate and label points for $\frac{2}{3}$, $\frac{3}{3}$, $\frac{4}{3}$, $\frac{5}{3}$, and $\frac{6}{3}$.

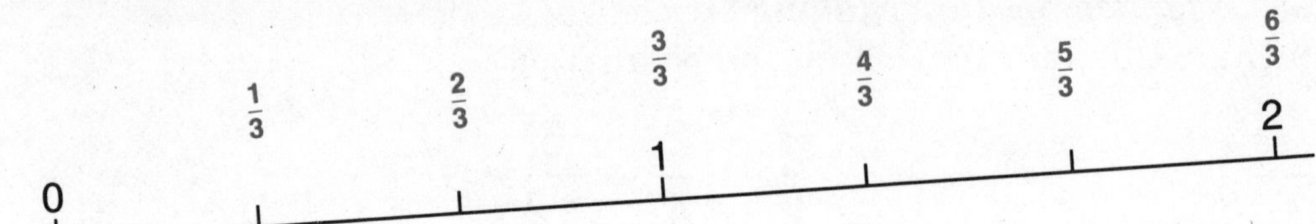

T: Explorer C took six steps to go from 0 to 1. Is C's step size longer or shorter than H's step size?
S: *Shorter; it took two of C's steps to equal one of H's.*
T: Good. Where on the number line did C's first step land?
S: *Halfway between 0 and $\frac{1}{3}$.*
Let a student label the point for $\frac{1}{6}$.

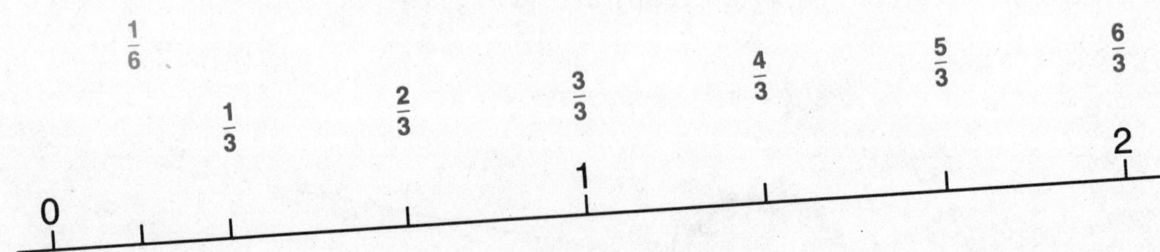

Continue by asking students to locate and label points for $\frac{2}{6}$, $\frac{5}{6}$, $\frac{6}{6}$, $\frac{9}{6}$, $\frac{10}{6}$, and $\frac{12}{6}$.

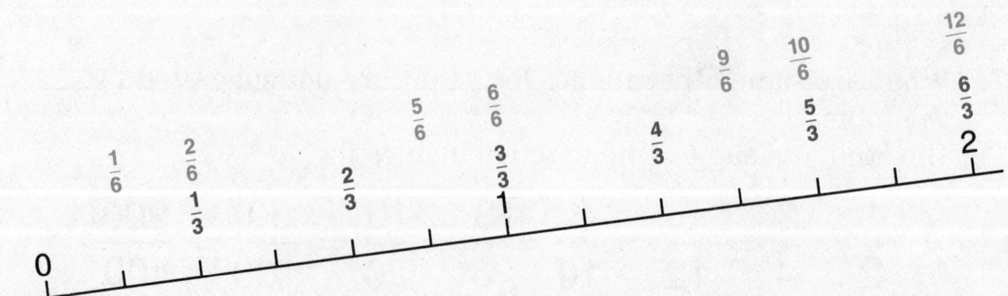

As this work proceeds, students should notice that $\frac{2}{6} = \frac{1}{3}$, $\frac{6}{6} = \frac{3}{3} = 1$, $\frac{10}{6} = \frac{5}{3}$, and $\frac{12}{6} = \frac{6}{3} = 2$.

Redraw the portion of the number line from 0 to 2 and ask the students to copy it on their papers.

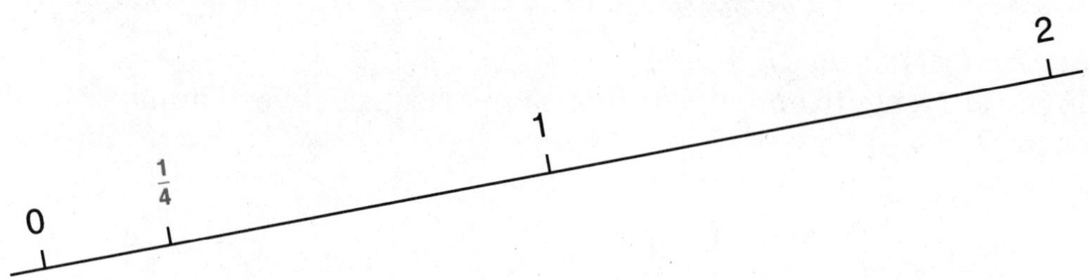

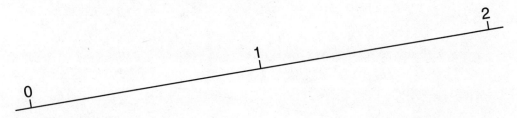

T: Explorer A took four steps to go from 0 to 1. Locate the point on your number line where A's first step landed and label it.

Let the class work on this problem independently for a while. Ask a student to locate $\frac{1}{4}$ at the board.

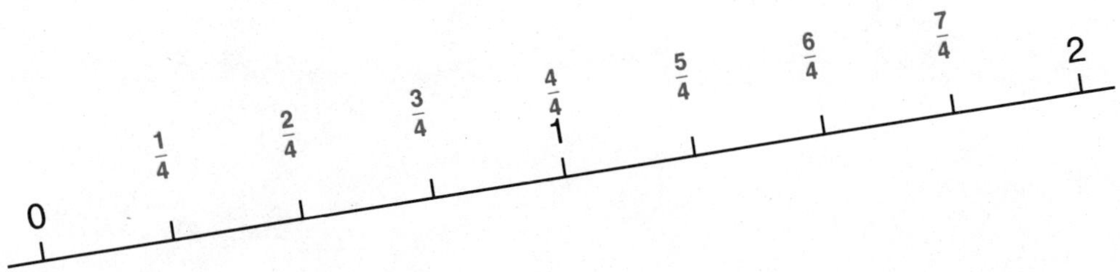

Instruct your students to locate A's second, third, fourth, fifth, sixth, and seventh steps on their papers, then on the board.

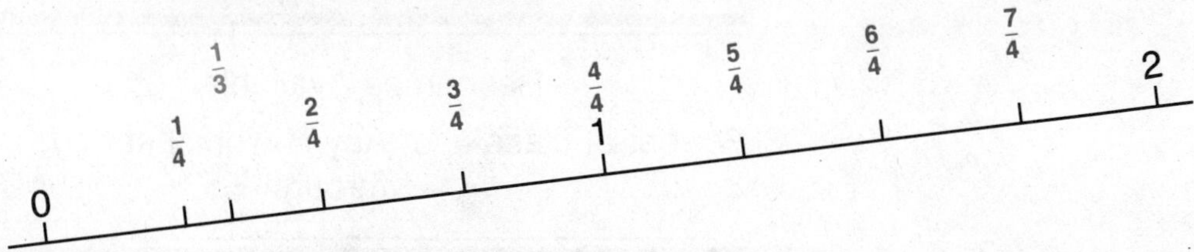

T: Explorer H took three steps to go from 0 to 1. Was H's first step to the right or to the left of $\frac{1}{4}$?

S: *$\frac{1}{3}$ is to the right of $\frac{1}{4}$; $\frac{1}{3}$ is larger than $\frac{1}{4}$.*

Invite a student to locate (approximately) $\frac{1}{3}$ on the number line. One way to do this is to give the student a pair of chalkboard compasses and let him or her use them to divide the segment from 0 to 1 into three segments of equal length.

37 38

In the same spirit, invite students to locate $\frac{2}{3}$, $\frac{3}{3}$, $\frac{4}{3}$, $\frac{5}{3}$, and $\frac{6}{3}$.

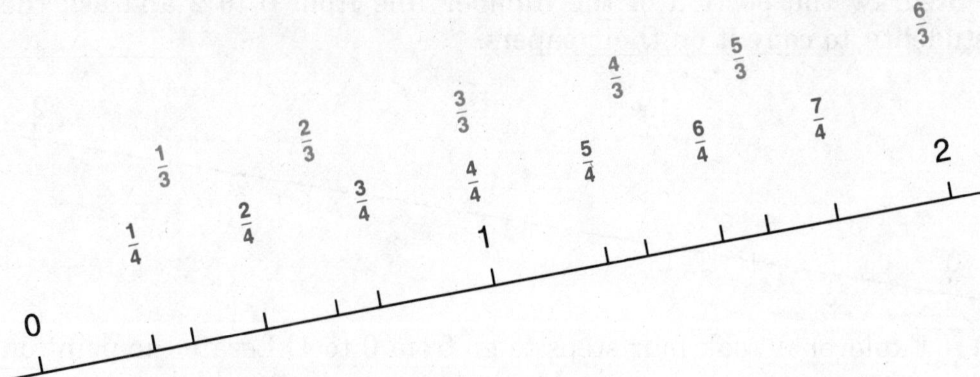

T: Which is larger, $\frac{5}{4}$ or $\frac{3}{2}$? $\left(\frac{3}{2}\right)$ Why?

S: *Because $\frac{3}{2} = \frac{6}{4}$ and $\frac{6}{4}$ is more than $\frac{5}{4}$.*

S: *And $\frac{3}{2}$ is to the right of $\frac{5}{4}$.*

Invite students to announce other comparisons between numbers. For example:

$$\frac{2}{3} > \frac{1}{2}, \frac{3}{4} < \frac{5}{4}, \text{ etc.}$$

Resources Available

For out-of-class use: Any H-worksheets up through H57

ACTIVITY 39
String Game (Analysis Version) 3

Materials Needed
Teacher: Numerical String Game kit, colored chalk
Students: String Game Analysis Sheets (a supply of these is at the back of the workbook), colored pencils

The analysis version of the String Game was introduced in Activity 6 of this volume. If you need to refresh your memory of this version of the game we suggest that you refer to that activity. In any case, begin this activity by reminding your class of the playing rules.

Play the analysis version of the String Game with your class. A possible game is outlined below.

Starting Clues

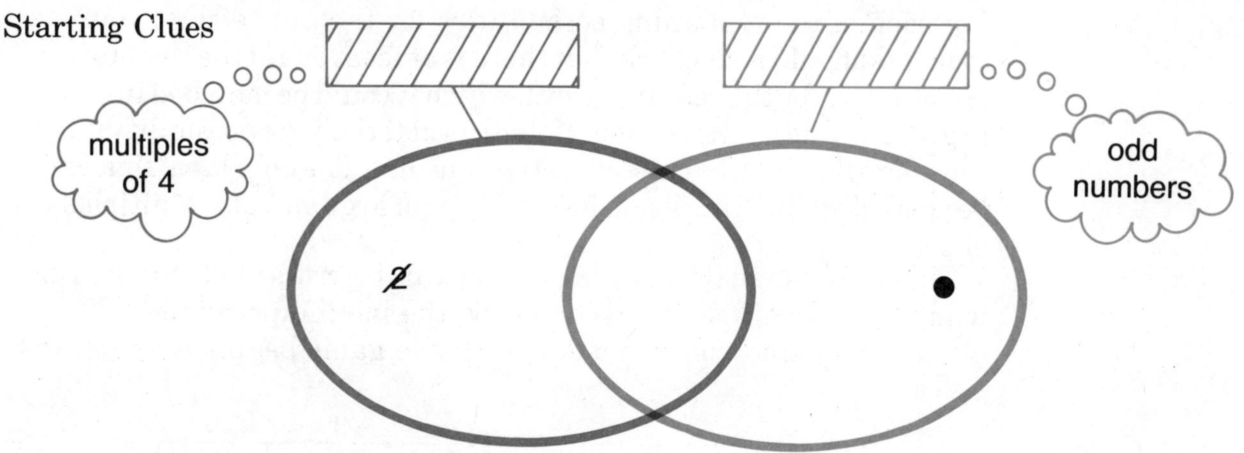

Correct Placement of Pieces

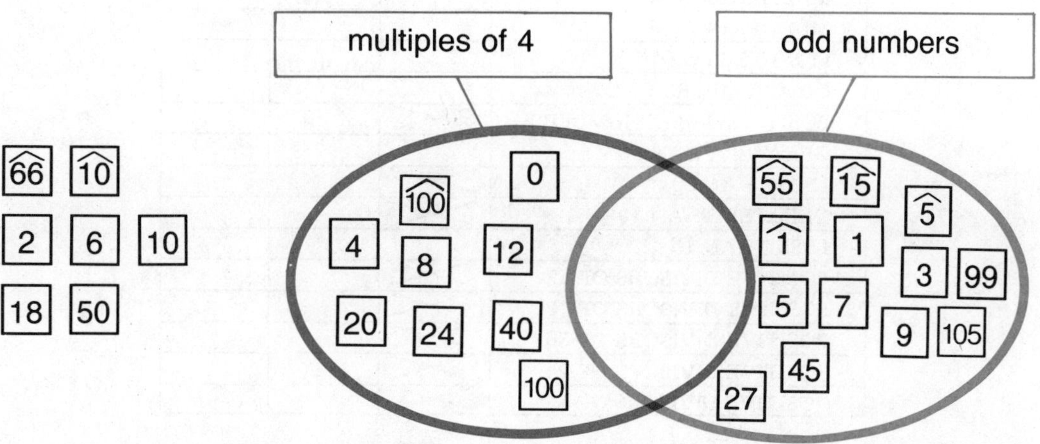

To analyze the starting situation, your students will probably begin by using the information that 2 does not belong to the indicated region (and hence, because of the hatching, it does not belong to the red string). This reasoning will lead to the following eliminations:

	Red	Blue	
MULTIPLES OF 2	X		
MULTIPLES OF 3			
MULTIPLES OF 4			
MULTIPLES OF 5			
MULTIPLES OF 10			
ODD NUMBERS			
POSITIVE PRIME NUMBERS	X		
GREATER THAN 50			
LESS THAN 50	X		
GREATER THAN $\widehat{10}$	X		
LESS THAN $\widehat{10}$			
POSITIVE DIVISORS OF 12	X		
POSITIVE DIVISORS OF 18	X		
POSITIVE DIVISORS OF 20	X		
POSITIVE DIVISORS OF 24	X		
POSITIVE DIVISORS OF 27	X		

For each of the remaining possibilities for the blue string, your students should next check that there is at least one of the remaining possibilities for the red string with which it could be matched in order to give an empty intersection. If there is not, then the possibility under consideration may be crossed off the Blue list. The only label that can be crossed off the Blue list using this type of argument is "Multiples of 3."

There are no additional labels that can be crossed off the Red list using the above line of reasoning. So the maximum number of eliminations that can be made before the game begins is as follows:

	Red	Blue	
MULTIPLES OF 2	X		
MULTIPLES OF 3		X	
MULTIPLES OF 4			
MULTIPLES OF 5			
MULTIPLES OF 10			
ODD NUMBERS			
POSITIVE PRIME NUMBERS	X		
GREATER THAN 50			
LESS THAN 50	X		
GREATER THAN $\widehat{10}$	X		
LESS THAN $\widehat{10}$			
POSITIVE DIVISORS OF 12	X		
POSITIVE DIVISORS OF 18	X		
POSITIVE DIVISORS OF 20	X		
POSITIVE DIVISORS OF 24	X		
POSITIVE DIVISORS OF 27	X		

Do not be concerned if your class does not reduce the possibilities for the two strings to this extent. Whatever reduction students manage to achieve forms the starting point for the playing of the game, as explained in Activity 6.

Resources Available

For class use: Worksheets L39 and L40
For out-of-class use: Any H-worksheet up through H60

ACTIVITY 40
Numerical String Game (High-Speed Version) 2

Materials Needed

Teacher: Numerical String Game kit, colored chalk
Students: String Game Analysis Sheets (a supply of these is at the back of the workbook), colored pencils

Play as many high-speed String Games as time permits. See Activity 22 for a description of the rules and a list of suggested starting positions.

Resources Available

For class use: Worksheets L41–46
For out-of-class use: Any H-worksheet up through H60

ACTIVITIES 41 and 42

Number Line Tug-of-War

Materials Needed
Teacher: Colored chalk
Students: None

Draw this portion of the number line on the board. Use a very large scale, at least 10 cm between successive marks.

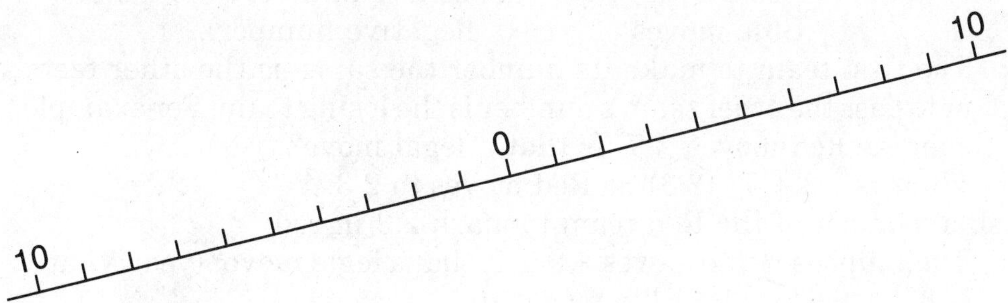

T: I am thinking of two numbers that are on this number line. They are $\overset{\frown}{9.3}$ and 8.6. Someone please make marks on the line to show these numbers.

After these two numbers have been located on the line to everyone's satisfaction, ask other students to mark the locations of 3.2, $\overset{\frown}{6.8}$, 3.1, $\overset{\frown}{6.7}$, 3.15, $\overset{\frown}{6.75}$, and other numbers if more experience is needed. The board will look somewhat like this. (In the following diagram, portions of the line have been magnified, but on the board this will not be necessary if the scale is sufficiently large.)

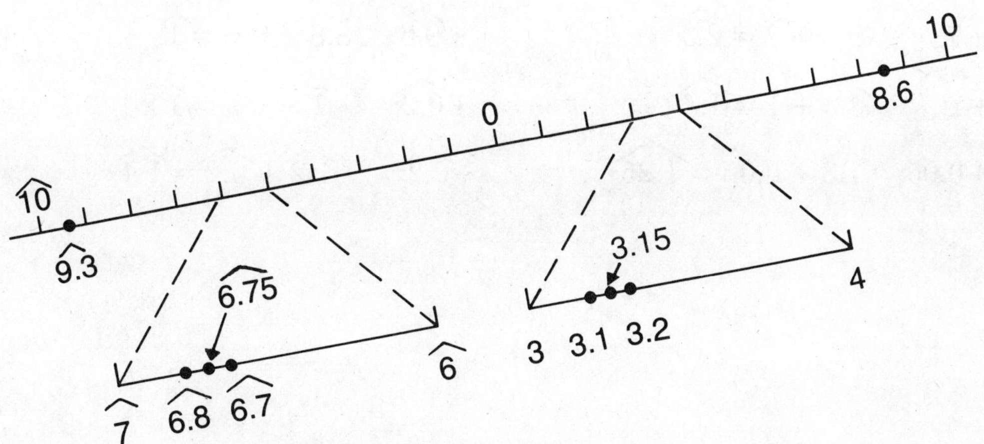

41
42

Then erase all the labels on the line except those for $\widehat{10}$, $\widehat{9.3}$, 0, 8.6, and 10, leaving:

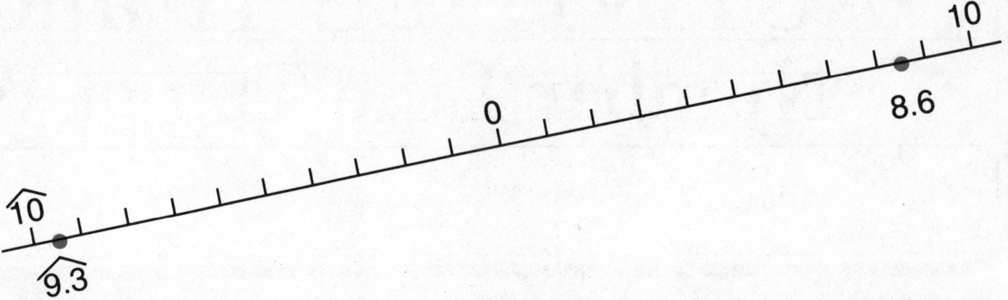

Divide the class into two teams, the Red team and the Blue team, and explain:

T: We are going to play the game of Number Line Tug-of-War. The Red team will start at $\widehat{9.3}$ and the Blue team will start at 8.6. Starting with Red, the teams will take turns to change their numbers by making these moves:

Write the following on the board as you say it aloud:

Red moves only + (a positive number).
Blue moves only + (a negative number).

T: The first team to make its number the same as the other team's or to pass the other team's number is the losing team. For example, suppose Red moves +7. Is that a legal move? (yes) What is $\widehat{9.3} + 7$? ($\widehat{2.3}$) So Red moves to $\widehat{2.3}$.

Ask a member of the Red team to mark $\widehat{2.3}$ in red.

T: Then suppose Blue moves $+\widehat{9.6}$. Is that a legal move? (yes) What is $8.6 + \widehat{9.6}$? ($\widehat{1}$) So Blue moves to $\widehat{1}$.

Ask a member of the Blue team to mark $\widehat{1}$ in blue.

T: Has the Blue number passed the Red number? (no) So let's continue the game.

Then let volunteers from the Red and Blue teams alternate. Each player should first announce the number to be added to his or her team's number (a positive number for Red and a negative number for Blue). Then the player should calculate the team's new number and mark that new number in red or blue, as appropriate.

The game might proceed as follows:

	Red		Blue
+7:	$\widehat{9.3} + 7 = \widehat{2.3}$	$+\widehat{9.6}$:	$8.6 + \widehat{9.6} = \widehat{1}$
+1:	$\widehat{2.3} + 1 = \widehat{1.3}$	$+\widehat{0.2}$:	$\widehat{1} + \widehat{0.2} = \widehat{1.2}$
+0.05:	$\widehat{1.3} + 0.05 = \widehat{1.25}$	$+\widehat{0.2}$:	$\widehat{1.2} + \widehat{0.2} = \widehat{1.4}$

41
42

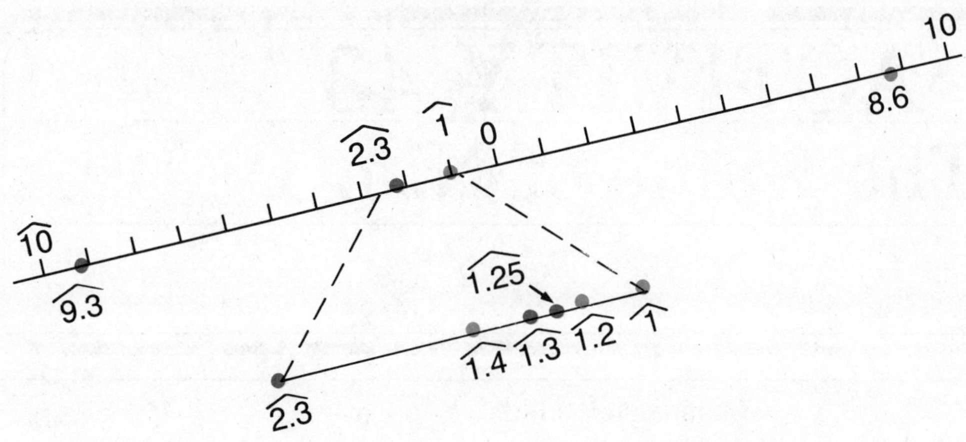

At this point both teams should realize that Blue has passed Red, and consequently Blue loses.

Many other sequences of moves are possible. For example, classes that are not as adept at adding decimals and negative numbers might blunder before the sixth move. Other classes might catch on quickly to the fact that it is possible to continue forever with neither team losing. (For example, if on the sixth move the Blue player had chosen $+\widehat{0.02}$ instead of $+\widehat{0.2}$, the game could have continued with the next Red player choosing $+0.02$, and so on.)

If there is enough time, play the game again with the same starting numbers but with the teams changing colors and hence directions of play. Do not give any hints concerning strategies for prolonging the game.

Resources Available

For out-of-class use: Any H-worksheet up through H63

ACTIVITY 43
The Game of Nim 1

Materials Needed

Teacher: Colored chalk (or, if your chalkboard is magnet-sensitive, the Minicomputer kit), the Nim Adder (see the blackline master and accompanying instructions at the end of this lesson)

Students: None

Note to the Teacher

Activities 43, 44, 49, 50, 53, 57, 58, 61, 62 and 65 form a sequence that culminates in the discovery of a method for determining winning moves (if there are any) in a game of 3-pile Nim. Stated at this stage, however, the method would appear to be more complex and unusable than it actually is. We therefore prefer to lead you in these activities through the same experiences as your students. We insure that you stay one or two steps ahead, however, by providing you with a means (the Nim Adder) of performing the calculations necessary for deciding what move to make next. Until you reach the end of the sequence of activities, you will remain as much in the dark about *why* the suggested "blind procedures" work as your students. If you feel insecure about being in such a controlling position without understanding the source of your power, we suggest that before you begin this sequence of activities you study the entire sequence.

These ideas can be extended to the point where winning moves in a game of Nim with any number of piles are determined in a similar way. It is then shown that a large number of so-called "impartial" games can be interpreted in terms of Nim, and winning moves in such games can therefore be determined by the techniques discovered during the course of these activities.

Before the activity begins, write these rules on the board:

Nim

Rule 1: Some piles of checkers.
Any number of checkers in each pile.

Rule 2: Two players take turns to pick up one or more checkers from one pile.

Rule 3: The winner is the one who picks up the last checker.

43

T: Have you ever heard of the game of Nim? It's a game for two people or two teams. You can play it almost anywhere and with practically no equipment. The great thing about it is that if you're playing with someone who doesn't know the trick, you can be almost certain to win.

Here's the first rule.

Point to rule 1 on the board and explain:

T: You start with some number of piles of checkers (or you could use matchsticks, coins, pebbles, marbles, scraps of paper, twigs, marks on paper, and so on).

Tell the students what you are going to use. If your board is magnet-sensitive, use Minicomputer checkers. If not, represent checkers by small circles drawn on the board.

T: There can be any number of checkers in any of the piles, there can be the same number of checkers in some of the piles, or the piles can all contain different numbers of checkers. For example, let's say we decide to have three piles, one containing three checkers, one containing five, and the other containing six.

Display three such piles on the board, either using Minicomputer checkers or by drawing with colored chalk:

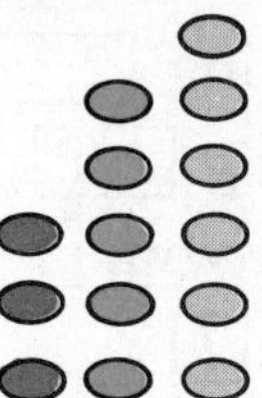

Point to rule 2 on the board and explain:

T: You play by taking turns to pick up some checkers from any one of the piles. You must pick up at least one checker, and you can pick up a whole pile if you want to.

If you are using circles drawn on the board instead of actual checkers, explain that you will pick up checkers by erasing them.

T: Who would like to suggest a first move in the game on the board?

Let a volunteer make a suggestion. For example:

S: *Take two from the yellow pile.*

If the suggestion is in accordance with the rules, then carry it out on the board; otherwise, ask for another suggestion. In the above example, change the situation on the board to:

Point to rule 3 on the board and explain:

T: To win the game, you have to be the one who picks up the last checker.

Play through the game on the board, with the students' moves made by volunteers. You can make sure that you win as follows: Whenever it is your turn, move into one of the following positions (where $\boxed{a, b, c}$ means one pile containing a checkers, one containing b, and one containing c; obviously, the positions $\boxed{a, b, c}$, $\boxed{a, c, b}$, $\boxed{b, a, c}$, $\boxed{b, c, a}$, $\boxed{c, a, b}$, and $\boxed{c, b, a}$ are all identical):

1, 2, 3	5, 5	0
1, 4, 5	4, 4	
2, 4, 6	3, 3	
	2, 2	
	1, 1	

These moves will always be possible; in fact, given the initial position suggested above, there will always be only one possibility for each move. Here is one possible development of the game:

Teacher: Take 2 from the red pile, leaving $\boxed{1, 5, 4}$.
Student: *Pick up the red pile, leaving* $\boxed{5, 4}$.
Teacher: Take 1 from the blue pile, leaving $\boxed{4, 4}$.
Student: *Take 2 from the yellow pile, leaving* $\boxed{4, 2}$.
Teacher: Take 2 from the blue pile, leaving $\boxed{2, 2}$.
Student: *Take 1 from the blue pile, leaving* $\boxed{1, 2}$.
Teacher: Take 1 from the yellow pile, leaving $\boxed{1, 1}$.
Student: *Pick up the yellow pile, leaving* $\boxed{1}$.
Teacher: Pick up the last checker. You win!

Play the game several more times, each time starting with one of the "hopeless positions" given in the following table and allowing the class to play first.

Some Hopeless Positions at Nim (entries: third pile)

first pile \ second pile	1	2	3	4	5	6	7	8	9	10	11	12	13	14	15
1	0														
2	3	0													
3	2	1	0												
4	5	6	7	0											
5	4	7	6	1	0										
6	7	4	5	2	3	0									
7	6	5	4	3	2	1	0								
8	9	10	11	12	13	14	15	0							
9	8	11	10	13	12	15	14	1	0						
10	11	8	9	14	15	12	13	2	3	0					
11	10	9	8	15	14	13	12	3	2	1	0				
12	13	14	15	8	9	10	11	4	5	6	7	0			
13	12	15	14	9	8	11	10	5	4	7	6	1	0		
14	15	12	13	10	11	8	9	6	7	4	5	2	3	0	
15	14	13	12	11	10	9	8	7	6	5	4	3	2	1	0

43

Each time it is your turn, pick up the last checker, if possible. If not, move so that the class is left in one of the hopeless positions. (Rather than searching through this table in order to determine your next move, you can instead use your Nim Adder as described at the end of this activity.)

After a while, the students will suspect that your use of the table or your Nim Adder is somehow biasing the game in your favor. They may demand the right to make you play first. In that case, start with one of the hopeless positions, modified by the addition of one checker to one of the piles (for example, [5, 10, 14]). Make the first move by removing the added checker (leaving the class facing the position [4, 10, 14] *), and then play as described above.

On the other hand, the students may demand the right to choose the starting position. Let them do so, and in addition let them decide who should go first. Such a situation is less predictable. At the earliest opportunity you should move so that the class is left in one of the hopeless positions. If this is not possible, simply take one checker off the largest pile. Once you manage to make a move that puts the class in a hopeless position, however, you should play as described above. Here is one possible game in which by chance the students have suggested a starting situation that is a hopeless position and have asked you to play first.

Starting position: [5, 9, 12]

Teacher: There is no winning move, so take 1 off the 2-pile, leaving [5, 9, 11] .

Student: *Take 3 off the 5-pile, leaving* [2, 9, 11] .

Teacher: By chance the student has hit on a winning move. There is no winning move for you, so take 1 off the 11-pile, leaving [2, 9, 10] .

Student: *Take 4 off the 9-pile, leaving* [2, 5, 10] .

Teacher: The students' luck has not held. You can put the class in a hopeless position. Take 3 off the 10-pile, leaving [2, 5, 7] .

Student: *Pick up the 7-pile, leaving* [2, 5] .

Teacher: Take 3 off the 5-pile, leaving [2, 2] .

Student: *Pick up one of the piles, leaving* [2] .

Teacher: Pick up the remaining pile. You win!

---

* Recall that [4, 10, 14] and [10, 4, 14] describe the same position, so in the above table find **10** in the "first pile" and **4** in the "second pile" giving **14** as the third entry.

If a student suggests starting with more than three piles of checkers, say that for the moment three piles will be quite complicated enough. You can, however, promise the class that in the future you will return to this situation and deal with four piles or more.

At some point interest will wane, students' frustration will reach an intolerably high level, pressure on you to dispense with your Nim Adder or this lesson plan will become overwhelming, or time will run out. You should then either proceed to Activity 44 or bring this activity to a close as follows:

- If you have won all the games, say:

T: You probably realize that I have been able to win all these games because I know something about Nim that you don't.

Then continue from ■ below.

- If you have won all but one or two games, which in your opinion the students managed to win by accident (such as by their choosing to start with [4, 4, 7] and making a first move of picking up the 7-pile), say:

T: Well, you beat me once (or twice, or . . .), but I don't think you know how you did it.

Then continue from ■ below.

- It is possible that at some point a student will suggest starting with [1, 1, 1] with the class playing first or with some other position involving a small number of checkers where it is possible for students to predict the flow of play and thereby choose who should start so as to insure that you lose. In this case, say:

T: I think some of you are beginning to see that it's possible to think ahead in this game and so force your opponent to lose the game. You've only seen this happen in simple cases, though. In fact, in any Nim position it is possible to predict who ought to win.

■ **T:** We're going to come back to Nim several times over the next few weeks, and we'll find out more about how to win the game. By the end of our work you will be able to foretell at the very beginning who should win the game if it is played carefully.

Appendix: The Nim Adder

The Nim Adder is a device that allows you to calculate hopeless positions in games of Nim. You can make one as follows: Make *two* photocopies onto card stock of the blackline master in the poster packet. Cut out one copy along the outer circle; cut out the other copy along the circle that runs through the middle of the black-and-white patterns. Attach the two disks, the smaller on top of the larger, with a paper fastener through their centers. The top disk should now be free to rotate relative to the larger disk.

43

The Nim Adder relies on the fact that given the sizes of two unequal piles, there is a unique size for a third pile such that the three piles constitute a hopeless position. The Nim Adder tells you the size of the third pile. (This fact will become apparent during this sequence of activities.)

You use the Nim Adder as follows: Suppose you want to find out what size of pile you need to go with a 3-pile and a 6-pile in order to make a hopeless position. Align the ③ on either disk with the ⑥ on the other:

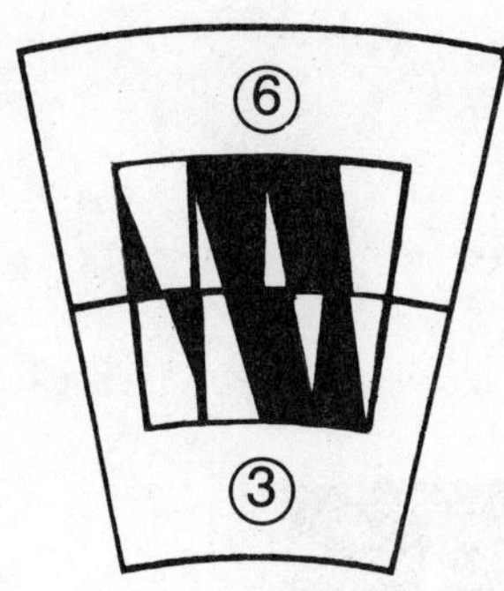

Read the result as follows. The black-and-white patterns should be perceived as forming four strips:

The strips have values as on the binary abacus:

Add the values of the strips containing either of these two patterns:

 or 

Do not add the values of the strips containing either of these two patterns:

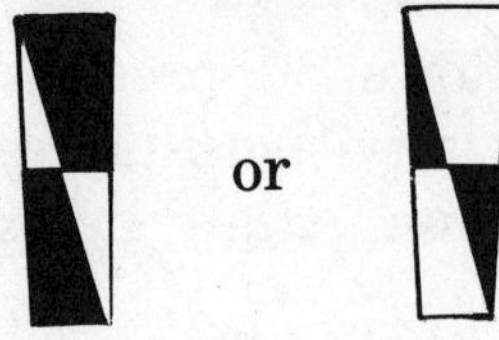

In the present case we have:

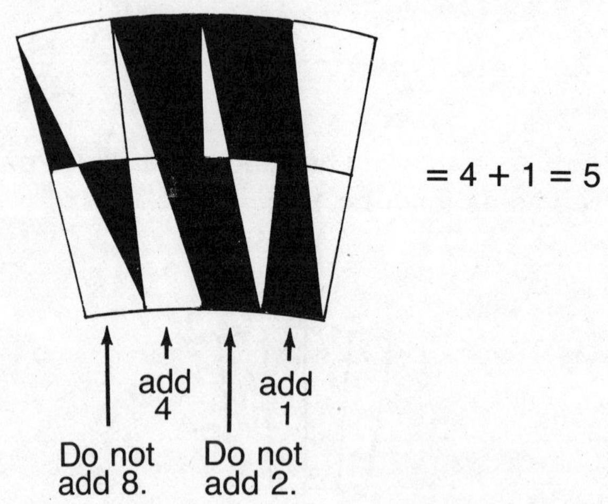

Hence, the hopeless position with a 3-pile and a 6-pile is [3, 6, 5]. (This was the position we chose for you to use in your introduction of the game of Nim.)

We suggest that you spend 10 or 15 minutes practicing using the Nim Adder and improving the ease with which you read the results. (You can check the accuracy of your readings by referring to the table of hopeless positions, which includes all the calculations that can be made with the Nim Adder.)

To determine what move to make during a game, Nim-add the sizes of two of the piles. There are three possibilities:

- The result is the size of the third pile, which means that the students have put you in a hopeless position. There is no winning move for you to make. Instead, make a stalling move as suggested in the plan of this activity by picking up one checker from the largest pile.

- The result is *larger* than the size of the third pile. Nim-add the sizes of a different pairing from the three piles. Repeat this if necessary (no more than three attempts will be needed) until:
- The result is *smaller* than the size of the third pile. A winning move then consists in lowering the third pile to the size indicated by the result of the Nim-addition.

Resources Available

For out-of-class use: Any H-worksheet up through H66

ACTIVITY 44
Nim Analysis 1

Materials Needed

Teacher: Colored chalk (or, if your chalkboard is magnet-sensitive, the Minicomputer kit), the Nim Adder (if you start by playing a game of Nim)

Students: Pencils

If you are able to move on to this activity immediately following Activity 43, start at ■ below. If not, start by reminding the class about their previous frustrating experience with the game of Nim. Remind them of the rules:

- Start with any number of piles of checkers (with any number of checkers in each pile).
- Take turns to pick up any number of checkers from one pile.
- The winner is the one who picks up the last checker.

Play the game once, starting with the position [5, 9, 12] and letting the class play first. Play as described in Activity 43, making use of your Nim Adder or the table of hopeless positions given in the description of that activity.

■ **T:** We're now going to look more closely at Nim and see if we can discover how to force a win. Remember that we can have any number of piles of checkers—it doesn't have to be three all the time. What's the simplest number of piles we could start with?

S: *One.*

T: Right. Let's suppose we start with one pile of checkers. What's the simplest number of checkers we could have in that pile?

S: *One.*

T: OK. Imagine that we're playing Nim starting with one pile containing one checker. Would you want to play first or second?

S: *First, because I would just pick up the checker and win.*

T: Very good. Let's call one pile with one checker a *safe position,* because if you are faced with it you can force a win.

Write on one side of the board:

Safe	Hopeless
[1]	

T: What if we started with one pile containing two checkers? Would you want to play first or second?

S: *First again, because I would pick up both checkers and win.*

T: So that's another safe position.

44

Add this information to your list on the board:

Safe	Hopeless
1	
2	

S: *It doesn't matter how many checkers there are in the pile if you only start with one pile. The first person to play just has to pick up the whole pile to win right away.*

T: Good thinking. Let's alter our list.

Safe	Hopeless
one pile of any size	

T: Now let's move on to two piles. What's the simplest starting position you can think of with two piles?

S: *One checker in each pile.*

T: Right. Here are the two piles.

Draw on the board (or use Minicomputer checkers to show this position):

T: Would you want to play first or second?

S (Elsie): *Second, because the first player can only pick up one of the checkers. That leaves me with the last one to pick up. So I would win.*

T: If you were the first to play from this position, is there any way you could avoid losing?

S: *No. It's just as Elsie said. If I play first I've got to pick up just one of the checkers—I can't do anything else. Then that leaves the last checker for my opponent to pick up. It's a hopeless position.*

Add this information to your list:

Safe	Hopeless
one pile of any size	1, 1

T: What's the next simplest starting position you can think of with two piles?

There are two likely responses at this stage. We deal with them below, one after the other.

S: *One pile of one checker and one of two.*

T: Right. Here are the two piles.

Draw on the board (or use Minicomputer checkers to show this position):

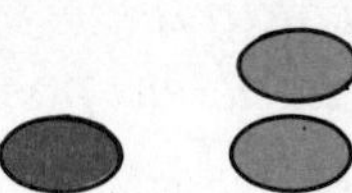

T: Would you want to play first or second?

S: *First, because I could take one checker off the blue pile, which would leave my opponent with two piles of one checker each, and that's a hopeless position.*

Point to the position on the board.

T: So what kind of position is this?
S: *A safe position.*
Modify your list on the board:

Safe	Hopeless
one pile of any size	1, 1
1, 2	

T: What if you started with one pile of one checker and one of six? Would you rather play first or second?
S: *First again, because I could take five off the 6-pile and leave my opponent with the same hopeless position.*
S: *The same thing works if you start with one pile of one checker and one pile of any number from 2 upward. You would simply take off all but one of the checkers in the larger pile.*
T: Excellent. That gives us a lot more safe positions.
Modify the list on the board:

Safe	Hopeless
one pile of any size	1, 1
1, 2 or more	

Go on now to consider the other likely response to your earlier question. If your students have not suggested it, do so yourself.
S: *Two piles with two checkers each.*
T: Right. Here are the two piles.
Draw on the board (or use Minicomputer checkers to show this position):

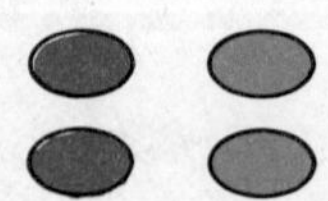

T: Would you want to play first or second?
S (David): *Second. I could win just by copying whatever my opponent did. If she took one checker off one pile, I would take one off the other. That would leave two piles of one checker each, which we know is a hopeless position. But if she started by picking up a whole pile, I would pick up the other one and win.*
T: Good. So we've found another hopeless position.

Modify your list on the board:

Safe	Hopeless
one pile of any size	1, 1
1, 2 or more	2, 2

S: *David's idea means that any position with two equal piles is a hopeless position.*

T: How do you figure that out?

S: *Well, if you play second, you can just play copycat. Whatever your opponent does, you copy it on the other pile. If he leaves some checkers in one pile, you leave the same number in the other. At some point he'll clear one of the piles, so you'll then clear the other and win.*

T: Excellent. Let's write that down.

Modify your list on the board:

Safe	Hopeless
one pile of any size	two equal piles of any size
1, 2, or more	

T: Let's suppose that instead we start with two unequal piles, say with 4 and 7 checkers. Would you want to play first or second?

S: *First, because I would begin by evening up the piles, taking three off the 7-pile. That would leave two equal piles, which I know is a hopeless position.*

S: *That works for all pairs of unequal piles. You begin by evening them up, and that puts your opponent in a hopeless position.*

Record this on the board:

Safe	Hopeless
one pile of any size	two equal piles of any size
two unequal piles of any size	

T: We're making progress. We now know all the safe and hopeless positions in 1- or 2-pile Nim. Next time we look at Nim we'll move on to 3-pile Nim. As you can probably guess, that's quite a bit more difficult.

Resources Available

For class use: Worksheets L47 and L48
For out-of-class use: Any H-worksheet up through H66

ACTIVITY 45
Composition 7

Materials Needed
Teacher: Colored chalk
Students: Paper and colored pencils

Draw this arrow picture on the board:

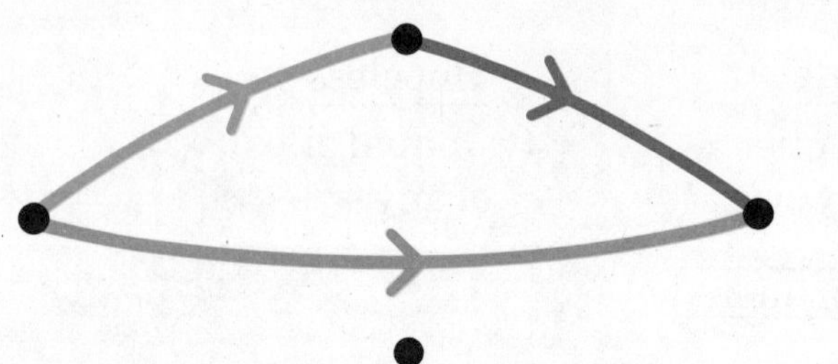

+9

+7

T: What could the green arrow be for?
S: +16.
Write +16 below the +7
T: Here's another name we could use for the green arrow.
Write $=(+9)\circ(+7)$ next to +16
Point to $(+9)\circ(+7)$ and ask:
T: Do you remember how we read this?
S: *+9 then +7.*
T: That's right.

Point to $+16=(+9)\circ(+7)$.
T: And we read this as "+16 is the same as +9 then +7."

Write on the board in white chalk:

$$(+7)\circ(+9).$$

T: What about this relation? Would someone please read this for me?
S: *+7 then +9.*
T: Is it the same relation as $(+9)\circ(+7)$ or different?
S: *The same.*

T: Why do you say that?
S: *Well, whether you add 9 and then add 7 or you add 7 and then 9, you've added 16 altogether.*
Erase $(+7)\circ(+9)$ and alter your arrow picture to the following:

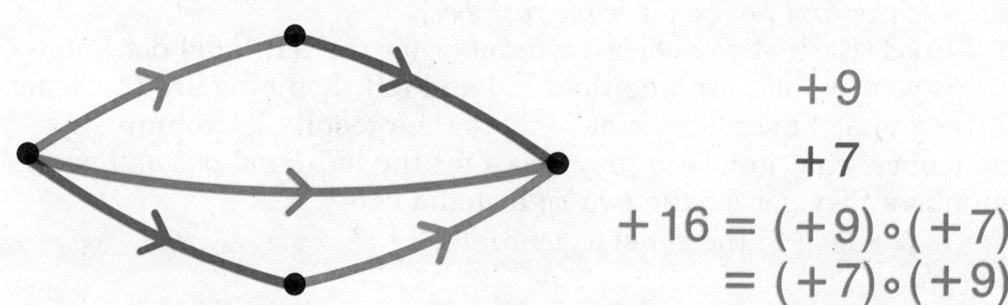

T: Can you think of relations R and S for which R∘S is *not* the same as S∘R?

This is a rather difficult question, so you may wish to continue:

T: How about "you are my father" and "you are my mother"?

Change your arrow picture on the board to the following:

T: What could the green arrow be for in this diagram?

S: *"You are my paternal grandmother."*

T: Now what about the relation M∘F?

Add to your picture as follows:

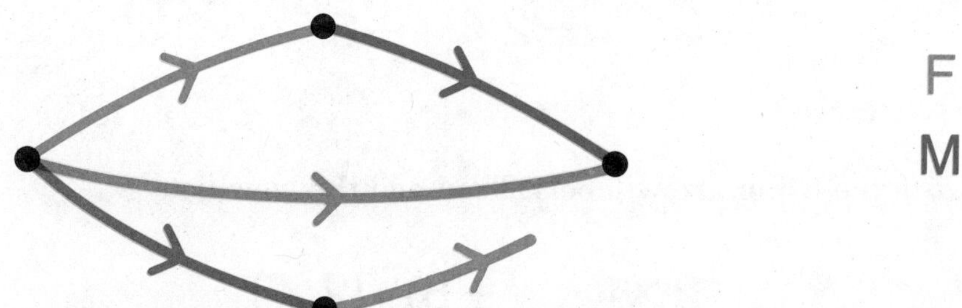

T: What does red then blue stand for?

S: *"You are my maternal grandfather."*

T: Is this the same as the green relation?

S: *No.*

T: Let's try to find an example with numbers. On your papers, let blue be for 2× and red be for +3.

While students work individually, change your drawing on the board to the following:

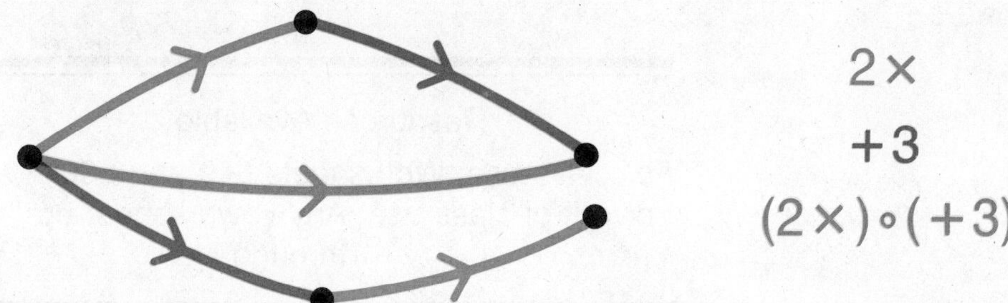

T: How can we check that red then blue is *not* green?
S: *Let the first dot be for some number.*
T: Good. Each of you choose a number for the left-hand dot and see if your results for blue then red and red then blue are the same.

After giving the students time to check their results, let volunteers announce what numbers they chose for the left-hand dot and what numbers they got for the two right-hand dots.

T: Is $(2\times)\circ(+3)$ the same as $(+3)\circ(+2\times)$?
S: *No.*

Erase your arrow picture from the board, and draw these two pictures:

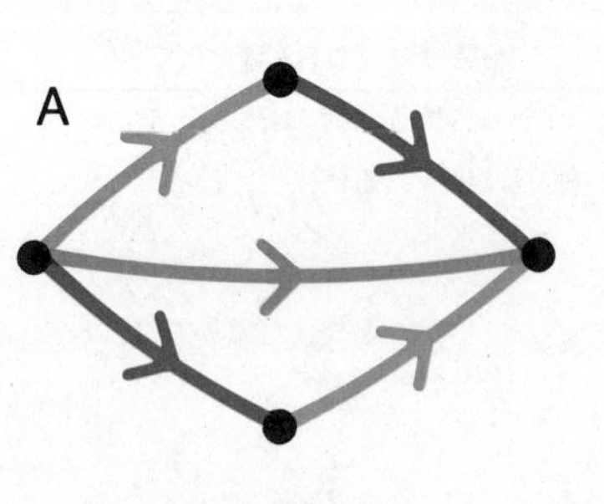

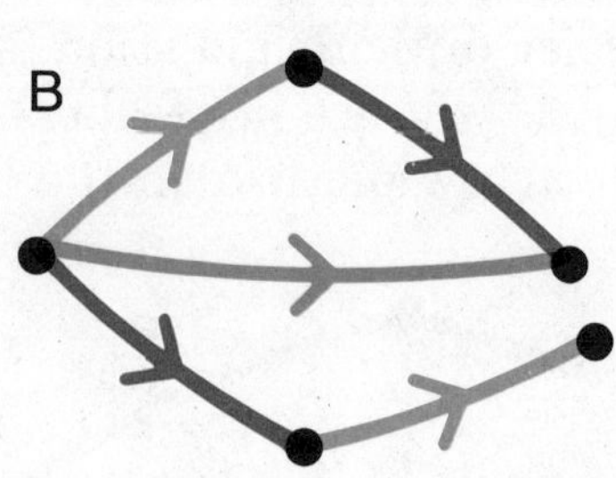

T: We've seen that it's possibile for $R\circ S$ to be the same relation as $S\circ R$, as in picture A, or for $R\circ S$ and $S\circ R$ to be different relations, as in picture B. Which picture is the correct one for these relations?

Write on the board:

+8   −2   +6

S: *A.*

Write A next to the list of arrow labels. Then add this new list:

+8   2× $(+8)\circ(2\times)$

T: What about these relations?
S: *Picture B.*

Write **B** next to the second list of arrow labels.

Finish the activity by letting the students work individually on Worksheets L49 and L50.

Resources Available

For class use: Worksheets L49 and L50
For out-of-class use: Any H-worksheet up through H69

ACTIVITY 46
Composition 8

Materials Needed
Teacher: Colored chalk
Students: Colored pencils

Draw this arrow picture on the board:

Point to **R∘R**.

T: How do we read this?
S: *"R then R."*
T: What does that mean?
S: *Whenever you have two red arrows in a row going the same way, you draw a blue arrow from the start of the first red arrow to the end of the second.*
T: Help me to draw the blue arrows in this picture.

As students draw the blue arrows, make sure they trace along two consecutive red arrows with their fingers. The completed picture should look like this:

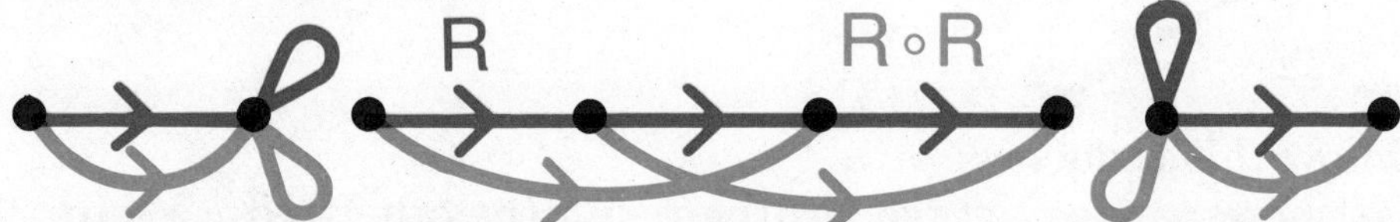

Now either erase the blue arrows and the key **R∘R** or redraw the original picture without the key **R∘R**. Write the new key **R̆** in its place.

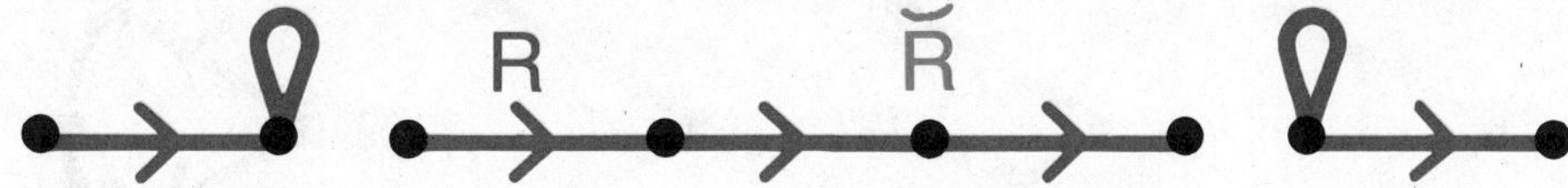

Point to **R̆**.

T: This is a new relation. You read this as "R converse." It is closely related to the red relation R. In fact, each red arrow gives us a green arrow that goes in exactly the opposite direction; the green arrows go *against* the direction of the red arrows. Help me draw the green arrows.

The completed picture should look like this:

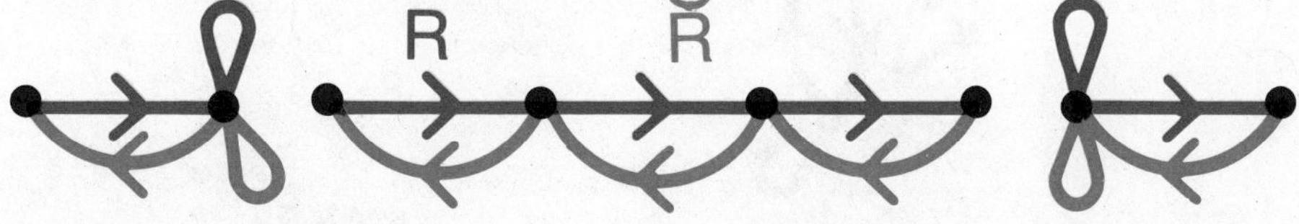

46

Redraw the original picture once again and introduce a third relation:

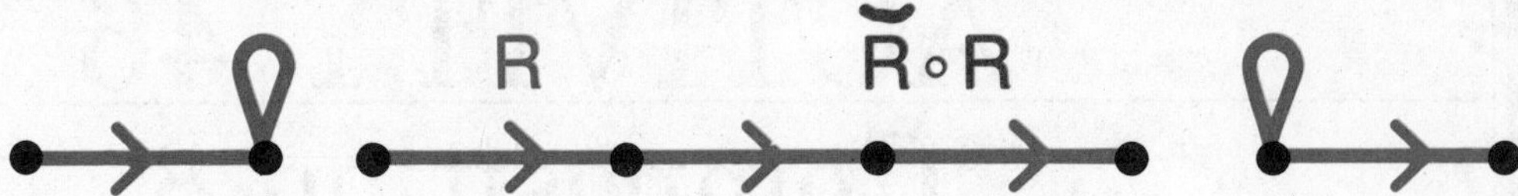

T: How do you read this?
S: *"R converse then R."*
T: What does that mean?
S: *You go* ***against*** *a red arrow, then along a red arrow, and you draw a purple arrow from the dot where you started to the one where you finished.*
T: Right. *Against* red then *with* red. Who can see where some purple arrows can be drawn?

The first purple arrows to be found will probably be the loops at the ending dots of the red arrows, leading to the following (partially completed) picture:

T: There are still two more purple arrows that can be drawn. Let me help you find them by showing you a separate example.

Draw the following on one side of the board:

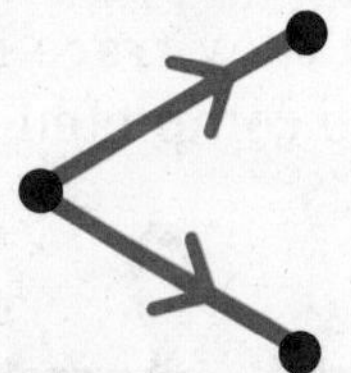

Now follow this sequence:

T: Start here . . . *against* red . . . then *with* the other red . . . join these two.

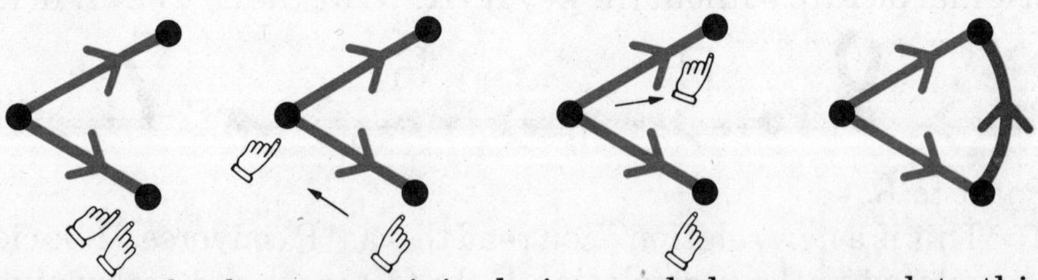

T: Before we go back to our original picture, help me complete this little picture.

The completed picture should look like this:

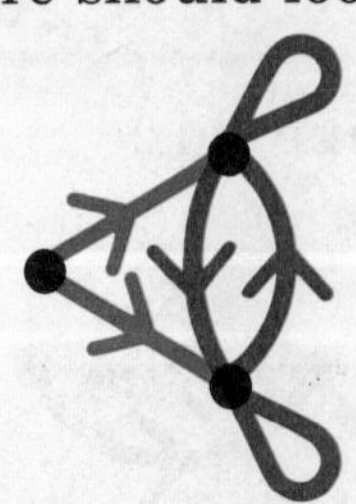

T: Now, can anyone find the last purple arrow in the first picture?

This problem is still far from easy, but students should eventually discover that the missing purple arrows belong on the right-hand side of the picture. The paths to be followed are shown here in dotted black:

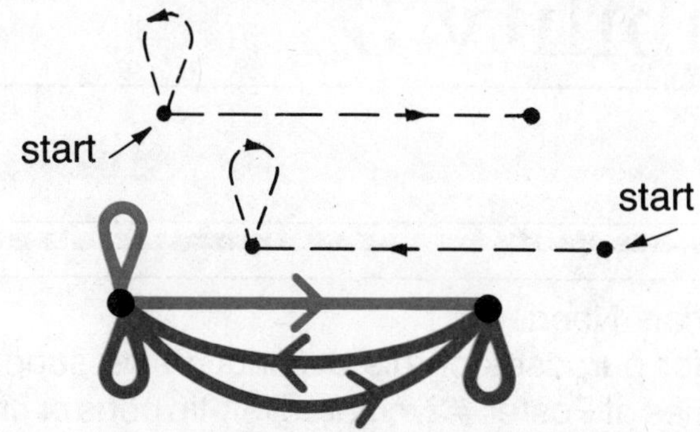

Redraw the original picture once more, including the additional 3-dot picture, ready for the last relation:

T: This time it's *with* red, then *against* red. Help me find the black arrows.

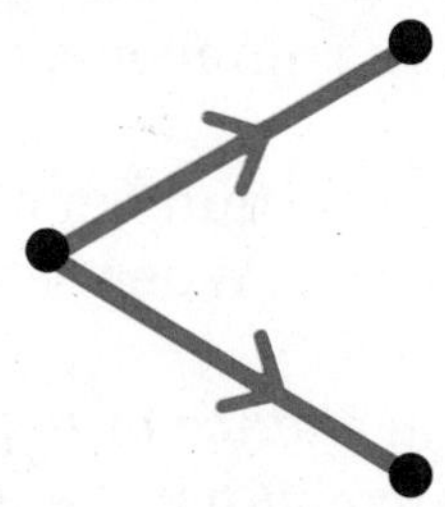

The completed picture should look like this:

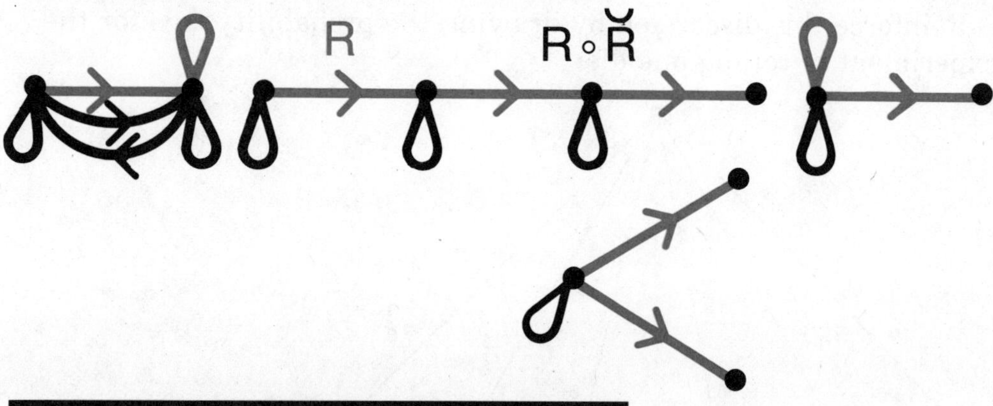

Resources Available

For class use: Worksheets L51 and L52

For out-of-class use: Any H-worksheet up through H69

ACTIVITIES 47 and 48
Probability 3

Materials Needed

Teacher: Two dice of different colors (for purposes of this description we suppose they are red and blue); four copies of Poster #2, colored felt-tip pens or crayons

Students: Colored pencils

Show the class your two dice.

T: How many faces does each die have? (6)
How many dots are there on this face? (1)
How many on this face? (2)
. . .
What about this face? (6)

Notice that, where appropriate, we use the singular form *die* of the plural *dice*. Some of your students may need you to explain this to them. Roll one of the dice and let a student read the number of dots on the top, say, 3.

T: We say the *outcome* of rolling the die is the number of dots on the top face of the die when it comes to rest. When I roll a die, what outcome do you think is most likely?

S: *None of them; they all have the same chance of happening.*

T: What is the probability that the outcome will be 3? $\left(\frac{1}{6}\right)$
What is the probability that the outcome will be 6? $\left(\frac{1}{6}\right)$

And so on.

Reinforce this discussion by drawing the probability tree for the experiment of rolling one die:

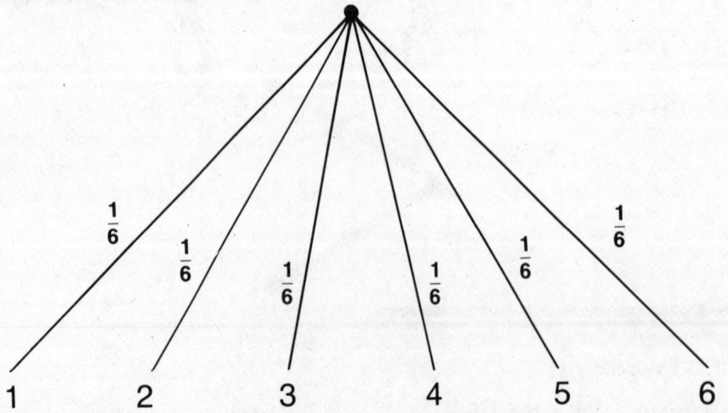

T: What is the probability that the outcome will be an odd number?

S: *Three chances in six;* $\frac{3}{6}$; $\frac{1}{2}$.

Explain this result by referring to the tree:

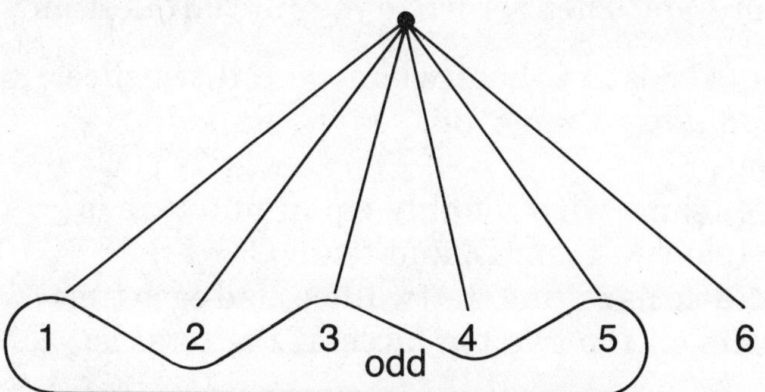

Ask further questions such as the following:
What is the probability of getting

at least 5? $\left(\frac{2}{6} \text{ or } \frac{1}{3}\right)$

at most 5? $\left(\frac{5}{6}\right)$

a prime number? $\left(\frac{3}{6} \text{ or } \frac{1}{2}\right)$

a divisor of 18? $\left(\frac{4}{6} \text{ or } \frac{2}{3}\right)$

Then erase everything you have drawn and written on the board, and take both dice in your hand.

T: How many outcomes will there be if I roll both dice at once? Let's look at a few trials.

Let a student roll the dice seven or eight times and describe each outcome to you. Record the outcome on the board, like this:

red 5, blue 4
red 5, blue 1
red 2, blue 2
and so on.

T: I wonder whether we could find an easier way to keep a record of the outcomes.

Display a copy of Poster #2, as shown below, and accept suggestions about how to represent on this grid the seven or eight outcomes that have already occurred.

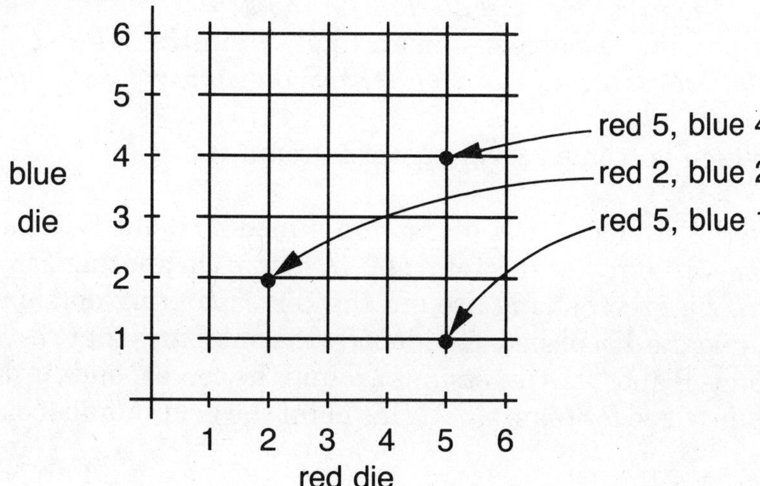

After all have agreed on how to represent outcomes on this grid, let the students roll the dice several more times and mark dots on the

47 48

grid for the outcomes. Mark some dots on the grid and ask the class what outcomes the dots represent. Then return to your initial question.

T: How many possible outcomes are there when we roll two dice?
S: *36, because there are 36 dots;* $6 \times 6 = 36$.
T: Now let us play a game.
Divide the class into three teams with roughly equal numbers of members. Call the teams team A, team B, and team C.
T: Now you're going to take turns rolling the two dice, and each time we will add the numbers on the two top faces. If the total is:

> 2, 3, 4, or 5, then team A gets a point.
> 6, 7, or 8, then team B gets a point.
> 9, 10, 11, or 12, then team C gets a point.

Record this information on the board below the grid:

Totals:	2 3 4 5	6 7 8	9 10 11 12
	A	B	C

T: Do you think this is a fair game?
Some might say, "No, because more totals give a point to A and C than to B." Others might realize that there are more outcomes (dots) corresponding to some totals than to others, so they might prefer to reserve judgment.

Play the game. (The team allegiance of the person rolling the dice has nothing to do with the result. For the sake of appearances, however, it is best to ask for a volunteer from each of the three teams in turn.) After about 12 rolls, or when it begins to appear as though team B is winning, direct attention back to the grid.

T: Let's analyze the game. How many outcomes are there when we roll two dice?
S: *36, because there are 36 dots on the grid.*
T: Is any of the outcomes more likely than the others?
S: *No. Unless the dice aren't fair, each outcome is just as likely as any other.*
T: Which outcomes give a point to team A?

Guide the students in a discussion aimed at identifying all the outcomes that result in a total of 2, 3, 4, or 5. On another copy of Poster #2 draw a green string around the corresponding dots on the grid. Continue the discussion and identify the outcomes that result in points for teams B and C. Draw strings around the corresponding dots (blue for team B, red for team C). At this point the grid should look like this:

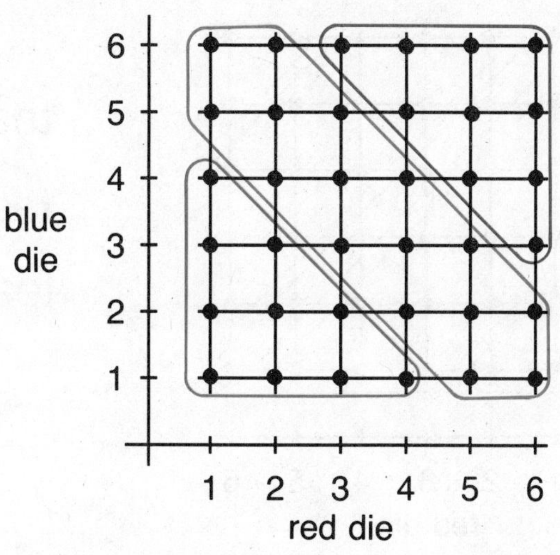

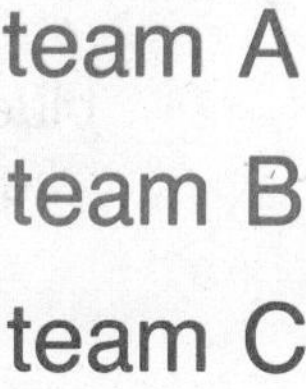

T: Now what do you think? Is it a fair game?
S: *Team B will win. It has 16 chances in 36.*
S: *And A and C each has only 10 chances in 36.*
T: What is the probability that team A will win this game? $\left(\frac{10}{36}\right)$
What about team B? $\left(\frac{16}{36}\right)$
and team C? $\left(\frac{10}{36}\right)$

Erase the colored strings on the grid.

T: Is there a way to change the game to make it fair? If we want it to be fair, how many chances out of 36 must each team have?
S: *12, because* $\frac{1}{3} \times 36 = 12$.
T: How could we do this?

Give the students a moment or two to think about this, and then ask for suggestions. Someone might suggest making a list of the number of outcomes that give each total. If not, make the suggestion yourself.

Total	2	3	4	5	6	7	8	9	10	11	12
Number of Outcomes	1	2	3	4	5	6	5	4	3	2	1

S: *I see a way. Let team A win if the total is 3, 5, or 7; team B if the total is 2, 6, 8 or 12; and team C if the total is anything else.*

Check this suggestion by making sure that each team would have 12 chances in 36.

S: *I see another. Team A wins if the total is 2, 3, 7, 11, or 12; team B wins if the total is 4, 5, or 6; otherwise team C wins.*

As before, check this suggestion. When one of the suggestions is preferred by the class—say, the second one above—display a clean copy of Poster #2 and have students draw colored strings on the grid for the resulting fair game, as follows:

47
48

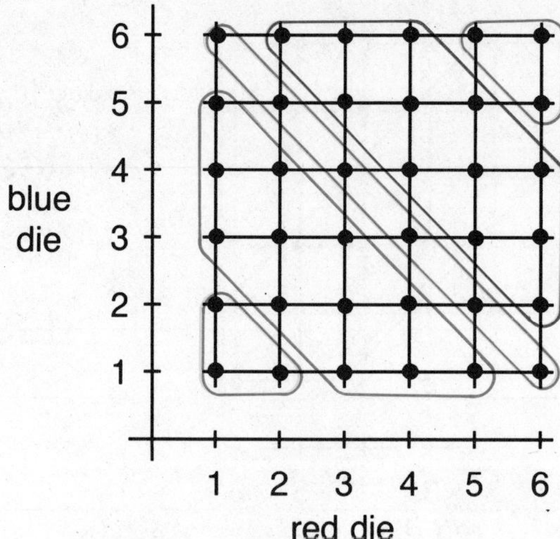

team A

team B

team C

Replace the grid poster with another copy.

T: When we roll the two dice, what is the probability that the total will be less than 5?

S: *It's 6 chances in 36, $\frac{6}{36}$, because I can see on the chart that there is one chance of getting the total 2, two chances of getting 3, and three chances of getting 4.*

After this response has been checked by the class, let someone draw a string around the dots for the outcomes that give a total of less than 5.

T: What is the probability that the total is at least 10?

S: *The same—$\frac{6}{36}$. There are 3 chances of getting 10, 2 chances for 11, and 1 for 12.*

Let a student draw a red string around the dots for outcomes giving a total of at least 10.

T: What is the probability that the total is a divisor of 24?

S: $\frac{17}{36}$. *The divisors of 24 are:*

1, with 0 chances.
2, with 1 chance.
3, with 2 chances.
4, with 3 chances.
6, with 5 chances.
8, with 5 chances.
12, with 1 chance.
24, with 0 chances.

Therefore, there is a total of 17 chances.

Ask a student to draw blue strings around these dots.

47
48

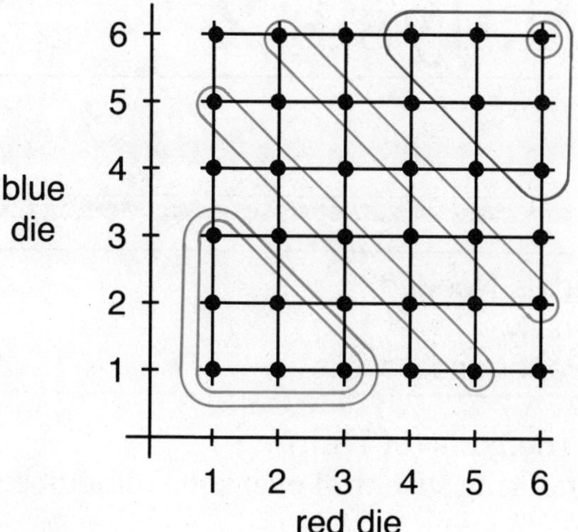

less than 5

at least 10

divisor of 24

Resources Available
For class use: Worksheets L53 and L54
For out-of-class use: Any H-worksheet up through H72

ACTIVITY 49
Nim Analysis 2

Materials Needed
Teacher: Chalk
Students: Paper and pencils

T: Who remembers the game of Nim?

Spend a few minutes making sure that everyone remembers the rules of the game:

- Start with any number of piles of checkers (with any number of checkers in each pile).
- Take turns to pick up any number of checkers from one pile.
- The winner is the one who picks up the last checker.

Also review from Activity 44 the results of the analysis of the safe and hopeless positions for 1- and 2-pile Nim. Record these results on the board:

Safe	Hopeless
one pile of any size	two equal piles of any size
two unequal piles of any size	

T: Today we're going to start work on 3-pile Nim. It's fairly complicated, so we'll take it quite slowly. What's the simplest starting position you can think of with three piles?

S: *Three piles with one checker each.*

T: Is that a safe position or a hopeless position? Would you want to play first or second?

S: *First, because I would pick up one checker, my opponent would have to pick up one of the other two checkers, and I would pick up the last checker.*

S: *Or you could say that when you pick up the first checkers you leave two equal piles, which is a hopeless position.*

T: In any case, three piles of one checker each is a safe position.

Put this information on your list on the board.

T: Does that suggest any other 3-pile starting positions that you think ought to be safe positions?

S: *Three equal piles.*

T: Convince me that it's a safe position. How can you make sure that at some stage you put your opponent in a hopeless position?

S: *It's easy! You just pick up all of one pile. That leaves two equal piles, which is a hopeless position.*

Modify your list on the board:

Safe	Hopeless
one pile of any size	two equal piles of any size
two unequal piles of any size	
three equal piles of any size	

T: What would happen if you made a mistake? Suppose you started with three equal piles and you took only *some* of the checkers from one pile, not the whole pile. Would that mean that your opponent could force you to lose?

S: *Yes. He or she would just have to clear the pile you had started on, and that would leave you with two equal piles, which is a hopeless position.*

T: So can we add any other kind of safe position to our list?

S: *Three piles, where two of them are equal.*

Modify your list on the board.

T: Let's take a break now and see if our work so far has made it any easier to play the game. Play 3-pile Nim a few times with your neighbor. Use paper and pencil, but instead of picking up checkers,* simply cross out drawings of them on your paper. Try to use the information we have learned so far and put your opponent in a hopeless position. Decide between the two of you what the starting positions should be and who should play first.

Let the students play the game for about 10 minutes. Discuss briefly whether the analysis so far has made it any easier to play the game. The general feeling will probably be that although we know quite a lot about safe positions, it would be useful to know some more hopeless positions, especially some 3-pile hopeless positions.

If you are able to do so, it would be beneficial to continue immediately with Activity 50. If this is not possible, bring the activity to a close as follows:

T: We're making progress with 3-pile Nim, and next time we'll find some hopeless 3-pile positions.

---

* Or erasing checkers, if that is what you have been doing.

Resources Available

For out-of-class use: Any H-worksheet up through H75

ACTIVITY 50
Nim Analysis 3

Materials Needed
Teacher: Chalk
Students: Paper and pencils

If you are able to move on to this activity immediately following Activity 49, start at ■ below. If not, start by reminding the class about the previous Nim analysis activities, as a result of which we have discovered the following:

Safe Positions	Hopeless Positions
one pile of any size	two equal piles of any size
two unequal piles of any size	
three equal piles of any size	
three piles of any size with two equal	

■ **T:** The time has come for us to find some 3-pile hopeless positions. What's the simplest 3-pile starting position you can think of where we don't yet know if it's a safe or a hopeless position?

S: *1, 1, 2* .

S: *No, that's a safe position: three piles with two equal.*

S: *1, 2, 3* .

Record this answer on the board.

T: Now,what we're going to do is write down all the positions that could be left after the first player has played. Then we'll look at those positions and see if any of them are hopeless positions. Suppose that one or more of the positions that could be left by the first player is a hopeless position. What would that tell you about the position 1, 2, 3 ?

S: *It would be a safe position, because if you can move and put your opponent in a hopeless position you can be sure to win.*

T: Suppose that no matter what the first player does, his or her opponent is left in a safe position. What does that tell you about the position 1, 2, 3 ?

S: *It would be a hopeless position, because no matter what you do, your opponent can always win.*
T: Let's try it and see. What could the first player do?
S: *He or she could pick up the 1-pile. That would leave* [2, 3] *, which is a safe position.*
Record on the board:

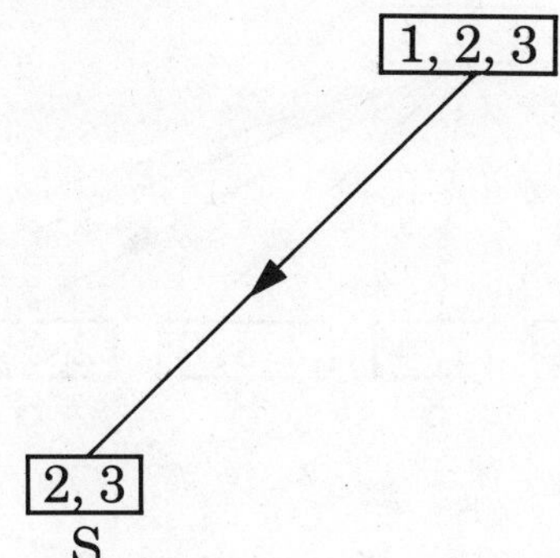

Elicit from the students all other possibilities. Encourage a systematic approach to the problem. Record each possibility on the board, as follows:

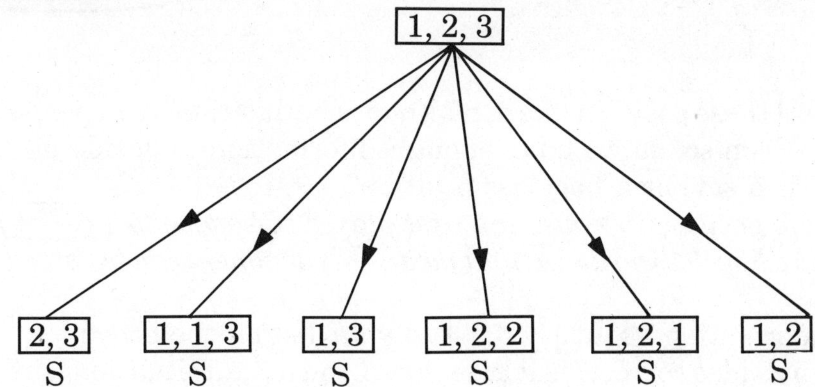

S: *They're all safe positions. So* [1, 2, 3] *must be a hopeless position; no matter what you do, your opponent can always win.*
T: So we've actually found a 3-pile hopeless position.
Add this result to your list on the board.
T: Look at the numbers of checkers in the piles: 1, 2, and 3. Does this suggest to you that there might have to be a relationship between the three numbers to make a hopeless position?
A variety of conjectures may be made at this point. Record them on the board and check them one by one with the class in the manner suggested by the following three examples (which represent the three most likely conjectures). If the students cannot think of any likely relationship, suggest the first of these to them.
1. **S: (Amy):** *Three numbers one after the other.*
T: After [1, 2, 3] , what's the next simplest situation involving three numbers one after the other?
S: [*4, 5, 6*] .

50

T: No. There's an even simpler one than that.
S: *2, 3, 4* .
Let the students work individually on listing all the possible results of the first player's move. After a few minutes, compile the class's work on the board:

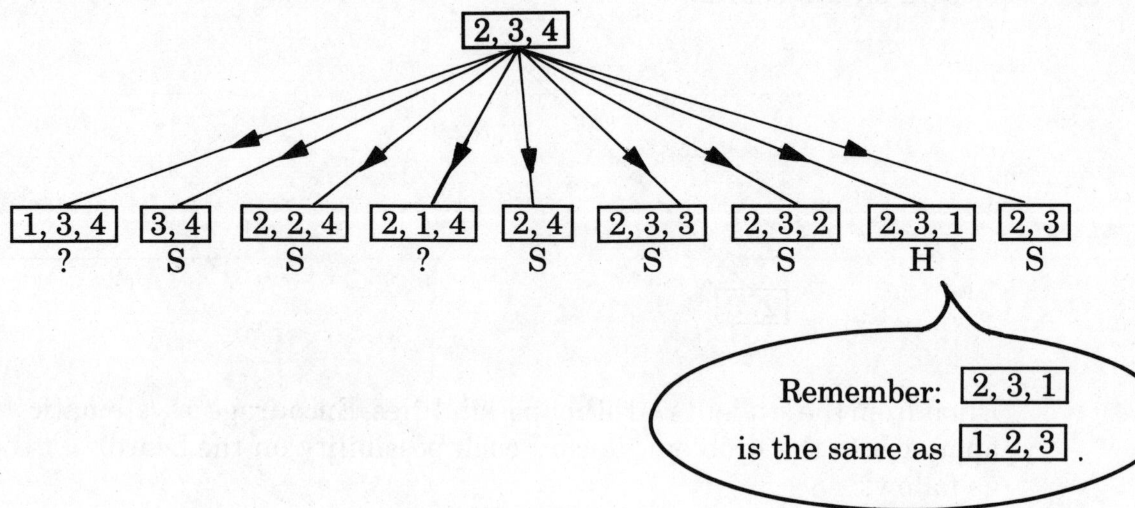

T: For two of these positions we don't know whether they're hopeless or safe. Even so, do we have enough information to decide if 2, 3, 4 is a safe or a hopeless position?
S: *It's a safe position, because the first player can move to 2, 3, 1 , which is a hopeless position; that means his opponent can be forced to lose.*
Add this information about 2, 3, 4 to your list on the board.
T: Was Amy's idea correct? Is it true that if you have a situation with three numbers one after the other it's a hopeless position?
S: *No. We've found one like that that's a safe position.*
2. **S (Barry):** *Two of the numbers add up to the third:* $1 + 2 = 3$.
T: After 1, 2, 3 , what's the next simplest situation involving three numbers where two of them add up to the third?
S: *1, 3, 4* .
S: *That's one of the positions we didn't know about.*
Proceed as above with individual work followed by collective discussion. Here are all the possibilities:

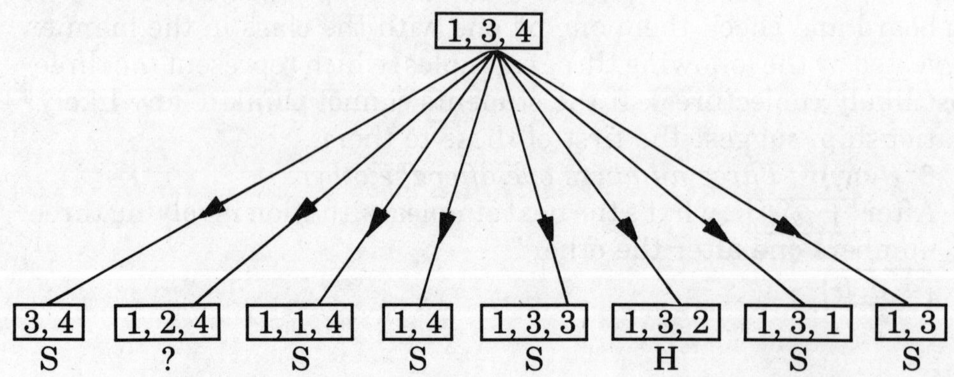

S: *1, 3, 4 is a safe position, because you can move to 1, 3, 2 , which is a hopeless position.*

T: Was Barry correct?

S: *No. His idea doesn't always work.*

3. **S (Cathy):** *One of the numbers is halfway between the other two.*

T: After 1, 2, 3 , what's the next simplest situation involving three numbers where one is halfway between the other two?

S: *1, 3, 5* .

Proceed as in the previous cases, and obtain the following:

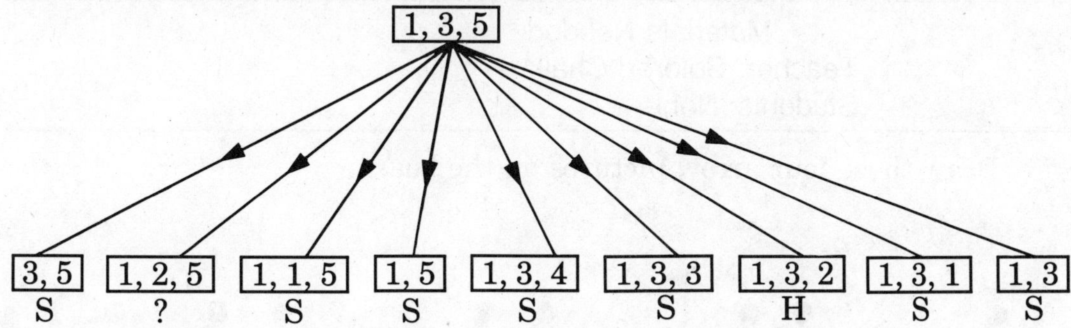

S: *1, 3, 5 is a safe position, because you can move to 1, 3, 2 , which is a hopeless position. So Cathy was wrong.*

T: Well, I think we'll leave it there for today. Next time we'll try to find some other 3-pile hopeless positions apart from 1, 2, 3 . You can try out some of your own ideas at home between now and then.

Note to the Teacher

Keep a record of which starting positions you try in response to students' conjectures, and make a note of whether they are safe or hopeless positions. You will want to refer to this information at the beginning of Activity 53.

Resources Available

For out-of-class use: Any H-Worksheet up through H75

ACTIVITY 51

Fractional Multipliers 2

Materials Needed
Teacher: Colored Chalk
Students: None

Draw these four arrow pictures on the board:

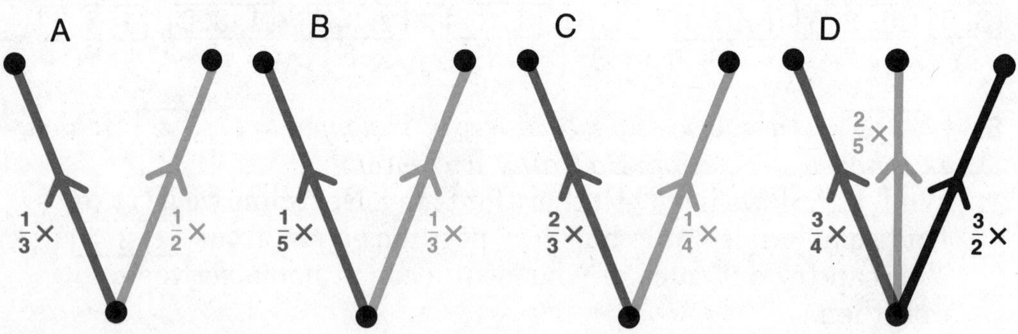

T: All these dots stand for positive whole numbers. What we have to do for each arrow picture is to work out which positive whole numbers the bottom dot could be for so that the top dots stand for positive whole numbers. Let's start with picture A.

Point to the bottom dot in picture A.

T: What positive whole number could this dot be for so that the top dots stand for positive whole numbers?

S: *6.*

Point to the left top dot in picture A.

T: If the bottom dot were for 6, what would this dot be for?

S: *2.* $\frac{1}{3} \times 6 = 2$.

Point to the third dot in picture A.

T: What about this dot?

S: *3.*

T: Are there any other numbers the bottom dot could be for? Remember, we want the top dots to stand for positive whole numbers.

Follow the same checking procedure for each answer. The possibilities for the bottom dot in picture A are the positive multiples of 6: 6, 12, 18, 24, 30 . . . .

Discuss pictures B and C in the same way. The bottom dot in picture B must be a multiple of 15, and the bottom dot in picture C must be a multiple of 12.

When you discuss picture C, students may need to be reminded about how to use a detour (see Activity 9) to do $\frac{2}{3}\times$. (Multiply by 2 and then divide by 3, or divide by 3 and then multiply by 2.)

Finally, move on to picture D.

T: Before we think about what numbers the bottom dot could be for, can anyone tell me which dot stands for the largest number?

S (Andy): *The dot at the end of the* $\frac{3}{2}\times$ *arrow, because the number there is the only one that is greater than the number at the bottom dot.*

T: Good. Which dot stands for the smallest number?

S: *That one at the end of the* $\frac{2}{5}\times$ *arrow.*

T: Now what positive whole number could the bottom dot be for? Remember, we want the top dots to stand for positive whole numbers too.

S: *20.*

In fact, any positive multiple of 20 will do. Point at the top dots from left to right.

T: If the bottom dot were for 20, what would these top dots be for?

S: *15, 8, and 30.*

T: Good. And notice that 30 is indeed the largest of these numbers, as Andy predicted.

Resources Available

For class use: Worksheets L55 and L56

For out-of-class use: Any H-worksheet up through H78

ACTIVITY 52
Fractional Multipliers 3

Materials Needed
Teacher: Colored chalk
Students: None

Draw the following arrow picture well spaced out on the board:

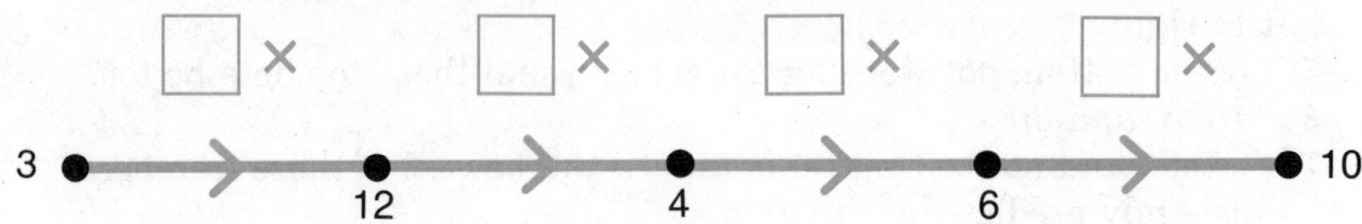

T: Each of these blue arrows is a multiplication arrow. Our job is to work out how to label the arrows. Let's start from the left.

S: *The first arrow is for 4×, because* $4 \times 3 = 12$.

Write **4** in the box next to the first arrow.

S: *The next arrow is for* $\div 3$.

T: True, but we're only using multiplication in this arrow picture.

S: $\frac{1}{3}\times$, *because* $\frac{1}{3} \times 12 = 4$.

Write $\frac{1}{3}$ in the box next to the second arrow.

T: The next two arrows are a bit more difficult. It will help if you think about detours.

Draw a detour for the third arrow:

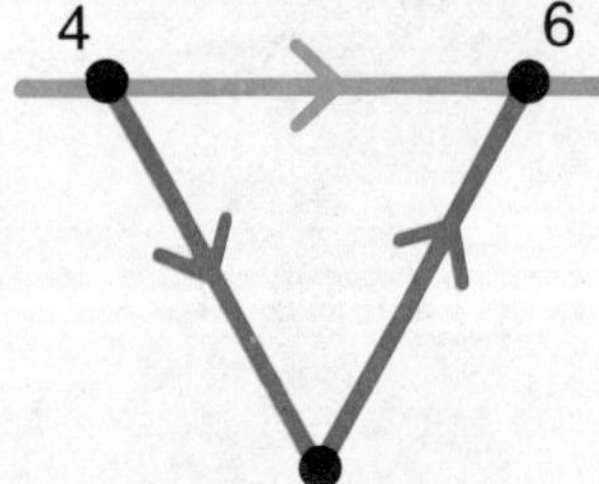

S: *It could be* $\div 2$ *then 3×.*

Let the student label the red arrows on the board:

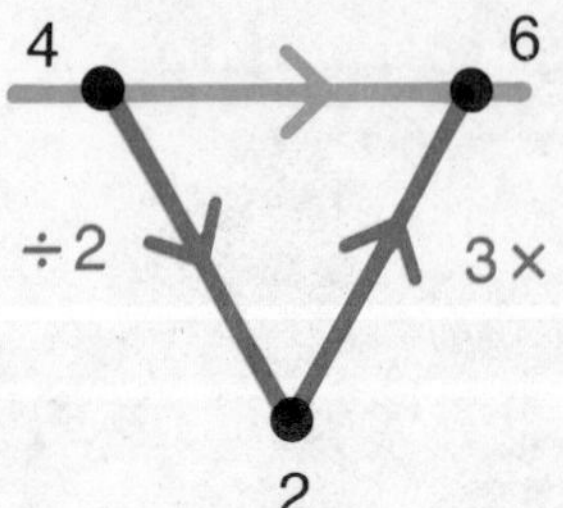

52

T: Good. How shall we label the blue arrow?
S: $\frac{3}{2}\times$.
Write $\frac{3}{2}$ in the box next to the third arrow. Deal with the fourth arrow in a similar fashion.

Your completed arrow picture should look like this (alternative reduce-to-one answers are given in parentheses):

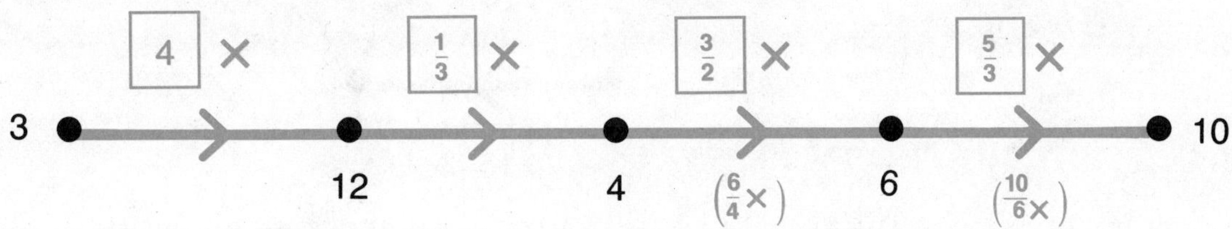

Draw these two arrow pictures on the board:

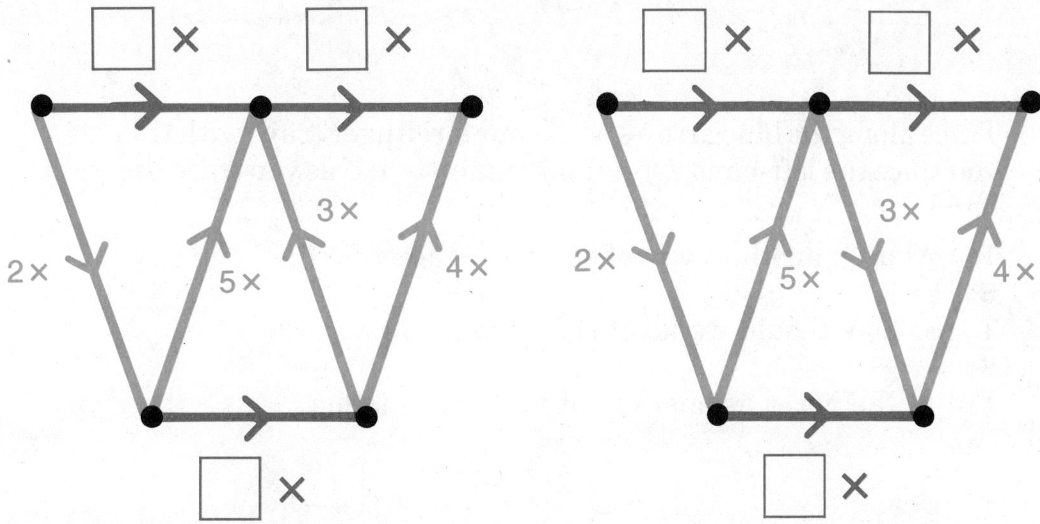

T: Here are two arrow pictures that look very much alike. Can anyone see the difference?
S: *In the picture on the right, some of the blue arrows go the other way.*
T: Remember that as we label the red arrows. Notice that they're all multiplication arrows again.
Point to the upper left-hand red arrow.
T: How should we label this arrow?
S: *10×.*
Fill in the boxes as answers are given for the left-hand picture, as shown in the next diagram.

In cases such as the third and fourth blue arrows, some students may use a reduce-to-one strategy to obtain a multiplier. According to this strategy, you divide by the old number (giving 1) and multiply by the new number. This leads to the (unreduced) multiplier $\frac{\text{new}}{\text{old}}\times$. Neither encourage nor discourage such thinking. Simply point out that there are other possible labels for the blue arrows.

52

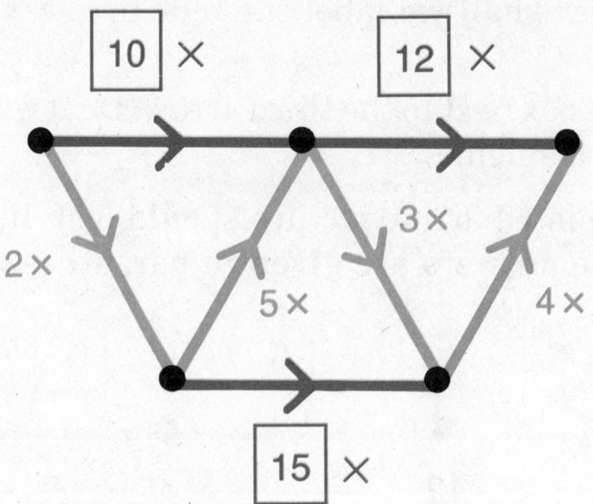

The right-hand picture is less straightforward. If the students do not do so, suggest the following strategy:

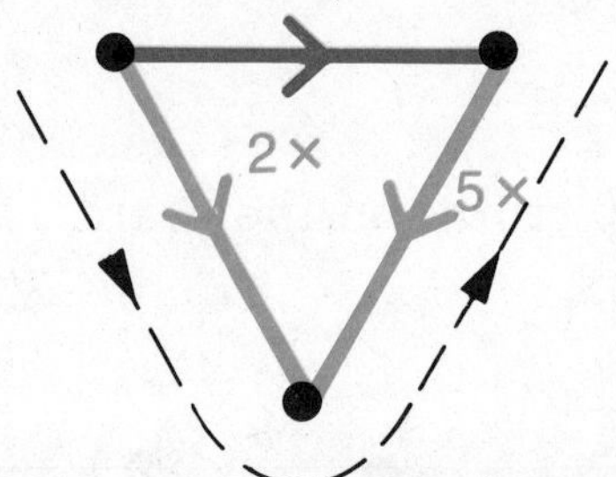

Trace along the blue arrows with your forefinger. Say "with this" as you trace the left-hand arrow and "against this" as you trace the right-hand one.

T: What is another way of saying "against 5 ×"?
S: $\frac{1}{5}\times$.
T: So how should we label this first arrow?
S: $\frac{2}{5}\times$.

Fill in the boxes as answers are given, as follows:

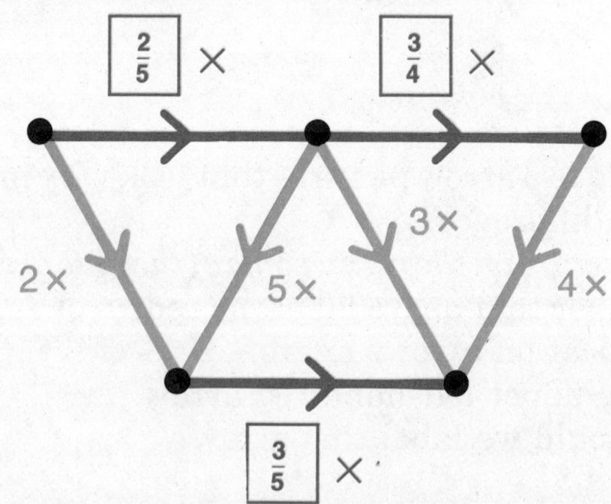

Resources Available
For out-of-class use: Any H-worksheet up through H78

ACTIVITY 53

The Game of Nim 2

Materials Needed
Teacher: Chalk
Students: Paper and pencils

T: Today I'm going to give you the chance to use what we've learned so far about Nim. In a little while you can play the game in pairs, but first let's remind ourselves what we have found out so far.

Write on the board:

Safe Positions	Hopeless Positions
one pile of any size	two equal piles of any size
two unequal piles of any size	[1, 2, 3]
three equal piles of any size	
three piles of any size with two equal	

[2, 3, 4]
[1, 3, 4]
[1, 3, 5]
} or whatever positions you tried in response to students' conjectures in Activity 50

T: There's one other thing I'd like you to realize before you start playing. We know that [1, 2, 3] is a hopeless position. What about [1, 2, 4] ?

S: *It has to be a safe position. If you take one checker off the 4-pile, you put your opponent in the position [1, 2, 3] , which is hopeless.*

T: What about [1, 2, 5] ?

S: *That's a safe position, too. You take two checkers off the 5-pile and leave [1, 2, 3] again.*

S: *The same argument works for [1, 2, any number bigger than 3]. You just take off enough checkers from the big pile to leave only three.*

T: Excellent. What about [1, 10, 3] ?

S: *It's the same idea. You take eight checkers off the 10-pile and leave [1, 2, 3] . So [1, 10, 3] is another safe position.*

S: *If your starting position has three piles, two of them agree with* [*1, 2, 3*]*, and the third pile has* more *checkers in it than the third of these numbers, then it's a safe position. You just pick up enough checkers from the pile that doesn't agree with* [*1, 2, 3*] *to leave* [*1, 2, 3*].

T: That's very good thinking. Try to remember that rule while you're playing; it will help you play better.

Let the students play Nim in pairs for the remainder of the time available. Encourage them to make use of the information on the board about safe and hopeless positions. If you feel that any student needs more explicit practice on using this information, give him or her Worksheets L57 and L58, which require the conscious application of the analytical work carried out so far.

Resources Available

For class use: Worksheets L57 and L58

For out-of-class use: Any H-worksheet up through H81

ACTIVITY 54
Ternary Abacus 1

Teacher: Minicomputer checkers
Students: None

If your chalkboard is magnet-sensitive, draw this abacus on it;

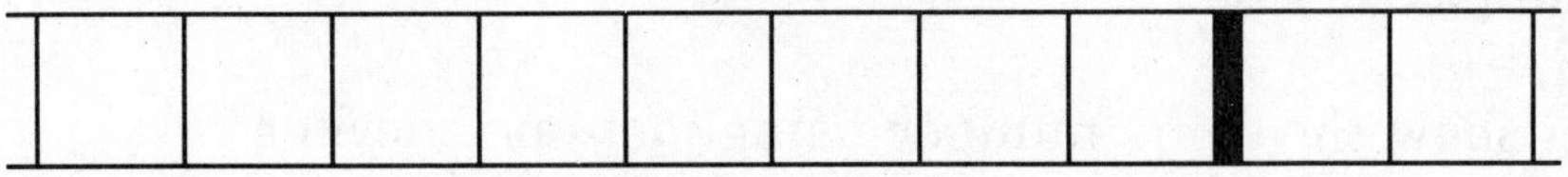

								‖	

otherwise, follow the suggestion at the beginning of Activity 30.

T: What was the rule of the *binary* abacus?
S: *Two checkers on a square show the same number as one checker on the next square to the left.*
T: Very good. That's the rule of the *binary* abacus. The word *binary* means "two." Now let's change the rule so that we have a *ternary* abacus. The word *ternary* means "three." What do you think the rule is for the ternary abacus?
S: ***Three*** *checkers on a square show the same number as one checker on the next square to the left.*

You might not get such a response immediately; you might even need to provide it yourself. In any case, write the rule on the board:

> Three checkers on a square show the same number as one checker on the next square to the left.

Place a checker on the abacus as follows:

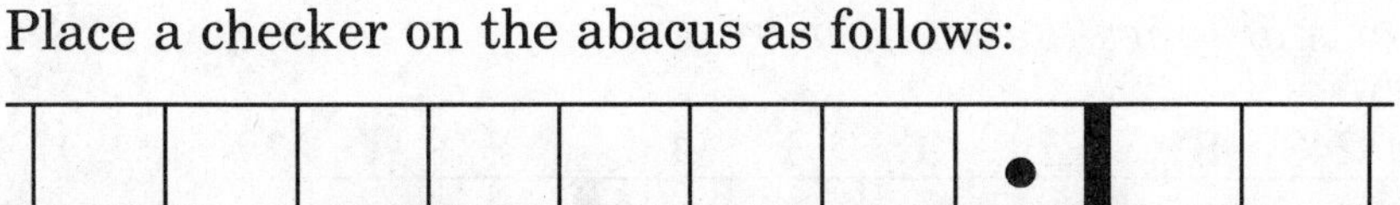

							• ‖	

T: What is this number? (1)
Label the square **1**.
T: And this number?

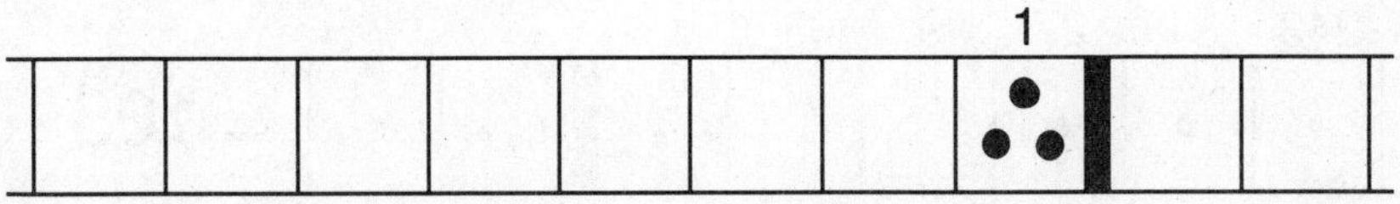

							1	
							••• ‖	

S: *3.*
T: This is a ternary abacus—a three-abacus. Can you show the same number with just one checker?
S: *One checker on the next square to the left.*
Let the student make the suggested robot move.

						3	1		
						•			

= 3

Place two more checkers on the 3-square.

						3	1		
						•••			

T: What number is this?
S: *9; $3 \times 3 = 9$.*
T: Can you show the same number using just one checker?
S: *One checker on the next square to the left.*
Again, let the student make the robot move.

					9	3	1		
					•				

= 9

Continue this process until seven or eight squares are labeled.

2,187	729	243	81	27	9	3	1		

T: Can anyone show 12 on the ternary abacus using at most two checkers?
S:

2,187	729	243	81	27	9	3	1		
					•	•			

= 12

T: What about 36?
S: *That's easy. You just have to move both checkers one square to the left. That multiplies the number by 3.*

2,187	729	243	81	27	9	3	1		
				•	•				

= 36

T: Now can you show 108 on the ternary abacus?
S: *That's 3×36. So move the checkers one more square to the left.*

2,187	729	243	81	27	9	3	1		
			•	•					

= 108

T: Let's check that. What's 81 + 27? (108)
OK. Now show 250 on the ternary abacus. Don't use more than two checkers on any square.

S:

2,187	729	243	81	27	9	3	1		
		•				••	•		

= 250

Move each checker one square to the left.

2,187	729	243	81	27	9	3	1		
	•				••	•			

T: What number is this?

S: *You move them all one square to the left. So the number is 3 × 250. That's 750.*

T: Here is a really big number. What is it?

2,187	729	243	81	27	9	3	1		
	••	••	••	••	••	••	•••		

Some students will begin to calculate, but others might see the possibility of making robot moves, starting in the 1-square.

S: *It's 2,187.*

Have a student who notices this short method come to the board and explain it.

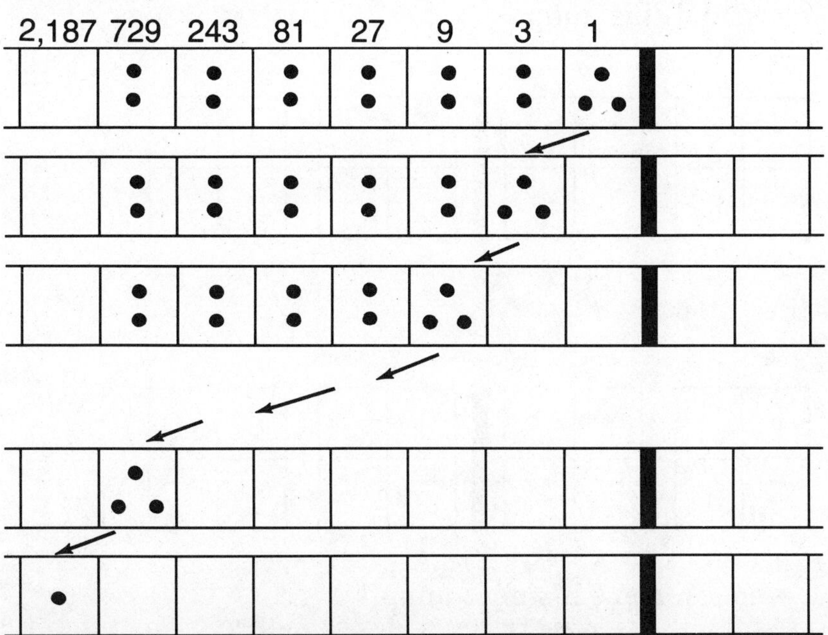

Resources Available

For class use: Worksheets L59 and L60
For out-of-class use: Any H-worksheet up through H81

ACTIVITIES 55 and 56
Decimals 7

Materials Needed
Teacher: Chalk and Minicomputer kit
Students: Paper and pencils

Set up your Minicomputer boards and one checker as follows:

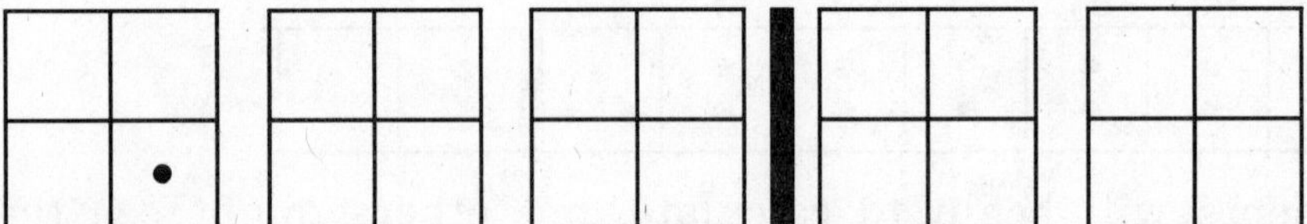

T: Let me tell you a story about Mr. 100, who is sitting here on the Minicomputer. Mr. 100 often daydreams. Last evening he imagined that he was doing his exercises on the Minicomputer. He dreamt he did this jump . . .

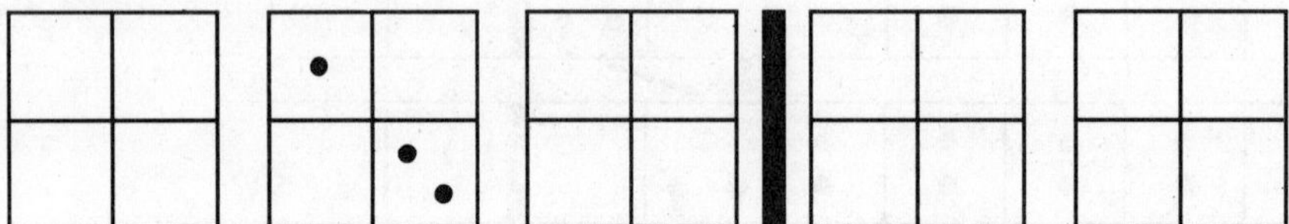

followed by this jump . . .

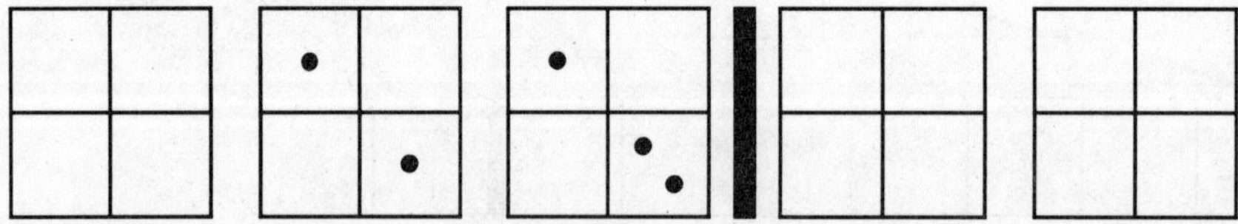

and then . . . who can show his next jump?
Let a student make the moves "1 = 0.8 + 0.2" and "0.2 = 0.1 + 0.1."

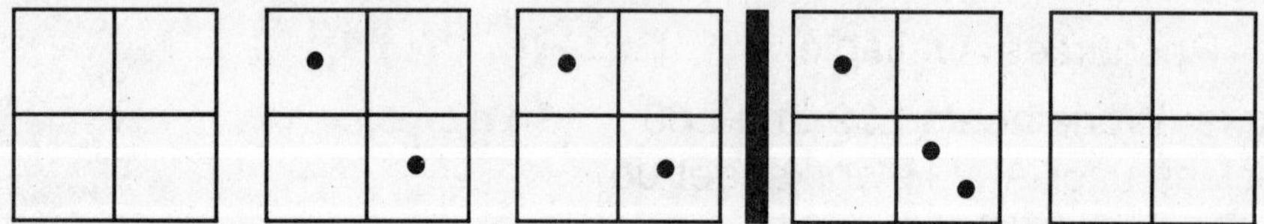

T: And his next jump?

55
56

S:

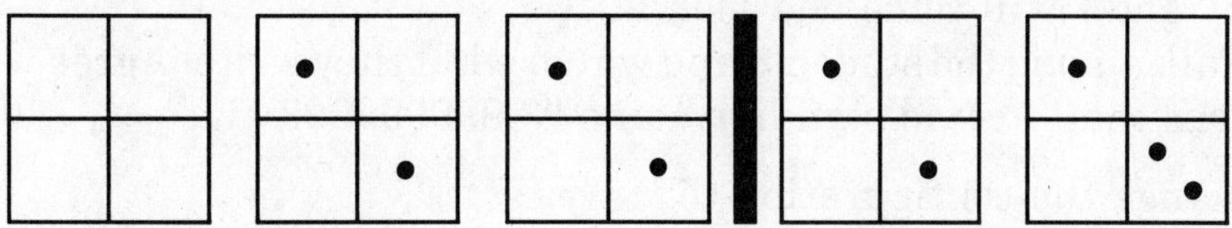

S: *We're running out of Mincomputer boards!*
Move the now-empty 100-board to the 0.001-board position.

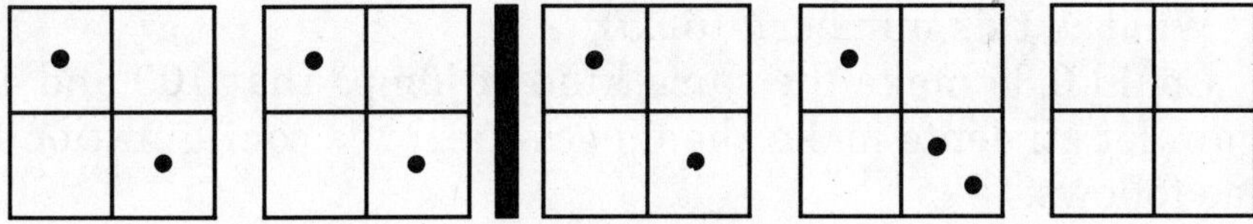

S: *Here's his next jump.*

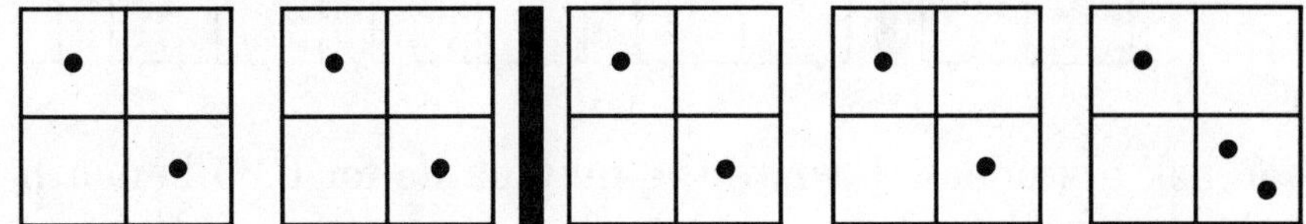

T: Could Mr. 100 continue his jumping exercises?
S: *Yes, but we neeed more boards.*
T: Well, in his daydream Mr. 100 imagined that he had all the Minicomputer boards he needed to go on jumping forever. This is the reason he now likes to sign his name "99.999999999 . . .," where the three dots at the end mean "and so on forever."

Change the configuration on the Minicomputer to:

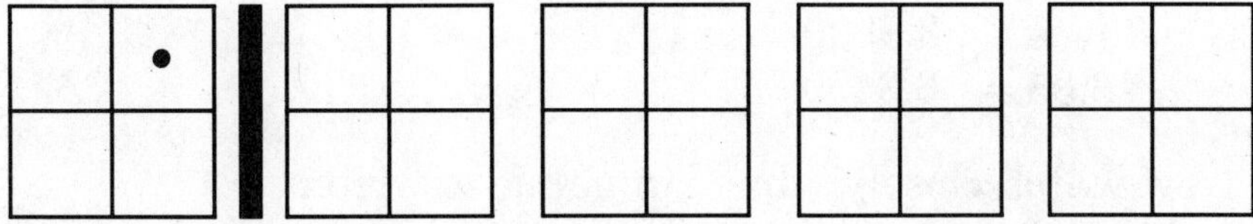

T: Do you think 4 could make the same sort of jumps that 100 did?
Let students come to the board and make jumps to obtain:

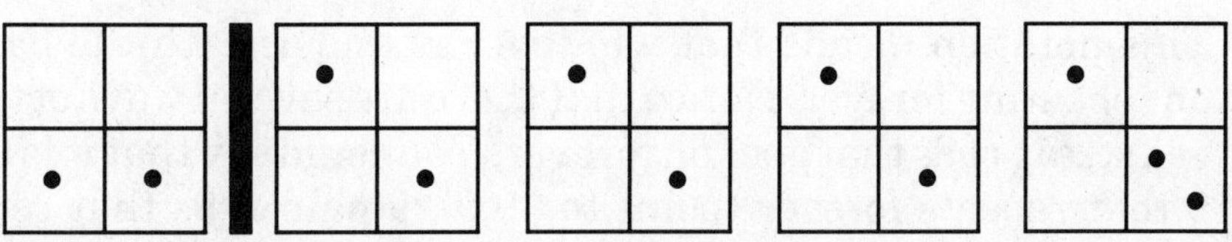

S: *And 4 can imagine more and more boards forever.*

T: How could 4 sign her name? Write 4's new name on your paper, and I will come and look at it.

Walk among the students and watch what they write. Agree with the class that 4 could sign her name "3.999999999 . . . ."

Change the configuration to:

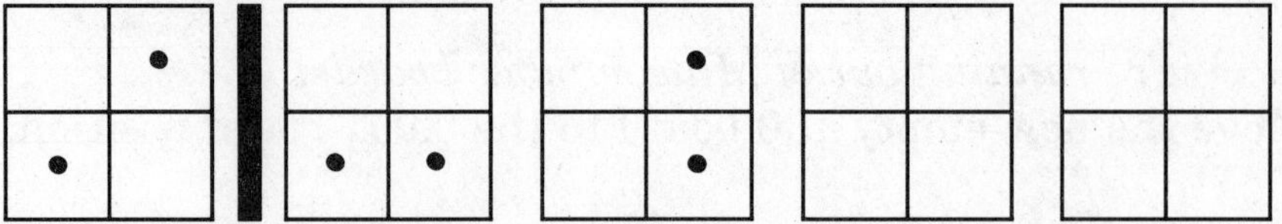

T: What is this number? (6.35)
Could 6.35 make the same kind of jumps that 100 and 4 did?

Again let students make the moves until the configuration for 6.35 is as follows:

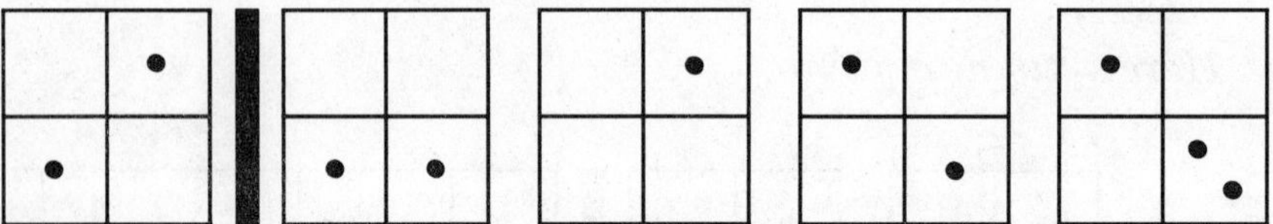

Then ask a student to write the new name for 6.35 beneath the Minicomputer boards.

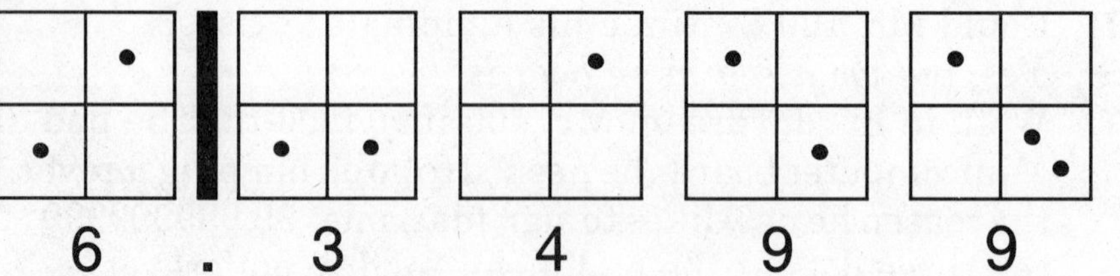

Add the new name for 6.35 to the others already written on the board:

$$100 = 99.9999\ldots$$
$$4 = 3.9999\ldots$$
$$6.35 = 6.3499\ldots$$

T: Now watch closely what I'm going to write.

Extend the above equalities as follows:

$$100 = 99.9999\ldots = 99.\overline{9} = 99.\overline{99} = 99.\overline{999} = 99.\overline{9999} = \ldots$$
$$4 = 3.9999\ldots = 3.\overline{9} = 3.\overline{99} = 3.\overline{999} = 3.\overline{9999} = \ldots$$
$$6.35 = 6.3499\ldots = 6.34\overline{9} = 6.34\overline{99} = 6.34\overline{999} = \ldots$$

T: This notation means that whatever is underneath the bar keeps on repeating forever. Notice that there are several ways of thinking of a string of 9s that goes on forever. You could say that it is one 9 that repeats forever (point to $99.\overline{9}$), a pair of 9s that repeats

forever (point to 99.$\overline{99}$), three 9s in a row that repeat forever (point to 99.$\overline{999}$), or two 9s followed by a pair of 9s that repeats forever (point to 99.99$\overline{99}$). Using the bar, we don't have to write out strings of 9s to help other people see the pattern that repeats. See if you can use this idea to help you write new names for 237 and 5.48.

After you see that most of the class has done at least one of these correctly, ask students to write the new names on the board. Accept names that use strings of 9s as well as those using the bar. For example:

$$237 = 236.999\ldots = 236.\overline{9} = 236.\overline{99}\ldots$$
$$5.48 = 5.47999\ldots = 5.47\overline{9} = 5.47\overline{99} = \ldots$$

Caution: It is important in the case of 5.48 that the bar does not encroach over the 7, thus:

$5.4\overline{79}$ Incorrect!

Remove the Minicomputer boards and erase everything you have written on the board.
Write the following on the board:

8		4		0	.	7	=	1.3

T: Each blank square stands for one of the operation keys (⊞, ⊟, ⊠, ⊡) on a calculator. Any one of the keys may be used as often as you like, but we want the calculator sentence to be true. That is, if you pressed the keys in the order that they are written on the board you would get 1.3 on the calculator display. Try to solve this problem on your papers.

Note to the Teacher

The above calculator sentence and those that follow describe calculations that could be performed on a calculator that "chains" operations. Such a calculator performs each operation as it is keyed in without keeping any calculations in reserve pending the result of a calculation keyed in later. Thus,

3	×	6	+	7	÷	5	=	5

indicates the calculation $[(3 \times 6) + 7] \div 5 = 5$.

Circulate among the students and check individuals' work until you see that some have found a solution. Then ask for a solution.
S: *I put "divided by" in the first blank square and "minus" in the other.*
Write these symbols in the blank squares.

8 ÷ 4 − 0 . 7 = 1.3

T: What is 8 ÷ 4? (2)
Then what is 2 − 0.7? (1.3)
So we have found a solution. Let's try another problem.

Write the following on the board:

Again give ample time for students to find the following solution individually:

If time allows, suggest other similar problems for classwork.

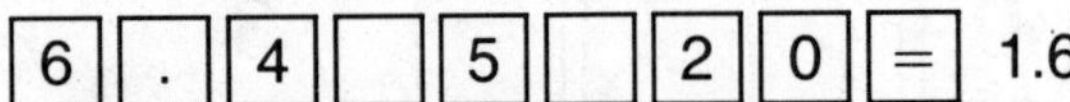

4 . 5 ☐ 4 ☐ 1 0 = 11.25

Solutions:

6 . 4 × 5 ÷ 2 0 = 1.6

4 . 5 ÷ 4 × 1 0 = 11.25

Resources Available

For class use: Worksheets L61 and L62
For out-of-class use: Any H-worksheet up through H84

ACTIVITIES 57 and 58
Nim Analysis 4

Materials Needed
Teacher: Chalk
Students: Paper and pencils

T: Today we're going to try to make more progress in understanding the game of Nim. So far we know quite a number of safe positions but not very many hopeless ones. Here is what we've found out.

Write on the board:

Safe Positions	Hopeless Positions
one pile of any size	two equal piles of any size
two unequal piles of any size	1, 2, 3
three equal piles of any size	
three piles of any size with two equal	
	2, 3, 4
	1, 3, 4
	1, 3, 5

(2, 3, 4; 1, 3, 4; 1, 3, 5 — or whatever positions you tried in response to students' conjectures in Activity 50)

T: We were having trouble finding 3-pile hopeless positions. Did any of you find any new 3-pile hopeless positions on your own?

If there are any volunteers, check their suggestions on the board with the help of the class, as in Activity 50. If anyone has indeed found a new 3-pile hopeless position, add it to the list on the board. Similarly, if a claim proves to be unjustified, extend the "safe" column. A starting position may be suggested that is undecidable at this stage. That is, once the results of all the possible first moves have been listed, it may be found that none of them whose status is known is a hopeless position; however, some of the resulting positions are of unknown status. In such a case, simply make a note of the student's suggestion and promise to come back to it later when more information is known. (The alternative approach of extending the exhaustive listing of all possible moves one or more stages further would be so time consuming at this

stage that it would divert the class from the simpler and more general reasoning on which we are about to embark.)

T: We're going to find quite a few more 3-pile hopeless positions today. But to begin with, I'd like to remind you about something you explained to me last time. Do you remember? If you have a 3-pile position, with two piles agreeing with [1, 2, 3] and the third pile having *more* checkers in it than the third of these numbers, then it's a safe position. Who can explain why?

S: *You pick up enough checkers from the pile that doesn't agree with [1, 2, 3] to leave [1, 2, 3].*

T: Does that work all the time? Suppose we know some 3-pile hopeless position. If we have a new position where two of the piles agree with the hopeless position and the third pile has *more* checkers than the other pile in the hopeless position, is that new position always a safe position?

S (Su Li): *Yes. You just pick up enough checkers from the pile that doesn't agree to make it agree. That puts your opponent in a hopeless position.*

T: Suppose instead you have a new position where two of the piles agree with the hopeless position and the third pile has *fewer* checkers than the other pile in the hopeless position. Could the new position also be a hopeless position?

S: *No, because if it were a hopeless position then the original position would have to have been a safe position by Su Li's argument. But we know it's a hopeless position.*

T: Here's what we've just found out: If we know a 3-pile hopeless position, then every other 3-pile position that has exactly two piles that agree with two piles in the hopeless position must be a safe position. In other words, if you have two unequal piles and you find a third pile that makes up a hopeless position, then that third pile is the *only possible* pile that will make a hopeless position. This information is very useful, because it will save us from doing a lot of searching around for hopeless positions that would not produce any results. For example, we know [1, 2, 3] is a hopeless position. Why would it be a waste of time to check if [2, 3, 5] is a hopeless position?

S: *Because there can't be any other size pile than a 1-pile that makes a hopeless position with a 2-pile and a 3-pile. So [2, 3, 5] must be a safe position.*

T: Right. Bearing that in mind, let's go in search of some more 3-pile hopeless positions. To begin with, let's check [1, 4, 5].

Discuss with the class all the possible first moves, as in the first such investigation in Activity 50. The result should be as follows:

57
58

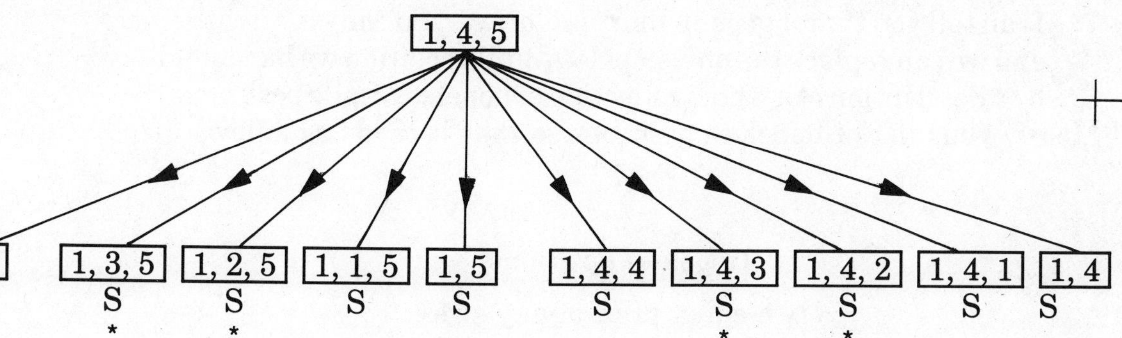

(By the foregoing argument, each position marked * is a safe position by virtue of the fact that [1, 2, 3] is a hopeless position.)

S: *They're all safe positions, so* [1, 4, 5] *must be a hopeless position.*

T: Very good. Now I want you by yourselves to investigate which of these are hopeless positions.

Write on the board:

1, 5, 6	1, 9, 10
1, 6, 7	1, 10, 11
1, 7, 8	1, 11, 12
1, 8, 9	1, 12, 13

T: Remember that sometimes you won't even have to bother to check.

S: *There's no need to check the first one, because we've just seen that you need a 4-pile with a 1-pile and a 5-pile to make a hopeless position. That means that if instead of a 4-pile you have a 6-pile, then it's a safe position.*

T: Good thinking. That's why I suggest you try three in the order I've listed them. You should quickly notice a pattern.

Let the students work their way through this list individually. In fact, every other one is a hopeless position. It then becomes unnecessary to check the next position, for a reason similar to that stated by the student above. Students will quickly realize that they are discovering hopeless positions of the form:

[1, even number, the next odd number]

As soon as a student (say, Amy) can contain herself no longer and blurts out this conjecture, discuss it with the whole class, as follows.

T: Well, it certainly seems to work to begin with. You've found:

1, 2, and the next odd number (3)
1, 4, and the next odd number (5)
1, 6, and the next odd number (7)

Continue the list as far as the students managed to reach before the conjecture was announced.

T: I can tell you that it goes on like that forever. So Amy is correct, and we can replace the only hopeless 3-pile position we had found by a description of a whole collection of hopeless 3-pile positions.

Modify your list of hopeless positions so that it reads as follows:

<u>Hopeless Positions</u>

two equal piles of any size

1, even number, the next odd number

T: For the rest of our time today I'd like you to work in pairs on finding some more 3-pile hopeless positions. Then next time we'll look at them closely and finally come up with a rule for recognizing 3-pile hopeless positions.

Distribute to each student a copy of Worksheet L63 and a supply of blank scratch paper. Tell students to work in pairs and list all the possible results of the first player's move on the scratch paper. Remind them that in each part, because two piles remain constant, if any of the given positions is a hopeless position, then all the others are safe. Worksheet L64 is available for especially fast and accurate workers.

For your convenience, explanations of the answer keys to Worksheets L63 and L64 appear on the following pages rather than at the back of the book.

Before you bring the activity to a close, compile on the board all the results discovered by the class. Also make a note of these results for use in Activities 61 and 62.

Resources Available

For class use: Worksheets L63 and L64
For out-of-class use: Any H-worksheet up through H84

Explanation of Key to L63

1. [2, 4, 5] → [1, 4, 5] H, so [2, 4, 5] safe.

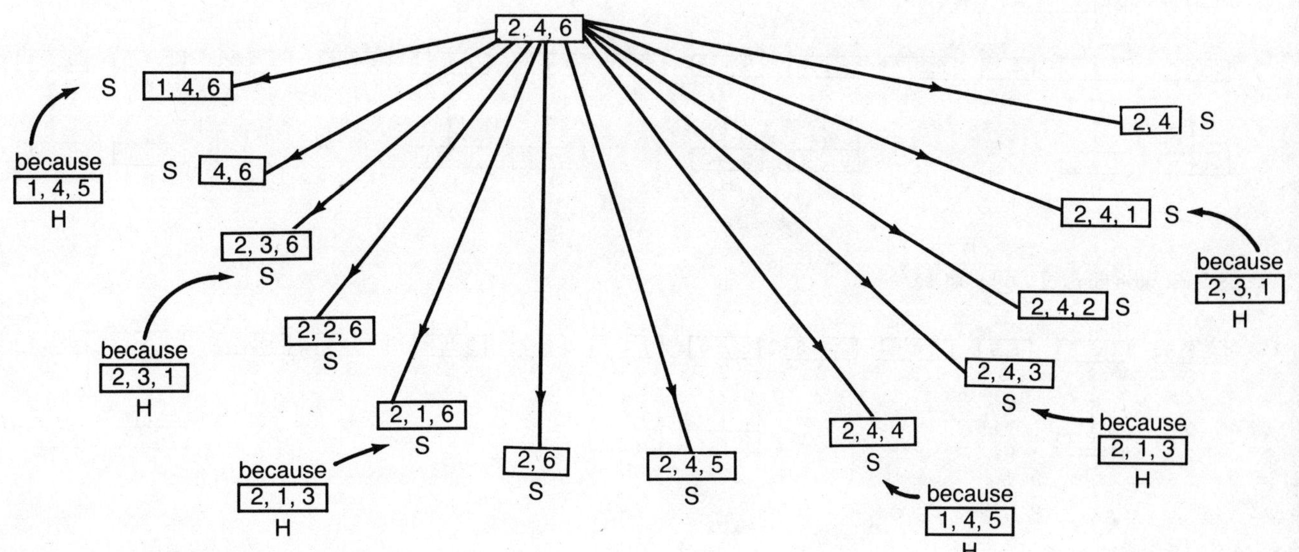

2. [2, 5, 6] → [2, 4, 6] H, so [2, 5, 6] safe.

First move from [2, 5, 7] could leave:

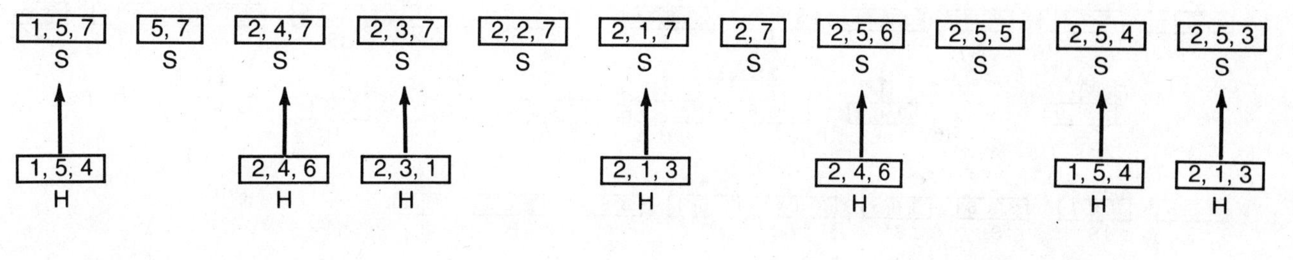

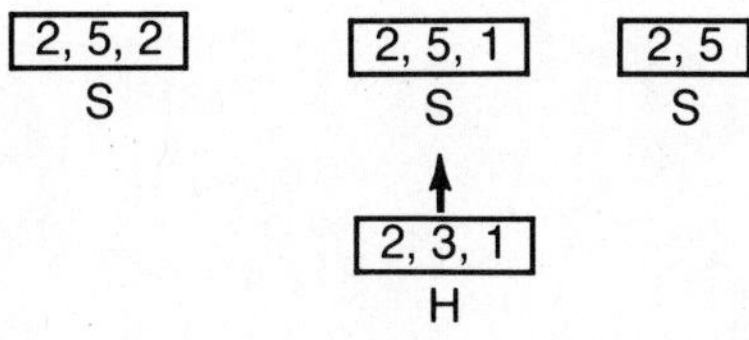

3. First move from [2, 8, 10] could leave:

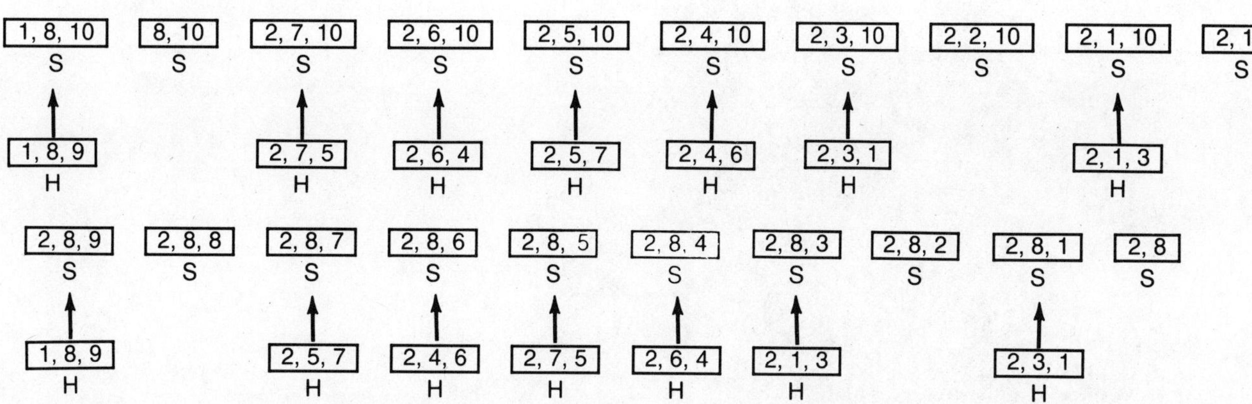

4. [3, 4, 5] → [1, 4, 5] H   [3, 4, 6] → [2, 4, 6] H

First move from [3, 4, 7] could leave:

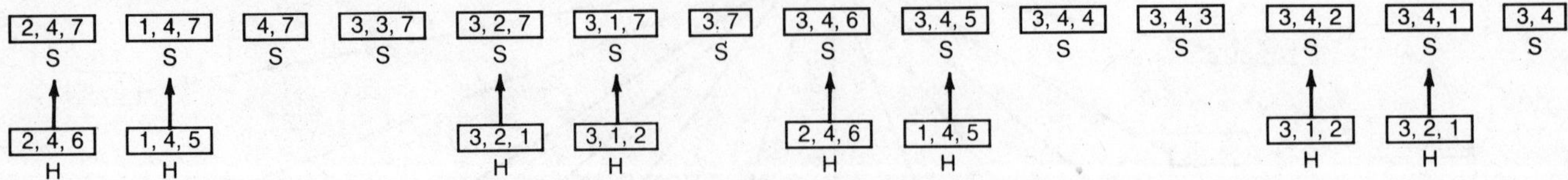

5. First move from [3, 5, 6] could leave:

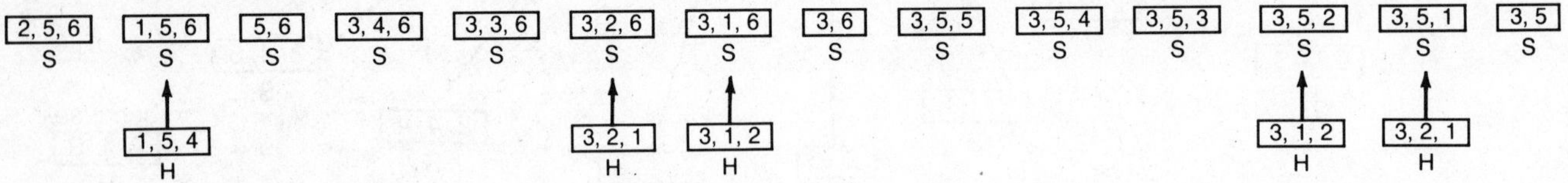

6. [3, 8, 10] → [2, 8, 10] H

First move from [3, 8, 11] could leave:

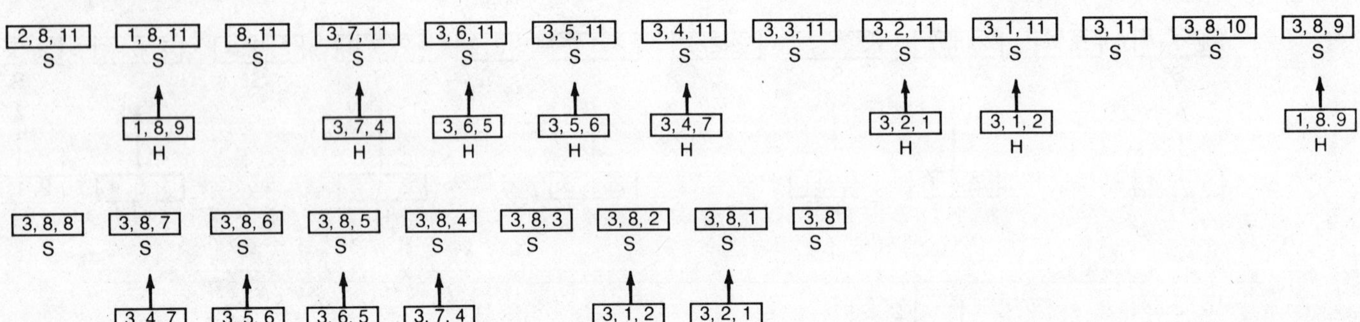

7. [4, 7, 9] → [4, 7, 3] H   [4, 7, 10] → [4, 7, 3] H   [4, 7, 11] → [4, 7, 3] H

8. 4, 8, 11 → 3, 8, 11 H

First move from 4, 8, 12 could leave:

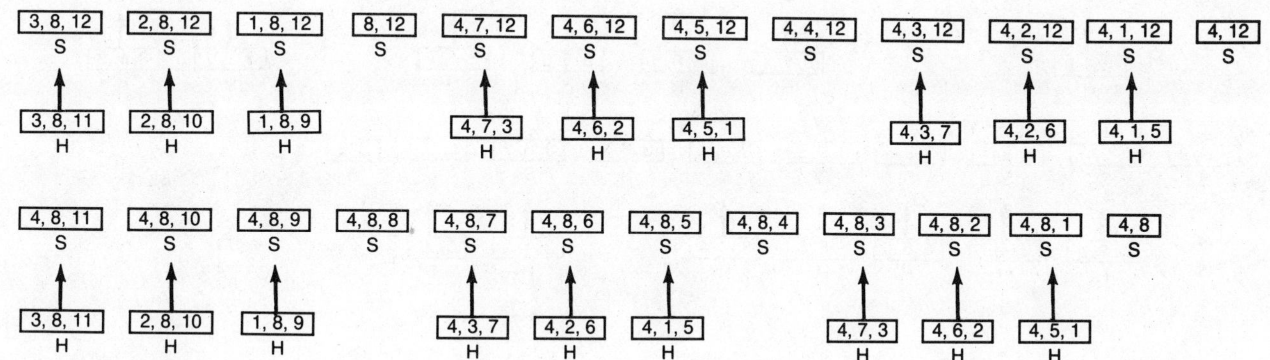

9. 5, 8, 11 → 3, 8, 11 H   5, 8, 12 → 4, 8, 12 H

First move from 5, 8, 13 could leave:

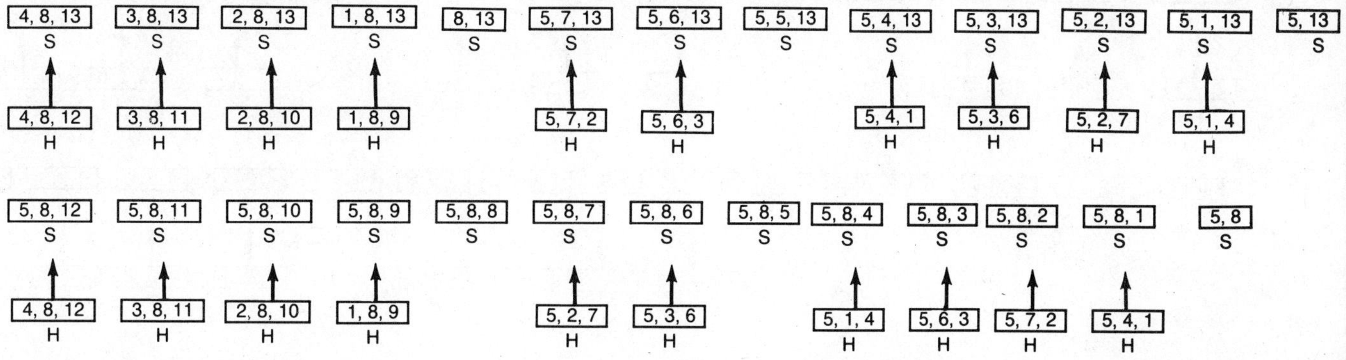

Explanation of Key to L64

1. 2, 9, 10 → 2, 8, 10 H

First move from 2, 9, 11 could leave:

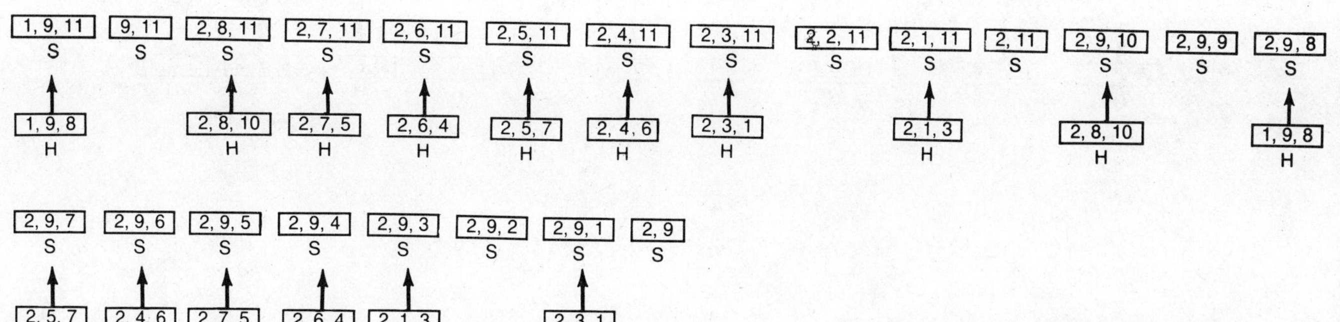

2. First move from [3, 9, 10] could leave:

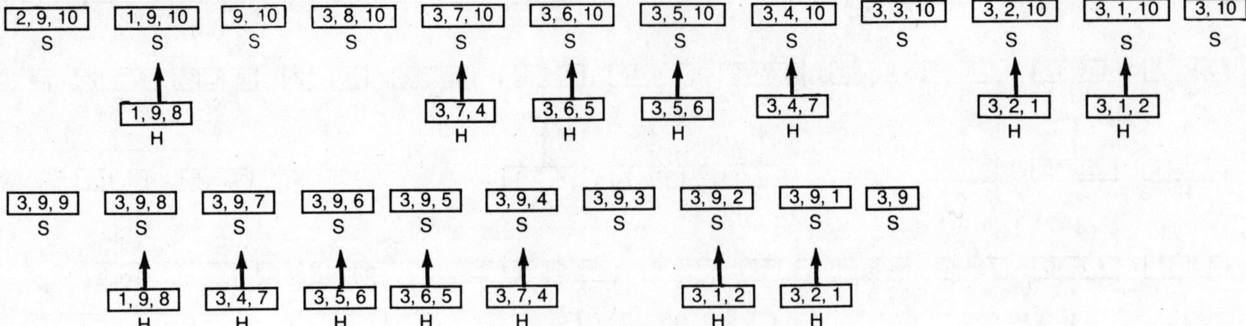

3. 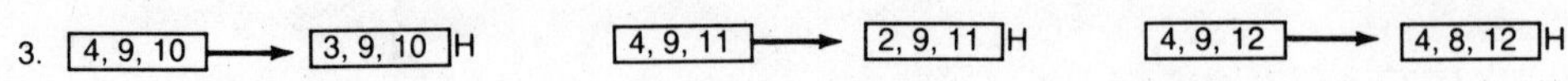

First move from [4, 9, 13] could leave:

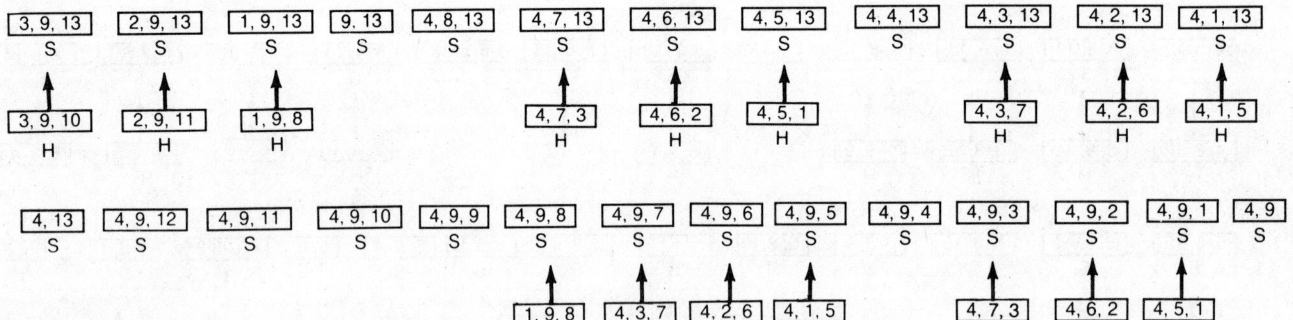

4. [5, 9, 10] → [3, 9, 10] H [5, 9, 11] → [2, 9, 11] H

First move from [5, 9, 12] could leave:

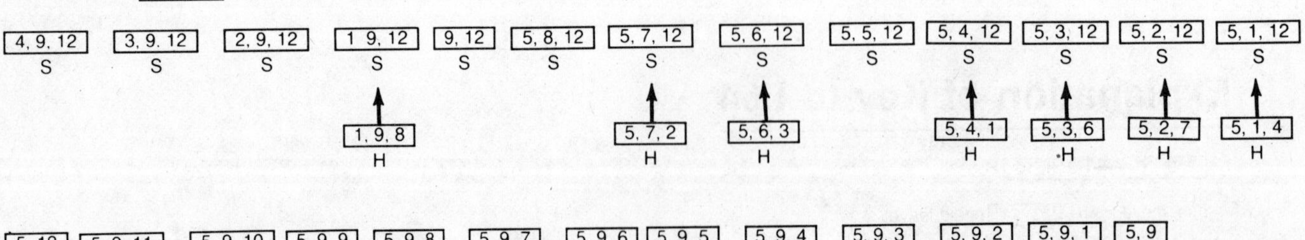

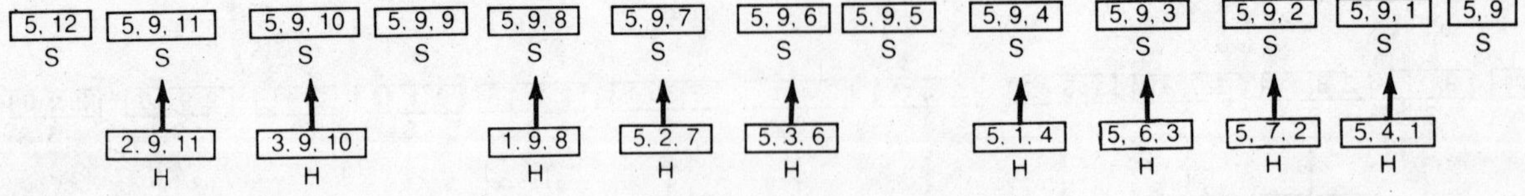

ACTIVITY 59
Composition 9

Materials Needed
Teacher: Colored chalk
Students: Pencils

This activity is based on Worksheets L65 and L66.

Ask the class to turn to Worksheet L65 and look at the arrow picture on the top left.

T: What is the blue arrow for?
What is the red arrow for?

As students respond, copy the arrow diagram and key arrows on the board:

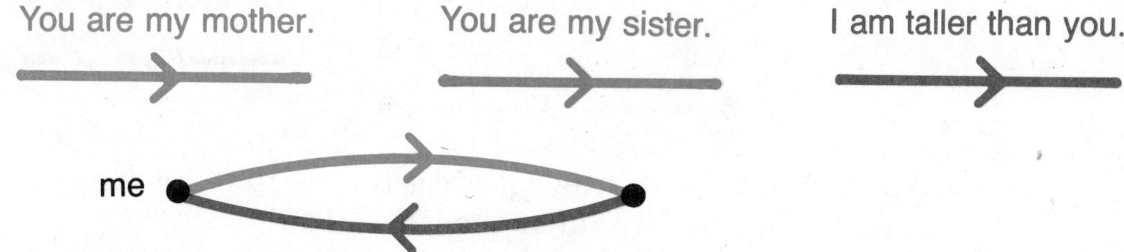

T: What is the message given by the picture?
S: *"You are my mother and you are taller than I am."*
S: *"My mother is taller than I am."*
S: *"I am shorter than my mother."*
T: You are all correct. Write your messages below the picture, and try to find the other seven messages.

Walk among the students as they work. Accept any phrasing of messages if they are correct, no matter how convoluted. Also accept "grandmother," even though "mother's mother" or "maternal grandmother" would be more accurate.

When some of the students have finished Worksheet L65, direct the class to put aside the worksheets. Add these letters to your key arrows on the board:

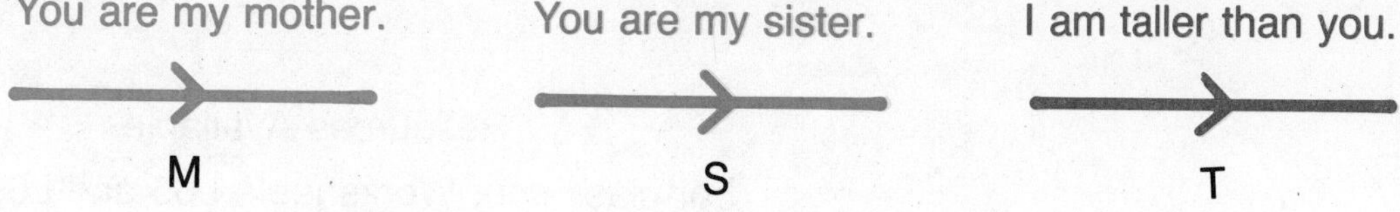

T: Now we're going to send some messages of a different kind using these three relations.

59

Draw this arrow picture on the board:

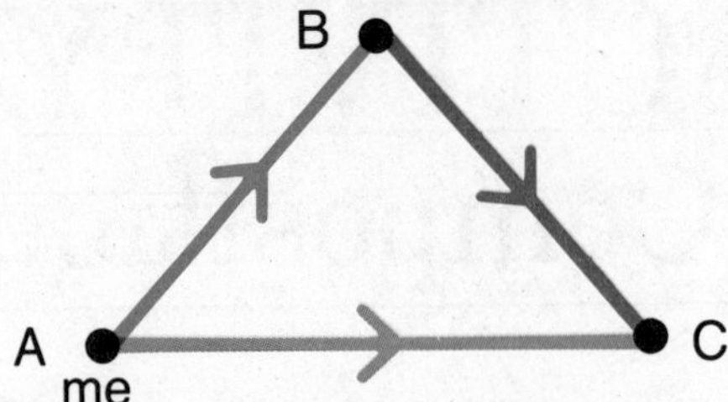

As you draw the orange arrow, ask:

T: What could the orange arrow be for?

S: *The relation $S \circ T$.*

T: That's right, but say it in words.

S: *"You are taller than my sister."*

S: *No. If I am A, then my sister is B. If you are C, then my sister is saying to you, "I am taller than you."*

Let the class discuss this until it is agreed that the orange arrow could be for "my sister is taller than you" or "you are shorter than my sister." Write the chosen formulation below the orange arrow.

Then draw the following diagram on the board:

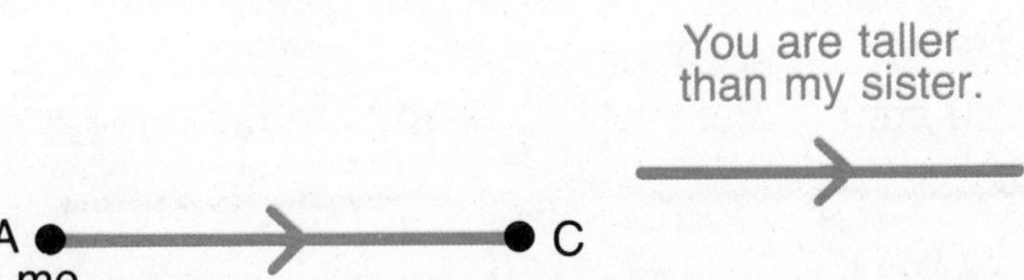

T: Will someone please draw colored arrows so that the orange arrow could be for "you are taller than my sister"?

Discuss responses until the diagram agreed on is as below:

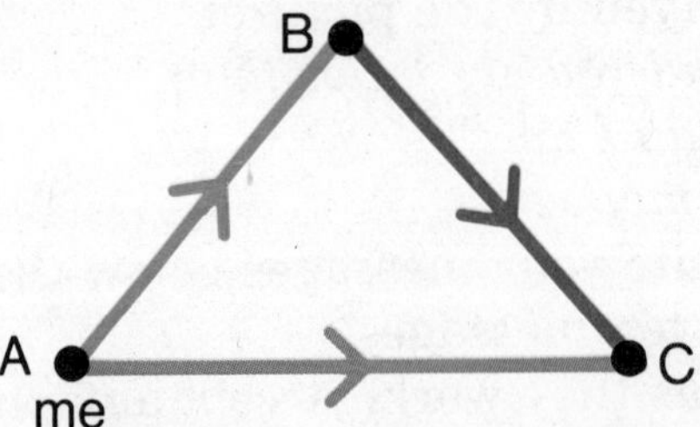

Point out how this diagram differs from the previous one.

For the remaining time, let students finish Worksheet L65 and start work on Worksheet L66.

Resources Available

For class use: Worksheets L65 and L66

For out-of-class use: Any H-worksheet up through H90

ACTIVITY 60
Ternary Abacus 2

Materials Needed
Teacher: Minicomputer checkers and colored chalk
Students: None

If your chalkboard is magnet-sensitive, draw this abacus on it;

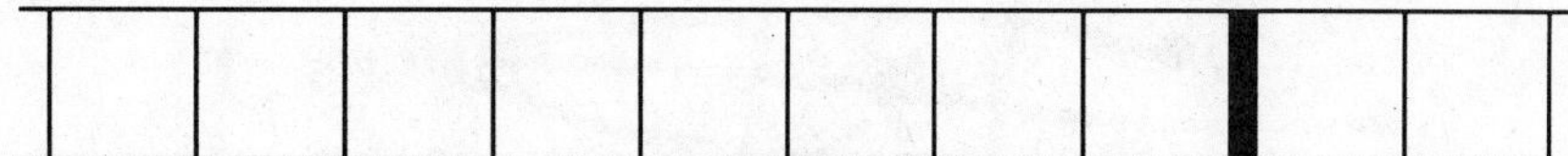

otherwise, follow the suggestion at the beginning of Activity 30.

T: What was the rule of the ternary abacus—the three-abacus?
S: *Three checkers on a square show the same number as one checker on the next square to the left.*
T: Very good.
Write the rule on the board. Then quickly review the ternary abacus by asking students to place checkers to show 25, 75, 225, etc.

2,187	729	243	81	27	9	3	1			
					••	••	•			= 25
				••	••	•				= 75
			••	••	•					= 225

Next draw two strings, one containing seven dots, the other containing three, as follows:

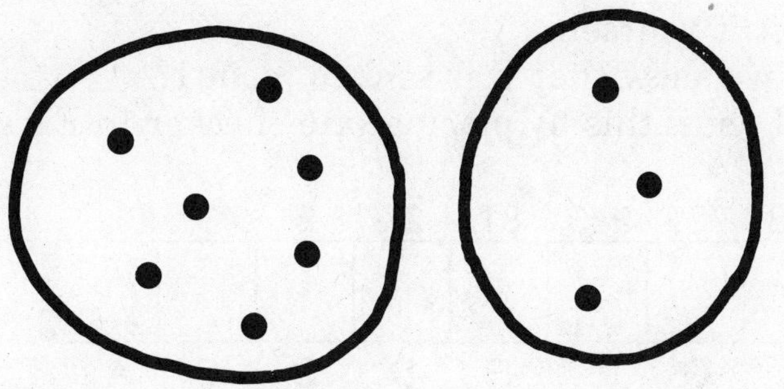

T: Suppose that a student helper group is formed, involving seven students. Let's give the students the code names A, B, C, and so on up through G.

Label the seven dots in the string on the left.

T: Also suppose that there are three special study rooms where the student helpers can help other students with their lessons during study periods. Let's give the three rooms the names 0, 1, 2.

Label the three dots in the string on the right.

T: The principal tells the student helpers which rooms to go to by using an arrow picture. One day she makes this assignment.

Draw these arrows:

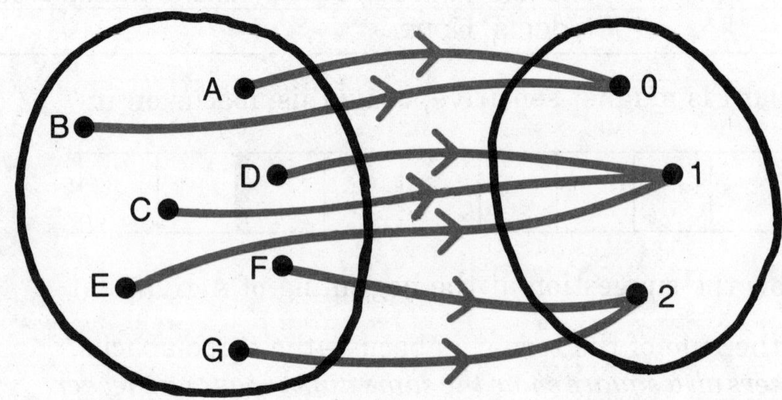

T: To which study room is E sent? (room 1)
Which helpers are sent to Room 2? (F and G)

Each day, the principal makes a new assignment. Some days she sends more helpers to one room than another, depending on how much help will be needed in the rooms. But it is a lot of bother to draw arrow diagrams to make assignments. Because there are three study rooms, she decides to use the ternary abacus to announce each day's assignment. How do you think she can use the abacus to do this?

A student will probably suggest labeling the squares of the abacus with the helpers' code names:

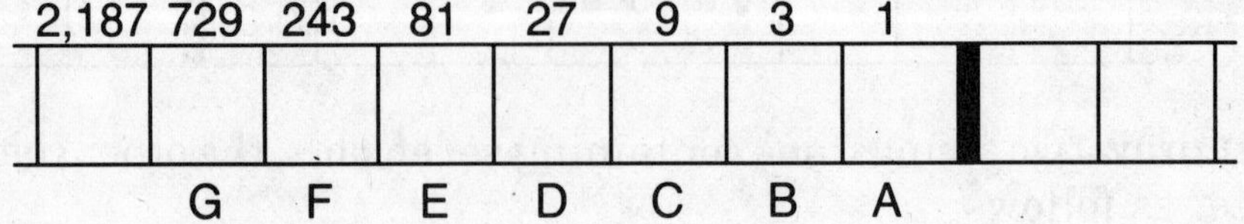

If not, suggest it yourself.

T: How can we show that E is sent to room 1?

Let a student show this by placing **one** checker in E's square.

2,187 729 243 81 27 9 3 1

G F E D C B A

In the same manner, let students place checkers for all the assignments.

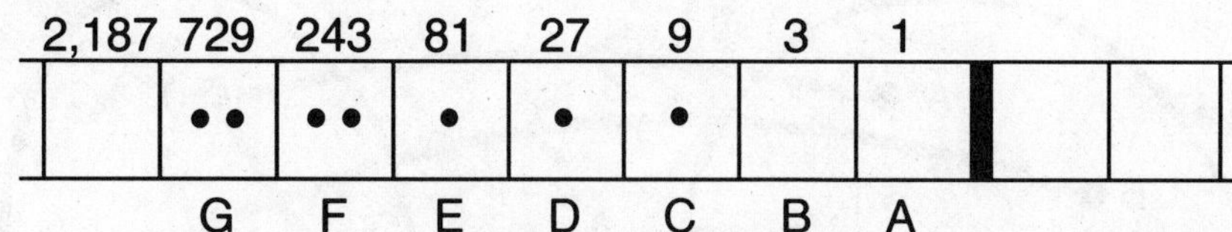

T: The principal could send this abacus message to the seven student helpers to give them their assignments for the day. But it is even more bother to draw the abacus than to draw the arrow picture. So she decided simply to send the number shown on the abacus. What number is on this abacus?

S: *2,061.*

T: Let's check:

$$
\begin{array}{r}
729 \\
729 \\
243 \\
243 \\
81 \\
27 \\
+ \quad 9 \\
\hline
2{,}061
\end{array}
$$

So the principal sends this message to the seven student helpers:

2,061 code 3

Erase the arrows in the arrow picture.

T: The next day the principal sent this message:

471 code 3

Please decode the message and draw the arrow picture to show the room assignments.

First ask a student to show 471 on the abacus.

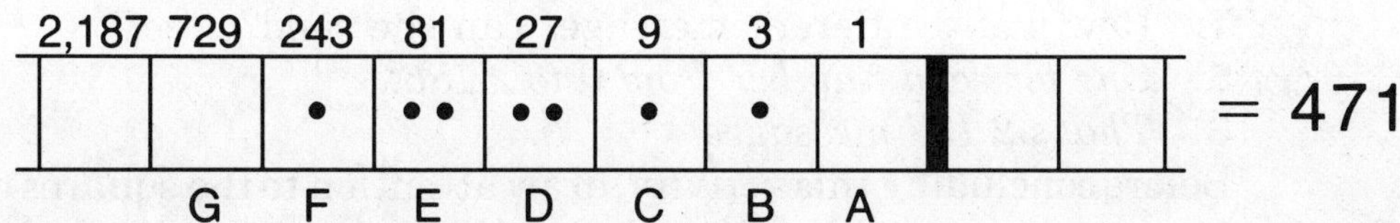

T: Good. To which room is C sent? (room 1)
To which room will F go? (room 1)
Where will G go? (room 0)

And so on. Ask students to draw arrows to show these assignments as they are mentioned.

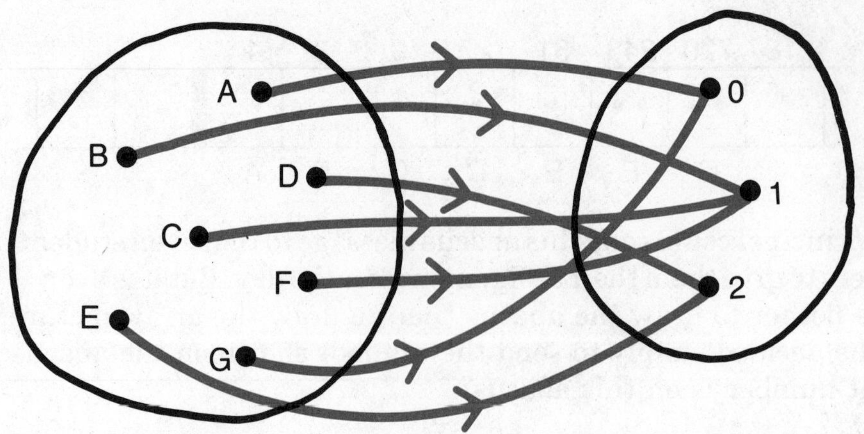

T: How many different messages can the principal send to the student helpers? What is the largest number she can send?
Let a student show this number on the abacus:

2,187	729	243	81	27	9	3	1	‖		
	••	••	••	••	••	••	••	‖		
	G	F	E	D	C	B	A			

S: *Every helper goes to room 2.*
If students suggest a quick way to determine this number, follow their suggestion. If not, put an extra checker on the 1-square.

2,187	729	243	81	27	9	3	1	‖		
	••	••	••	••	••	••	•••	‖		
	G	F	E	D	C	B	A			

In Activity 54 this was found to be the number 2,187 (by making a series of robot moves). Thus, the largest number the principal can send is 2,187 − 1 = 2,186.
T: What is the smallest number she can send?
S: *The number telling everybody to help in room 0.*
S: *The smallest number is 0.*
T: How many different messages can she send?
S: *One for each number from 0 to 2,186.*
S: *That's 2,187 messages.*
Before concluding this activity, draw attention to the squares on the ternary abacus to the right of the bar by placing a checker as follows:

2,187	729	243	81	27	9	3	1	‖		
								‖	•	
	G	F	E	D	C	B	A			

T: What is this number? $\left(\frac{1}{3}\right)$ Why?

If no student can explain this answer, place two more checkers in this square and let a volunteer make a robot move.

S: *The number is $\frac{1}{3}$ because $3 \times \frac{1}{3}$ is 1.*

Continue this line of questioning to establish that the second square has value $\frac{1}{9}$ and the third $\frac{1}{27}$.

Conclude the activity by posing several kinds of problems, as follows.

1. What number is on the ternary abacus?

2,187	729	243	81	27	9	3	1	$\frac{1}{3}$	$\frac{1}{9}$	
		•		••					••	$= 298\frac{2}{9}$

2. Show $1{,}173\frac{4}{9}$ on the ternary abacus. Don't use more than two checkers in a square.

2,187	729	243	81	27	9	3	1	$\frac{1}{3}$	$\frac{1}{9}$	
	•	•	••	•	•	•		•	•	$= 1{,}173\frac{4}{9}$

Resources Available

For class use: Worksheets L67 and L68

For out-of-class use: Any H-worksheet up through H90

ACTIVITIES 61 and 62
Nim Analysis 5

Materials Needed
Teacher: Chalk, Minicomputer checkers
Students: Paper and pencils

T: Today we're finally going to find out how to play 3-pile Nim. Remember that in the worksheets at the end of our last Nim analysis you discovered quite a number of 3-pile hopeless positions. Here they are.

Write the following list on the board:

1. [2, 4, 6]
2. [2, 5, 7]
3. [2, 8, 10]
4. [3, 4, 7]
5. [3, 5, 6]
6. [3, 8, 11]
7. [4, 8, 12]
8. [5, 8, 13]
9. [2, 9, 11]
10. [3, 9, 10]
11. [4, 9, 13]
12. [5, 9, 12]
13. [1, even number, next odd number]

T: Some of these make it look as though the numbers of checkers in two of the piles have to add up to the numbers of checkers in the third pile. But remember that we showed that wasn't true in an earlier lesson: [2, 3, 5] is *not* a hopeless position because the next player can move to [2, 3, 1], which *is* a hopeless position. Which of these hopeless positions I've listed do *not* involve three numbers where two of them add up to the third?

S: *Positions 5, 10, and 12.*

T: Let's look at them more closely. I'll now give you the crucial clue that will help us solve this problem. Show *on the binary abacus* the number of checkers in each pile.

If your chalkboard is magnet-sensitive, draw the following on it, otherwise, use the top row of your Minicomputer boards, as suggested in Activity 30.

16	8	4	2	1

T: Let's look at position 5. Who can show 3 on the binary abacus?

S:

16 8 4 2 1

Proceed similarly for the other two piles in position 5, using Minicomputer checkers of different colors to represent the numbers of checkers in the three piles.

position 5: 16 8 4 2 1

T: Do the same thing for positions 10 and 12 on your papers.

After a couple of minutes, ask a volunteer to record his or her work on the board:

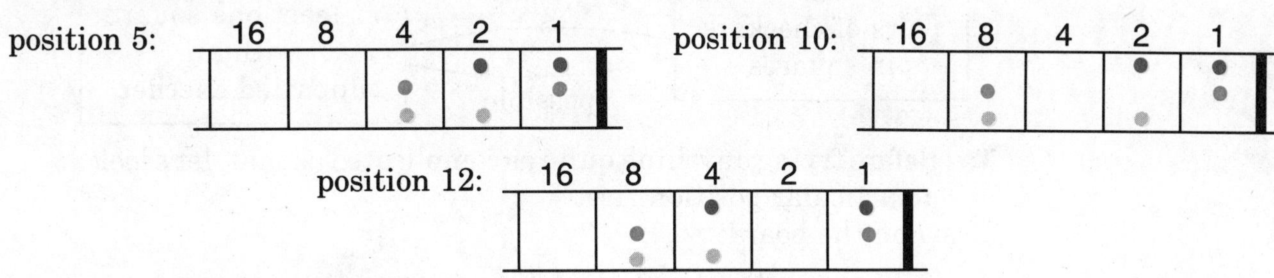

T: Look at these abacuses. What do you think has to be true for a hopeless position?

S: *Pairs of checkers in the squares.*

T: Let's see if that's true for some of these other hopeless positions.

Assign pairs of students to work on designated positions chosen from positions 1, 2, 3, 4, 6, 7, 8, 9, and 11. Let each pair report the result of its work.

T: Well, it certainly seems to work for positions 1 through 12. Let's think about position 13. What does an even number look like on the binary abacus if you use at most one checker in each square?

S: *It has no checker in the 1-square.*

T: Right. What does an odd number look like on the binary abacus if you use at most one checker in each square?

S: *It has exactly one checker in the 1-square and perhaps some other checkers in other squares.*

T: If you have an even number on the binary abacus, what do you have to do to change it into the next odd number?

S: *Put a checker on the 1-square.*

T: So position 13 looks like this.

Draw on the board:

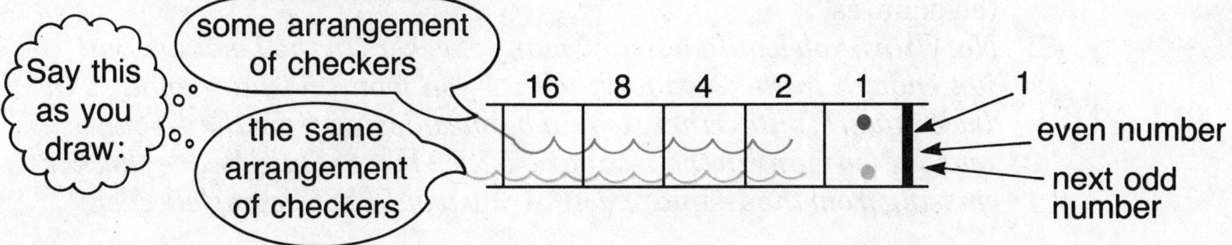

T: Does this obey the rule "pairs of checkers in the squares?"

S: *Yes. Except for the checker in the 1-square for the odd number, the arrangements of checkers for the even number and the odd number are exactly the same. So wherever there are checkers outside the 1-square they must be in pairs. In the 1-square, the checker for the 1-pile matches the checker from the odd number.*

T: So the rule works for all the hopeless positions we have found. I can tell you that in fact it works all the time. But to see why, we'll have to show two things:

- If you make a move from a position that obeys the rule, then you *always* reach a position that does not obey the rule.
- From any position that does not obey the rule it is always *possible* to move into a position that does obey the rule.

Write on the board:

WE MUST SHOW:

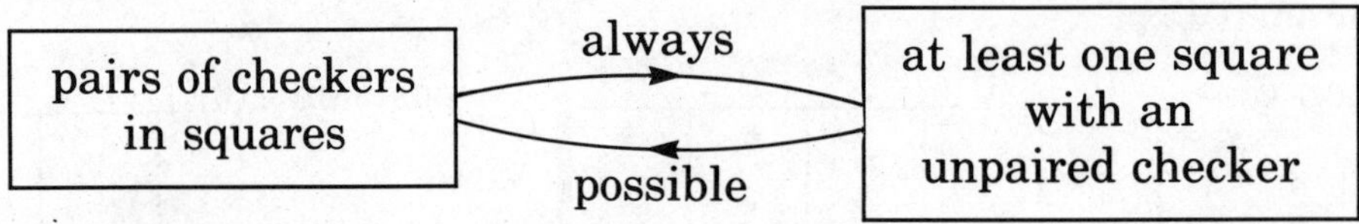

T: Before trying anything quite as complicated as that, let's look at a particular position first.

Draw on the board:

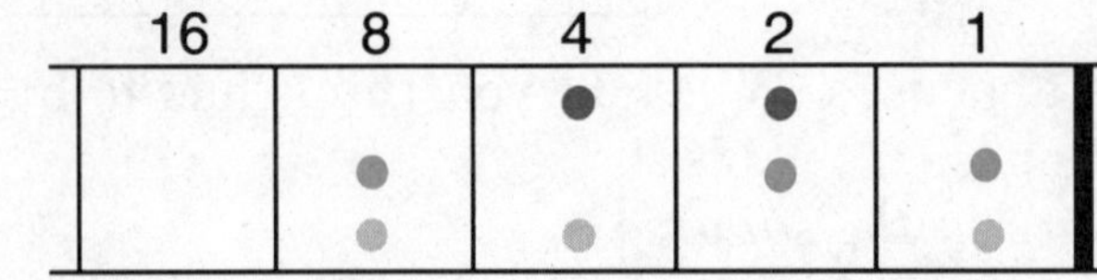

T: What position is this?

S: *6, 11, 13* .

T: Notice that it's a "pairs of checkers in the squares" position. Let's show that, no matter what the next player does, it will always result in at least one square with an unpaired checker. Let's say the next player picks up some number of checkers from the 6-pile. How many checkers could be left in that pile?

S: *5, 4, 3, 2, 1, or 0 .*

T: Who would like to show these on the binary abacus?

Let volunteers do this on separate drawings on the board:

5: 4: 3:

2: 1: 0:

T: Could I replace 6 on this binary abacus (point to your drawing *) by any of these numbers and still have pairs of checkers in the squares?

S: *No. With 5 you would have too many checkers in the 1-square and not enough in the 2-square; with 4 you wouldn't have enough in the 2-square; with 3 there would be one missing from the 4-square and one too many in the 1-square; with 2 there would be one checker missing from the 4-square; with 1 you would be missing checkers*

in the 4-square and the 2-square and have one too many in the 1-square; and with 0 you would be missing checkers in the 4-square and the 2-square.

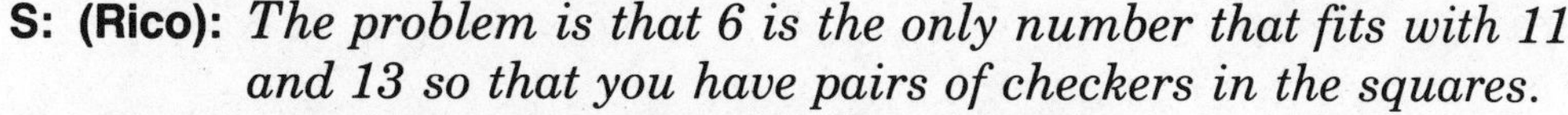

S: (Rico): *The problem is that 6 is the only number that fits with 11 and 13 so that you have pairs of checkers in the squares.*

T: That's very important, Rico. Look at this.

Erase the checkers for 6 on the binary abacus (*).

16	8	4	2	1
	●●	●	●	●●

T: Here are the 11-pile and the 13-pile. We want a third pile to fit with them so that we have pairs of checkers in the squares. Where *must* we put checkers?

S: *Here and here:*

16	8	4	2	1
	●●	●●	●●	●●

T: Could we put checkers anywhere else as well?

S: *No; they would be unpaired.*

If anyone suggests putting additional *pairs* of checkers on the abacus in the course of representing the number of checkers in the proposed third pile, explicitly state the assumption in the "pairs of checkers in the squares" rule that the size of each pile is represented on the abacus using at most one checker in each square.

S: *That works all the time. If you've got two numbers on the binary abacus, there's only one way to put a third number on so that you have pairs of checkers in the squares.*

T: So, if you start with three numbers where you have pairs of checkers in the squares and you alter *one* of the numbers, it obviously ends up not being the only number that fits with the other two. In other words, we've shown this. (Point to the arrow labeled **always** in the "we must show" diagram.) Now let's show the other half. We'll start with an example again.

Draw on the board:

16	8	4	2	1
	●●	●●●	●●	●

T: What position is this?

S: *7, 12, 14* .

T: Do we have pairs of checkers in the squares?

S: *No; there are unpaired checkers in the 4-square and the 1-square.*

T: Now remember that to make a move we must pick up some checkers from one of the piles; that is, we must *decrease* one of the numbers shown on this abacus. Look at the 4-square. How could we make it contain a pair of checkers?

61
62

S: *Take off one of the checkers.*
T: Which one?
S: *It doesn't matter. Let's say the top one.*
Draw on the board:

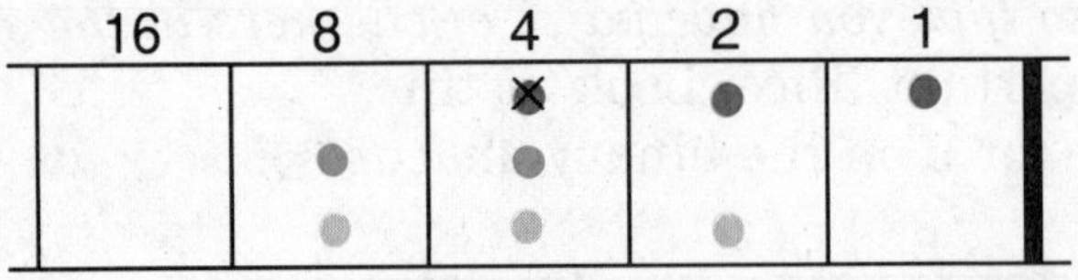

16 8 4 2 1

T: That means you've decided to decrease the 7-pile. The other place where we have an unpaired checker is in the 1-square. What should we do to the top number to make sure we only have pairs of checkers in the squares?
S: *Put another checker in the 1-square.*
T: That would give us two checkers in the 1-square for the top number, and we're supposed to show each number on the abacus with at most one checker in each square. Remember that if there are *no* checkers in a square it would be true that the checkers in the square are in pairs.
S: *Take that checker off the 1-square.*
Draw on the board:

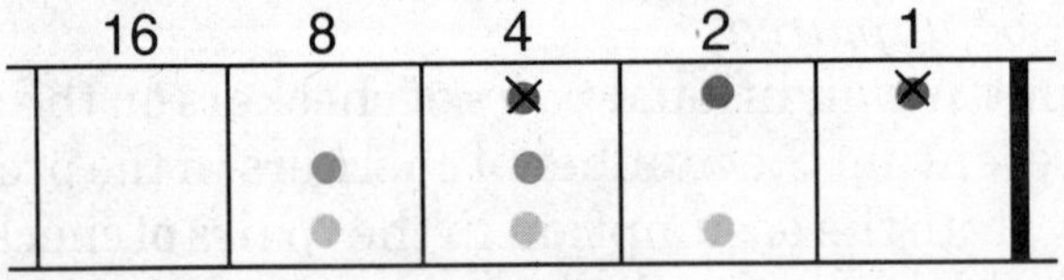

16 8 4 2 1

T: Now do we have pairs of checkers in the squares?
S: *Yes.*
T: So what have we shown you can do to get from [7, 12, 14] to a position with pairs of checkers in the squares?
S: *Take 5 off the 7-pile, leaving [2, 12, 14].*
Proceed similarly with the other two possible moves:

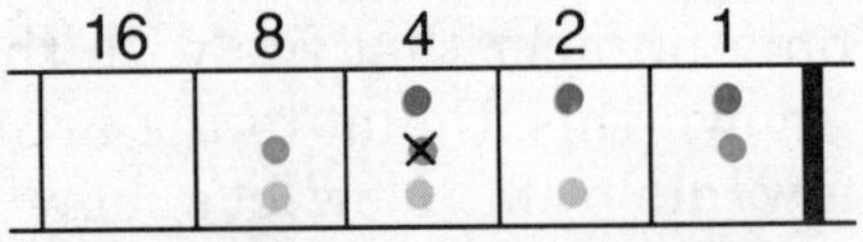

16 8 4 2 1

[7, 12, 14] → [7, 9, 14]

16 8 4 2 1

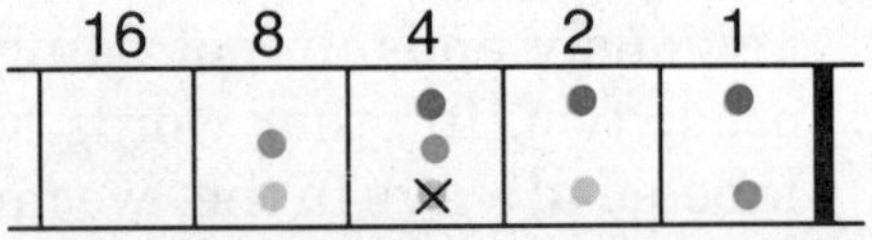

[7, 12, 14] → [7, 12, 11]

Draw the following on the board:

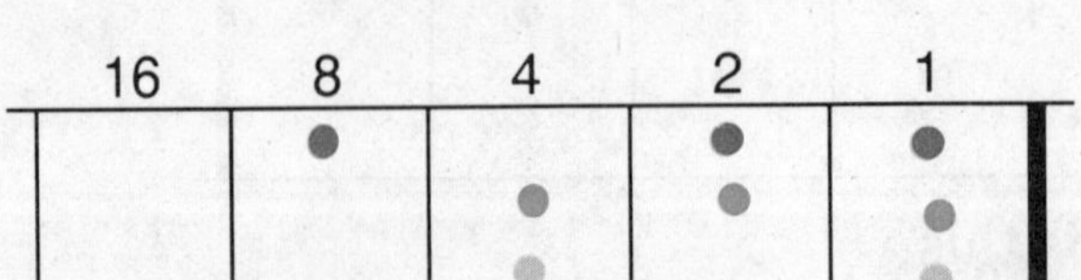

16 8 4 2 1

T: What position is this?
S: *[11, 7, 5].*
T: It obviously doesn't have pairs of checkers in the squares. What could we do about the unpaired checker in the 8-square?
S: *Take it off.*
S: *Or you could put another one on.*

T: Suppose we put another checker in the 8-square for one of the numbers. We then have to move on and try to pair up all the other checkers. Remember that we're supposed to decrease a pile. We would have added 8 by putting on the extra checker. Could we take off more than 8 by removing one checker from some or all of the other squares?

S: *No. The most you could take off is one from each square, and $4 + 2 + 1 = 7$, which is less than 8.*

T: Remember we saw that once on the binary abacus: if you have one checker in each square up to a certain value and you add one more checker in the 1-square, that shows the same number as one checker in the next square to the left.

Draw on the board:

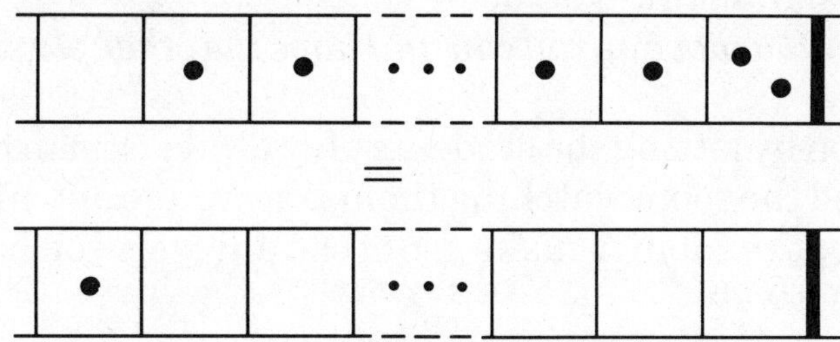

T: So one checker on the binary abacus is worth one more than one checker on each square to the right, all the way to the bar. This means that to make sure we are decreasing a pile we've got to *take off* the highest-value unpaired checker. Then we know that no matter how many smaller-value squares we *add* checkers to, we won't be adding more than we've already taken off. So what move should we make here?

S:

16 8 4 2 1

11, 7, 5 to *2, 7, 5*

T: Suppose we have some other position where there are unpaired checkers. What should we do so that we end up with pairs of checkers in the squares?

S: *Take off the highest-value unpaired checker. Then go through the rest of that row on the abacus, taking off or putting on checkers so that you have pairs of checkers in the squares.*

T: That's fine. So we've now shown this. (Point to the "possible" arrow in your "we must show" diagram.) That means we know how to play from any position where we have at least one square with an unpaired checker. Each time *we* play we can move to a position with pairs of checkers in the squares. Each time our opponent plays he or she *has* to move back to a position with at least one unpaired checker. What's going to happen eventually?

S: *Someone's going to pick up the last checker in one of the piles.*

T: If the other player does that, what can you say about the two piles that are left?

S: *They'll be unequal because the other player can only move to a position with at least one unpaired checker.*

T: So we can then even up the piles, and the other player is bound to lose. On the other hand, if *we* pick up the last checker in one of the three piles and we've been playing correctly, what can you say about the two piles that are left?

S: *They'll be equal, so the other player's bound to lose.*

T: That shows that any position with at least one unpaired checker is a safe position and also that the positions with pairs of checkers in squares are hopeless positions. Suppose you're playing 3-pile Nim, it's your turn to start, and you're faced with a hopeless position. What should you do?

S: *Make as small a move as you can and hope the other player makes a mistake!*

Finish the lesson by letting the students play 3-pile Nim in pairs. As you walk around the room watching them, encourage any individuals you see playing at random to make use of the analysis you have just completed collectively.

Resources Available

For out-of-class use: Any H-Worksheet up through H93

ACTIVITIES 63 and 64
Random Art 1

Materials Needed
Teacher: Colored chalk, one red marble, one blue marble
Students: Colored pencils

T: Today I want to tell you a story about a friend of mine named Tom. One of Tom's interests is painting. But instead of portraits or landscapes, Tom paints random pictures of red and blue squares. Here's what he does.

Draw the following picture on the board:

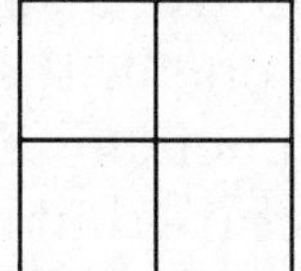

T: He starts by drawing this outline. Then he takes a red marble and a blue marble and shakes them in his cupped hands. Without looking, he puts his hands behind his back and chooses one marble to bring forward.

With the help of two marbles, act out this part of the story as you tell it. For the sake of this description we suppose that you choose the red marble.

T: We got the red marble, so Tom would paint the first square (in the lower right hand corner) red.

Color the lower right-hand square so that it agrees with the color of the marble you choose.

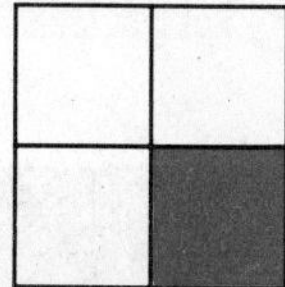

T: After he's colored the first square, Tom puts both marbles back in his hands, shakes them, and puts them behind his back. He again chooses one marble to bring forward. He colors the next square with the color of the marble he chooses.

Repeat the shaking and drawing three more times and color your picture according to the results. Color the small squares in the following order:

4th	3rd
2nd	1st

For example, you might arrive at the following coloring:

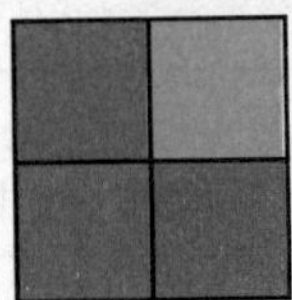

T: How many different four-square pictures do you think Tom could paint if he paints each square either red or blue?

Record the estimates in one corner of the board for future reference. Ask the students to turn to Worksheet L69.

T: Color as many of the different pictures that Tom could paint as you can.

While the students are working independently on this problem, draw 19 more picture outlines on the board. One at a time, ask students to reproduce on the board one of the colored pictures from their worksheets. Each time a student goes to the board, ask him or her to try to avoid redrawing a picture that is already there, but do not worry for the moment if there are some duplications.

For the sake of this description, let us suppose that the pictures drawn by the students are as follows:

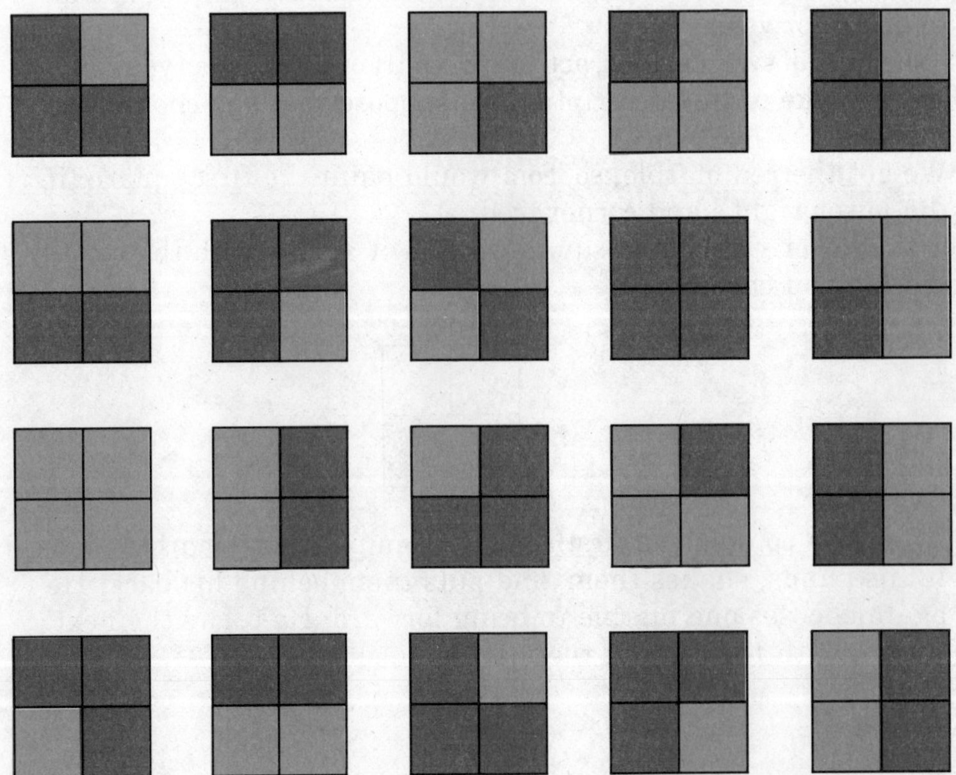

T: How good were your estimates of the number of different pictures?
Let the students discuss this topic. The students might see that there are some duplicates on the board (for example, 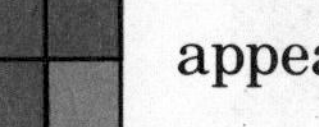 appears twice in the above display of pictures). They might decide that estimates in the region of 15 to 20 are close to the actual number of pictures. In any case, lead the discussion to the conclusion that what is needed is a systematic way of checking that we have all the different pictures with no duplicates.

T: I have an idea for a code that will help us determine how many different pictures Tom could paint; it will also show up duplicates if we have any. Watch as I number the pictures and see if you can discover my code.

Slowly number the pictures one by one according to this code:

> Treat each picture as the ones' board of a Minicomputer. Red squares should be treated as though they contained one regular checker; blue squares should be treated as though they are empty.

For example:

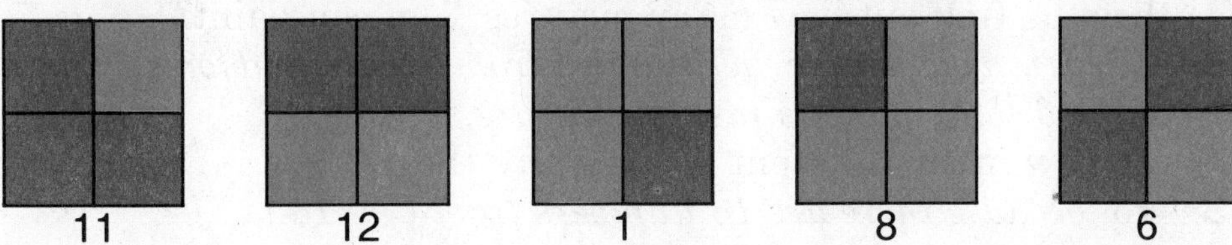

After you have numbered two or three of the pictures, let students try to guess what the next picture will be numbered, but do not let them give away your code. If after nine or ten pictures have been numbered some students still have not discovered the code, give the following hint:

T: Think about the Minicomputer.

Continue numbering the pictures and letting students guess the numbers. When only a few pictures are left without numbers, ask a student to explain the code. Then all the students will have a chance to try out the code on the last few pictures.

With all the previous pictures numbered, the board will look like this:

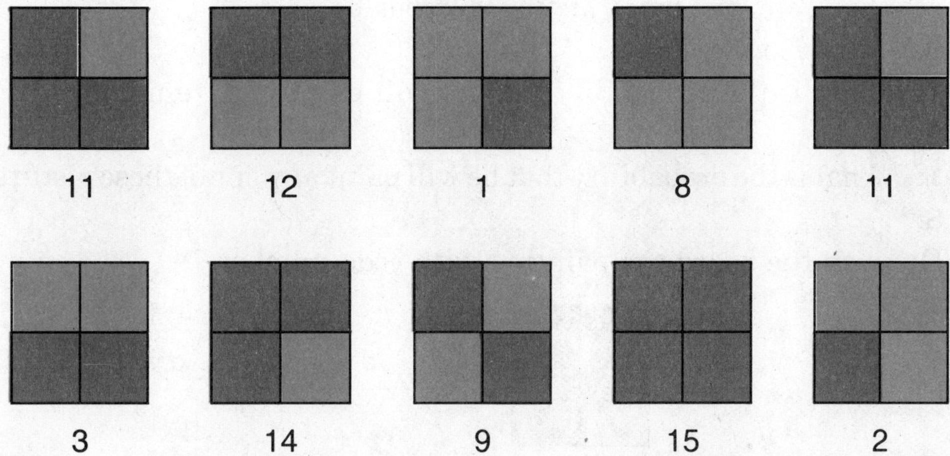

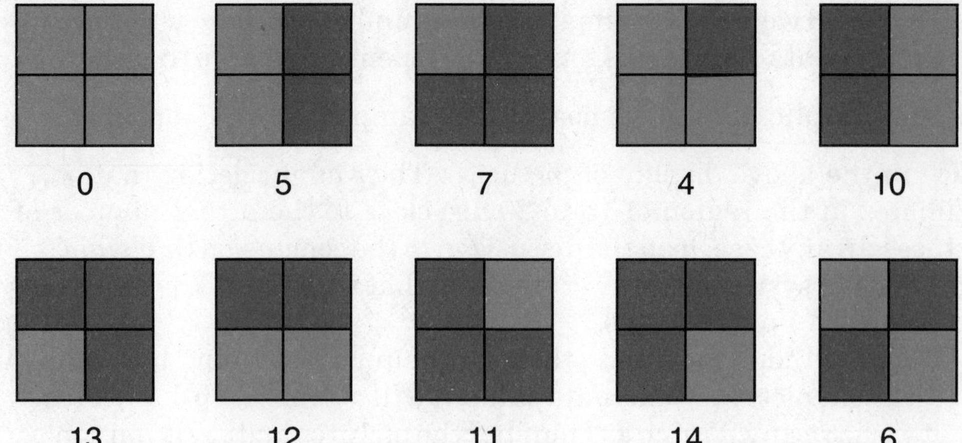

T: What is the largest number we can give to one of Tom's pictures?
S: *15: the picture with all four squares painted red.*
T: What is the smallest number?
S: *0: the picture with all four squares painted blue.*
T: Do you think there is a picture for each of the numbers between 0 and 15? (yes) How does this code help us to check for duplicates? (Pictures with the same number are duplicates.) How does this code help us find out how many pictures Tom can paint?
S: *There is a picture for each number from 0 to 15, and for each number from 0 to 15 there is just one picture.*
T: So how many different pictures are there?
S: *16, because there are 16 numbers from 0 to 15.*
T: Tom enjoys painting, but he also likes to sell his pictures. He knows that he can expect to get a better price for rare pictures than for those that are more common. What do you think a rare painting would be?

Let the class discuss what the word *rare* means in this context and how Tom should decide which of the 16 possible pictures could be called rare. Students might suggest that picture number 0 or 15 is rare because it is the smallest or largest number possible. Other students might suggest that number 8 is not rare because it is a lot like picture numbers 1, 2, and 4. Accept any comments and then proceed with the following discussion, which picks up the latter idea.

T: Suppose Tom is going to paint a picture. He uses the red and blue marbles to decide how to color each square. What is the probability that Tom will paint picture number 6?
S: *$\frac{1}{16}$ (or 1 out of 16).*
T: What is the probability that he will paint picture number 12?
S: *$\frac{1}{16}$.*
T: What is the probability that he will paint any one of these pictures?
S: *$\frac{1}{16}$.*

Draw on the board the painting with code number 7:

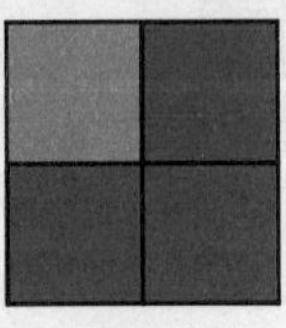

T: One day Tom sold picture number 7 to a man who thought he was buying a one-of-a-kind painting. What do you think?

Let the students react; someone might suggest that by turning the painting it could also be number 11 or number 13 or number 14. If this does not happen, turn the painting yourself and let the students note the different possibilities.

S: *If you turn number 7 you can make number 11 or number 13 or number 14. They are really all the same painting.*

List these four numbers in a box on the board: [7, 11, 13, 14].

T: What is the probability that Tom will paint a picture with one of these numbers?

S: *4 out of 16, or $\frac{1}{4}$.*

Write $\frac{1}{4}$ next to the boxed-in list of numbers.

Draw on the board the painting with code number 8:

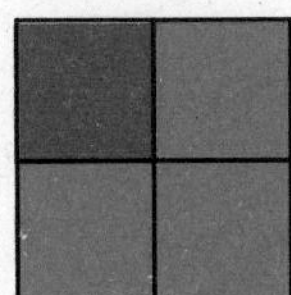

T: Suppose the man had bought picture number 8. Do you think that it is a one-of-a-kind painting?

S: *No, it is the same as number 2 and number 1 and number 4. Just turn it.*

List these four numbers in a second box on the board.

T: What is the probability that Tom will paint a picture with one of these four numbers?

S: $\frac{1}{4}$.

Write $\frac{1}{4}$ next to the second boxed-in list of numbers.

7, 11, 13, 14	$\frac{1}{4}$
1, 2, 4, 8	$\frac{1}{4}$

T: What do you think about number 0?

S: *It's one of a kind.*

Continue in this way, letting the students classify the pictures and give the probabilities for each classification. The final results should be as follows:

7, 11, 13, 14	$\frac{1}{4}$	0	$\frac{1}{16}$
1, 2, 4, 8	$\frac{1}{4}$	15	$\frac{1}{16}$
3, 5, 10, 12	$\frac{1}{4}$	6, 9	$\frac{1}{8}$

T: Suppose Tom has painted 160 pictures using his red and blue marbles to decide the colors of the squares. About how many would be like number 7? (11, 13, and 14)

S: *40.*

Repeat this question for each classification. For your information, answers are given in parentheses.

7, 11, 13, 14	$\frac{1}{4}$	(40)	0	$\frac{1}{16}$	(10)
1, 2, 4, 8	$\frac{1}{4}$	(40)	15	$\frac{1}{16}$	(10)
3, 5, 10, 12	$\frac{1}{4}$	(40)	6, 9	$\frac{1}{8}$	(20)

T: Which pictures are the rarest? (0 and 15)
Which are the most common? (1, 3, 7, and their likes)

T: Tom decided to price his pictures according to how rare they are. He decided to charge 20 dollars each for the rarest pictures, numbers 0 and 15. How much should he charge for a picture with code number 7, 11, 13, or 14?

S: *5 dollars. There are four alike and* $\frac{1}{4} \times 20 = 5$.

T: How much should he charge for number 3, 5, 10, or 12 and for number 1, 2, 4, or 8? (5 dollars each) How much should he charge for a picture with code number 6 or 9?

S: *10 dollars. There are two alike, and* $\frac{1}{2} \times 20 = 10$.

T: Tom had soon painted and sold at least one of each kind of his four-square pictures. He was getting tired of these pictures, and his customers were no longer interested in this kind of painting because they did not want to have the same paintings as other people. Tom decided to try something new. This time he would start with a square divided into nine smaller squares.

Draw this outline on the board:

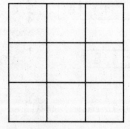

T: As before, Tom decided to use his red and blue marbles to make up his mind how to color each square. How many different pictures of this type do you think Tom could paint?

Record the estimates somewhere on the board for future reference.

T: Can you find a code that Tom could use?

S: *Give each square a number: 1, 2, 4, 8, 16, 32, 64, 128, 256.*

This suggestion may not be given, so you may have to start the process of assigning numbers to the squares. Begin in the lower right-hand corner and label the squares, step by step asking the students to make suggestions as you proceed.

256	128	64
32	16	8
4	2	1

S: *It's like the binary abacus, only in a square rather than in a line.*
T: Very good. How can we use these numbers to make a code?
S: *Count a red square as being a square with a checker on it, and count a blue square as being empty.*

Color your picture as shown here:

256	128	64
32	16	8
4	2	1

T: Which code number would this picture have? (74) Who can draw the picture whose code number is 22?

Invite a student to come to the board and draw the corresponding picture, as follows:

256	128	64
32	16	8
4	2	1

T: How many different nine-square pictures could Tom paint if he paints each square either red or blue?

Give the students an opportunity to change their estimates. You will probably find that most students will want to increase their estimates. Do not expect the students to say that there are exactly 512 such pictures, and do not give the answer away at this point. In Activities 69 and 70 the problem will be solved completely.

If there is time, let the students work on Worksheets L70 and L71, and then check them collectively. In any case, tell the students that the story of Tom is not yet complete. Tom is interested in knowing how many nine-square pictures are rare and how many of them are two of a kind, and so on. These questions will be investigated later.

Resources Available

For class use: Worksheets L69–L71
For out-of-class use: Any H-worksheet up through H96

ACTIVITY 65
Nim Addition

Materials Needed

Teacher: Nim Adder (from poster packet), colored chalk (or, if your chalkboard is magnet-sensitive, the Minicomputer kit)

Students: One Nim Adder each, paper and pencils

Before class begins, make preparations for the students to make their own Nim Adders by making two card copies of the blackline master in the poster packet for each student. Either cut out the pairs of disks as described in Activity 43 or have the students do it for themselves.

T: Do you remember our work with the game of Nim? A couple of lessons ago we finally figured out how to make winning moves in 3-pile Nim. Now that we've done that, I want to explain to you what I was doing to help myself win the first time we ever played Nim.

Show the class your Nim Adder.

T: This is called a Nim Adder—I'll explain why in a minute. It works because of something we argued about in an earlier lesson. Do you remember that if you are given the sizes of two piles, then there is only one size pile that can go with them to make a hopeless Nim position?

If your chalkboard is magnet-sensitive, draw the following on it; otherwise use the top of your Minicomputer boards, as suggested in Activity 30.

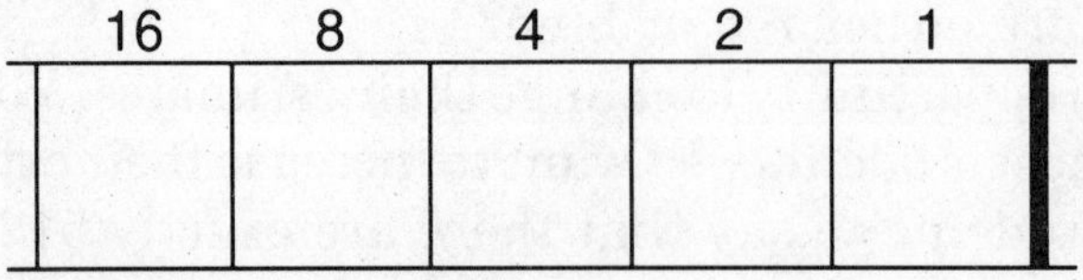

16	8	4	2	1

Then add checkers as follows:

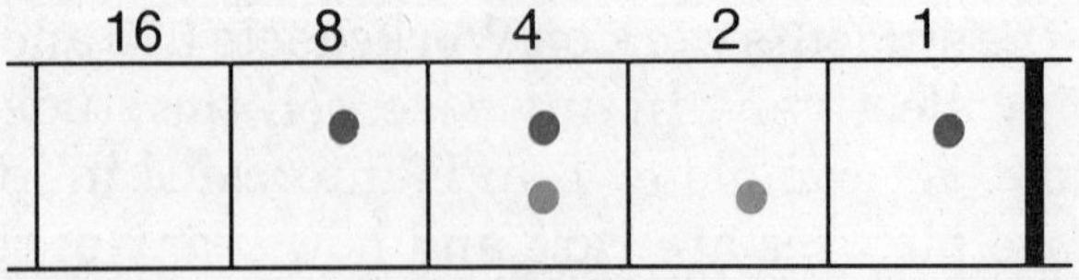

16	8	4	2	1

T: Where should I put checkers (no more than one to a square) so that we have pairs of checkers in squares?

S: *Here, here, and here:*

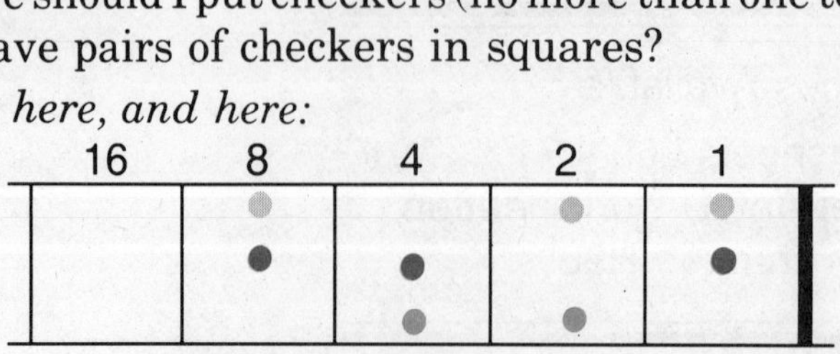

16	8	4	2	1

T: What were the original two numbers on the abacus?
S: *13 and 6.*
T: And what's the number you've just put on to make this hopeless position?
S: *11.*
T: I'm going to write that like this.
Write on the board: $\mathbf{13} +_{\mathbf{N}} \mathbf{6} = \mathbf{11}$.
T: And I'll call what we've done "Nim addition." That's why I've written the N by the plus sign. We can read this as "thirteen Nim-plus six equals eleven." It's also the reason why I call this (show your Nim Adder) a Nim Adder: it helps me do Nim additions. I've got a Nim Adder for each of you. Let's see if we can figure out how it works.
Distribute the pairs of prepared card disks, and give each student a paper fastener. Explain how to put them together to make a Nim Adder, illustrating what you say with the help of your own Nim Adder.
T: Now I claim that we can use this to show that $13 +_N 6 = 11$. Line up the (13) on the inner ring with the (6) on the outer ring.
Do this on your own Nim Adder, and help any students who are unable to do so by themselves.
T: Look at the black-and-white pattern. Concentrate just on the half that's on the (13) side.
Draw the following on the board next to the binary abacus:

T: Can anyone explain why this pattern shows 13?
If no one volunteers a correct response immediately, give a hint as follows:
T: It's got something to do with the binary abacus. What is it about the pattern for 13 that shows the squares of the abacus, and how can you tell when there's a checker in a square and when there's not?
S: *We need four squares on the binary abacus to show 13, so the squares must be like this:*

Then, whenever the pattern is like this, there's a checker in the square:

When it's like this, there's no checker in the square.

Check with the class that, with this interpretation, the black-and-white pattern really does show 13.

T: Now let's concentrate on the half that's on the ⑥ side. Why does that pattern show 6?

S: *The squares of the abacus are shown in the same way. But this time there's a checker in the square when the pattern is like this:*

There's no checker when the pattern is like this:

Check with the class that, with this interpretation, the black-and-white pattern really does show 6.

T: Now the answer is supposed to be 11.

Modify your drawing on the board so that it looks like this:

T: How can we see that the whole black-and-white pattern shows 11?

S: *Well, you have to think of the pattern in four long strips, like this:*

Then there's no checker on the square when the pattern is like this, but there is for any other pattern:

65

Check that, with this interpretation, the black-and-white pattern shows 11.

T: Very good. Now try to use your Nim Adder to do this.

Write on the board: $\mathbf{12 +_N 14 =}$

S: *6.*

T: No, that's not correct. Let's find out what the answer should be by using the binary abacus.

16 8 4 2 1

S: *There's only one unpaired checker—on the 2-square. So the answer's 2.*

T: Look at your Nim Adder again. Why does it show 2?

S: *It must be that there's also no checker on a square when the pattern is like this:*

T: That's right. Perhaps it's easier to see if I tell you that there *is* a checker on a square when the pattern forms two large triangles, side by side, that go right across the pattern like this:

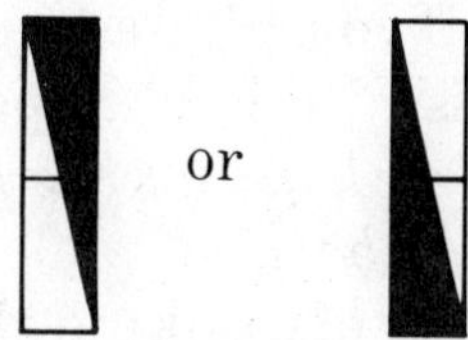

Let the students work individually on Worksheet L72. Then check through it rapidly with the class, going into detail only for those problems that have created difficulty.

T: Now try this on your Nim Adder.

Write on the board: $\mathbf{6 +_N 6 =}$

S: *The answer's 0.*

T: That's right. It means that you must add *no* checkers to two piles with six checkers in each in order to make a hopeless position; it's already hopeless!

Complete the statement on the board, and write the following: $\mathbf{7 +_N 7 =}$

S: *That's the same. The answer's 0.*

S: *Any number Nim-plus itself is zero.*

T: Excellent. Now let's use that information to find some interesting results.

65

Write on the board: $\mathbf{3 +_N 5 = 6}$

T: You found this out just now for your worksheet. Let's see what happens if we Nim-add 6 on both sides of the equals sign.

Modify the number sentence on the board: $\mathbf{3 +_N 5 +_N 6 = 6 +_N 6}$

S: *Six Nim-plus six is zero.*

Modify the sentence again: $\mathbf{3 +_N 5 +_N 6 = 0}$

T: Look at the other results on Worksheet L72, and tell me what you think about these.

Write on the board:

$$5 +_N 2 +_N 7 =$$
$$4 +_N 11 +_N 15 =$$
$$6 +_N 4 +_N 2 =$$
$$15 +_N 7 +_N 8 =$$

S: *They're all zero, because you get them all the same way. For example, $5 +_N 2$ is 7. So if you Nim-add 7 to both sides you get*

$$5 +_N 2 +_N 7 = 7 +_N 7,$$

which is zero.

T: What would happen if you Nim-added the numbers of checkers in the piles of a hopeless 3-pile Nim position?

S: *You would get zero. In a hopeless position the checkers are in pairs on the squares of the abacus.*

T: That's correct. One way of thinking about that is like this: If you're faced with a hopeless position it's just as if you have already lost—there's nothing you can do about it if your opponent doesn't make a mistake. But if you've already lost, your opponent has just picked up the last checker and you're sitting there looking at an empty table with *zero* checkers on it. That's why every hopeless position always gives you an answer of zero when you Nim-add the numbers of checkers in the piles. If you want to be thinking ahead, that's the clue to winning at Nim with more than three piles.

Finish the lesson by letting the students work individually on Worksheet L73.

Note to the Teacher

The above description deals with how to read the Nim Adder to determine the size of a third Nim pile that together with two piles of given sizes makes a hopeless position. It does not explain *why* it works. If a student asks for such an explanation, you can answer as follows:

There is an unpaired checker in the binary representation of the sizes of the two given piles if:

there is a checker on a square for one number

but not for the other

or vice versa.

There is no unpaired checker if:

there is a checker on a square for one number

and a checker on the same square for the other

or

there is no checker on a square for one number

and no checker on the same square for the other.

The size of the third pile of a hopeless position must have checkers in its binary representation exactly on those squares containing unpaired checkers. Its size may therefore be read as explained in the description of the lesson.

You could ask students who are interested to design a Nim Adder that works for 1 through 31 rather than only 1 through 15.

Resources Available

For class use: Worksheets L72 and L73

For out-of-class use: Any H-worksheet up through H99

ACTIVITY 66
Fractional Multipliers 4

Materials Needed
Teacher: Colored chalk
Students: Paper and pencils

Draw the following on the board:

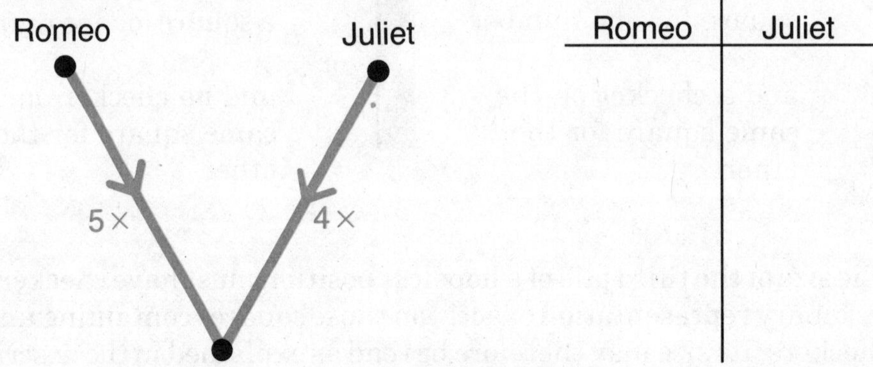

T: Romeo and Juliet are secret numbers. All I'll tell you about them is that they are both positive whole numbers. What numbers could Romeo and Juliet be?

S: *Romeo could be 4 and Juliet could be 5.*

Ask the student to record his or her suggestion on the chart on the board. Make sure the numbers are written in the correct column. Let other volunteers suggest further possibilities for Romeo and Juliet and record them in the chart. For example:

Romeo	Juliet
4	5
12	15
8	10
16	20
20	25
100	125
24	30

T: Do you notice anything about the possibilities for Romeo?

S: *They're multiples of 4.*

T: What about the possibilities for Juliet?

S: *They're multiples of 5.*
Modify your arrow picture:

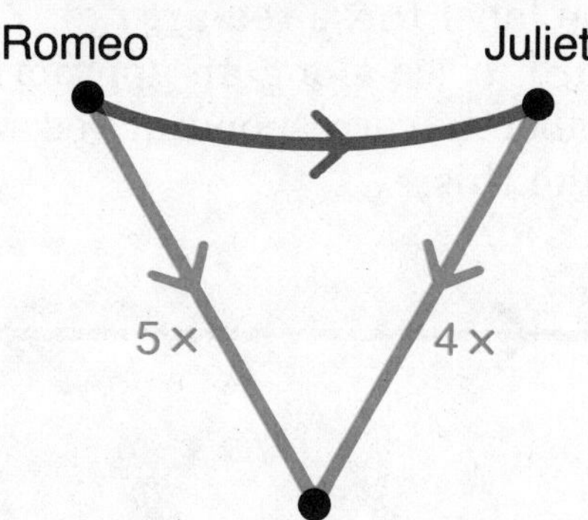

Trace along the blue arrows from Romeo to Juliet as you say:

T: With 5×, then against 4×. How can we label the red arrow?

S: $\frac{5}{4}$×.

Label the red arrow accordingly, and then add a green arrow as follows:

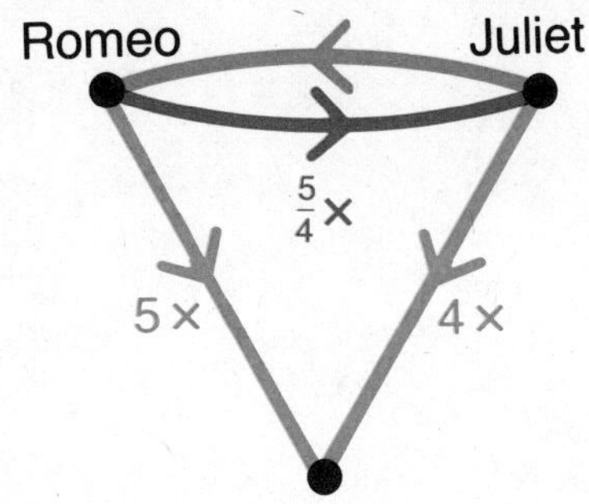

Let a volunteer trace along the blue arrows from Juliet to Romeo. Encourage the student to describe the route out loud.

S: *With 4×, then against 5×.*

T: So how could we label the green arrow?

S: $\frac{4}{5}$×.

Write the following problems on the board, and let the students work on them individually. (Answers are given in parentheses.)

$\frac{5}{4} \times 20 =$ ____(15)	$\frac{4}{5} \times 15 =$ ____(12)
$\frac{4}{5} \times 20 =$ ____(16)	$\frac{4}{5} \times 12.5 =$ ____(10)
$\frac{5}{4} \times 10 =$ ____(12.5)	$\frac{5}{4} \times 16 =$ ____(20)

While the class is working on these problems, draw the following arrow picture on the board:

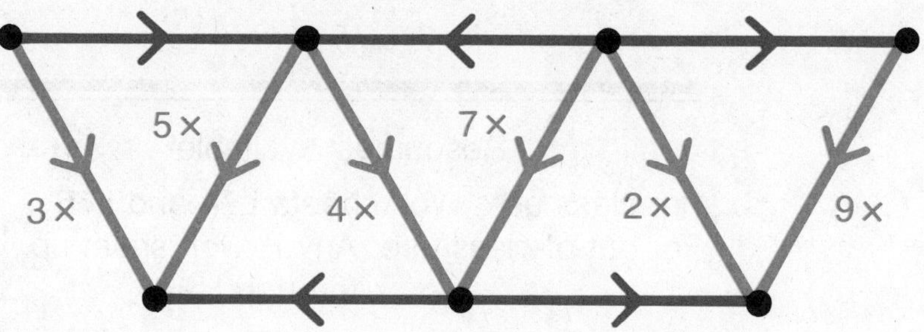

Check through the six multiplications with the whole class. Then continue as follows:

T: Now I'd like you to help me label these red arrows.

Let volunteers come to the board, trace along an appropriate blue route, describe it out loud, and label the corresponding red arrow. The completed diagram will look like this:

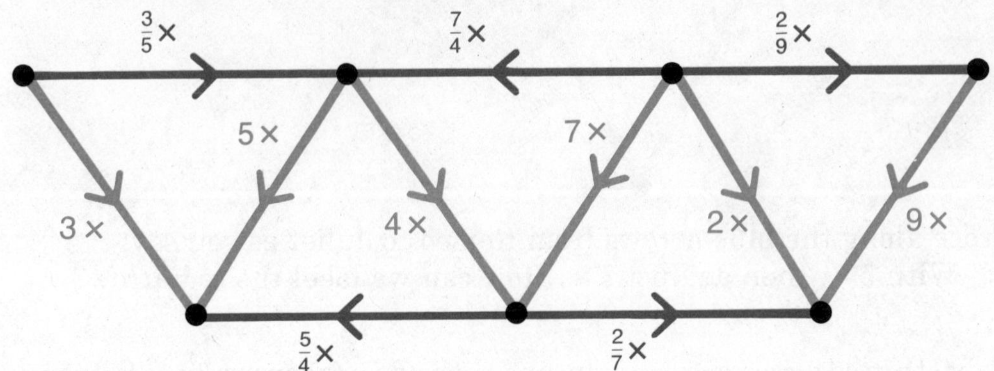

Resources Available

For class use: Worksheets L74 and L75

For out-of-class use: Any H-worksheet up through H99

ACTIVITY 67
Weighted Checkers 2

Materials Needed
Teacher: Minicomputer kit, colored chalk
Students: None

Display four Minicomputer boards and the following configuration of checkers:

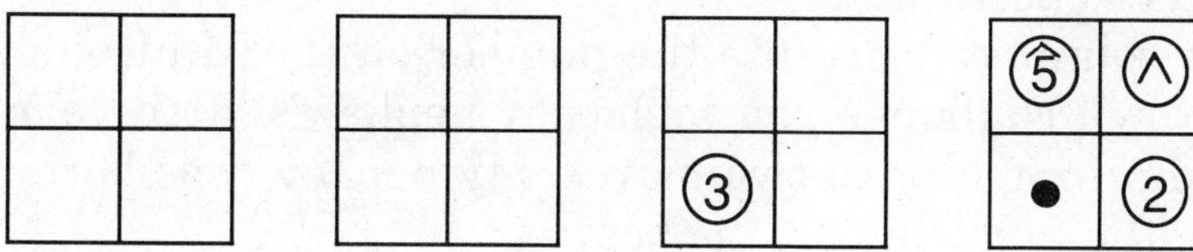

T: What is this number?
S: *20.*
Record this number on the board. Then add these checkers on the tens' board:

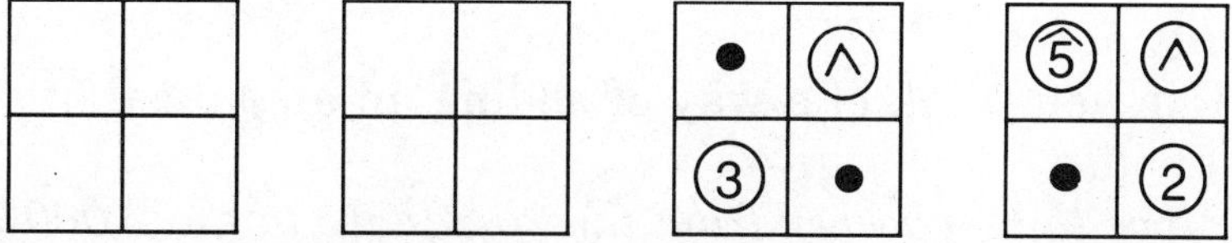

T: What number is on the Minicomputer now?
S: *70; we added 50 to 20.*
T: Today I'm going to draw an arrow picture on the board. I want you to help me make the plays shown by the arrows. Each play should involve moving just *one* checker.
Draw the leftmost arrow of this arrow picture on the board:

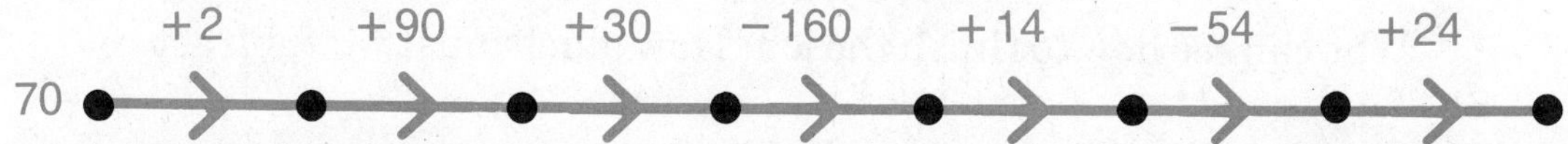

T: How can we add 2?
S: *Move the regular checker from the 2-square to the 4-square.*
S: *Or you could move the negative checker from the 4-square to the 2-square.*
Make sure that both these moves are mentioned, and then make one of them.
T: What number is on the Minicomputer now?
S: *72.*
Label the dot at the end of the +2 arrow **72**. Continue in this way,

67

drawing one arrow at a time, until you have completed the above arrow diagram and labeled all the dots. Here are the plays:

+90: Move the regular checker from the 10-square to the 100-square.
+30: Move the $\hat{5}$-checker from the 8-square to the 2-square.
−160: Move the negative checker from the 40-square to the 200-square.
+14: Move the 2-checker from the 1-square to the 8-square.
−54: Move the 3-checker from the 20-square to the 2-square.
+24: Move the 2-checker from the 8-square to the 20-square.

Your completed arrow picture should look like this:

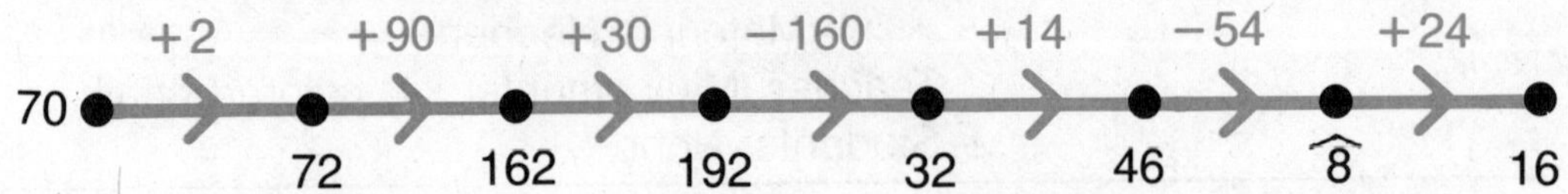

T: What number is on the Minicomputer?
S: *16.*
T: Let's check that.

Let a volunteer calculate the number on the Minicomputer.

T: Now I challenge you to get my nephew's birth year on the Minicomputer in two moves. My nephew was born in 1971.

Draw the following on the board:

16 ● → ● → ● 1,971

Give students a few minutes to think. If after a short while no one seems to be making any progress, suggest a strategy:

T: How much must we add?
S: *1,955.*
T: Can you think of a way of adding an amount that's quite near 1,955?
S: *Move the 2-checker from the 20-square to the 1,000-square.*
T: How much does that add?
S: *1,960, because you add 2 × 1,000—that's 2,000—and you subtract 2 × 20—that's 40.*

Record this information on the arrow picture:

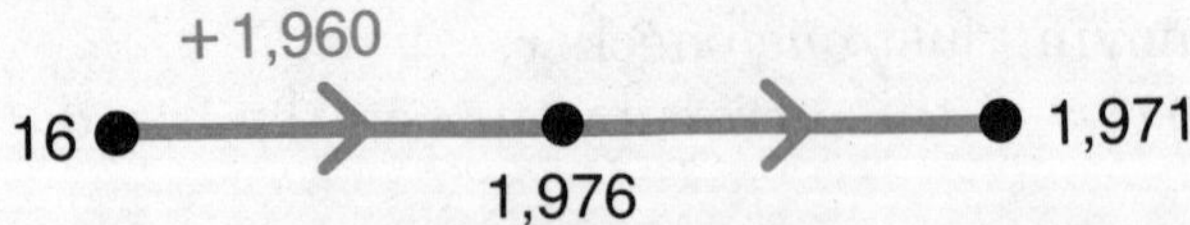

T: Who can see how to finish the job? How much must we subtract?
S: *5.*
T: Can we do that?
S: *Yes. Move the $\hat{5}$-checker from the 2-square to the 1-square.*

Resources Available

For class use: Worksheets L76 and L77
For out-of-class use: Any H-worksheet up through H102

ACTIVITY 68
Minicomputer Golf

Materials Needed
Teacher: Minicomputer kit, Colored Chalk
Students: None

Display three Minicomputer boards and build up the following configuration by slowly placing checkers one at a time.

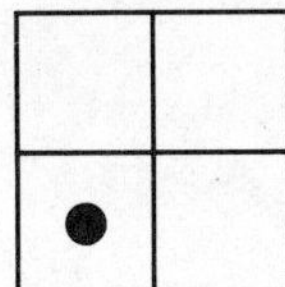 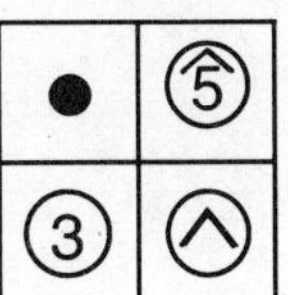 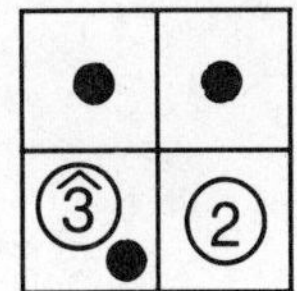

T: What number is this?
S: *140.*
T: Now we will play a game of Minicomputer Golf using this as the starting number.

Divide the class into teams A and B. Write on the board:

goal: 1,000

team A ⟶ (red)
team B ⟶ (blue)

T: We start this game at 140, and the goal is 1,000. Teams A and B will take turns to play, and each of you will make a play before anyone has a second turn. Each player must move one checker from any square to any other square. This will make the number increase and decrease. The first team to reach the goal wins. Who would like to play first for team A?

Suppose the first player for team A moves the 3-checker from the 20-square to the 200-square.

T: Is the number on the Minicomputer larger or smaller? (larger) How much larger? (540 larger) What number is on the Minicomputer now?
S: *140 + 540 = 680.*

Draw on the board:

+540
140 ⟶ 680
③ (20 ⟶ 200)

Suppose the next player (from team B) moves a regular checker from the 200-square to the 400-square.

T: Is the number larger or smaller? (larger) By how much? (200 larger) What is the new number?
S: *680 + 200 = 880.*
Continue recording the information on the board.

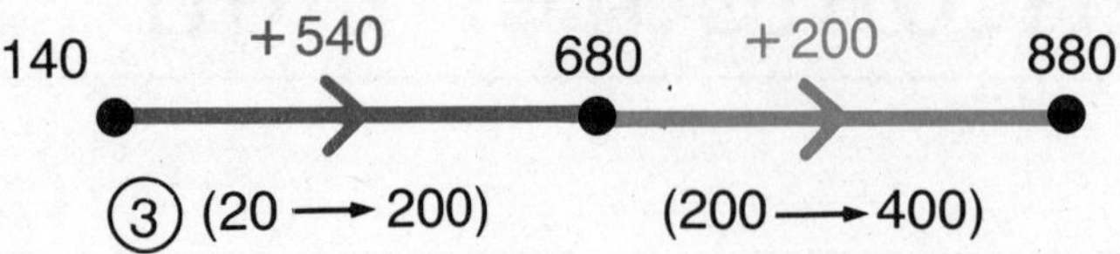

Here is one way in which the game might develop:

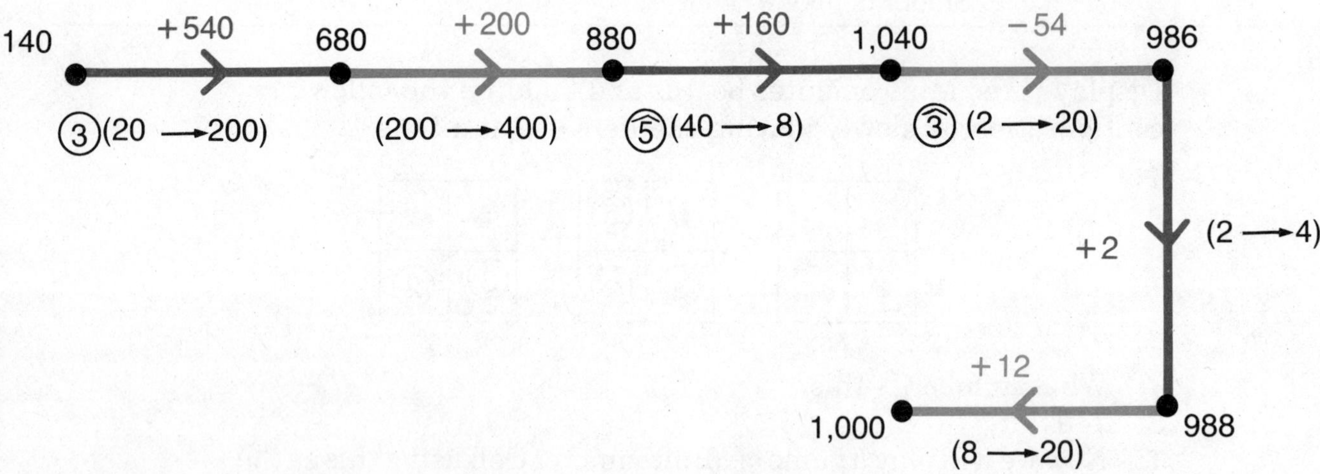

Note: ③ (20 → 200) indicates a play in which the 3-checker is moved from the 20-square to the 200-square, and (200 → 400) indicates a regular checker being moved from the 200-square to the 400-square.

For the remaining time, let the same teams play the game again, this time with team B making the first play. The following is a flexible starting configuration:

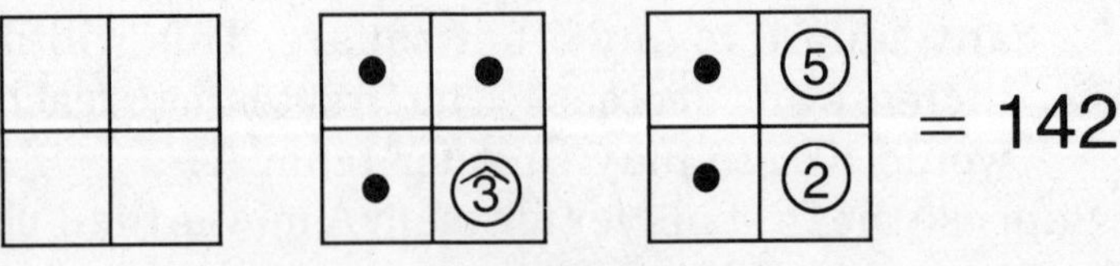

goal: 700

(If you select your own starting configuration, be sure to test it before class and insure that the configuration includes enough checkers for the goal to be reached.)

Note to the Teacher

An interesting variation of Minicomputer Golf that your students might want to play instead of the above version has the following rules:

- Given a starting configuration and a goal, the members of one team play in turn until the goal is reached.
- The scoring diagram is then erased and the members of the other team play in turn (from the same starting configuration to the same goal).
- The winning team is the one that uses the *least* number of moves. In case of a tie, the team playing first wins; this takes into account the possibility of the second team merely copying the first team's moves.

This variation more closely resembles the actual game of golf, in which the least number of strokes from tee (starting number) to cup (goal) determines the winner.

Resources Available

For out-of-class use: Any H-worksheet up through H102

ACTIVITIES 69 and 70
Random Art 2

Materials Needed
Teacher: Minicomputer kit, Colored chalk
Students: Paper and colored pencils

T: Do you remember the story of my friend Tom and his random red and blue paintings?

Let the students tell as much of the story from Activities 63 and 64 as they can recall. Remind them that Tom can paint 16 different four-square red and blue pictures; but when we take into account the fact that some of the pictures are exactly the same as other pictures when they are turned, there are only six different pictures.

T: After Tom got tired of painting four-square pictures, he decided to create some nine-square red and blue pictures in the same way.

Draw this outline on the board:

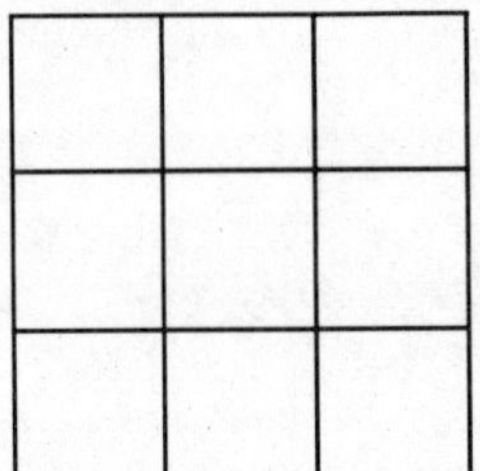

T: How many different nine-square red and blue pictures do you think Tom could paint?

Record some estimates in one corner of the board for future reference.

T: Do you remember the code we invented to number the pictures Tom could paint?

S: *The squares were numbered like a binary abacus: 1, 2, 4, 8, 16, 32, 64, 128, 256.*

Label the squares of your picture:

256	128	64
32	16	8
4	2	1

69
70

Color your pictures as shown here:

256	128	64
32	16	8
4	2	1

T: What is the code number of this picture?
S: *152, because 128 + 16 + 8 = 152.*
T: Now I'd like someone to draw the picture with code number 175 on the board.
Invite a student to come to the board and draw the following picture:

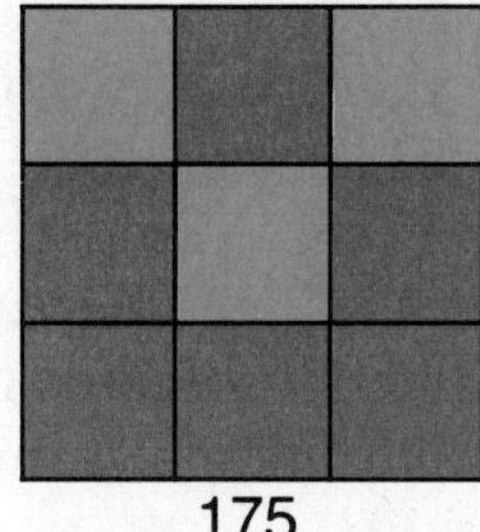

175

T: What's the largest code number one of Tom's paintings could have?
Give the students a few minutes to consider this question.
S: *511.*
S: *512.*
T: Someone come to the board and paint the picture with the largest code number.
S: *Color all the squares red; it's the same as putting one checker on each square of a binary abacus.*
T: That's a good idea. What number is this?
Draw a binary abacus (or use the top row of the Minicomputer boards) and place checkers like this:

512	256	128	64	32	16	8	4	2	1
	•	•	•	•	•	•	•	•	•

T: How can we calculate quickly what number this is?
S: *Put another checker on the ones' board.*

512	256	128	64	32	16	8	4	2	1
	•	•	•	•	•	•	•	•	• •

Let a volunteer make the plays to obtain 512.

512	256	128	64	32	16	8	4	2	1
•									

T: Is 512 the largest number?
S: *No. We added an extra checker, so the largest number is $512 - 1 = 511$.*
T: Very good. What's the smallest number?
S: *0.*
T: Could Tom paint a picture for every number from 0 through 511?
S: *Yes.*

If your class is not convinced of this, start with 0 on the binary abacus and keep adding 1 to get 1, 2, 3, 4, 5, 6, . . . , and so on. You will not need to continue this very long before most students realize that every number between 0 and 511 is the code number for a picture.

T: How many pictures is that altogether?
S: *From 0 to 511 there are 512 numbers, so there must be 512 pictures.*
T: Tom's customers are still interested in buying the rarest pictures. They would like to have one-of-a-kind pictures. What would make a picture one of a kind?
S: *No matter how you turn it, it is the same.*
T: Can you draw some of these one-of-a-kind pictures?

Let students work on this problem independently. As the one-of-a-kind pictures are discovered, invite students to draw them on the board. There are eight such pictures. They are shown below together with their code numbers.

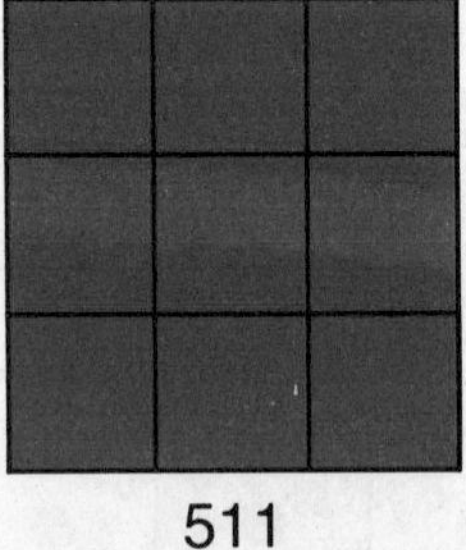
511

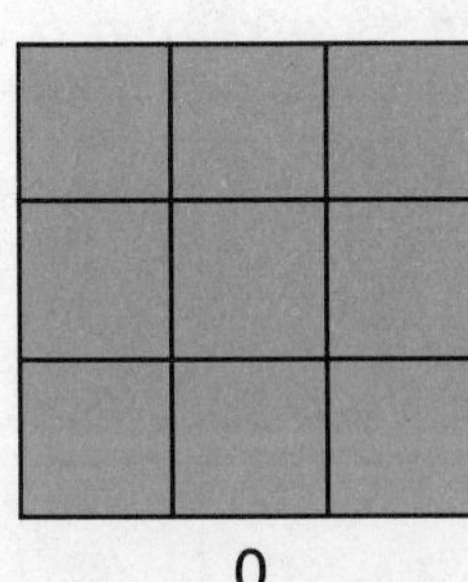
0

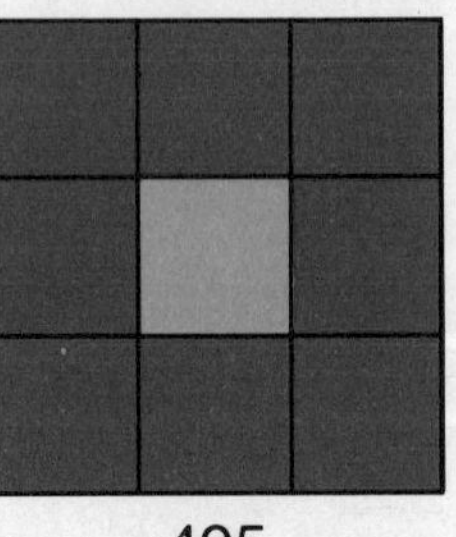
495

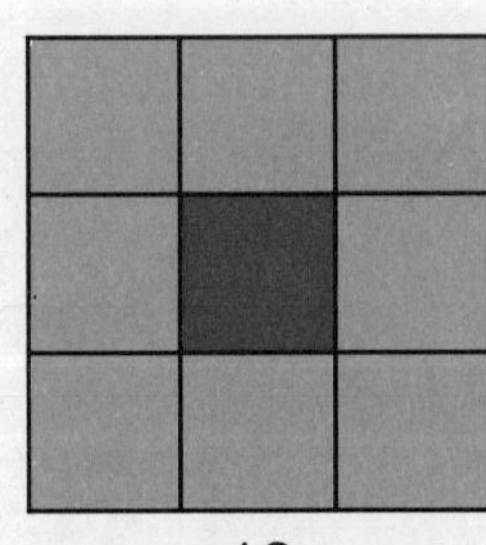
16

69
70

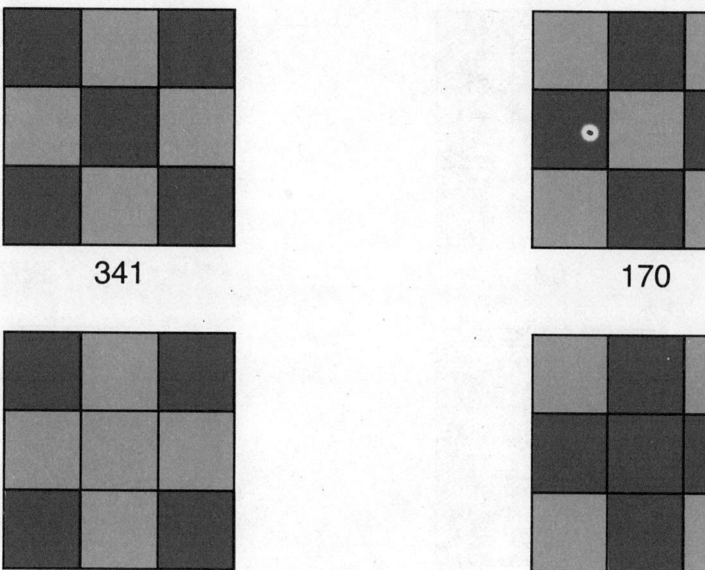

341 170 325 186

T: We've found eight one-of-a-kind pictures. What do you notice about these pictures?

S: *They come in pairs. If you find one one-of-a-kind picture and then reverse the colors (red for blue and blue for red), you will get another one-of-a-kind picture.*

A student might suggest that the sum of the code numbers of a complementary pair of pictures is 511 (for example, 495 + 16 = 511). Do not force this observation, however, if it is not volunteered.

T: Good. Remember that Tom's pictures come in pairs—it will be useful to us later.

Tom charges 60 dollars for a one-of-a-kind picture. How much do you think he would charge for a two-of-a-kind picture?

S: *30 dollars.* $\frac{1}{2} \times 60 = 30$.

T: Let's try to find all the two-of-a-kind pictures. Are there any two-of-a-kind pictures with exactly one red square?

S: *No. Pictures that have only one red square are either one of a kind or four of a kind.*

Sketch the following two pictures on the board to illustrate this comment.

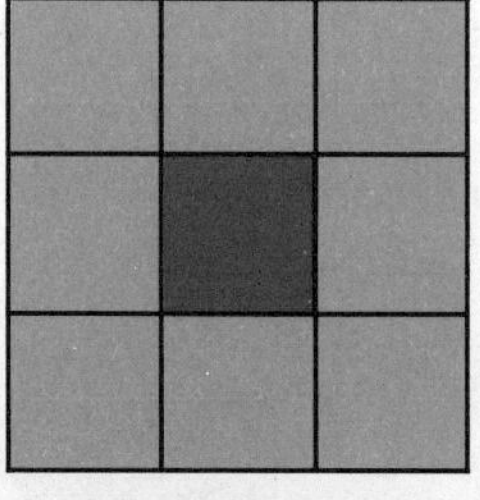

one of a kind

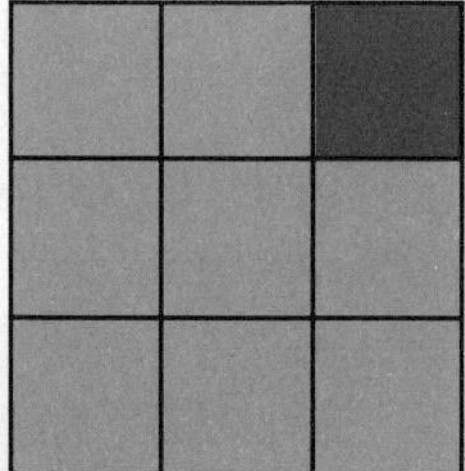

four of a kind

T: Are there any two-of-a-kind pictures with exactly two red squares?

Invite students to draw them on the board. (There are four.) To save time, suggest that only the color red be used in the drawings on the board, leaving the blue squares blank. (In this description, however, we continue to use both colors.)

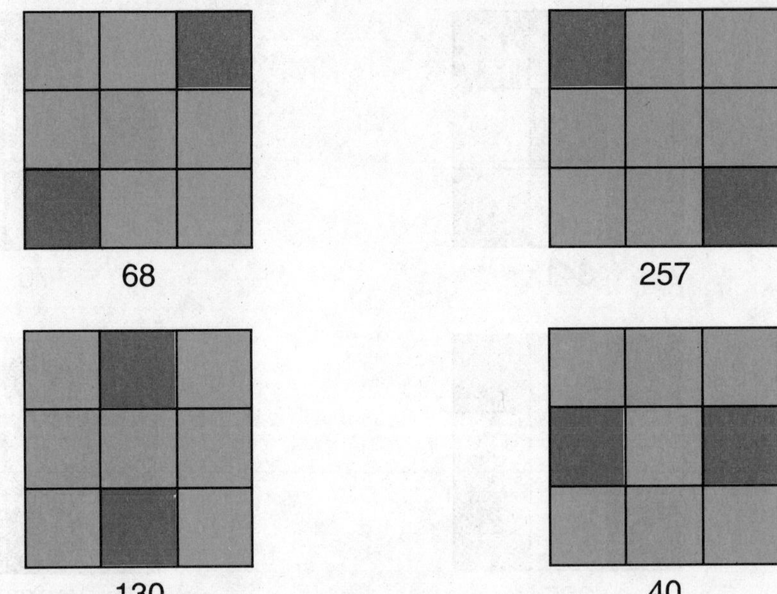

68 257

130 40

S: *If we reverse the colors (red for blue and blue for red), we'll get four more pictures.*

Ask students to draw these four complementary pictures on the board.

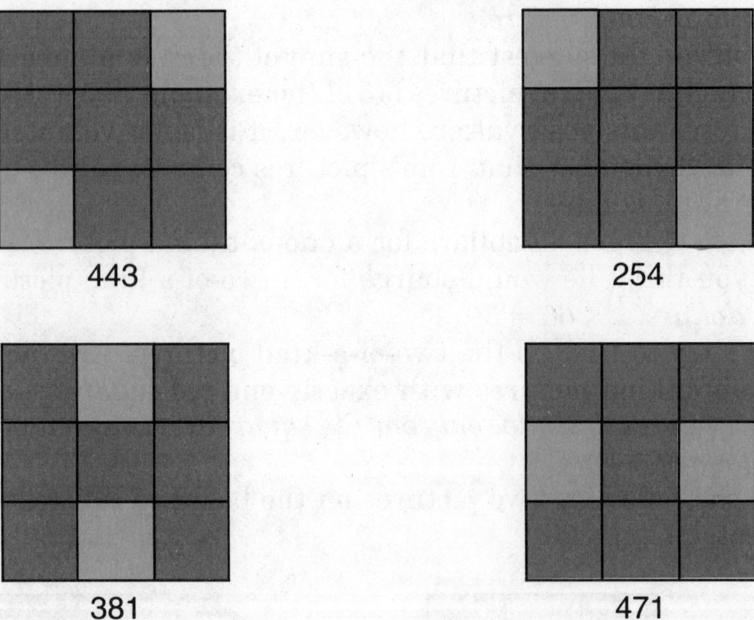

443 254

381 471

Continue in this manner for the two-of-a-kind pictures with exactly three red squares and their complements . . .

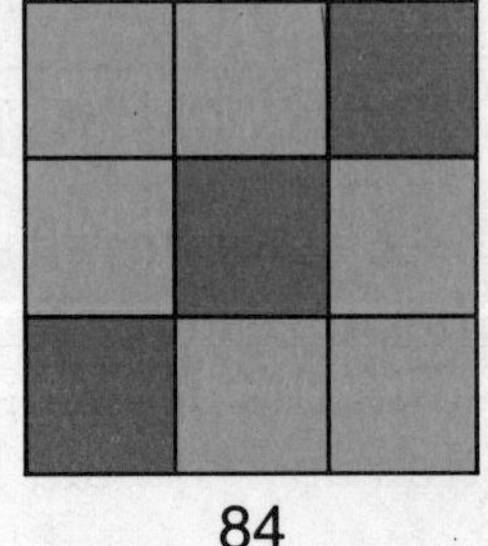

84

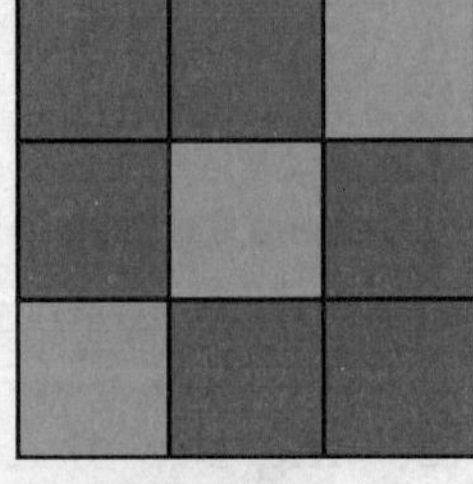

427

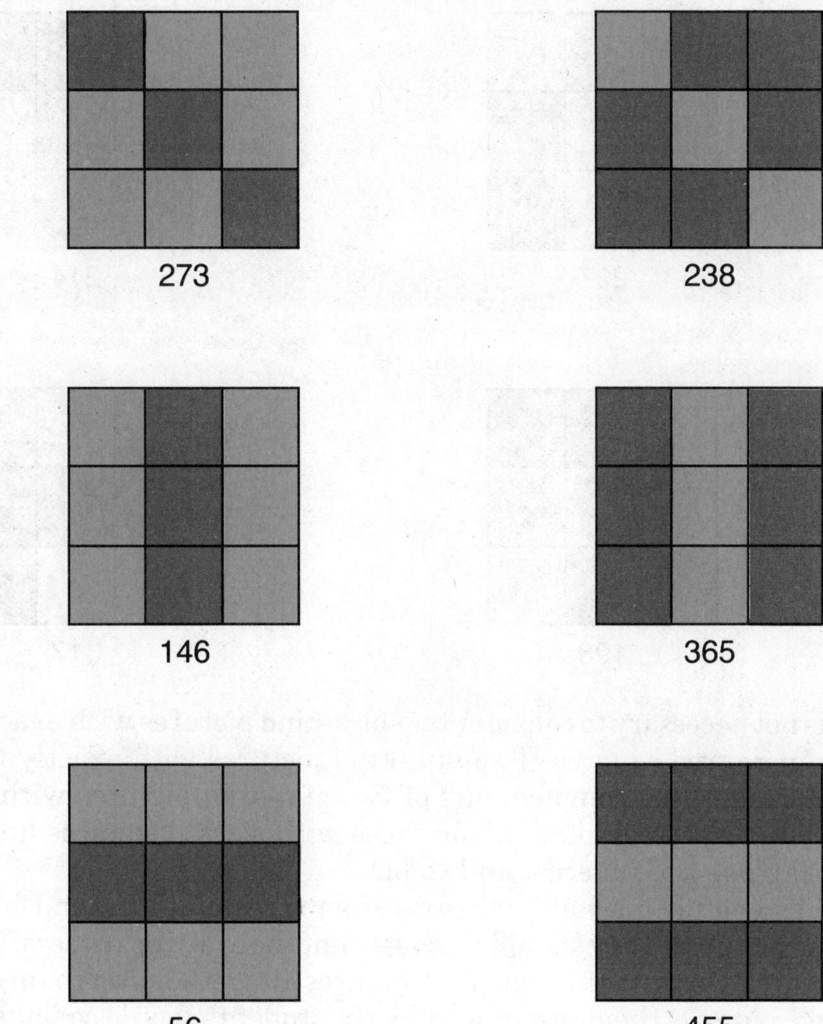

273 238

146 365

56 455

. . . and the two-of-a-kind pictures with exactly four red squares and their complements.

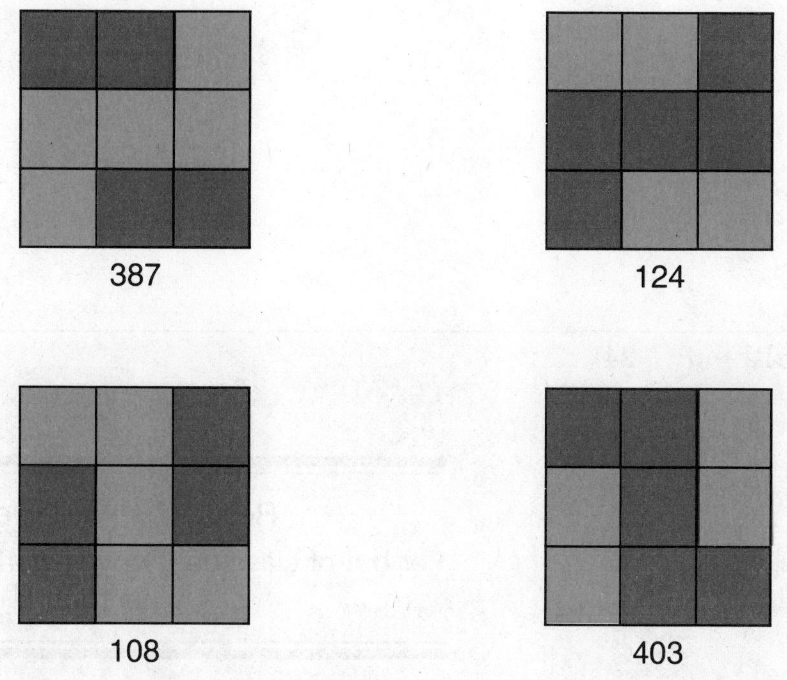

387 124

108 403

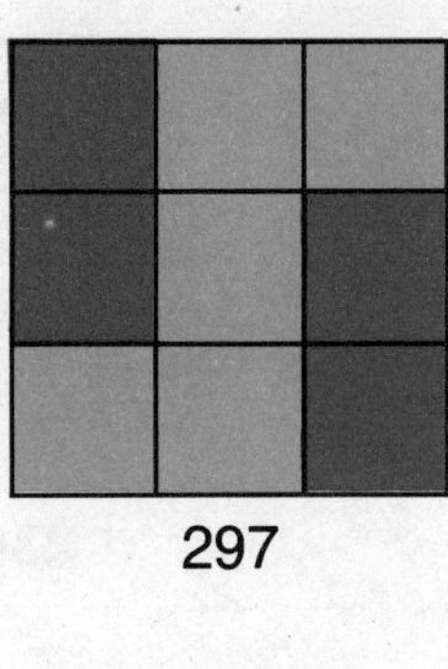

297

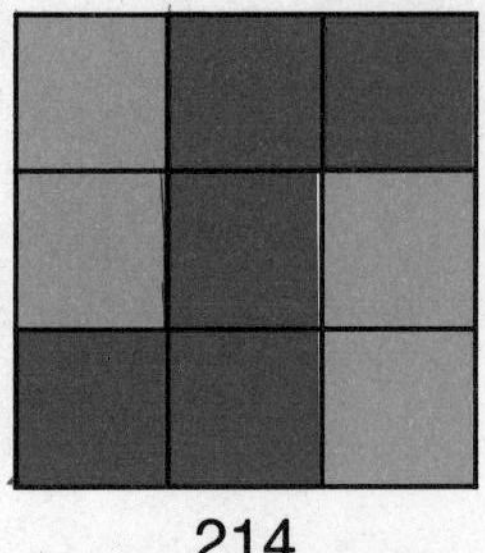

214

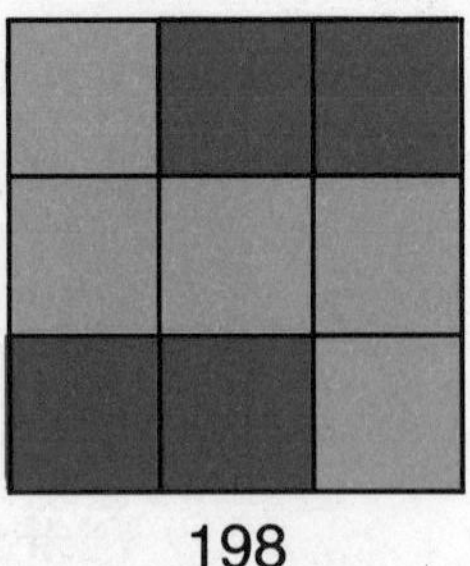

198

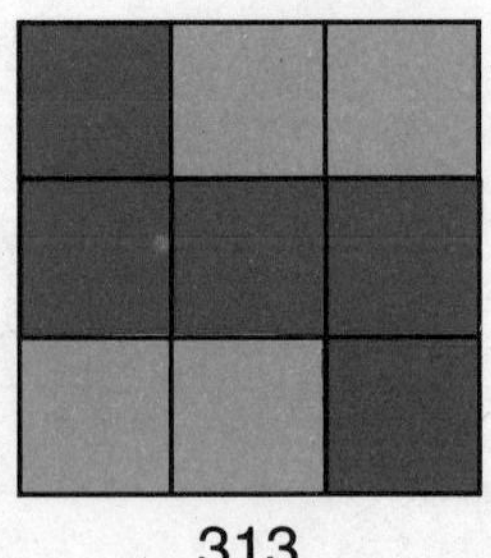

313

It is not necessary to consider two-of-a-kind pictures with exactly five (or more) red squares. Two-of-a-kind pictures with exactly five red squares are the complements of two-of-a-kind pictures with exactly four red squares; likewise for those with six red squares and those with three red squares, and so on.

Faster students may wish to consider three-of-a-kind and four-of-a-kind pictures. They should discover that there are no three-of-a-kind pictures. Because there are 512 pictures altogether, 8 of them one-of-a-kind and 24 of them two-of-a-kind, the students should conclude that there are 480* four-of-a-kind pictures.

---

*512 − (8 + 24)

Resources Available

For out-of-class use: Any H-worksheets up through H105

APPENDIX
The String Game

Introduction

The String Game is introduced in Volume 1 of *Challenge: A Program for the Mathematically Talented* and appears in various guises throughout the program. Through the medium of a game, it gives students an opportunity to become familiar with the language of strings, which provides a precise, pictorial, and nonverbal means of recording and communicating information about classifications. The abilities to classify, to reason about classification, and to extract information from a classification are important skills for everyday life, for intellectual activity in general, and for the study and understanding of mathematics in particular. The language of strings helps young students to think logically and creatively and to report their thinking without the need for extensive verbalization.

The String Game is first played using shapes, but later variations of the game involve numbers. In this appendix we provide the necessary information and examples to enable you to play the game using shapes or numbers, and we spell out some of the many ways in which the game can be organized. The variations of the game described in this appendix are referred to in several of the activities in *Challenge*; however, we suggest that you do not restrict your playing of the String Game just to the few occasions when it is specifically scheduled. Experience has shown that the game is most beneficial (and enjoyable) for students if you make a regular practice of playing it about once every two weeks as well as whenever you have 10 or 15 minutes to spare during the course of the day.

Equipment

The Playing Surface

To play the String Game you will need a playing surface divided up as follows:

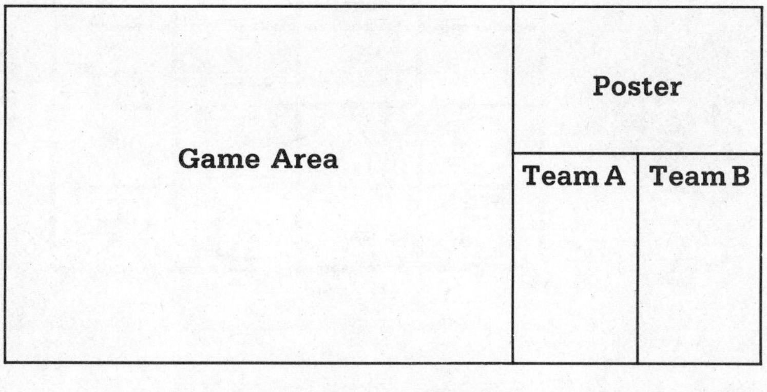

<table>
<tr><td rowspan="2">Game Area</td><td colspan="2">Poster</td></tr>
<tr><td>Team A</td><td>Team B</td></tr>
</table>

It will be most convenient if this playing surface is a large area of chalkboard (say, at least 3 feet by 6 feet) to which magnetic material will adhere. Use a Minicomputer checker to test your permanently mounted chalkboard and any portable chalkboard or gridboard the school has available to find one that is magnet-sensitive.

If you are only partially successful and discover a magnet-sensitive surface large enough for the game area, you can improvise the right-hand third of the playing surface by obtaining a sheet of metal (minimum size 2 feet by 3 feet) or locating a convenient metallic surface in the classroom such as the side of a file cabinet. You can use a heavy felt-tip pen to draw the three regions labeled **Poster**, **Team A**, and **Team B** on a large sheet of paper and then tape this paper to your metallic surface.

If you are completely unsuccessful, you can use your regular chalkboard as the game area and a large piece of poster board (minimum size 2 feet by 3 feet), marked with heavy felt-tip pen into three regions, for the remainder of the playing surface.

Game Pieces, String Cards, and Posters

Each variation of the String Game requires one set of game pieces, two sets of string cards, and a poster of possible string labels, all of which are included in the appropriate String Game kit.

The game pieces for the Shapes String Game are as follows:

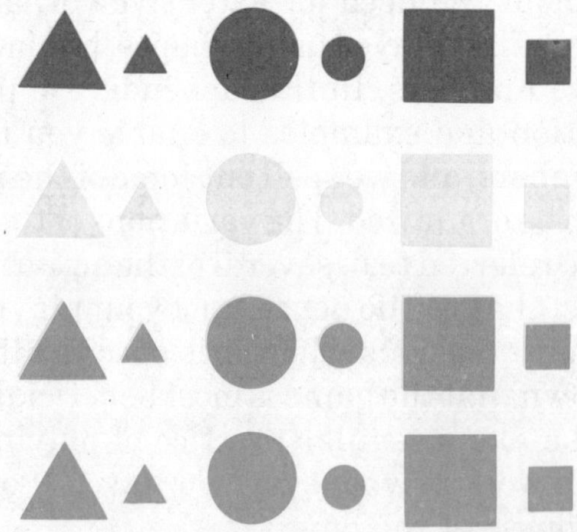

The string cards are as follows:

RED	YELLOW	GREEN	BLUE
NOT RED	NOT YELLOW	NOT GREEN	NOT BLUE
○	△	□	BIG
NOT ○	NOT △	NOT □	LITTLE

In this version of the game there are two posters of possible string labels:

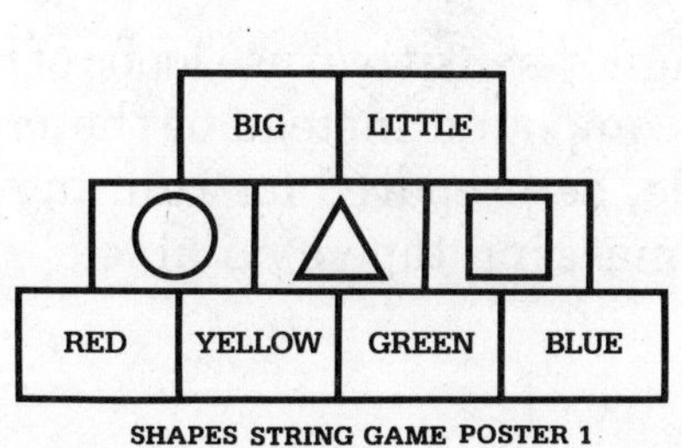

SHAPES STRING GAME POSTER 1

RED	YELLOW	GREEN	BLUE
NOT RED	NOT YELLOW	NOT GREEN	NOT BLUE
○	△	□	BIG
NOT ○	NOT △	NOT □	LITTLE

SHAPES STRING GAME POSTER 2

The game pieces for the Numerical String Game are as follows:

$\widehat{100}$	$\widehat{66}$	$\widehat{55}$	$\widehat{15}$	$\widehat{10}$
$\hat{5}$	$\hat{1}$	0	1	2
3	4	5	6	7

8	$\underline{9}$	10	12	18
20	24	27	40	45
50	53	$\underline{99}$	100	105

The string cards are as follows:

MULTIPLES OF 2	MULTIPLES OF 3
MULTIPLES OF 10	POSITIVE DIVISORS OF 12
POSITIVE DIVISORS OF 24	POSITIVE DIVISORS OF 27

LESS THAN 50	LESS THAN $\widehat{10}$
MULTIPLES OF 4	MULTIPLES OF 5

POSITIVE DIVISORS OF 18	POSITIVE DIVISORS OF 20
GREATER THAN 50	GREATER THAN $\widehat{10}$
ODD NUMBERS	POSITIVE PRIME NUMBERS

In this version of the game there is one poster of possible string labels:

MULTIPLES OF 2	MULTIPLES OF 3	MULTIPLES OF 4	MULTIPLES OF 5
MULTIPLES OF 10	POSITIVE DIVISORS OF 12	POSITIVE DIVISORS OF 18	POSITIVE DIVISORS OF 20
POSITIVE DIVISORS OF 24	POSITIVE DIVISORS OF 27	GREATER THAN 50	GREATER THAN $\widehat{10}$
LESS THAN 50	LESS THAN $\widehat{10}$	ODD NUMBERS	POSITIVE PRIME NUMBERS

NUMERICAL STRING GAME POSTER 1

If you have a magnet-sensitive playing surface, magnetize the game pieces by sticking a small piece of magnetic material (provided in the

String Game kit) to the back of each piece. The string cards, on the other hand, can be magnetized by sticking a small piece of magnetic material to the *front* of each piece, taking care not to obscure the printing.

If your playing surface is not magnet-sensitive, use loops of masking tape or wads of plastic caulking compound instead of the magnetic material. If you use masking tape, be prepared for running repairs by having a sufficient supply of masking tape available.

Preparation

Preparation will vary slightly according to how you organize the playing of the game. Use different colors of chalk (or felt-tip pen) to draw two (or in more complicated variations three) large, overlapping strings on the game area of the playing surface (as shown at the end of this appendix). Next to each of these strings attach one string card face down. If the remainder of the playing surface is not physically attached to the game area, arrange for it to be nearby.

Divide the class into the required number of teams using whatever method is acceptable to your class; for example, boys vs. girls or rows 1, 2, 3 vs. rows 4, 5, 6. Call the teams team A, team B, and so on.

Give at least two clues before play begins. These could be correctly placing some of the game pieces in the string picture, drawing a number of crossed-out game pieces in the string picture (which indicates that the piece does not belong to that region), and/or hatching one or more of the regions of the string picture (which indicates that the region concerned contains no pieces other than those already placed there). The provision of these clues means that early players do not need to play using pure guesswork. You can influence how long a game lasts by the number of clues you give at the outset.

If the version of the game you are playing calls for it, distribute the remaining game pieces to the sections of the playing surface labeled **Team A** and **Team B** by placing one-half of the pieces, chosen at random, in one section and the remainder in the other section.

Object of the Game

The object of the game is to determine what is written on the face-down string cards. Once this goal has been achieved, the decision about which team has won will depend on which of the various organizations of the game you are using.

General Rules

1. The game should be played in silence so each student has the chance to analyze successive plays for him- or herself. If a student talks or calls out, his or her team loses its next turn.
2. The teams take turns to play, as do the members of each team. A play consists of a student's placing one of the unplayed game pieces in one of the regions of the string picture.
3. You are the judge. If the piece is correctly placed, say yes. Leave the piece in the string picture and let the player take a second (and

final) turn. On the other hand, if the piece is *not* correctly placed, say no. (In the case of the Numerical String Game, when you say no, draw the numeral in the suggested region and cross it out.) The player must then return the piece to the place from which it was taken, and the next team to play sends a member to the board.

To help you in your role as judge, prepare a crib sheet, preferably one that shows the correct position of each game piece but at the very least one that reminds you of what is written on the face-down string cards. If at any time you discover that you have made an error in the play just completed, say so immediately and correct it. If you discover an error made previously, apologize, clear the board, and begin another game. You will be respected for your decisiveness and will avoid many complications of repositioning game pieces.

Possible Organizations of the Game

1. When a class is learning to play the String Game, an appropriate organization is the one described in Volume 1, Activity 4, and used again when the numerical version is introduced in Volume 2, Activity 14.
   - The class is divided into two teams, and the game pieces are distributed evenly between the two teams and placed in the appropriate sections of the playing surface.
   - The teams play alternately, the members of each team taking turns.
   - When all of a team's pieces have been correctly placed, the player placing the final piece may immediately attempt to identify the string cards. If this is done successfully, then that team has won. If any of the string cards are misidentified, simply indicate that a mistake has been made and let the game continue.
   - When it is the turn of a team whose stock of game pieces has been exhausted, that team's representative must attempt to identify the string cards. Deal with this attempt as indicated above.

2. Once the class is familiar with the String Game and analytical methods have been introduced, players who make good use of the analysis sheets quickly become frustrated if their skill does not influence the outcome of the game. To alleviate this situation you can use the special scoring rules introduced in Volume 2, Activity 70, and modified slightly in Volume 3, Activity 18.
   - There are two teams, the game pieces are distributed evenly, and plays are made as described under (1).
   - Two plays, one by each team, form a **round**. Before the first play and after each round, ask the class if anyone wants to say at that point what the string labels are. Those who do should circle one label for each string on their analysis sheets and hand them to you. Those who do not wish to commit themselves at that point should keep their analysis sheets for the next round.
   - Make a note of the round after which you received each analysis sheet.

- Score the analysis sheets that have been handed to you as follows:

If all the strings are correct before play begins:	250 points
After round 1:	200 points
After round 2:	150 points
After round 3:	100 points
After round 4:	75 points
After round 5:	50 points
After round 6:	25 points
If any string is incorrect:	0 points

  Students have only one opportunity to score in this fashion.
- After round 6, the game continues as described under (1) until completed.
- The team that first exhausts all its pieces and correctly identifies the strings is awarded 100 points plus 10 points for each unplaced piece still in the opposing team's section of the playing surface. At this stage, all the points scored by the members of both teams are totaled and the team with the most points is declared the winner.

Note that this form of organization would be appropriate on any occasion when you decide to play the Shapes String Game with a class that has studied Volume 1.

3. For more mature students, an organization that was introduced in Volume 4, Activity 6, might be appropriate.
   - Once again, there are two teams, the game pieces are distributed evenly, and plays are made alternately as described under (1). In this organization, however, a player is restricted to a single play. After each play on which a piece is correctly placed, analyze the resulting situation as a class.
   - A team is awarded five points each time a member's play eliminates at least one-fourth of the remaining possible labels for the strings (calculated to the nearest whole number). The team is awarded an additional two points for each possibility eliminated over the number required to score. If fewer than the required number are eliminated, there is no score.
   - Before a team makes a play, help the students decide what is the smallest number of possibilities that must be eliminated in order for the team to score. After each play, compute and record the score.
   - Continue until the strings are determined. The team with the highest score wins.

4. If your students would prefer a faster-paced game, the organization introduced in Volume 4, Activity 22, may be appropriate.
   - Divide the class into four teams of as nearly equal numbers and average ability as possible. Do *not* distribute the game pieces; all the unplaced pieces at each stage of the game remain available to the team whose turn it is.
   - The teams take turns to play, as do the members within each team.

- Plays are made as described under (1) and (2), with a second play being allowed any player whose first play is successful.
- After a visit to the board but before sitting down again, a player may indicate that he or she wishes to identify the string cards. As soon as this announcement is made, the current round of the game is over.
- If the player correctly identifies all the strings, his or her team is awarded two points. If any string is misidentified, each of the other three teams is awarded one point.
- In either case, start a new round of the game with new starting clues and the next scheduled player. Continue playing in this fashion until one of the teams has three points. That team is declared the winner.

Encourage the students to use their String Game analysis sheets while they are playing the game in this way.

Different Versions of the Game

In all versions of the game there are various levels of difficulty. The principal ones, in order of difficulty, are:

Two strings with no empty regions.
Two strings with at least one empty region.
Three strings with no empty regions.
Three strings with at least one empty region.

Similarly, the kinds of starting clues that you provide vary in ease of interpretation. In order of difficulty, they are:

A correctly placed game piece.
A crossed-out drawing of a game piece.
An unidentified dot, indicating that a region is *not* empty.
Hatching to show that a region is empty.
Hatching and dots to show that a region has exactly the indicated number of members.

Obviously, you should match the level of difficulty of the game and your starting clues to the level of maturity, experience, and preparedness of your students. The String Game should be challenging and stimulating without becoming dishearteningly difficult.

1. Shapes String Game (simplified version)
   The simplified version uses only the nine string cards displayed on Shapes String Game Poster 1:

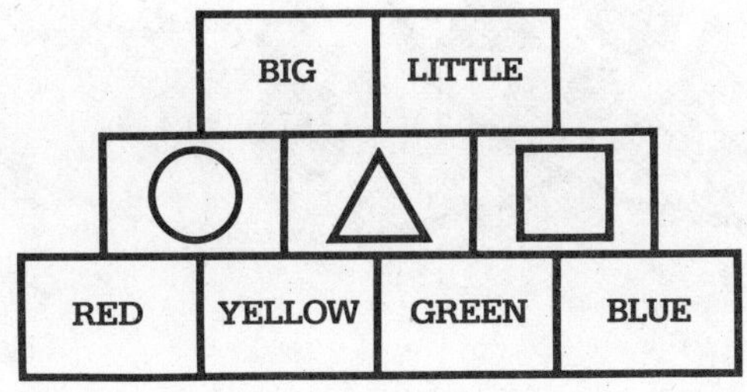

For example:

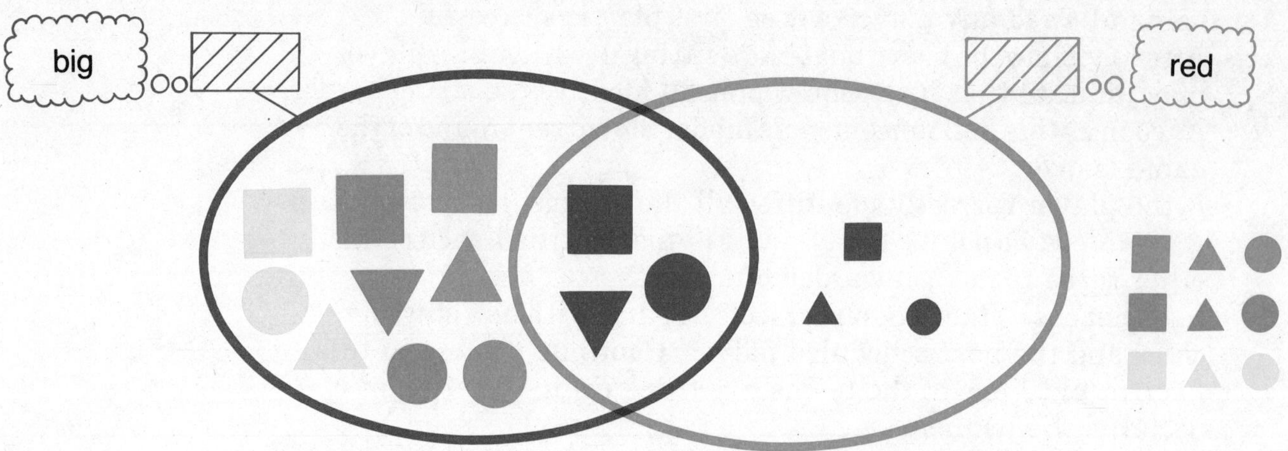

2. Shapes String Game
The full version uses the 16 string cards displayed on Shapes String Game Poster 2:

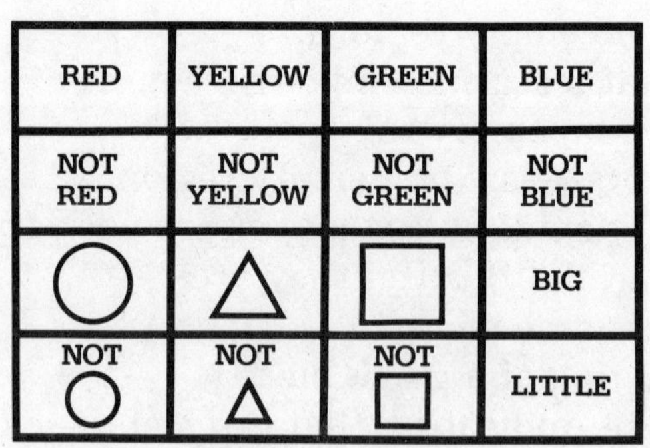

RED	YELLOW	GREEN	BLUE
NOT RED	NOT YELLOW	NOT GREEN	NOT BLUE
○	△	□	BIG
NOT ○	NOT △	NOT □	LITTLE

For example:

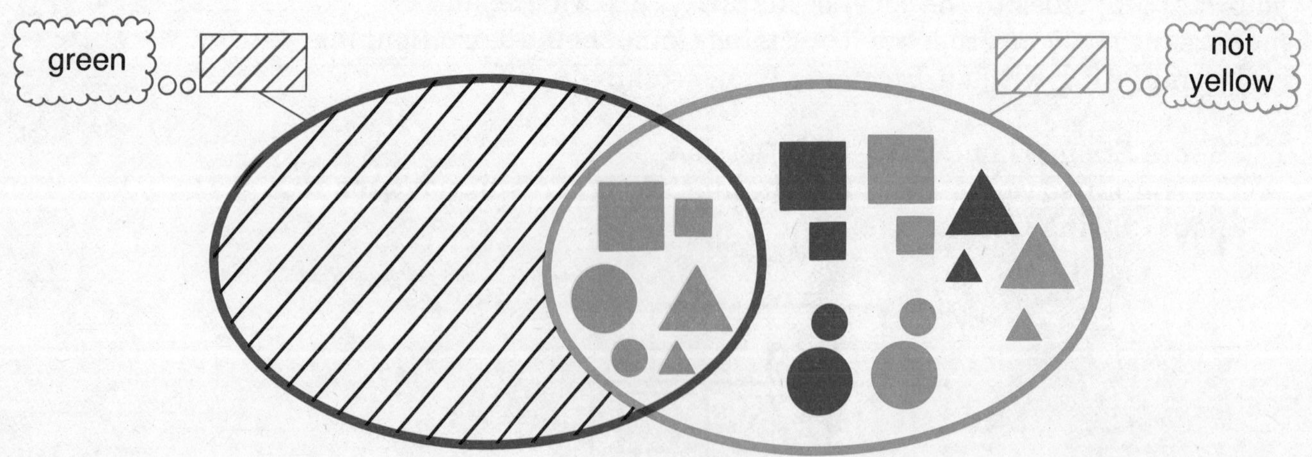

Note that because **not big** and **little** describe exactly the same shapes—and similarly for **not little** and **big**—such a "not-card" is redundant. If any student asks why these two "not-cards" are missing, let the class discuss why they are unnecessary.

3. Numerical String Game
   This version of the game uses the 16 string cards displayed on Numerical String Game Poster 1:

MULTIPLES OF 2	MULTIPLES OF 3	MULTIPLES OF 4	MULTIPLES OF 5
MULTIPLES OF 10	POSITIVE DIVISORS OF 12	POSITIVE DIVISORS OF 18	POSITIVE DIVISORS OF 20
POSITIVE DIVISORS OF 24	POSITIVE DIVISORS OF 27	GREATER THAN 50	GREATER THAN $\widehat{10}$
LESS THAN 50	LESS THAN $\widehat{10}$	ODD NUMBERS	POSITIVE PRIME NUMBERS

For example:

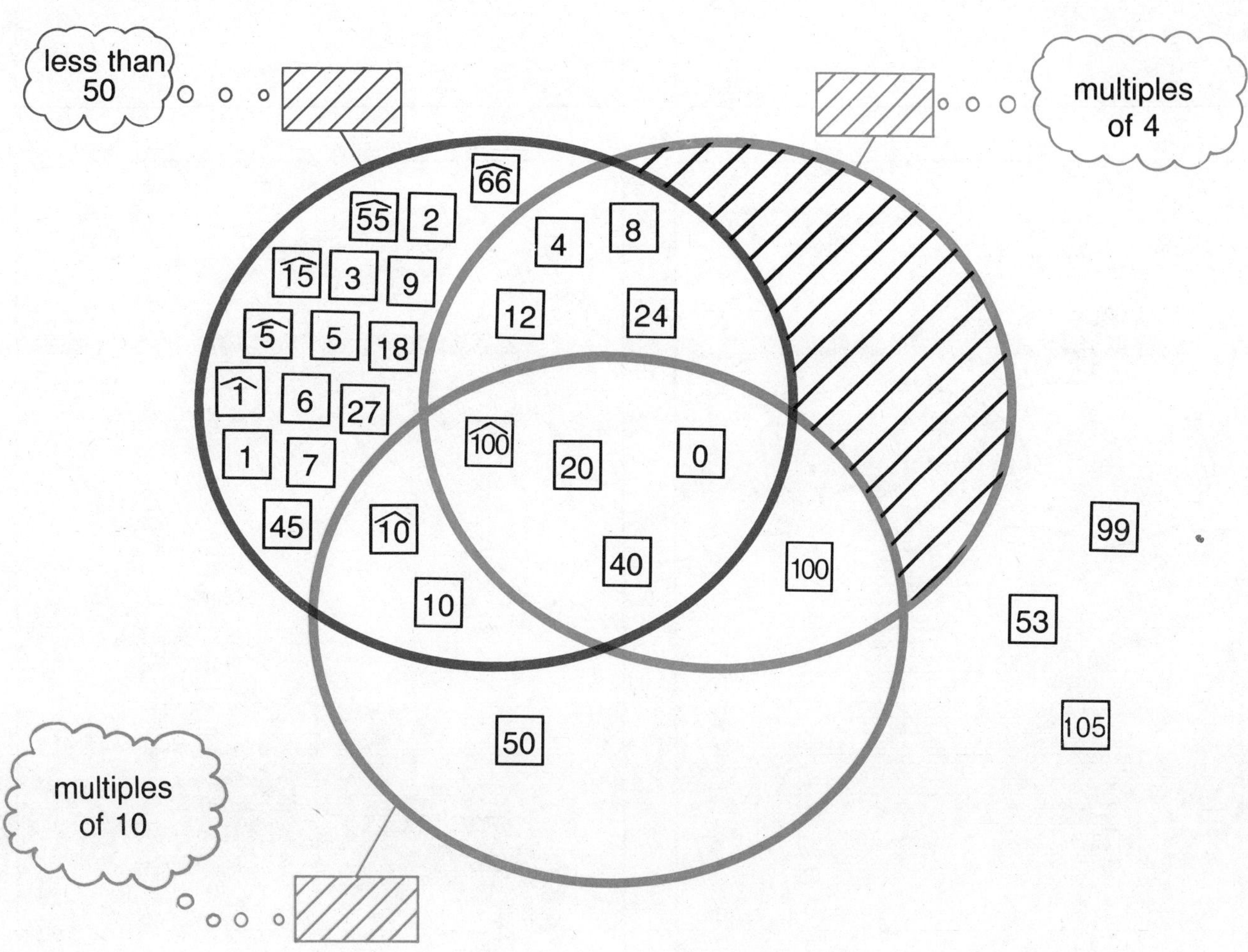

Answer Keys

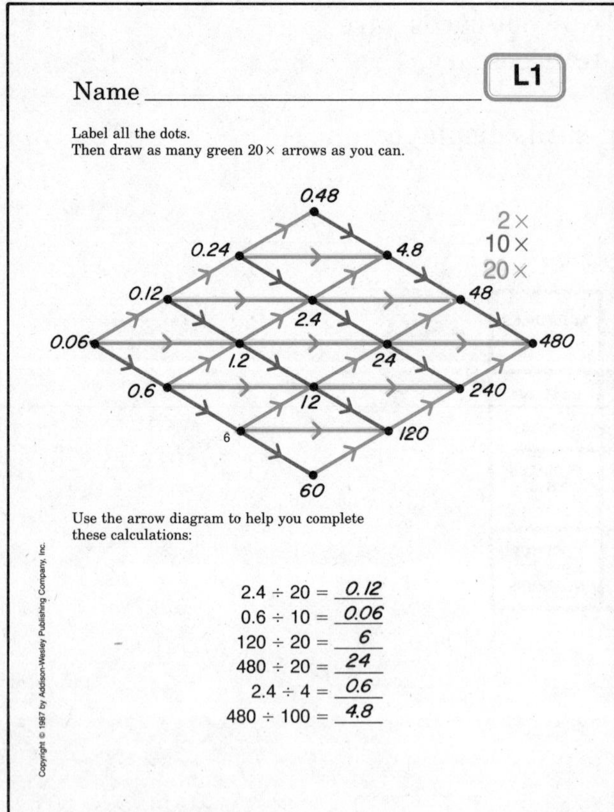

L1

Name ____________________

Label all the dots.
Then draw as many green 20× arrows as you can.

Use the arrow diagram to help you complete these calculations:

2.4 ÷ 20 = 0.12
0.6 ÷ 10 = 0.06
120 ÷ 20 = 6
480 ÷ 20 = 24
2.4 ÷ 4 = 0.6
480 ÷ 100 = 4.8

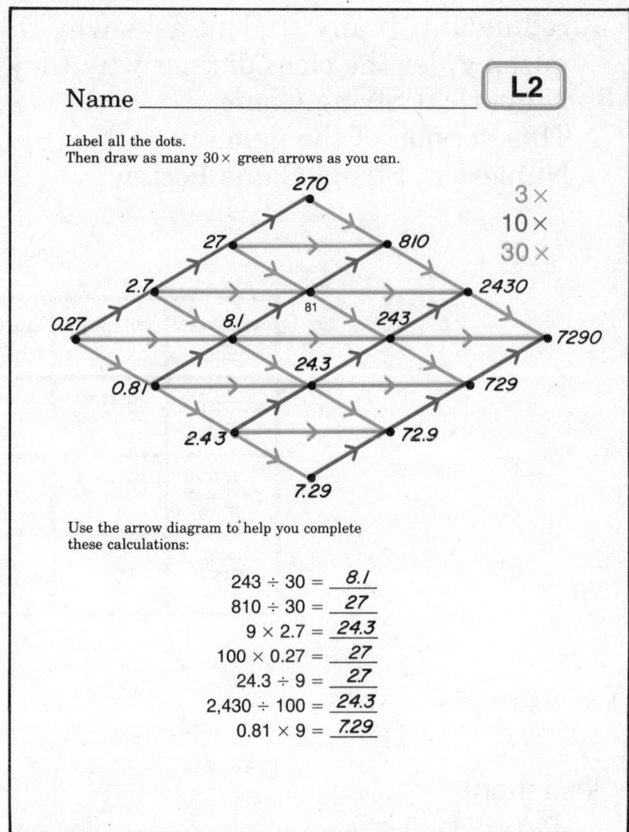

L2

Name ____________________

Label all the dots.
Then draw as many 30× green arrows as you can.

Use the arrow diagram to help you complete these calculations:

243 ÷ 30 = 8.1
810 ÷ 30 = 27
9 × 2.7 = 24.3
100 × 0.27 = 27
24.3 ÷ 9 = 2.7
2,430 ÷ 100 = 24.3
0.81 × 9 = 7.29

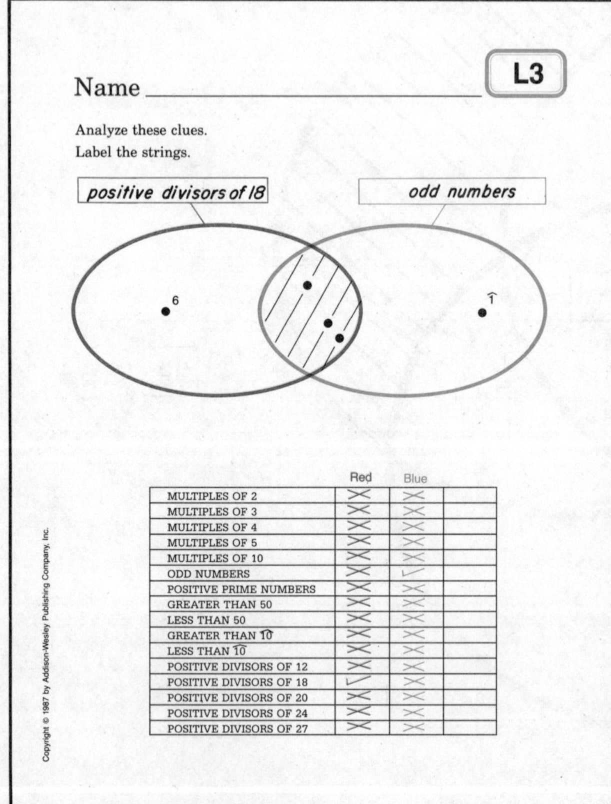

L3

Name ____________________

Analyze these clues.
Label the strings.

	Red	Blue	
MULTIPLES OF 2	X	X	
MULTIPLES OF 3	X	X	
MULTIPLES OF 4	X	X	
MULTIPLES OF 5	X	X	
MULTIPLES OF 10	X	X	
ODD NUMBERS	X	✓	
POSITIVE PRIME NUMBERS	X	X	
GREATER THAN 50	X	X	
LESS THAN 50	X	X	
GREATER THAN 1̂0	X	X	
LESS THAN 1̂0	X	X	
POSITIVE DIVISORS OF 12	X	X	
POSITIVE DIVISORS OF 18	✓	X	
POSITIVE DIVISORS OF 20	X	X	
POSITIVE DIVISORS OF 24	X	X	
POSITIVE DIVISORS OF 27	X	X	

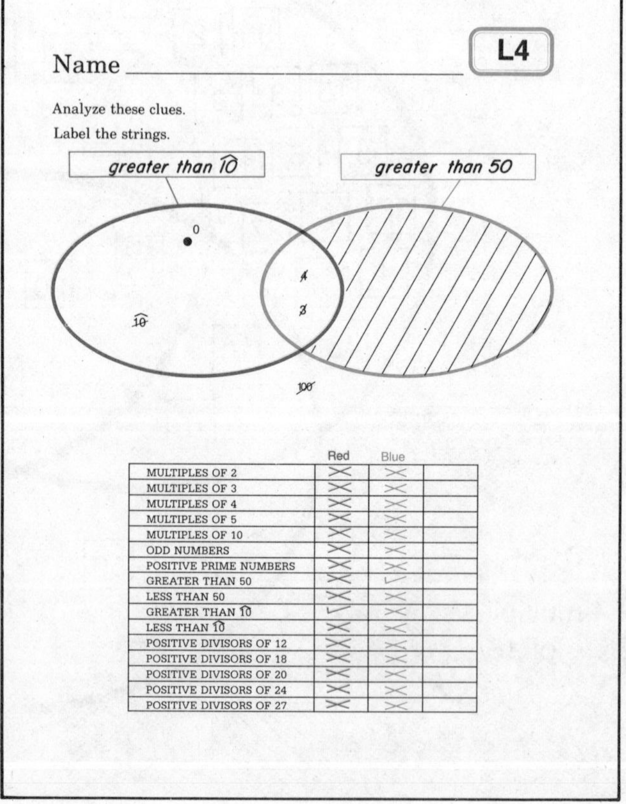

L4

Name ____________________

Analyze these clues.
Label the strings.

	Red	Blue	
MULTIPLES OF 2	X	X	
MULTIPLES OF 3	X	X	
MULTIPLES OF 4	X	X	
MULTIPLES OF 5	X	X	
MULTIPLES OF 10	X	X	
ODD NUMBERS	X	X	
POSITIVE PRIME NUMBERS	X	X	
GREATER THAN 50	X	✓	
LESS THAN 50	X	X	
GREATER THAN 1̂0	✓	X	
LESS THAN 1̂0	X	X	
POSITIVE DIVISORS OF 12	X	X	
POSITIVE DIVISORS OF 18	X	X	
POSITIVE DIVISORS OF 20	X	X	
POSITIVE DIVISORS OF 24	X	X	
POSITIVE DIVISORS OF 27	X	X	

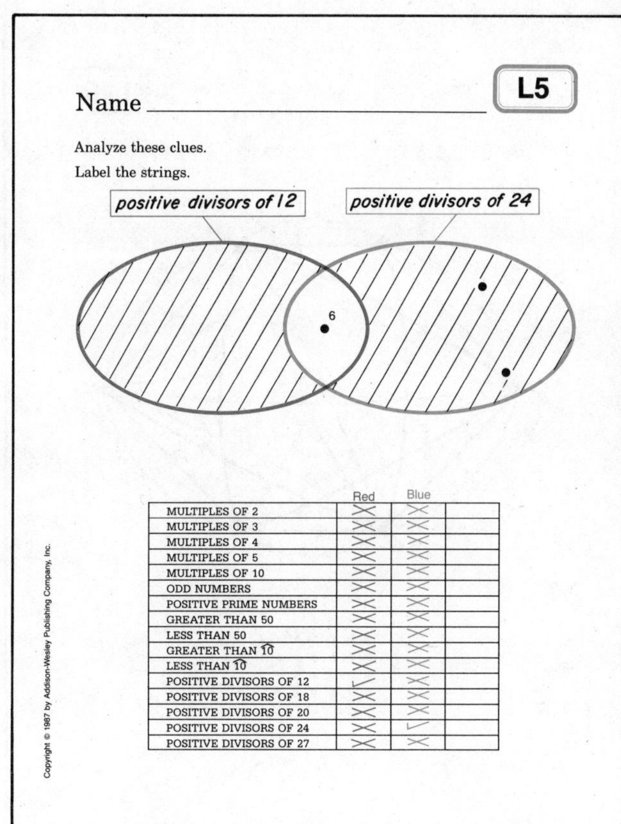

Name ______________________ **L5**

Analyze these clues.
Label the strings.

	Red	Blue	
MULTIPLES OF 2	X	X	
MULTIPLES OF 3	X	X	
MULTIPLES OF 4	X	X	
MULTIPLES OF 5	X	X	
MULTIPLES OF 10	X	X	
ODD NUMBERS	X	X	
POSITIVE PRIME NUMBERS	X	X	
GREATER THAN 50	X	X	
LESS THAN 50	X	X	
GREATER THAN 10	X	X	
LESS THAN 10	X	X	
POSITIVE DIVISORS OF 12	✓	X	
POSITIVE DIVISORS OF 18	X	X	
POSITIVE DIVISORS OF 20	X	X	
POSITIVE DIVISORS OF 24	X	✓	
POSITIVE DIVISORS OF 27	X	X	

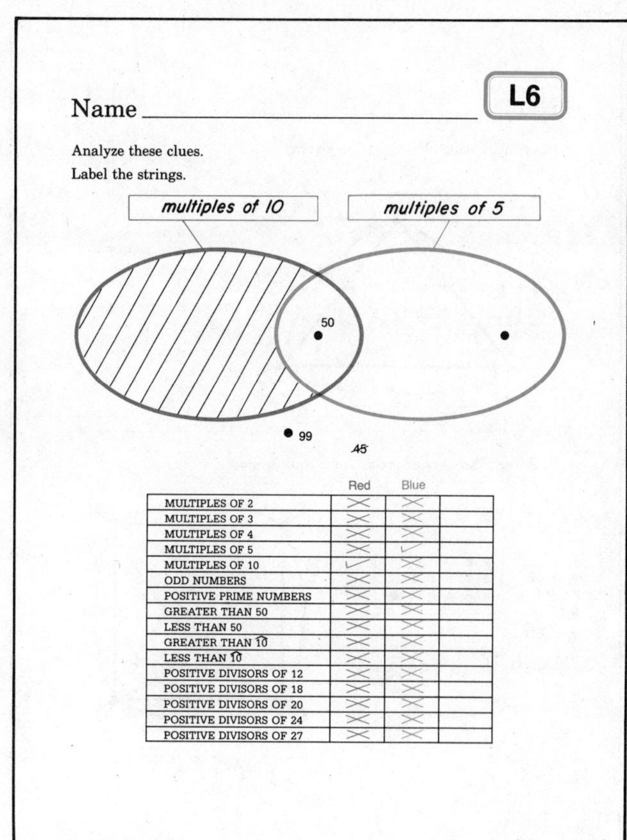

Name ______________________ **L6**

Analyze these clues.
Label the strings.

	Red	Blue	
MULTIPLES OF 2	X	X	
MULTIPLES OF 3	X	X	
MULTIPLES OF 4	X	X	
MULTIPLES OF 5	X	✓	
MULTIPLES OF 10	✓	X	
ODD NUMBERS	X	X	
POSITIVE PRIME NUMBERS	X	X	
GREATER THAN 50	X	X	
LESS THAN 50	X	X	
GREATER THAN 10	X	X	
LESS THAN 10	X	X	
POSITIVE DIVISORS OF 12	X	X	
POSITIVE DIVISORS OF 18	X	X	
POSITIVE DIVISORS OF 20	X	X	
POSITIVE DIVISORS OF 24	X	X	
POSITIVE DIVISORS OF 27	X	X	

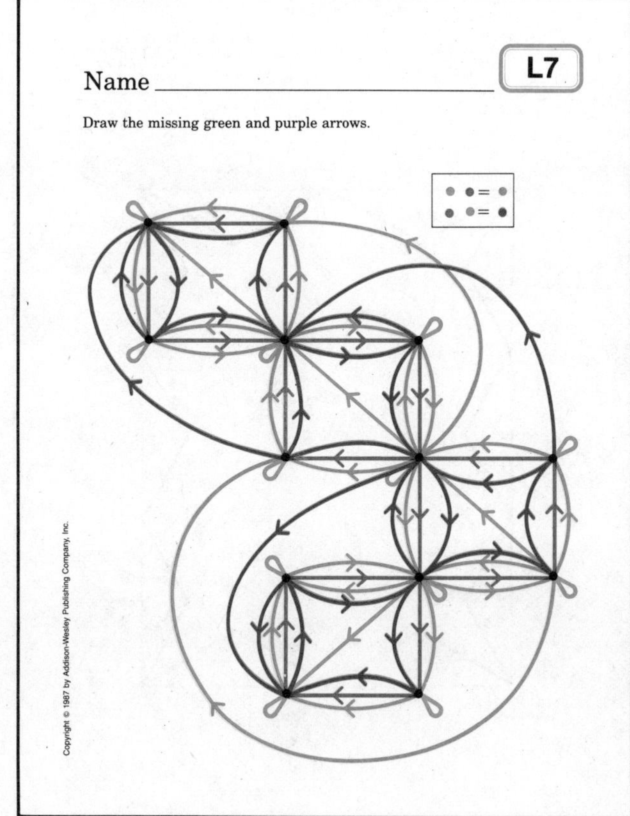

Name ______________________ **L7**

Draw the missing green and purple arrows.

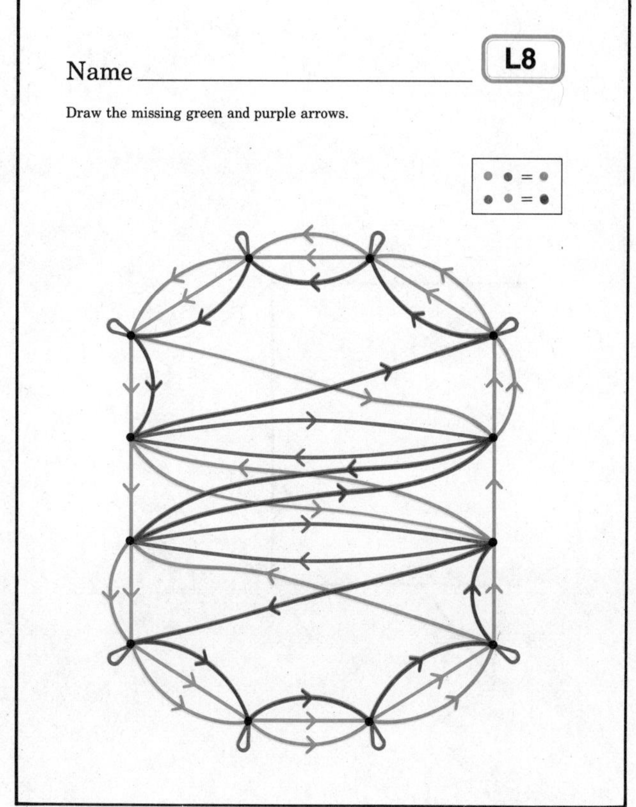

Name ______________________ **L8**

Draw the missing green and purple arrows.

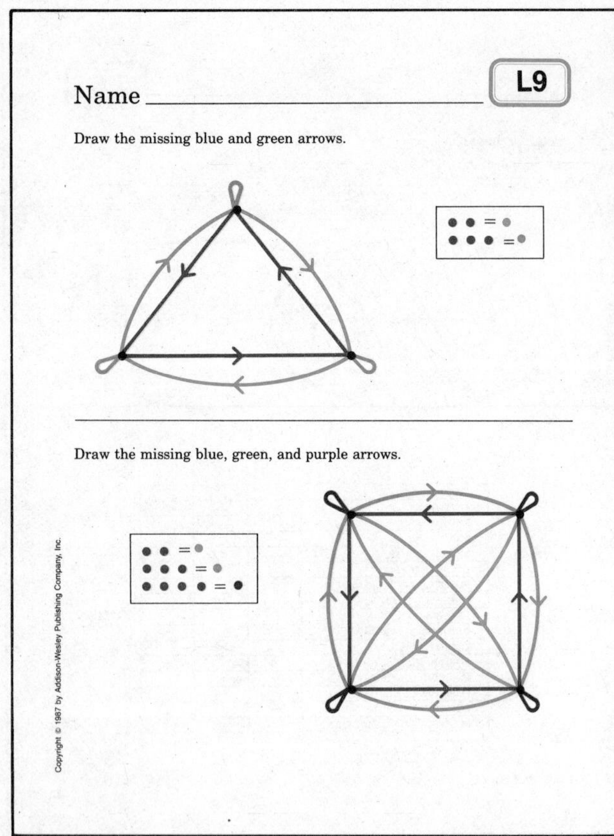
Name
L9
Draw the missing blue and green arrows.
Draw the missing blue, green, and purple arrows.
Copyright © 1987 by Addison-Wesley Publishing Company, Inc.

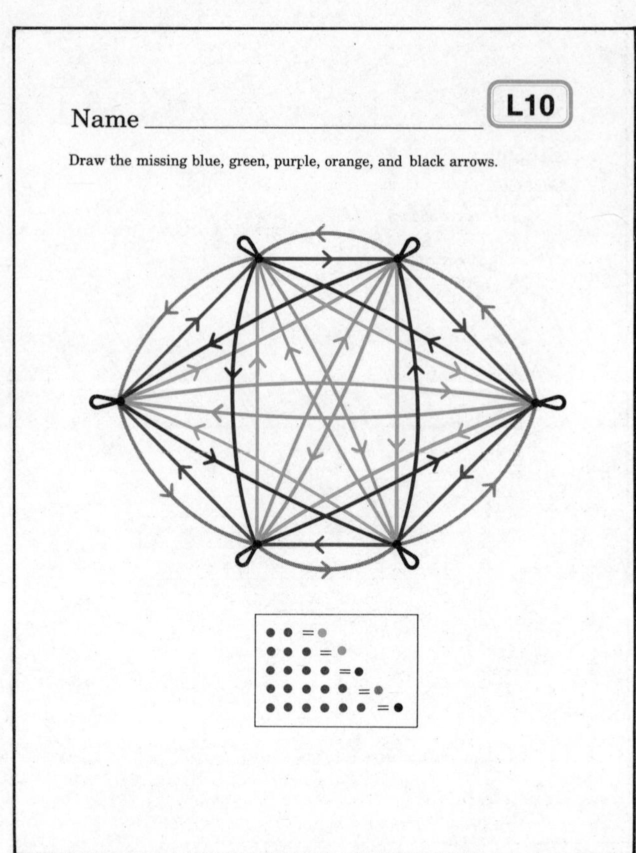
Name
L10
Draw the missing blue, green, purple, orange, and black arrows.

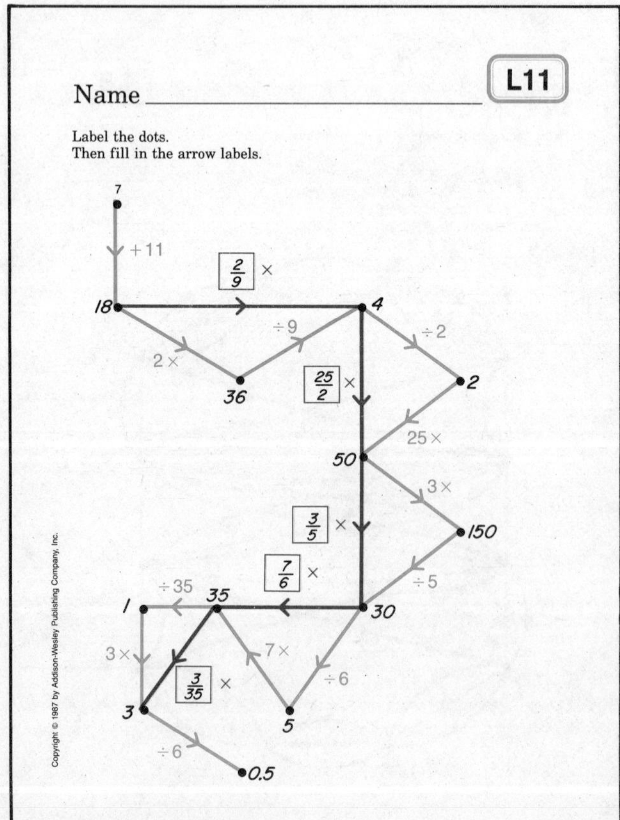
Name
L11
Label the dots.
Then fill in the arrow labels.
7
+11
2/9 ×
18
4
÷9
÷2
2×
36
25/2 ×
2
25×
50
3×
3/5 ×
150
7/6 ×
÷5
1
÷35
35
30
3×
7×
3/35 ×
÷6
3
5
÷6
0.5
Copyright © 1987 by Addison-Wesley Publishing Company, Inc.

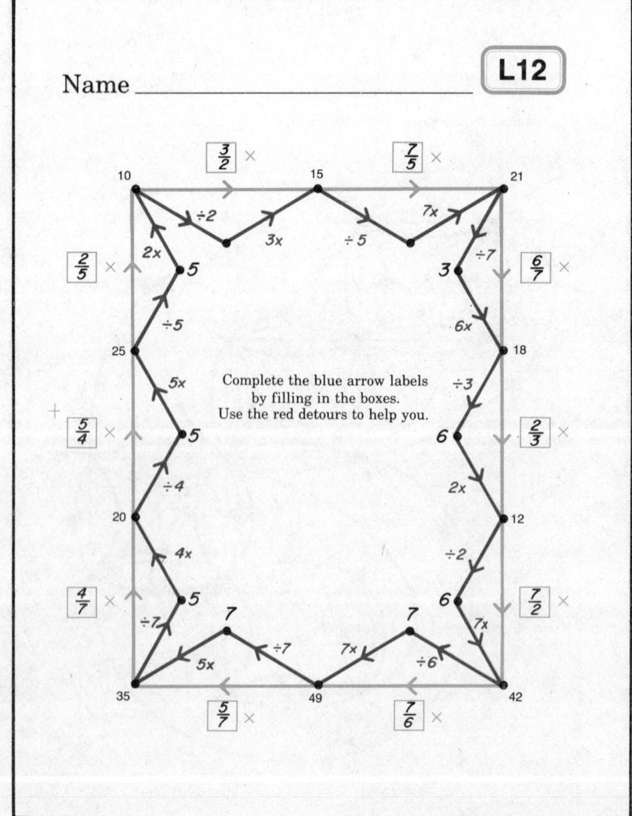
Name
L12
3/2 ×
7/5 ×
10
15
21
÷2
7x
3x
÷5
2x
÷7
2/5 ×
5
3
6/7 ×
÷5
6x
25
18
5x
Complete the blue arrow labels
by filling in the boxes.
Use the red detours to help you.
÷3
5/4 ×
5
6
2/3 ×
÷4
2x
20
12
4x
÷2
4/7 ×
5
6
7/2 ×
÷7
7
7
7x
5x
÷7
7x
÷6
35
49
42
5/7 ×
7/6 ×

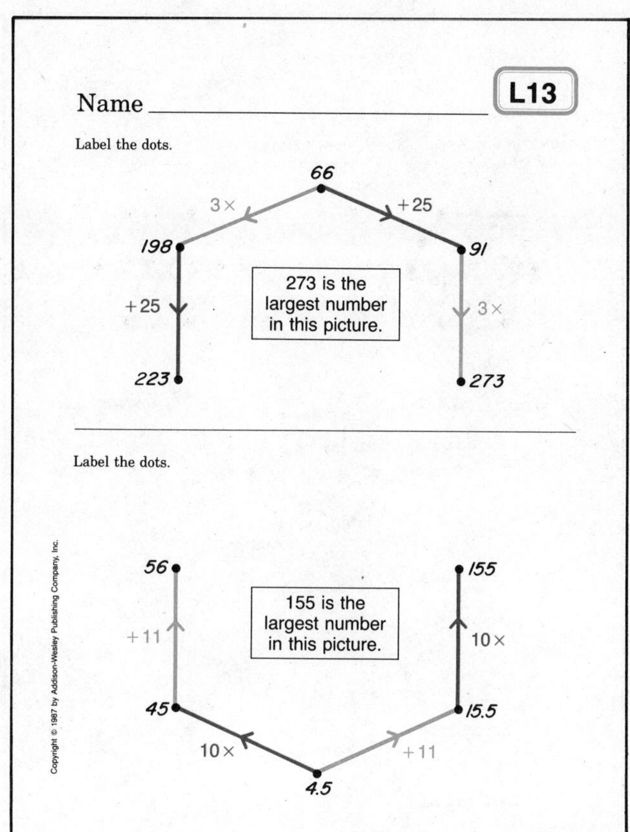

Name ____________ **L13**

Label the dots.

Label the dots.

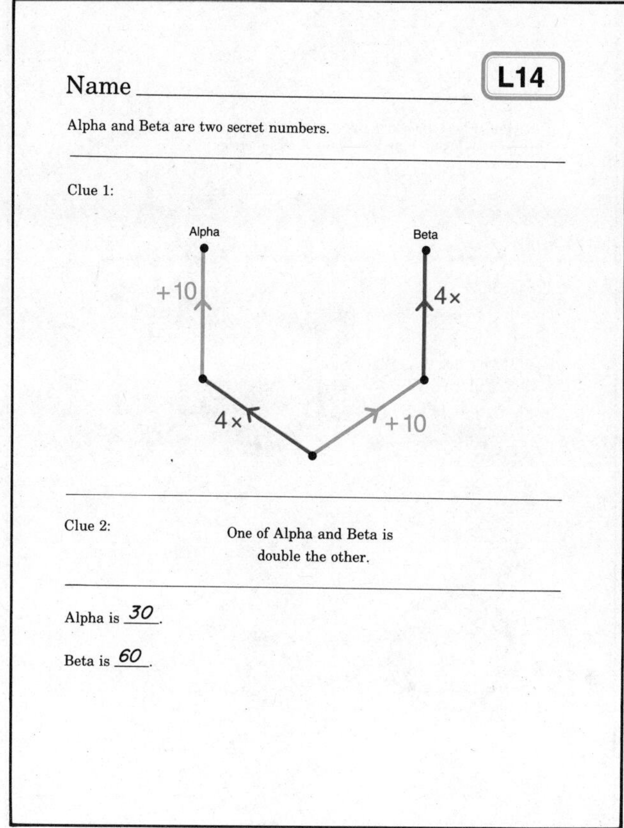

Name ____________ **L14**

Alpha and Beta are two secret numbers.

Clue 1:

Clue 2:

One of Alpha and Beta is double the other.

Alpha is 30.

Beta is 60.

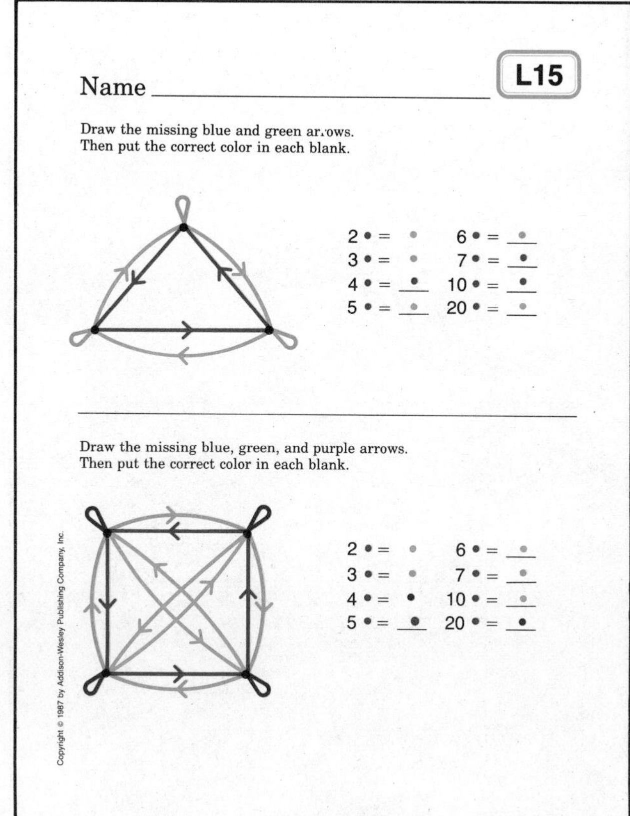

Name ____________ **L15**

Draw the missing blue and green arrows.
Then put the correct color in each blank.

2 • = • 6 • = •
3 • = • 7 • = •
4 • = • 10 • = •
5 • = • 20 • = •

Draw the missing blue, green, and purple arrows.
Then put the correct color in each blank.

2 • = • 6 • = •
3 • = • 7 • = •
4 • = • 10 • = •
5 • = • 20 • = •

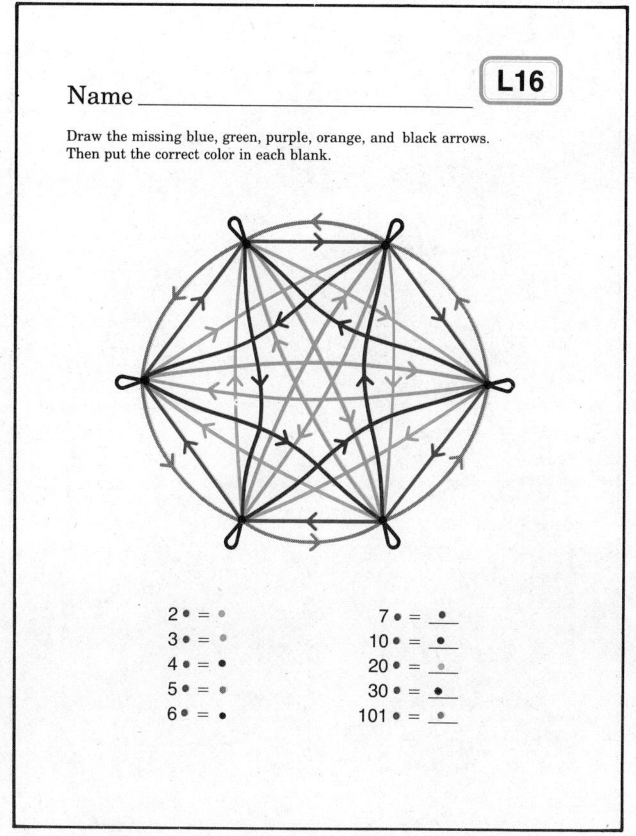

Name ____________ **L16**

Draw the missing blue, green, purple, orange, and black arrows.
Then put the correct color in each blank.

2 • = • 7 • = •
3 • = • 10 • = •
4 • = • 20 • = •
5 • = • 30 • = •
6 • = • 101 • = •

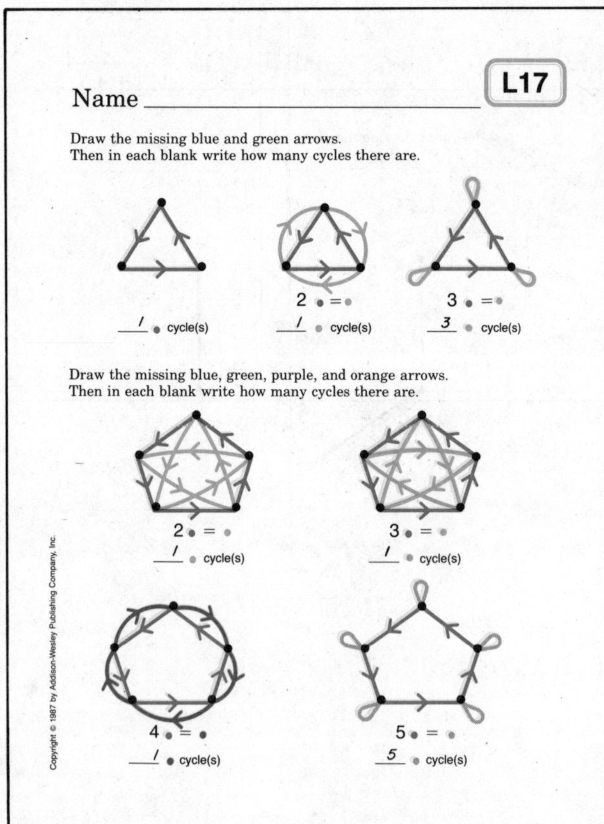

Name ______________________ **L17**

Draw the missing blue and green arrows.
Then in each blank write how many cycles there are.

1 ● cycle(s)

2 ● = ●
1 ● cycle(s)

3 ● = ●
3 ● cycle(s)

Draw the missing blue, green, purple, and orange arrows.
Then in each blank write how many cycles there are.

2 ● = ●
1 ● cycle(s)

3 ● = ●
1 ● cycle(s)

4 ● = ●
1 ● cycle(s)

5 ● = ●
5 ● cycle(s)

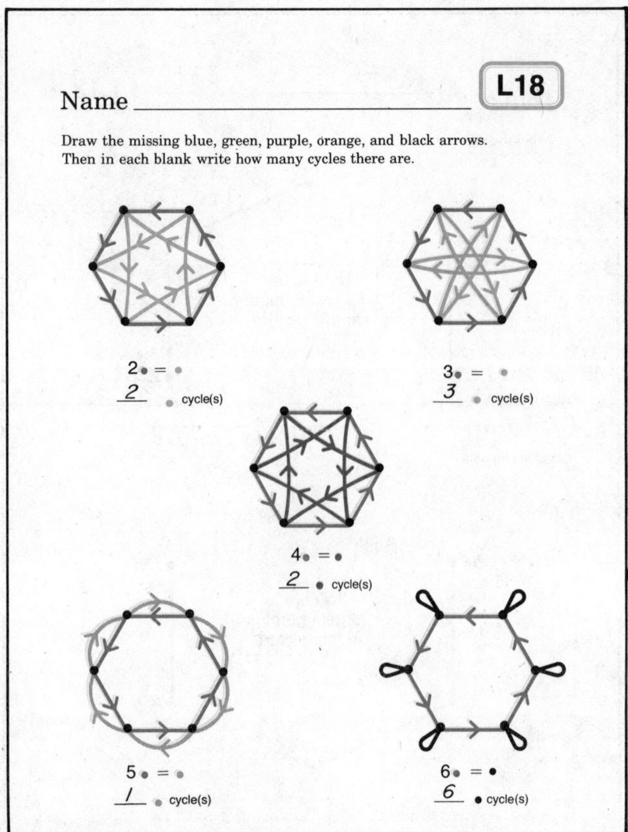

Name ______________________ **L18**

Draw the missing blue, green, purple, orange, and black arrows.
Then in each blank write how many cycles there are.

2 ● = ●
2 ● cycle(s)

3 ● = ●
3 ● cycle(s)

4 ● = ●
2 ● cycle(s)

5 ● = ●
1 ● cycle(s)

6 ● = ●
6 ● cycle(s)

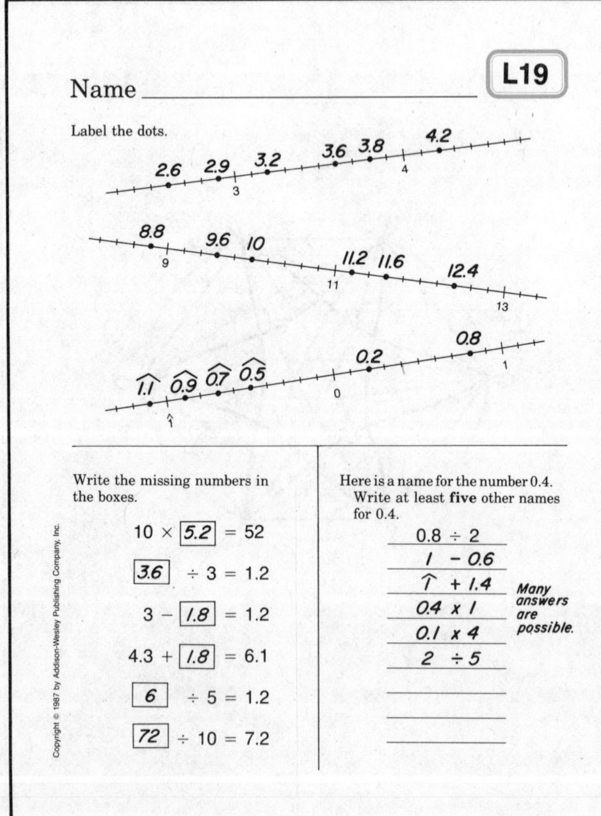

Name ______________________ **L19**

Label the dots.

Write the missing numbers in the boxes.

10 × [5.2] = 52

[3.6] ÷ 3 = 1.2

3 − [1.8] = 1.2

4.3 + [1.8] = 6.1

[6] ÷ 5 = 1.2

[72] ÷ 10 = 7.2

Here is a name for the number 0.4.
Write at least **five** other names for 0.4.

0.8 ÷ 2
1 − 0.6
1̂ + 1.4
0.4 x 1
0.1 x 4
2 ÷ 5

Many answers are possible.

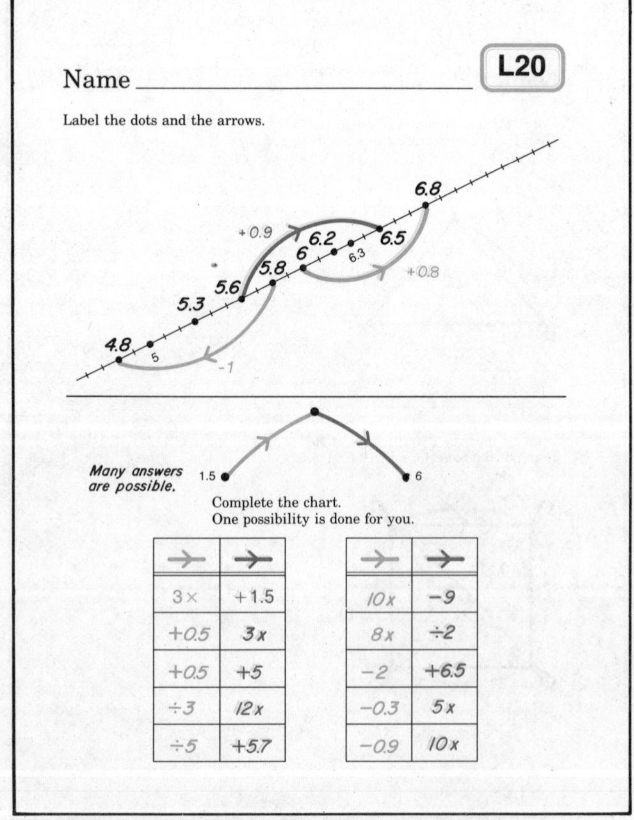

Name ______________________ **L20**

Label the dots and the arrows.

Many answers are possible. 1.5 6

Complete the chart.
One possibility is done for you.

→	→
3×	+1.5
+0.5	3x
+0.5	+5
÷3	12x
÷5	+5.7

→	→
10x	−9
8x	÷2
−2	+6.5
−0.3	5x
−0.9	10x

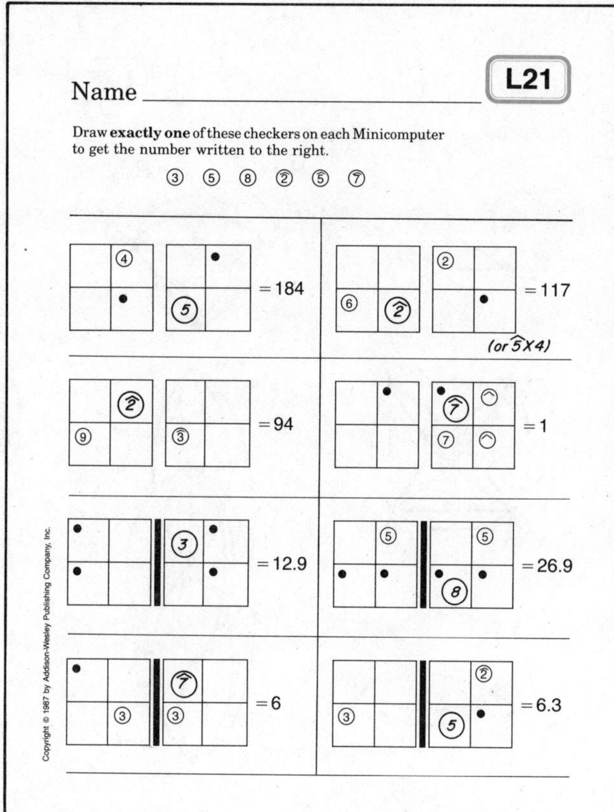

Name ____________________ **L21**

Draw **exactly one** of these checkers on each Minicomputer to get the number written to the right.

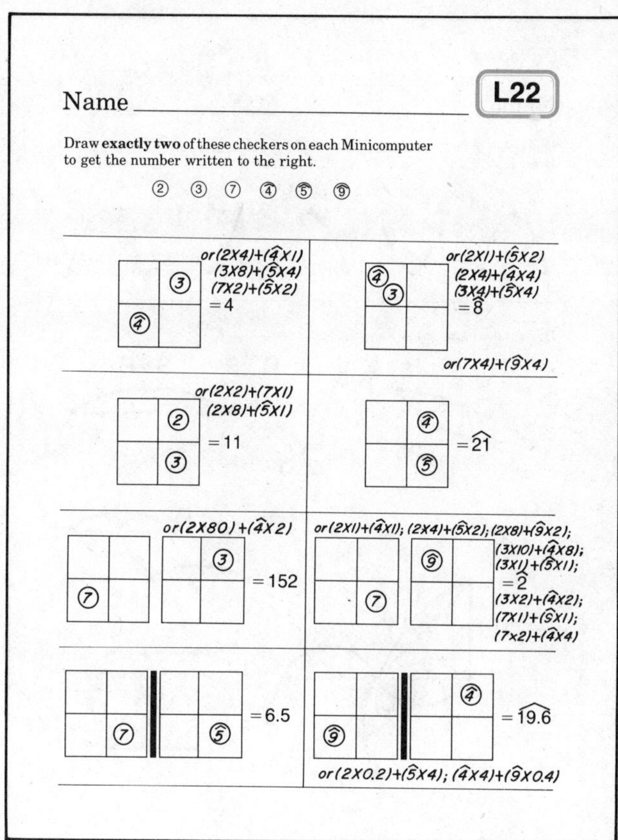

Name ____________________ **L22**

Draw **exactly two** of these checkers on each Minicomputer to get the number written to the right.

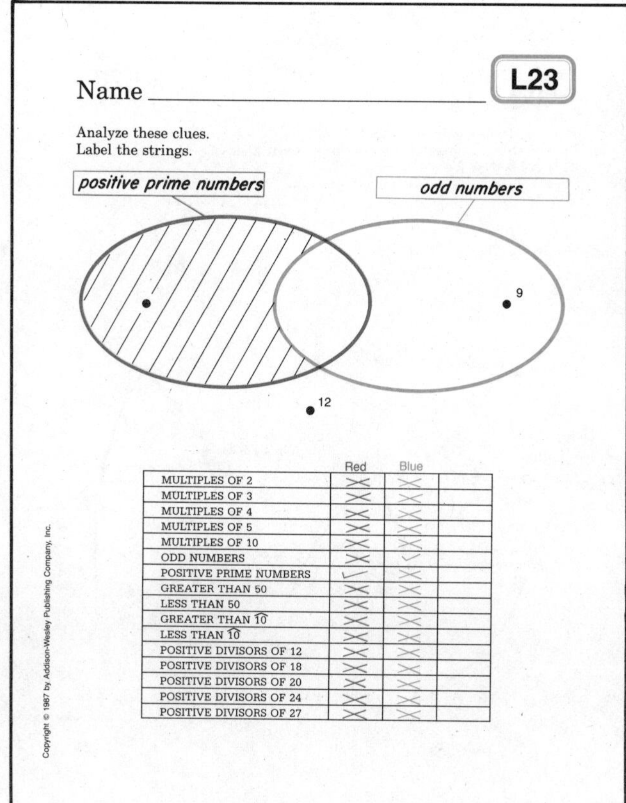

Name ____________________ **L23**

Analyze these clues.
Label the strings.

	Red	Blue	
MULTIPLES OF 2	X	X	
MULTIPLES OF 3	X	X	
MULTIPLES OF 4	X	X	
MULTIPLES OF 5	X	X	
MULTIPLES OF 10	X	X	
ODD NUMBERS	X	✓	
POSITIVE PRIME NUMBERS	✓	X	
GREATER THAN 50	X	X	
LESS THAN 50	X	X	
GREATER THAN 1̂0	X	X	
LESS THAN 1̂0	X	X	
POSITIVE DIVISORS OF 12	X	X	
POSITIVE DIVISORS OF 18	X	X	
POSITIVE DIVISORS OF 20	X	X	
POSITIVE DIVISORS OF 24	X	X	
POSITIVE DIVISORS OF 27	X	X	

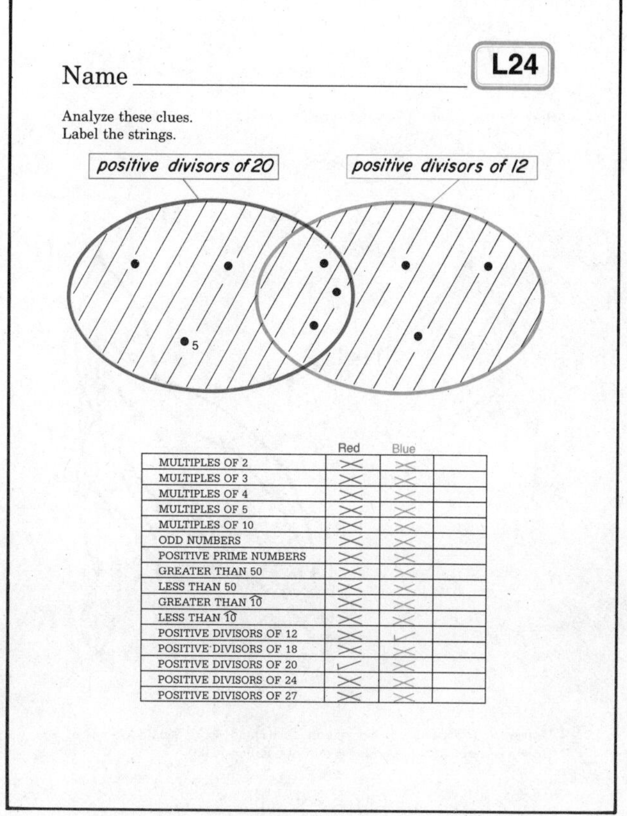

Name ____________________ **L24**

Analyze these clues.
Label the strings.

	Red	Blue	
MULTIPLES OF 2	X	X	
MULTIPLES OF 3	X	X	
MULTIPLES OF 4	X	X	
MULTIPLES OF 5	X	X	
MULTIPLES OF 10	X	X	
ODD NUMBERS	X	X	
POSITIVE PRIME NUMBERS	X	X	
GREATER THAN 50	X	X	
LESS THAN 50	X	X	
GREATER THAN 1̂0	X	X	
LESS THAN 1̂0	X	X	
POSITIVE DIVISORS OF 12	X	✓	
POSITIVE DIVISORS OF 18	X	X	
POSITIVE DIVISORS OF 20	✓	X	
POSITIVE DIVISORS OF 24	X	X	
POSITIVE DIVISORS OF 27	X	X	

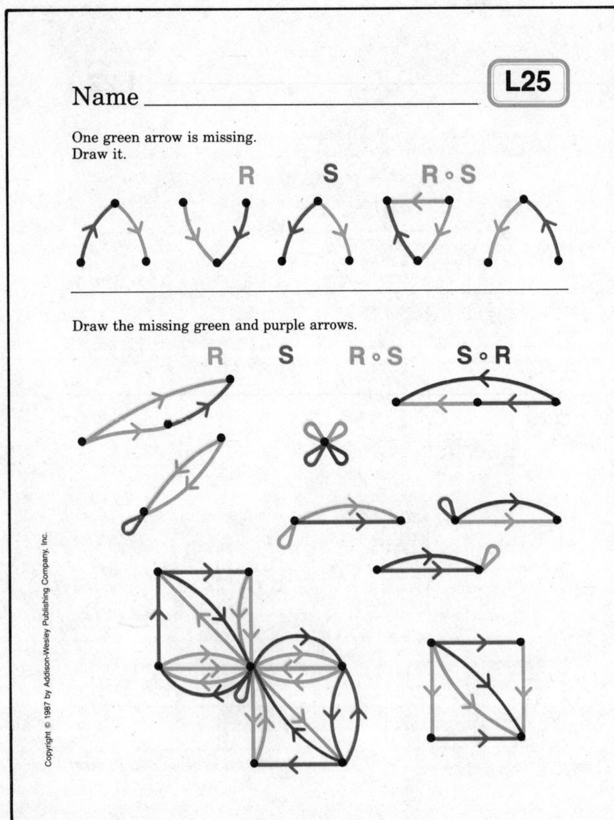

Name
L25
One green arrow is missing.
Draw it.
R
S
R∘S
Draw the missing green and purple arrows.
R
S
R∘S
S∘R
Copyright © 1987 by Addison-Wesley Publishing Company, Inc.

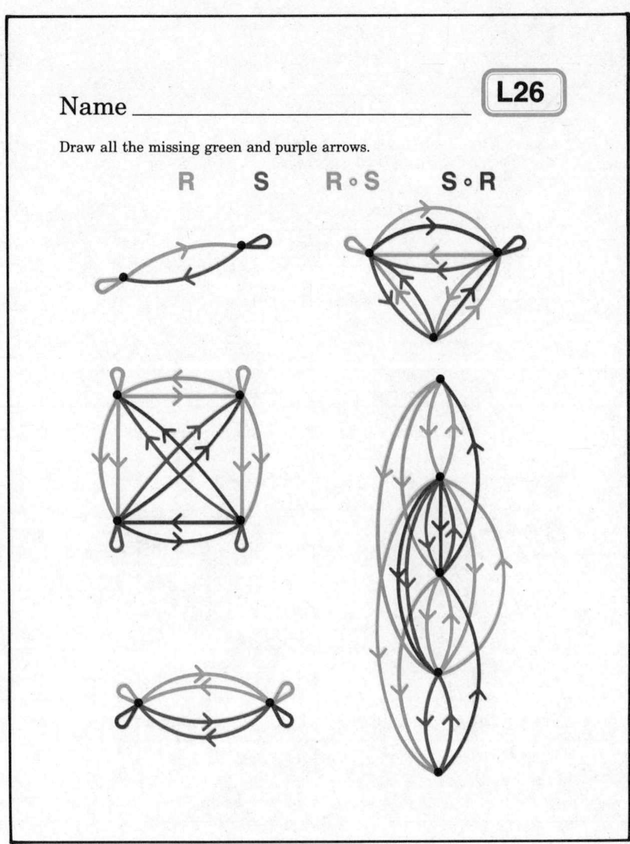

Name
L26
Draw all the missing green and purple arrows.
R
S
R∘S
S∘R

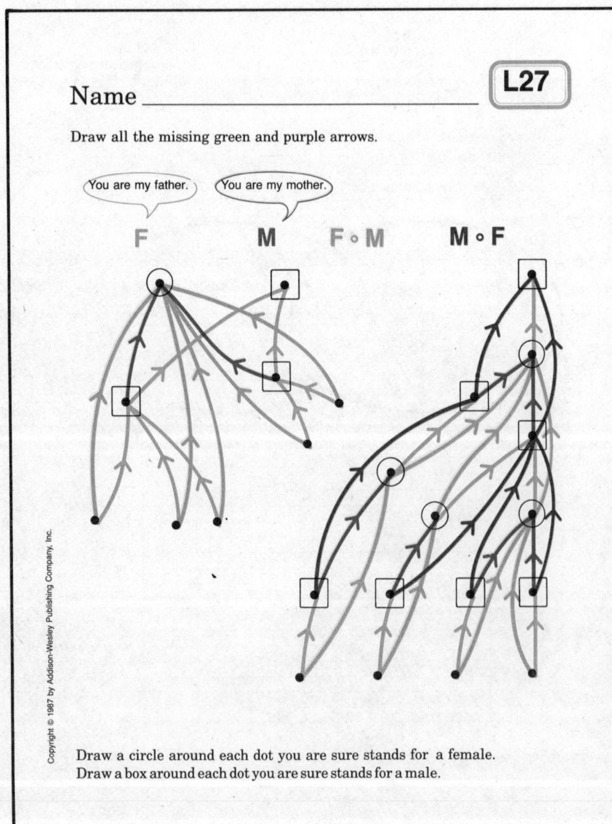

Name
L27
Draw all the missing green and purple arrows.
You are my father.
You are my mother.
F
M
F∘M
M∘F
Draw a circle around each dot you are sure stands for a female.
Draw a box around each dot you are sure stands for a male.
Copyright © 1987 by Addison-Wesley Publishing Company, Inc.

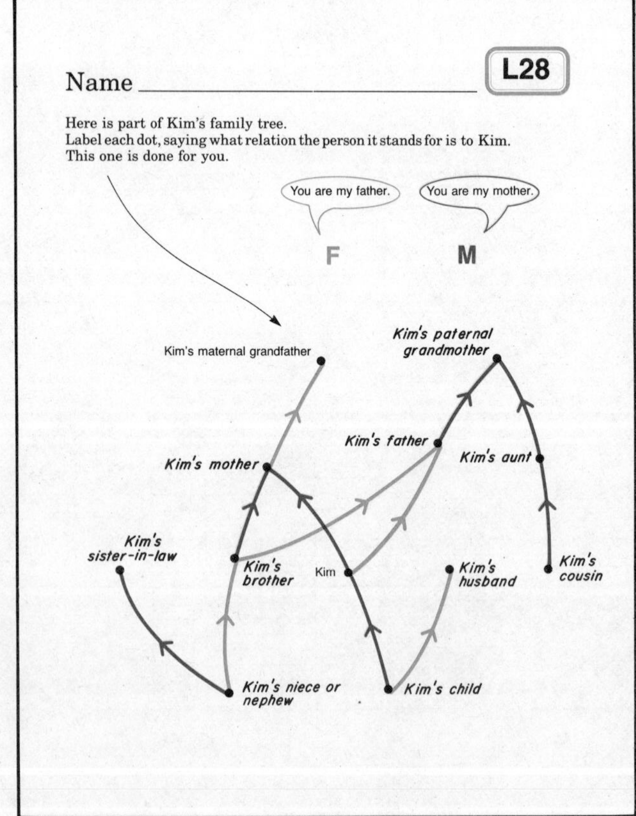

Name
L28
Here is part of Kim's family tree.
Label each dot, saying what relation the person it stands for is to Kim.
This one is done for you.
You are my father.
You are my mother.
F
M
Kim's maternal grandfather
Kim's paternal grandmother
Kim's father
Kim's aunt
Kim's mother
Kim's sister-in-law
Kim's brother
Kim
Kim's husband
Kim's cousin
Kim's niece or nephew
Kim's child

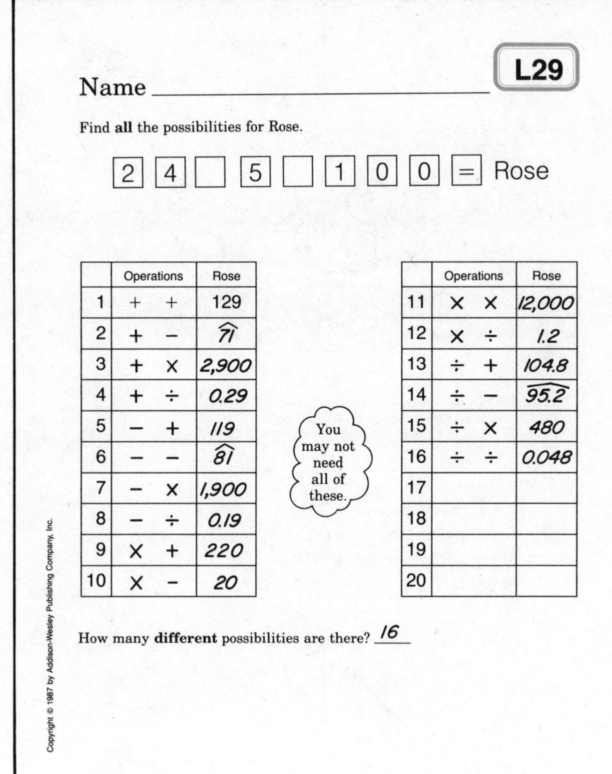

Name ______________ **L29**

Find **all** the possibilities for Rose.

2 4 ☐ 5 ☐ 1 0 0 = Rose

	Operations	Rose
1	+ +	129
2	+ −	71
3	+ ×	2,900
4	+ ÷	0.29
5	− +	119
6	− −	81
7	− ×	1,900
8	− ÷	0.19
9	× +	220
10	× −	20

	Operations	Rose
11	× ×	12,000
12	× ÷	1.2
13	÷ +	104.8
14	÷ −	95.2
15	÷ ×	480
16	÷ ÷	0.048
17		
18		
19		
20		

You may not need all of these.

How many **different** possibilities are there? 16

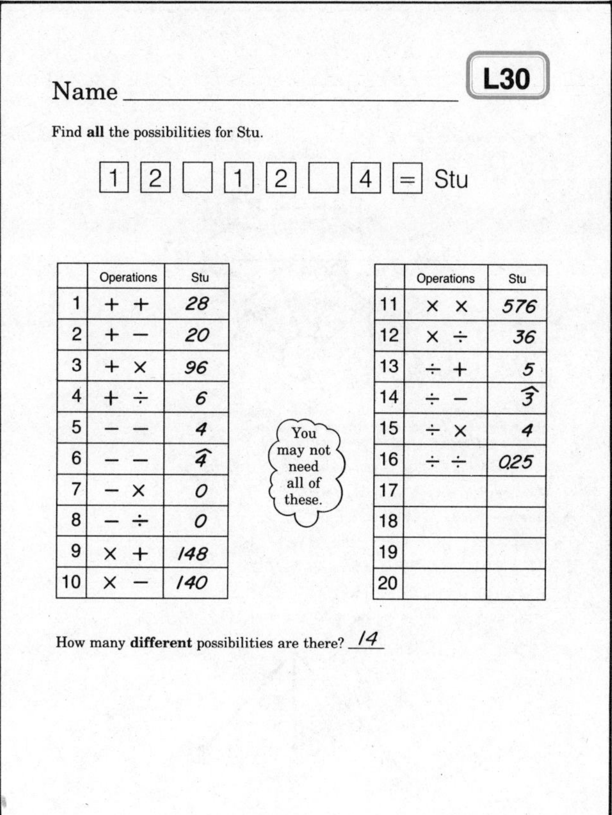

Name ______________ **L30**

Find **all** the possibilities for Stu.

1 2 ☐ 1 2 ☐ 4 = Stu

	Operations	Stu
1	+ +	28
2	+ −	20
3	+ ×	96
4	+ ÷	6
5	− −	4
6	− −	4
7	− ×	0
8	− ÷	0
9	× +	148
10	× −	140

	Operations	Stu
11	× ×	576
12	× ÷	36
13	÷ +	5
14	÷ −	3
15	÷ ×	4
16	÷ ÷	0.25
17		
18		
19		
20		

You may not need all of these.

How many **different** possibilities are there? 14

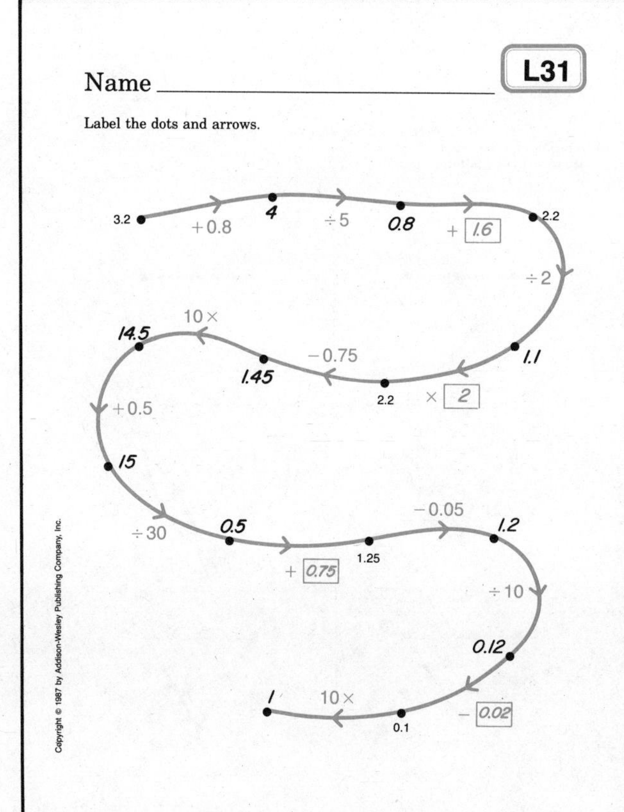

Name ______________ **L31**

Label the dots and arrows.

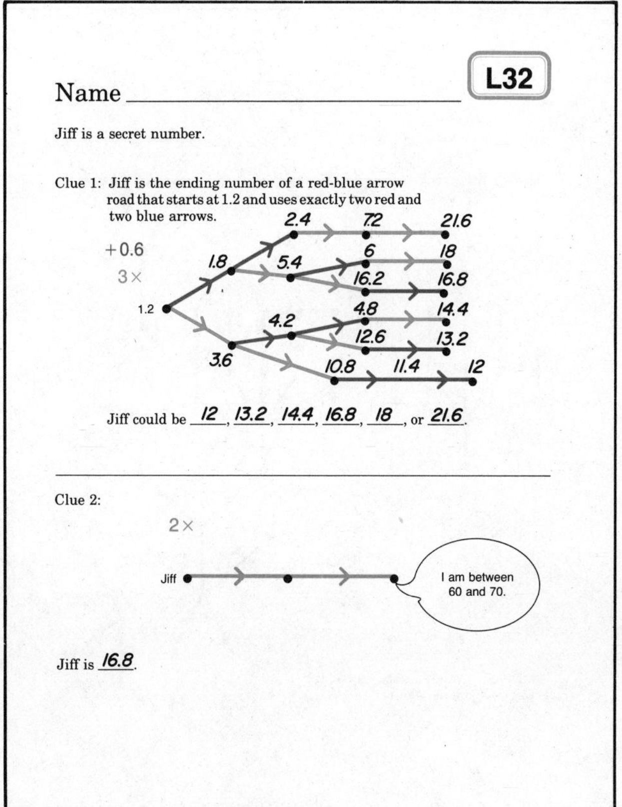

Name ______________ **L32**

Jiff is a secret number.

Clue 1: Jiff is the ending number of a red-blue arrow road that starts at 1.2 and uses exactly two red and two blue arrows.

Jiff could be 12, 13.2, 14.4, 16.8, 18, or 21.6.

Clue 2:

Jiff is 16.8.

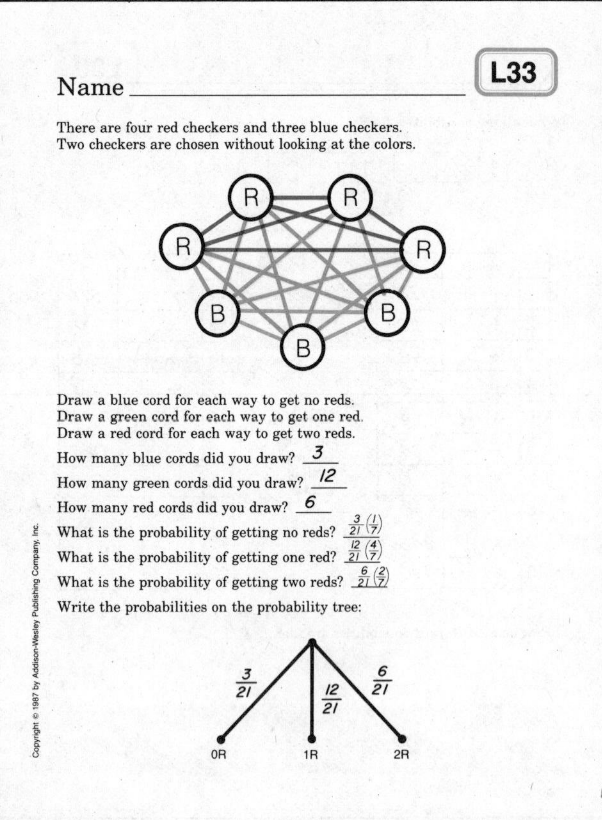

Name ____________ **L33**

There are four red checkers and three blue checkers.
Two checkers are chosen without looking at the colors.

Draw a blue cord for each way to get no reds.
Draw a green cord for each way to get one red.
Draw a red cord for each way to get two reds.

How many blue cords did you draw? 3

How many green cords did you draw? 12

How many red cords did you draw? 6

What is the probability of getting no reds? $\frac{3}{21}$ $(\frac{1}{7})$

What is the probability of getting one red? $\frac{12}{21}$ $(\frac{4}{7})$

What is the probability of getting two reds? $\frac{6}{21}$ $(\frac{2}{7})$

Write the probabilities on the probability tree:

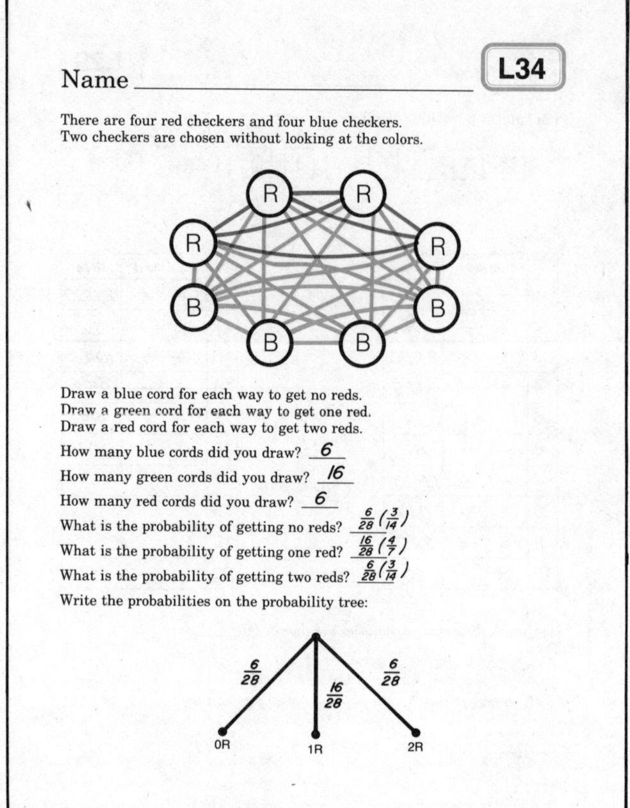

Name ____________ **L34**

There are four red checkers and four blue checkers.
Two checkers are chosen without looking at the colors.

Draw a blue cord for each way to get no reds.
Draw a green cord for each way to get one red.
Draw a red cord for each way to get two reds.

How many blue cords did you draw? 6

How many green cords did you draw? 16

How many red cords did you draw? 6

What is the probability of getting no reds? $\frac{6}{28}$ $(\frac{3}{14})$

What is the probability of getting one red? $\frac{16}{28}$ $(\frac{4}{7})$

What is the probability of getting two reds? $\frac{6}{28}$ $(\frac{3}{14})$

Write the probabilities on the probability tree:

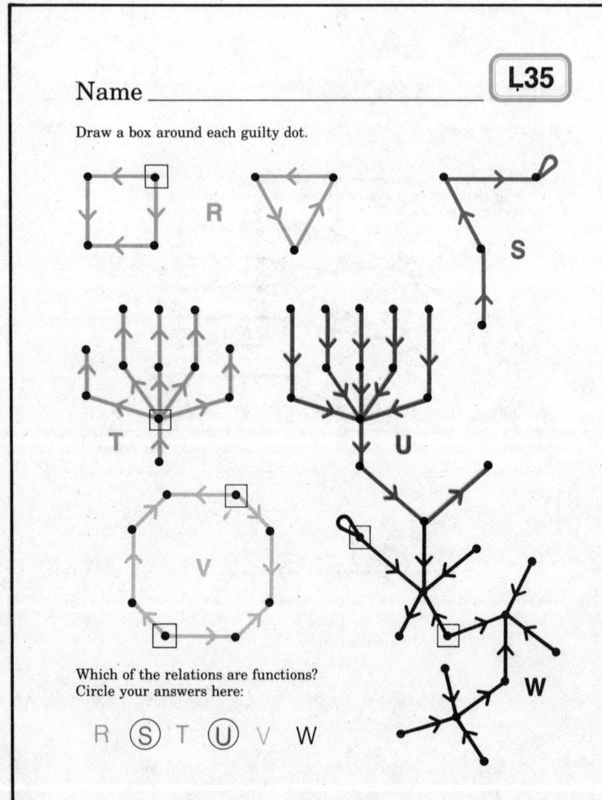

Name ____________ **L35**

Draw a box around each guilty dot.

Which of the relations are functions?
Circle your answers here:

R (S) T (U) V W

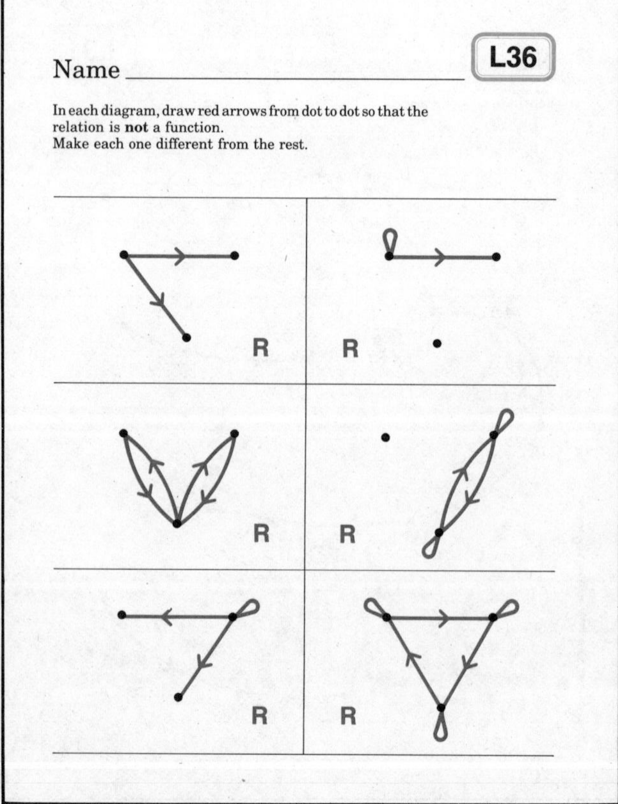

Name ____________ **L36**

In each diagram, draw red arrows from dot to dot so that the relation is **not** a function.
Make each one different from the rest.

Name ____________ **L37**

Complete these equations.

$2 +_{10} 4 +_{10} 6 +_{10} 8 = \boxed{0}$

$2 \times_{10} 4 \times_{10} 6 \times_{10} 8 = \boxed{4}$

$1 +_{10} 3 +_{10} 5 +_{10} 7 +_{10} 9 = \boxed{5}$

$1 \times_{10} 3 \times_{10} 5 \times_{10} 7 \times_{10} 9 = \boxed{5}$

$3 +_{10} 4 +_{10} 5 +_{10} 6 = \boxed{8}$

$3 \times_{10} 4 \times_{10} 5 \times_{10} 6 = \boxed{0}$

For each equation, list all the numbers less than 10 that could be in the box.

$\square \times_{10} 7 = 3$ 9

$4 \times_{10} \square = 2$ 3,8

$5 \times_{10} \square = 5$ 1,3,5,7,9

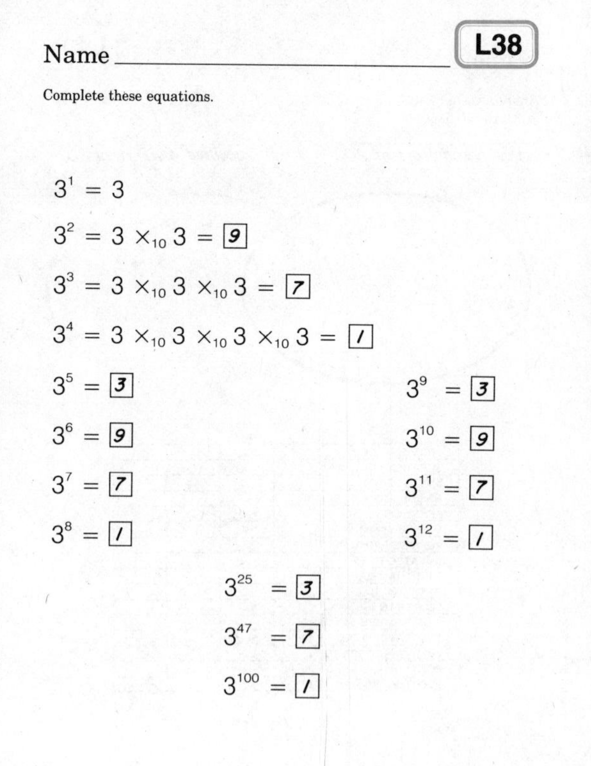

Name ____________ **L38**

Complete these equations.

$3^1 = 3$

$3^2 = 3 \times_{10} 3 = \boxed{9}$

$3^3 = 3 \times_{10} 3 \times_{10} 3 = \boxed{7}$

$3^4 = 3 \times_{10} 3 \times_{10} 3 \times_{10} 3 = \boxed{1}$

$3^5 = \boxed{3}$ $3^9 = \boxed{3}$

$3^6 = \boxed{9}$ $3^{10} = \boxed{9}$

$3^7 = \boxed{7}$ $3^{11} = \boxed{7}$

$3^8 = \boxed{1}$ $3^{12} = \boxed{1}$

$3^{25} = \boxed{3}$

$3^{47} = \boxed{7}$

$3^{100} = \boxed{1}$

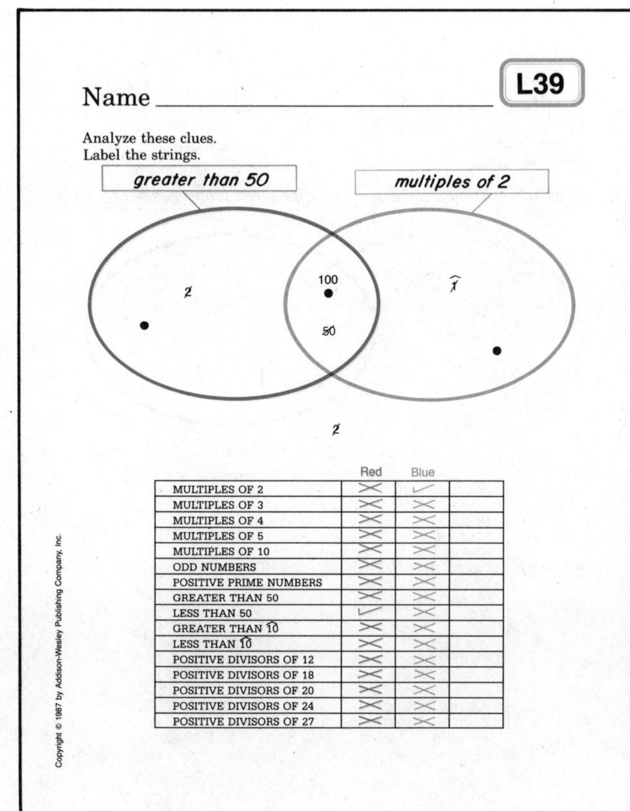

Name ____________ **L39**

Analyze these clues.
Label the strings.

	Red	Blue	
MULTIPLES OF 2	X	✓	
MULTIPLES OF 3	X	X	
MULTIPLES OF 4	X	X	
MULTIPLES OF 5	X	X	
MULTIPLES OF 10	X	X	
ODD NUMBERS	X	X	
POSITIVE PRIME NUMBERS	X	X	
GREATER THAN 50	X	X	
LESS THAN 50	✓	X	
GREATER THAN $\widehat{10}$	X	X	
LESS THAN $\widehat{10}$	X	X	
POSITIVE DIVISORS OF 12	X	X	
POSITIVE DIVISORS OF 18	X	X	
POSITIVE DIVISORS OF 20	X	X	
POSITIVE DIVISORS OF 24	X	X	
POSITIVE DIVISORS OF 27	X	X	

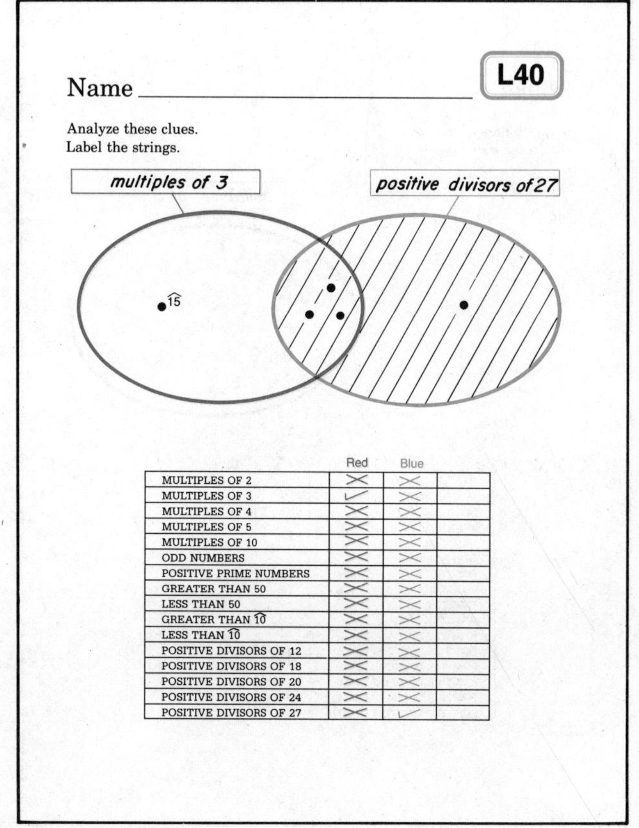

Name ____________ **L40**

Analyze these clues.
Label the strings.

	Red	Blue	
MULTIPLES OF 2	X	X	
MULTIPLES OF 3	✓	X	
MULTIPLES OF 4	X	X	
MULTIPLES OF 5	X	X	
MULTIPLES OF 10	X	X	
ODD NUMBERS	X	X	
POSITIVE PRIME NUMBERS	X	X	
GREATER THAN 50	X	X	
LESS THAN 50	X	X	
GREATER THAN $\widehat{10}$	X	X	
LESS THAN $\widehat{10}$	X	X	
POSITIVE DIVISORS OF 12	X	X	
POSITIVE DIVISORS OF 18	X	X	
POSITIVE DIVISORS OF 20	X	X	
POSITIVE DIVISORS OF 24	X	X	
POSITIVE DIVISORS OF 27	X	✓	

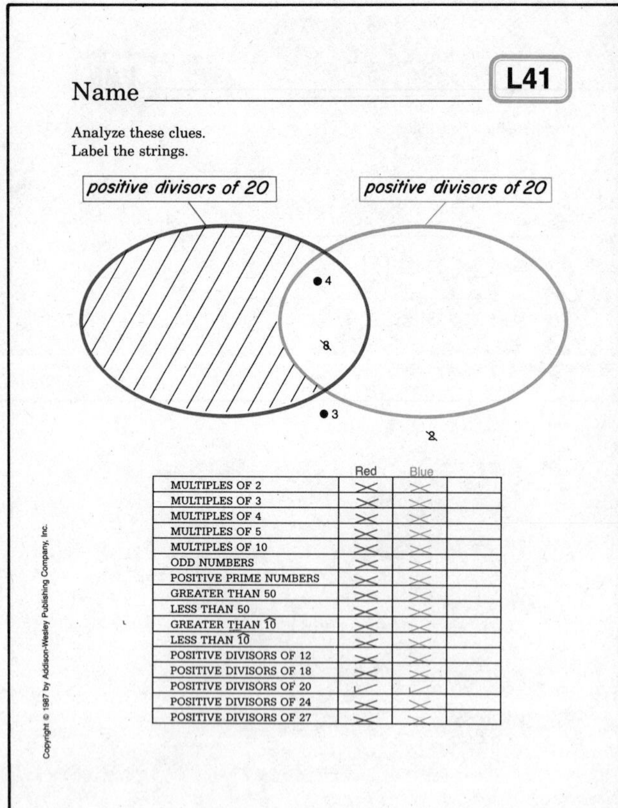
Name ______________ **L41**

Analyze these clues.
Label the strings.

	Red	Blue	
MULTIPLES OF 2	X	X	
MULTIPLES OF 3	X	X	
MULTIPLES OF 4	X	X	
MULTIPLES OF 5	X	X	
MULTIPLES OF 10	X	X	
ODD NUMBERS	X	X	
POSITIVE PRIME NUMBERS	X	X	
GREATER THAN 50	X	X	
LESS THAN 50	X	X	
GREATER THAN 10	X	X	
LESS THAN 10	X	X	
POSITIVE DIVISORS OF 12	X	X	
POSITIVE DIVISORS OF 18	X	X	
POSITIVE DIVISORS OF 20	✓	✓	
POSITIVE DIVISORS OF 24	X	X	
POSITIVE DIVISORS OF 27	X	X	

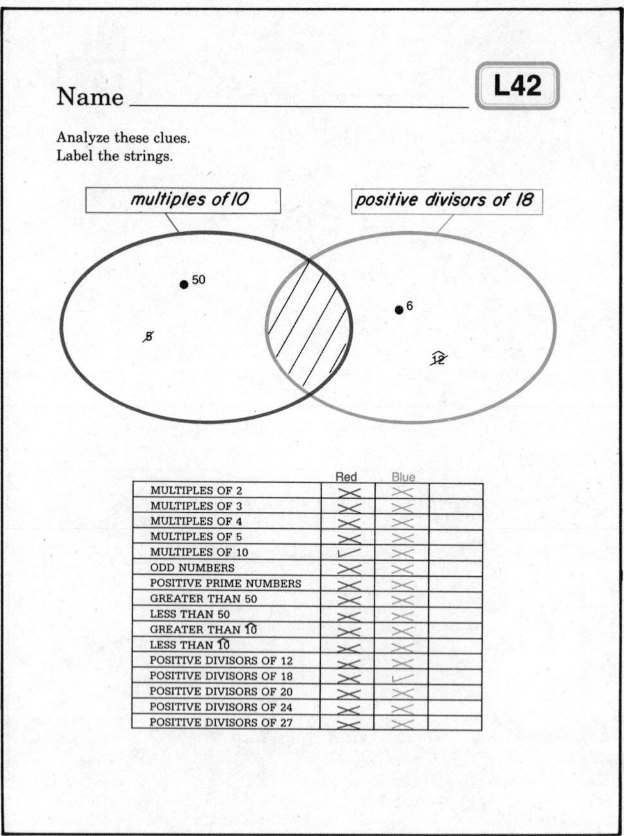
Name ______________ **L42**

Analyze these clues.
Label the strings.

	Red	Blue	
MULTIPLES OF 2	X	X	
MULTIPLES OF 3	X	X	
MULTIPLES OF 4	X	X	
MULTIPLES OF 5	X	X	
MULTIPLES OF 10	✓	X	
ODD NUMBERS	X	X	
POSITIVE PRIME NUMBERS	X	X	
GREATER THAN 50	X	X	
LESS THAN 50	X	X	
GREATER THAN 10	X	X	
LESS THAN 10	X	X	
POSITIVE DIVISORS OF 12	X	X	
POSITIVE DIVISORS OF 18	X	✓	
POSITIVE DIVISORS OF 20	X	X	
POSITIVE DIVISORS OF 24	X	X	
POSITIVE DIVISORS OF 27	X	X	

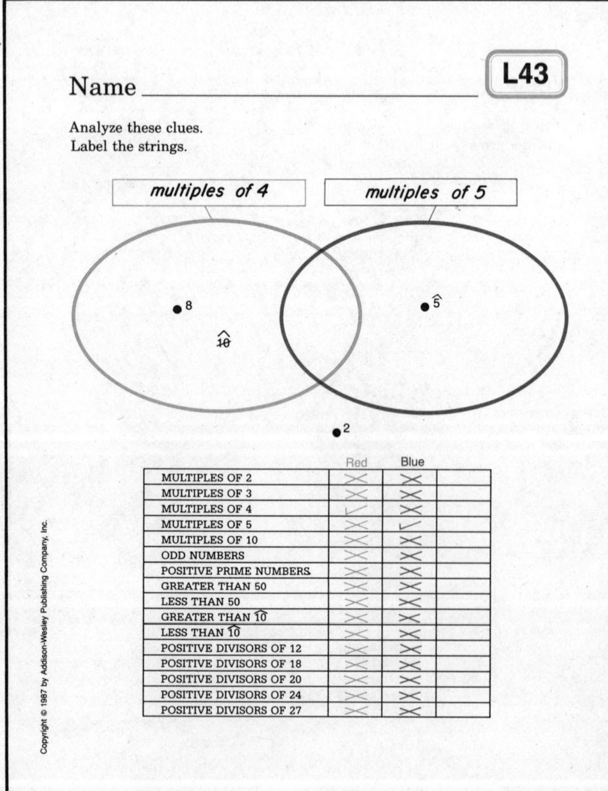
Name ______________ **L43**

Analyze these clues.
Label the strings.

	Red	Blue	
MULTIPLES OF 2	X	X	
MULTIPLES OF 3	X	X	
MULTIPLES OF 4	✓	X	
MULTIPLES OF 5	X	✓	
MULTIPLES OF 10	X	X	
ODD NUMBERS	X	X	
POSITIVE PRIME NUMBERS	X	X	
GREATER THAN 50	X	X	
LESS THAN 50	X	X	
GREATER THAN 10	X	X	
LESS THAN 10	X	X	
POSITIVE DIVISORS OF 12	X	X	
POSITIVE DIVISORS OF 18	X	X	
POSITIVE DIVISORS OF 20	X	X	
POSITIVE DIVISORS OF 24	X	X	
POSITIVE DIVISORS OF 27	X	X	

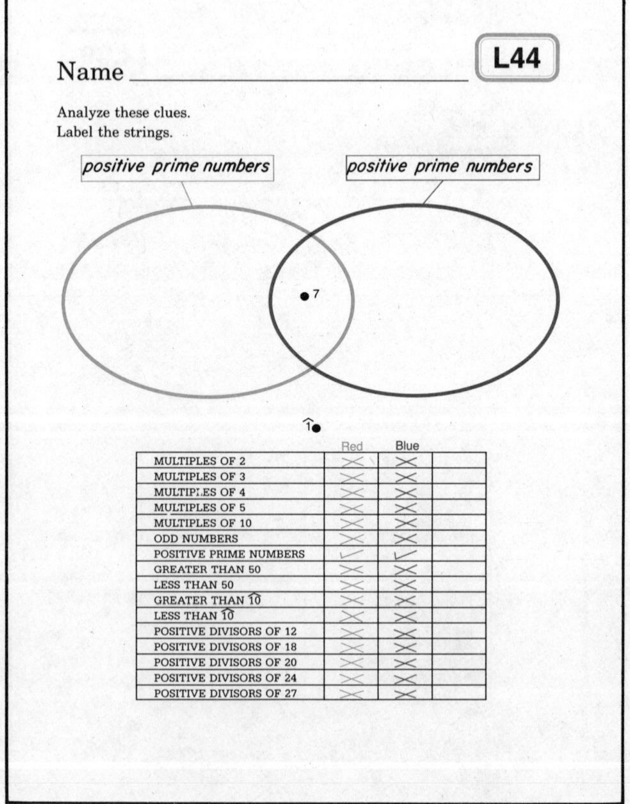
Name ______________ **L44**

Analyze these clues.
Label the strings.

	Red	Blue	
MULTIPLES OF 2	X	X	
MULTIPLES OF 3	X	X	
MULTIPLES OF 4	X	X	
MULTIPLES OF 5	X	X	
MULTIPLES OF 10	X	X	
ODD NUMBERS	X	X	
POSITIVE PRIME NUMBERS	✓	✓	
GREATER THAN 50	X	X	
LESS THAN 50	X	X	
GREATER THAN 10	X	X	
LESS THAN 10	X	X	
POSITIVE DIVISORS OF 12	X	X	
POSITIVE DIVISORS OF 18	X	X	
POSITIVE DIVISORS OF 20	X	X	
POSITIVE DIVISORS OF 24	X	X	
POSITIVE DIVISORS OF 27	X	X	

Name ______________________ **L45**

Analyze these clues.
Label the strings.

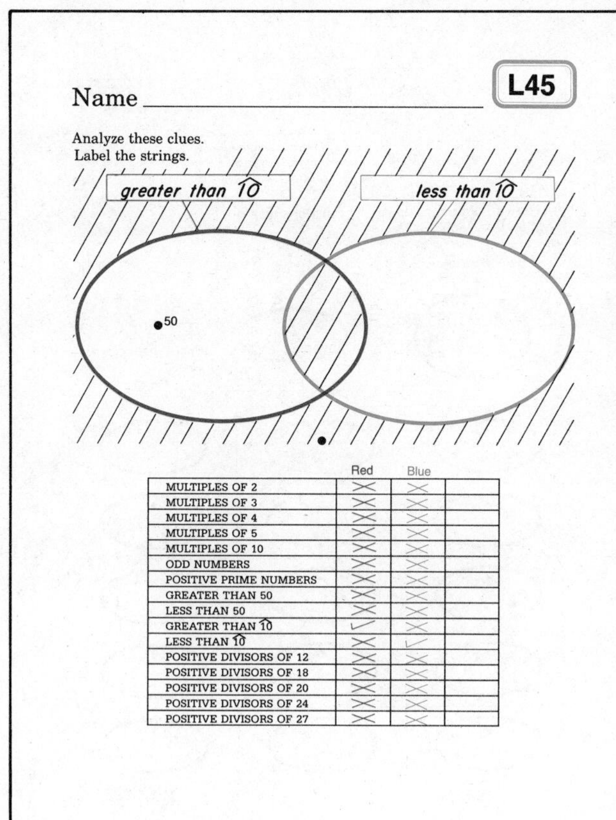

	Red	Blue	
MULTIPLES OF 2	✗	✗	
MULTIPLES OF 3	✗	✗	
MULTIPLES OF 4	✗	✗	
MULTIPLES OF 5	✗	✗	
MULTIPLES OF 10	✗	✗	
ODD NUMBERS	✗	✗	
POSITIVE PRIME NUMBERS	✗	✗	
GREATER THAN 50	✗	✗	
LESS THAN 50	✗	✗	
GREATER THAN $\widehat{10}$	✓	✗	
LESS THAN $\widehat{10}$	✗	✓	
POSITIVE DIVISORS OF 12	✗	✗	
POSITIVE DIVISORS OF 18	✗	✗	
POSITIVE DIVISORS OF 20	✗	✗	
POSITIVE DIVISORS OF 24	✗	✗	
POSITIVE DIVISORS OF 27	✗	✗	

Name ______________________ **L46**

Analyze these clues.
Label the strings.

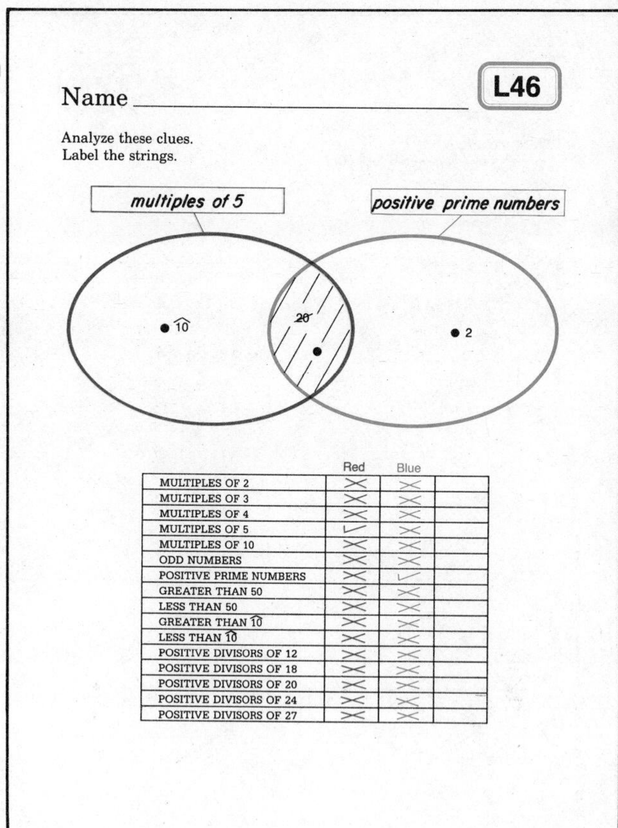

	Red	Blue	
MULTIPLES OF 2	✗	✗	
MULTIPLES OF 3	✗	✗	
MULTIPLES OF 4	✗	✗	
MULTIPLES OF 5	✓	✗	
MULTIPLES OF 10	✗	✗	
ODD NUMBERS	✗	✗	
POSITIVE PRIME NUMBERS	✗	✓	
GREATER THAN 50	✗	✗	
LESS THAN 50	✗	✗	
GREATER THAN $\widehat{10}$	✗	✗	
LESS THAN $\widehat{10}$	✗	✗	
POSITIVE DIVISORS OF 12	✗	✗	
POSITIVE DIVISORS OF 18	✗	✗	
POSITIVE DIVISORS OF 20	✗	✗	
POSITIVE DIVISORS OF 24	✗	✗	
POSITIVE DIVISORS OF 27	✗	✗	

Name ______________________ **L47**

Nim

The numbers tell how many checkers are in each pile.
In each part, circle "safe" or "hopeless."
For each safe position, describe the best move to make by filling in the blanks.
The first one is done for you.

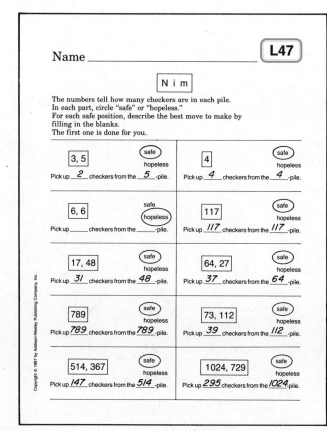

3, 5 — (safe) hopeless Pick up *2* checkers from the *5*-pile.	**4** — (safe) hopeless Pick up *4* checkers from the *4*-pile.
6, 6 — safe (hopeless) Pick up ____ checkers from the ____-pile.	**117** — (safe) hopeless Pick up *117* checkers from the *117*-pile.
17, 48 — (safe) hopeless Pick up *31* checkers from the *48*-pile.	**64, 27** — (safe) hopeless Pick up *37* checkers from the *64*-pile.
789 — (safe) hopeless Pick up *789* checkers from the *789*-pile.	**73, 112** — (safe) hopeless Pick up *39* checkers from the *112*-pile.
514, 367 — (safe) hopeless Pick up *147* checkers from the *514*-pile.	**1024, 729** — (safe) hopeless Pick up *295* checkers from the *1024*-pile.

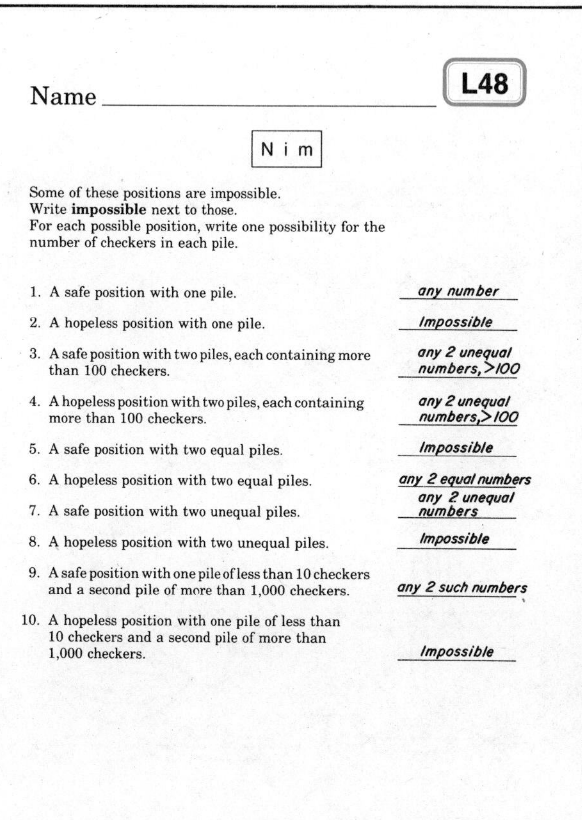
Name ______________________ **L48**

Nim

Some of these positions are impossible.
Write **impossible** next to those.
For each possible position, write one possibility for the number of checkers in each pile.

1. A safe position with one pile. — *any number*
2. A hopeless position with one pile. — *impossible*
3. A safe position with two piles, each containing more than 100 checkers. — *any 2 unequal numbers, >100*
4. A hopeless position with two piles, each containing more than 100 checkers. — *any 2 unequal numbers, >100*
5. A safe position with two equal piles. — *impossible*
6. A hopeless position with two equal piles. — *any 2 equal numbers*
7. A safe position with two unequal piles. — *any 2 unequal numbers*
8. A hopeless position with two unequal piles. — *impossible*
9. A safe position with one pile of less than 10 checkers and a second pile of more than 1,000 checkers. — *any 2 such numbers*
10. A hopeless position with one pile of less than 10 checkers and a second pile of more than 1,000 checkers. — *impossible*

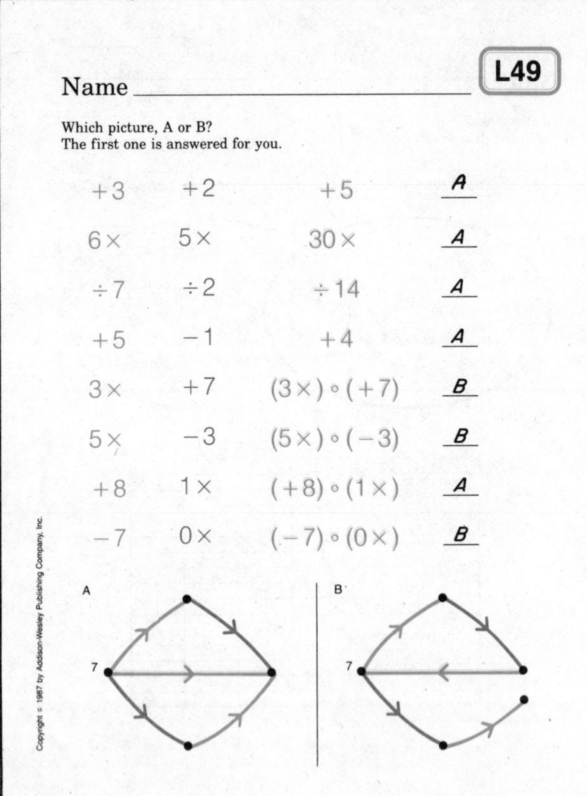

Name ________________ **L49**

Which picture, A or B?
The first one is answered for you.

+3	+2	+5	A
6×	5×	30×	A
÷7	÷2	÷14	A
+5	−1	+4	A
3×	+7	(3×)∘(+7)	B
5×	−3	(5×)∘(−3)	B
+8	1×	(+8)∘(1×)	A
−7	0×	(−7)∘(0×)	B

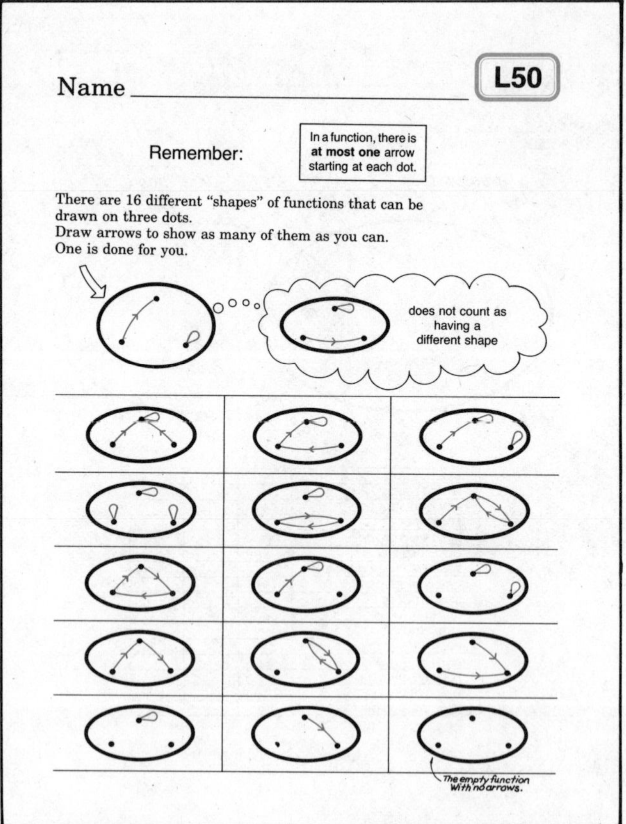

Name ________________ **L50**

Remember: In a function, there is **at most one** arrow starting at each dot.

There are 16 different "shapes" of functions that can be drawn on three dots.
Draw arrows to show as many of them as you can.
One is done for you.

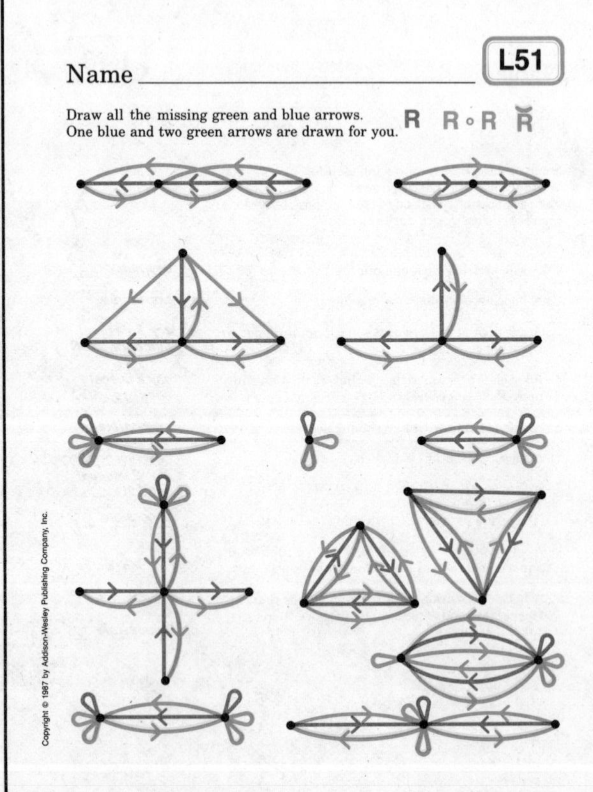

Name ________________ **L51**

Draw all the missing green and blue arrows.
One blue and two green arrows are drawn for you.

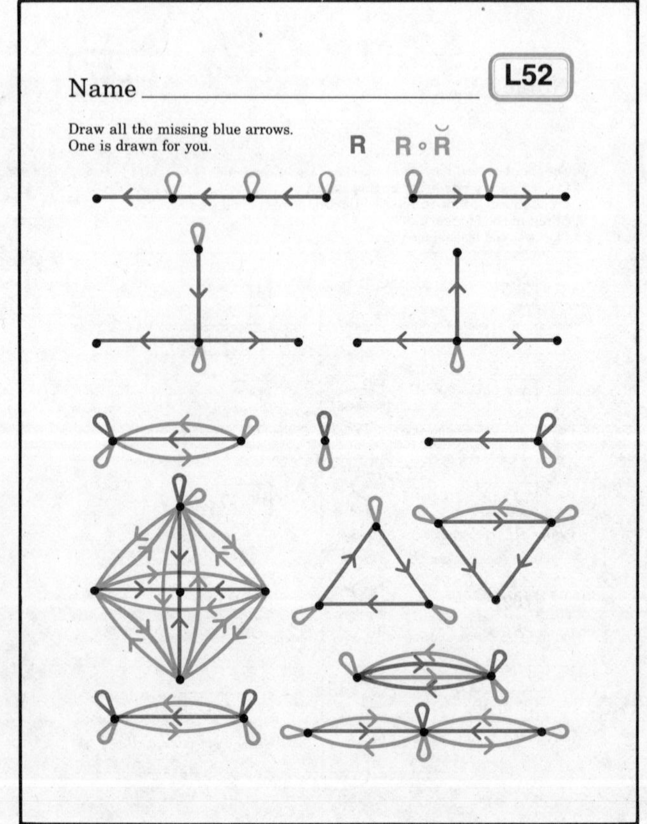

Name ________________ **L52**

Draw all the missing blue arrows.
One is drawn for you.

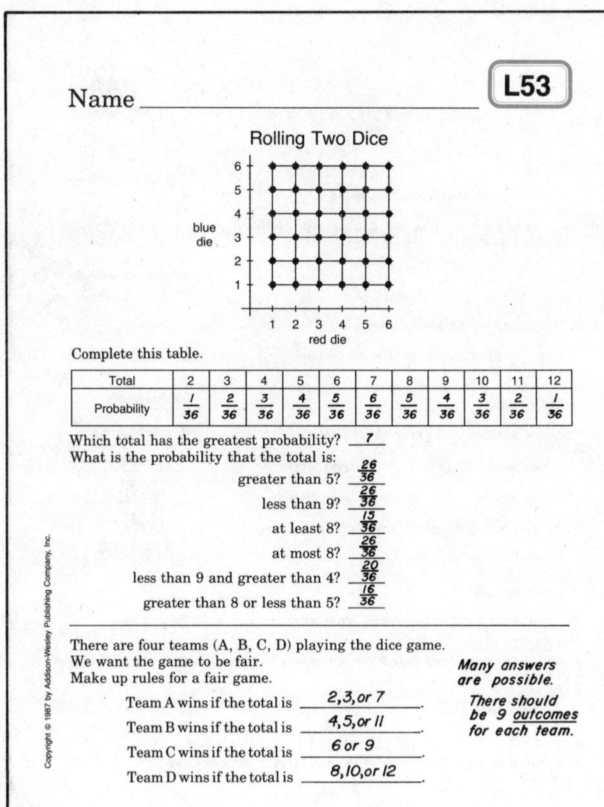

Name ________________ **L53**

Rolling Two Dice

Complete this table.

Total	2	3	4	5	6	7	8	9	10	11	12
Probability	1/36	2/36	3/36	4/36	5/36	6/36	5/36	4/36	3/36	2/36	1/36

Which total has the greatest probability? 7

What is the probability that the total is:

greater than 5? 26/36

less than 9? 26/36

at least 8? 15/36

at most 8? 26/36

less than 9 and greater than 4? 20/36

greater than 8 or less than 5? 16/36

There are four teams (A, B, C, D) playing the dice game.
We want the game to be fair.
Make up rules for a fair game.

Team A wins if the total is 2,3,or 7.

Team B wins if the total is 4,5,or 11.

Team C wins if the total is 6 or 9.

Team D wins if the total is 8,10,or 12.

Many answers are possible. There should be 9 outcomes for each team.

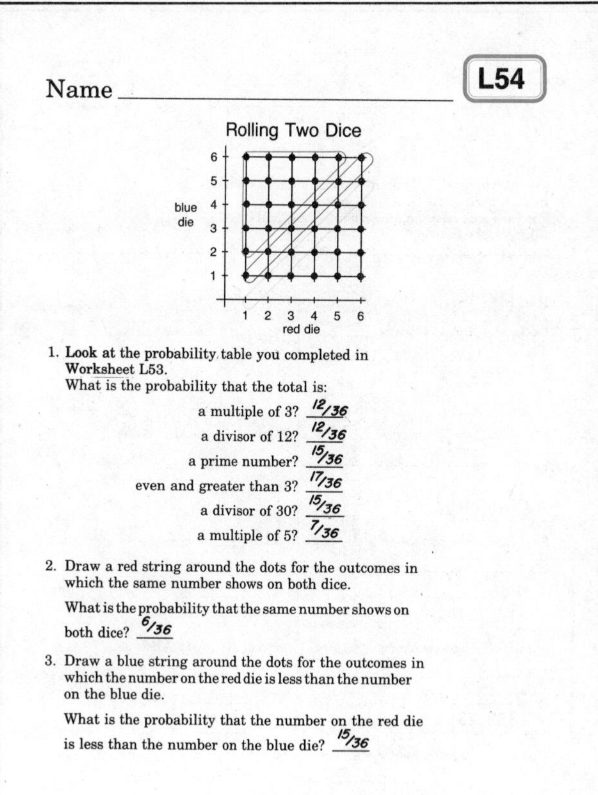

Name ________________ **L54**

Rolling Two Dice

1. Look at the probability table you completed in Worksheet L53.
   What is the probability that the total is:

   a multiple of 3? 12/36

   a divisor of 12? 12/36

   a prime number? 15/36

   even and greater than 3? 17/36

   a divisor of 30? 15/36

   a multiple of 5? 7/36

2. Draw a red string around the dots for the outcomes in which the same number shows on both dice.

   What is the probability that the same number shows on both dice? 6/36

3. Draw a blue string around the dots for the outcomes in which the number on the red die is less than the number on the blue die.

   What is the probability that the number on the red die is less than the number on the blue die? 15/36

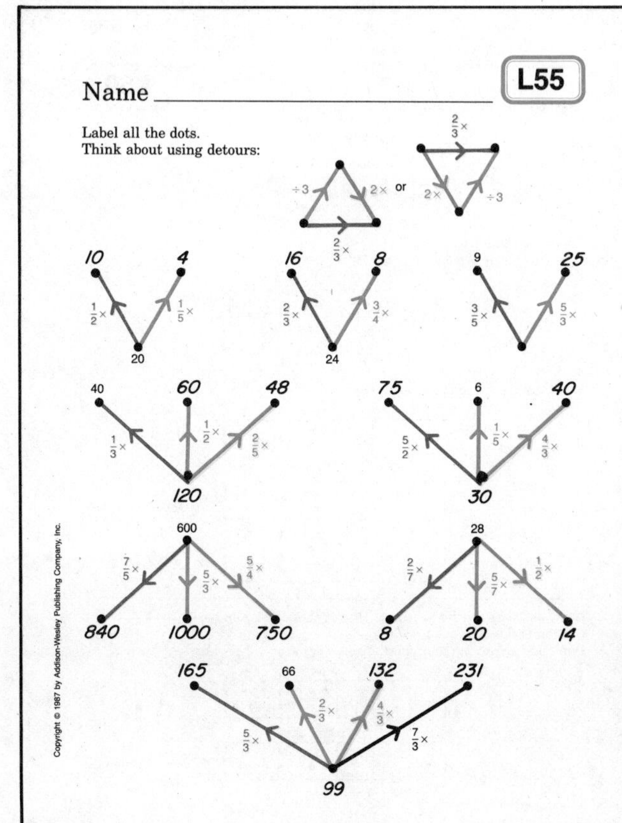

Name ________________ **L55**

Label all the dots.
Think about using detours:

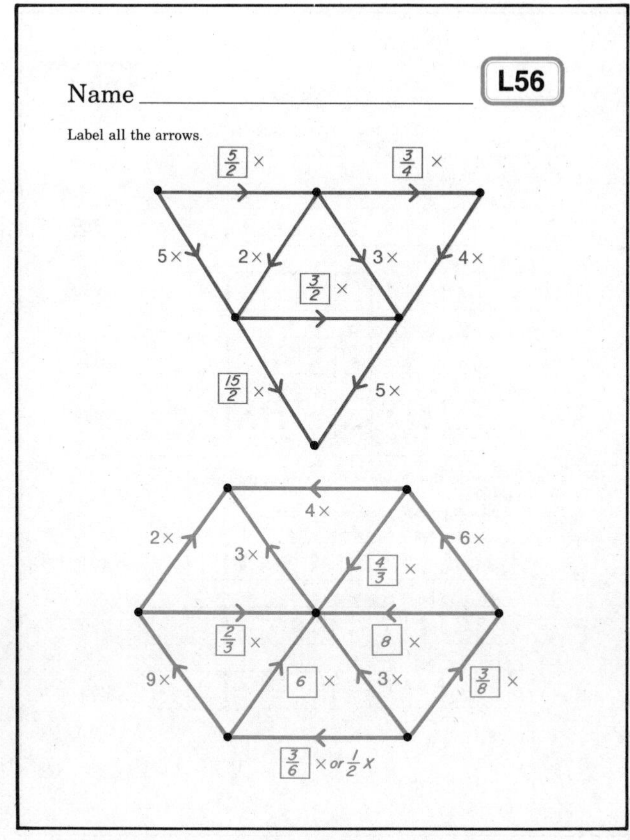

Name ________________ **L56**

Label all the arrows.

L57

Name ______________________

Nim

The numbers tell how many checkers are in each pile.
In each part, circle "safe" or "hopeless."
For each safe position, describe the best move to make by filling in the blanks.

Position	safe / hopeless	Move
12, 12	safe / (hopeless)	Pick up ____ checkers from the ____-pile.
1, 3, 13	(safe) / hopeless	Pick up *11* checkers from the *13*-pile.
1, 2, 3	safe / (hopeless)	Pick up ____ checkers from the ____-pile.
3, 1, 2	safe / (hopeless)	Pick up ____ checkers from the ____-pile.
4, 3, 4	(safe) / hopeless	Pick up *3* checkers from the *3*-pile.
8, 8, 8	(safe) / hopeless	Pick up *8* checkers from ~~the~~ *any 8*-pile.
3, 2, 4	(safe) / hopeless	Pick up *3* checkers from the *4*-pile.
21, 2, 1	(safe) / hopeless	Pick up *18* checkers from the *21*-pile.
32, 23	(safe) / hopeless	Pick up *9* checkers from the *32*-pile.
10, 10, 9	(safe) / hopeless	Pick up *9* checkers from the *9*-pile. *or 7 from one of the 10-piles*

L58

Name ______________________

Nim

Some of these positions are impossible.
Write **impossible** next to those.
For each possible position, write one possibility for the number of checkers in each pile.

1. A safe position with three piles. *any 3 piles with 2 equal or 3 equal.*
2. A hopeless position with three piles. *1,2,3*
3. A safe position with three piles, two of them equal. *any such piles*
4. A hopeless position with three piles, two of them equal. *impossible*
5. A safe position with three equal piles. *any such piles*
6. A hopeless position with three equal piles. *impossible*
7. A safe position with three piles, all different. *1,2,4*
8. A hopeless position with three piles, all different. *1,2,3*
9. A safe position with four piles. (Hint: Use what you know about hopeless 3-pile positions.) *1,2,3,any number*

For problems 1,2,7,8,& 9, check other answers with your Nim-Adder.
Nim Adder Checks:
1. Position is safe if and only if the nim-sum of 2 piles is NOT the third pile.
2. Position is hopeless if and only if the nim-sum of 2 piles is EQUAL to the third pile.
3. As 1
4. As 2
5. Position is safe if and only if the nim-sum of all the piles is NOT zero.

L59

Name ______________________

The Ternary Abacus

What number is on the ternary abacus?

2,187	729	243	81	27	9	3	1	
		•		••		•	•	= *301*
	•		••		•	•		= *903*
			••	••	••	•••		= *243*
		••	••	•••		••	•••	= *738*

Draw checkers on the abacus so that it shows the number written beside it.
Don't use more than two checkers on a square.

2,187	729	243	81	27	9	3	1	
			•	•	••	•	••	= 131
		••	••	••	••			= 720
		•						= 243

L60

Name ______________________

The Five-Abacus

Five checkers on a square show the same number as one checker on the next square to the left.

Label the squares.
(The first three are done for you.)

3125	*625*	*125*	25	5	1

What number is on the five-abacus?

			25	5	1	
			••••	•••••		= *125*
			••	•	••	= *57*
		••	•	••		= *285*

Draw checkers on the abacus so that it shows the number written beside it.
Don't use more than four checkers on a square.

			25	5	1	
			••••	••	•••	= 113
			•••	••	••	= 87

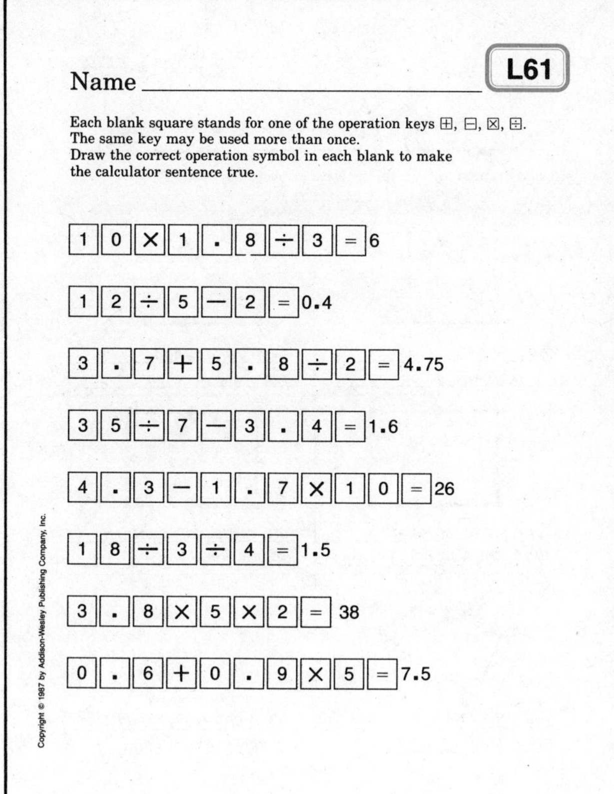

Name ______________________ **L61**

Each blank square stands for one of the operation keys [+], [−], [×], [÷].
The same key may be used more than once.
Draw the correct operation symbol in each blank to make the calculator sentence true.

[1] [0] [×] [1] [.] [8] [÷] [3] [=] 6

[1] [2] [÷] [5] [−] [2] [=] 0.4

[3] [.] [7] [+] [5] [.] [8] [÷] [2] [=] 4.75

[3] [5] [÷] [7] [−] [3] [.] [4] [=] 1.6

[4] [.] [3] [−] [1] [.] [7] [×] [1] [0] [=] 26

[1] [8] [÷] [3] [÷] [4] [=] 1.5

[3] [.] [8] [×] [5] [×] [2] [=] 38

[0] [.] [6] [+] [0] [.] [9] [×] [5] [=] 7.5

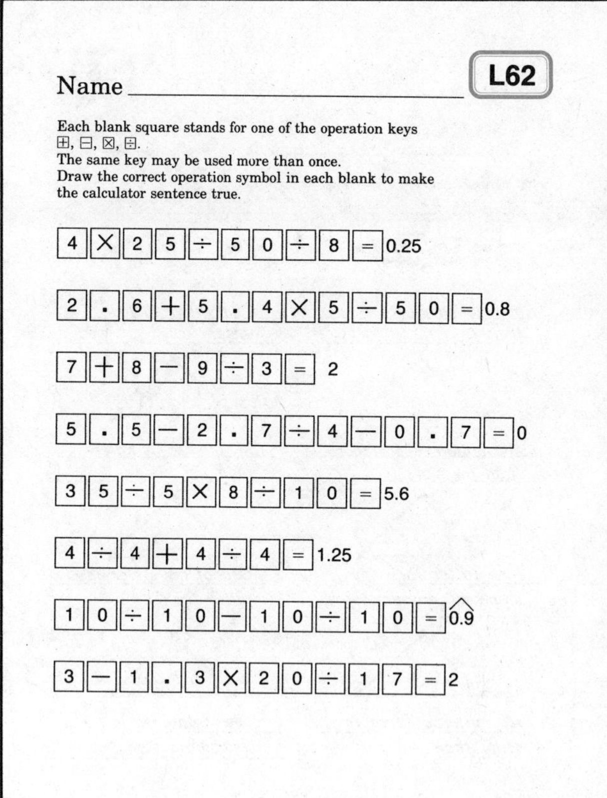

Name ______________________ **L62**

Each blank square stands for one of the operation keys [+], [−], [×], [÷].
The same key may be used more than once.
Draw the correct operation symbol in each blank to make the calculator sentence true.

[4] [×] [2] [5] [÷] [5] [0] [÷] [8] [=] 0.25

[2] [.] [6] [+] [5] [.] [4] [×] [5] [÷] [5] [0] [=] 0.8

[7] [+] [8] [−] [9] [÷] [3] [=] 2

[5] [.] [5] [−] [2] [.] [7] [÷] [4] [−] [0] [.] [7] [=] 0

[3] [5] [÷] [5] [×] [8] [÷] [1] [0] [=] 5.6

[4] [÷] [4] [+] [4] [÷] [4] [=] 1.25

[1] [0] [÷] [1] [0] [−] [1] [0] [÷] [1] [0] [=] 0.9

[3] [−] [1] [.] [3] [×] [2] [0] [÷] [1] [7] [=] 2

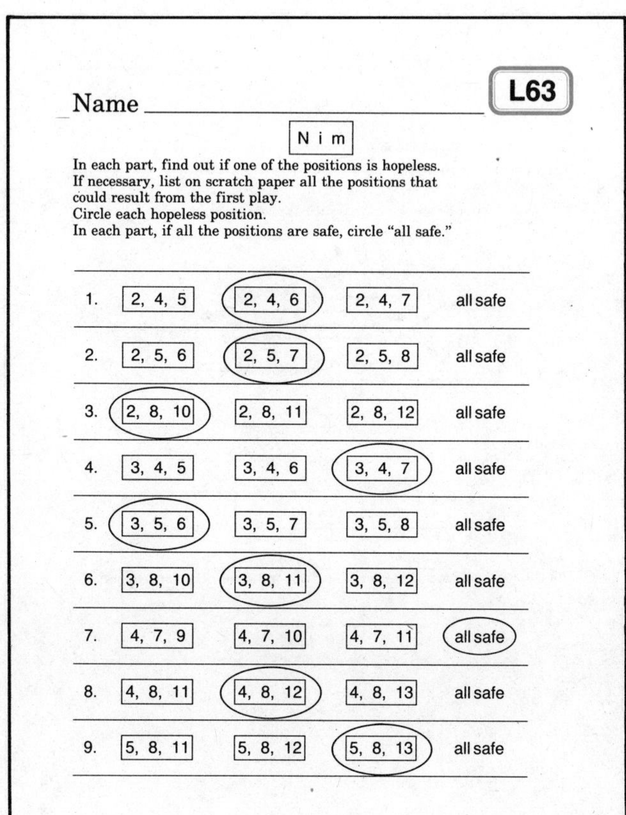

Name ______________________ **L63**

[Nim]

In each part, find out if one of the positions is hopeless.
If necessary, list on scratch paper all the positions that could result from the first play.
Circle each hopeless position.
In each part, if all the positions are safe, circle "all safe."

1.	2, 4, 5	(2, 4, 6)	2, 4, 7	all safe
2.	2, 5, 6	(2, 5, 7)	2, 5, 8	all safe
3.	(2, 8, 10)	2, 8, 11	2, 8, 12	all safe
4.	3, 4, 5	3, 4, 6	(3, 4, 7)	all safe
5.	(3, 5, 6)	3, 5, 7	3, 5, 8	all safe
6.	3, 8, 10	(3, 8, 11)	3, 8, 12	all safe
7.	4, 7, 9	4, 7, 10	4, 7, 11	(all safe)
8.	4, 8, 11	(4, 8, 12)	4, 8, 13	all safe
9.	5, 8, 11	5, 8, 12	(5, 8, 13)	all safe

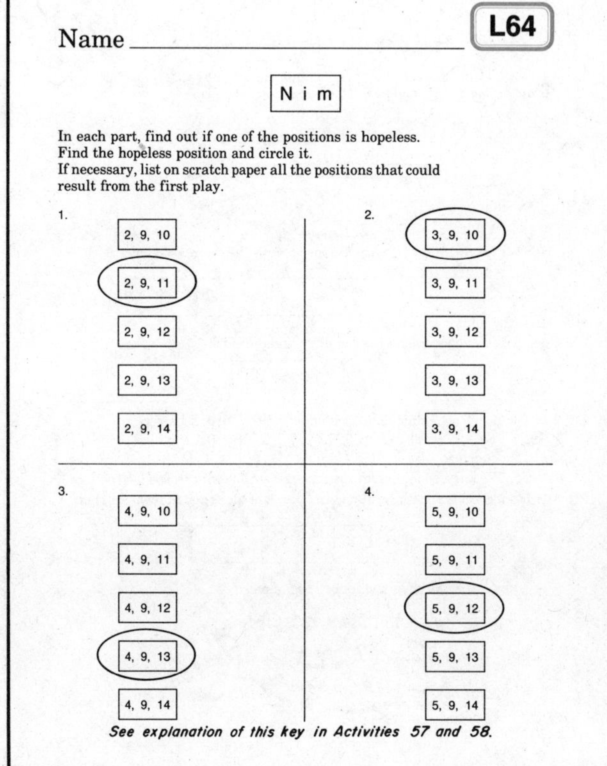

Name ______________________ **L64**

[Nim]

In each part, find out if one of the positions is hopeless.
Find the hopeless position and circle it.
If necessary, list on scratch paper all the positions that could result from the first play.

1.
- 2, 9, 10
- (2, 9, 11)
- 2, 9, 12
- 2, 9, 13
- 2, 9, 14

2.
- (3, 9, 10)
- 3, 9, 11
- 3, 9, 12
- 3, 9, 13
- 3, 9, 14

3.
- 4, 9, 10
- 4, 9, 11
- 4, 9, 12
- (4, 9, 13)
- 4, 9, 14

4.
- 5, 9, 10
- 5, 9, 11
- (5, 9, 12)
- 5, 9, 13
- 5, 9, 14

See explanation of this key in Activities 57 and 58.

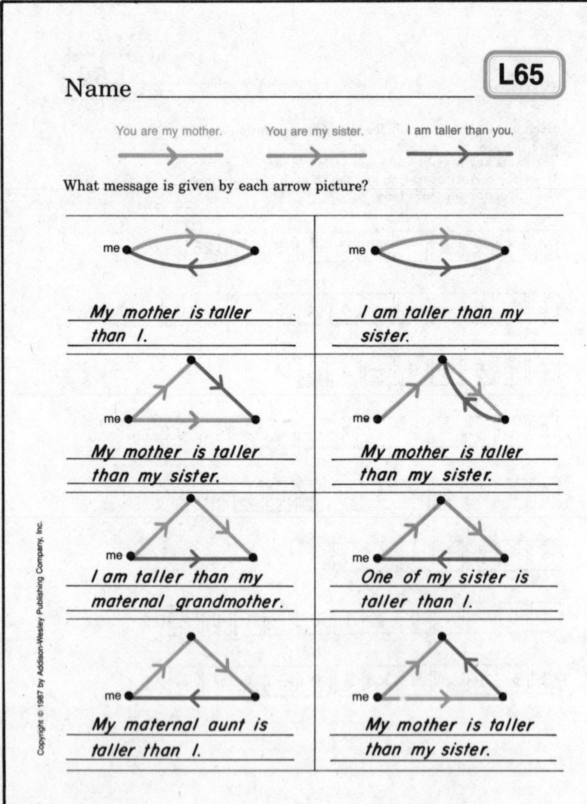

Name
L65
You are my mother.
You are my sister.
I am taller than you.
What message is given by each arrow picture?
me
My mother is taller than I.
I am taller than my sister.
My mother is taller than my sister.
My mother is taller than my sister.
I am taller than my maternal grandmother.
One of my sister is taller than I.
My maternal aunt is taller than I.
My mother is taller than my sister.
Copyright © 1987 by Addison-Wesley Publishing Company, Inc.

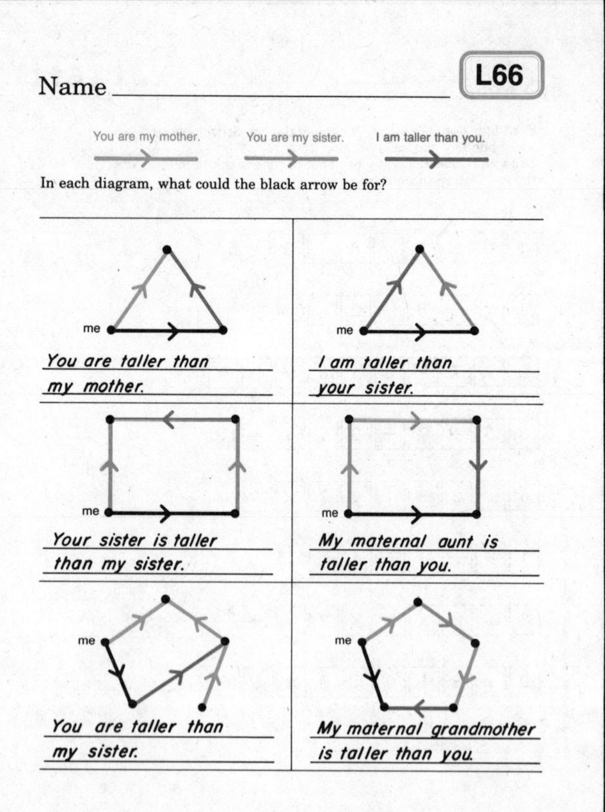

Name
L66
You are my mother.
You are my sister.
I am taller than you.
In each diagram, what could the black arrow be for?
me
You are taller than my mother.
I am taller than your sister.
Your sister is taller than my sister.
My maternal aunt is taller than you.
You are taller than my sister.
My maternal grandmother is taller than you.

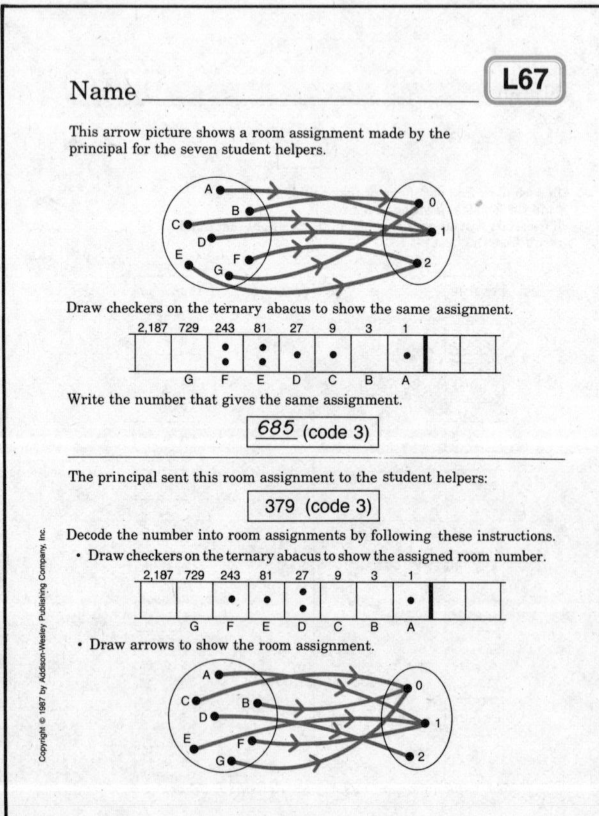

Name
L67
This arrow picture shows a room assignment made by the principal for the seven student helpers.
A B C D E F G 0 1 2
Draw checkers on the ternary abacus to show the same assignment.
2,187 729 243 81 27 9 3 1
G F E D C B A
Write the number that gives the same assignment.
685 (code 3)
The principal sent this room assignment to the student helpers:
379 (code 3)
Decode the number into room assignments by following these instructions.
• Draw checkers on the ternary abacus to show the assigned room number.
2,187 729 243 81 27 9 3 1
G F E D C B A
• Draw arrows to show the room assignment.
Copyright © 1987 by Addison-Wesley Publishing Company, Inc.

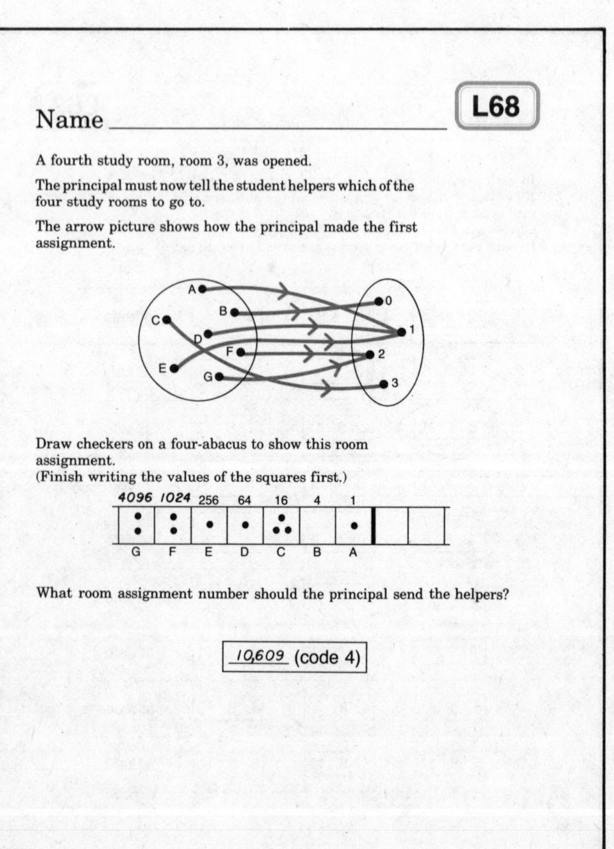

Name
L68
A fourth study room, room 3, was opened.
The principal must now tell the student helpers which of the four study rooms to go to.
The arrow picture shows how the principal made the first assignment.
A B C D E F G 0 1 2 3
Draw checkers on a four-abacus to show this room assignment.
(Finish writing the values of the squares first.)
4096 1024 256 64 16 4 1
G F E D C B A
What room assignment number should the principal send the helpers?
10,609 (code 4)

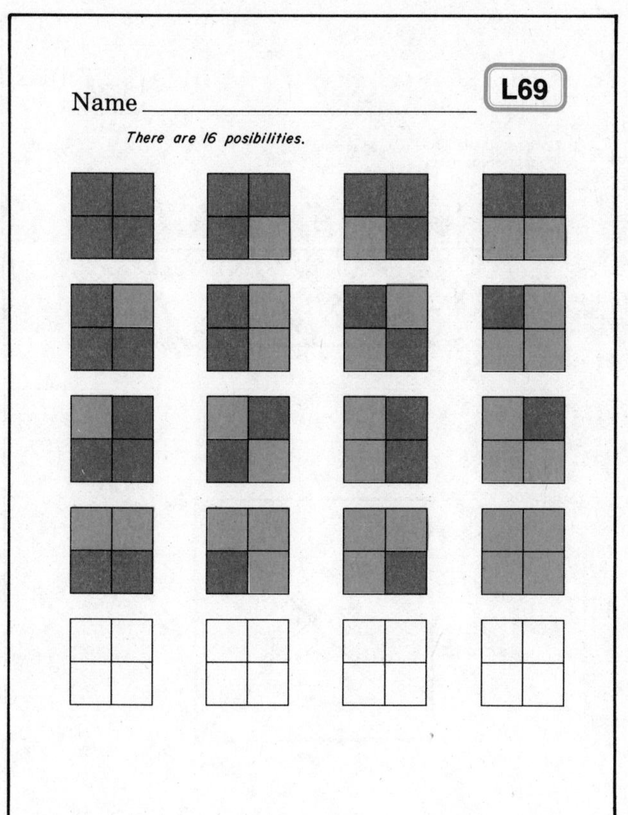
Name
L69
There are 16 posibilities.

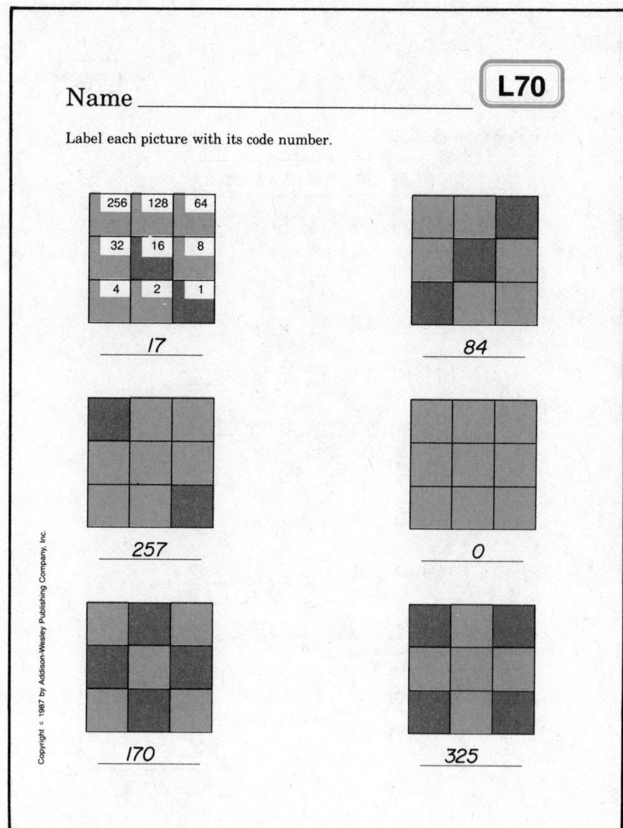
Name
L70
Label each picture with its code number.
256
128
64
32
16
8
4
2
1
17
84
257
0
170
325
Copyright © 1987 by Addison-Wesley Publishing Company, Inc.

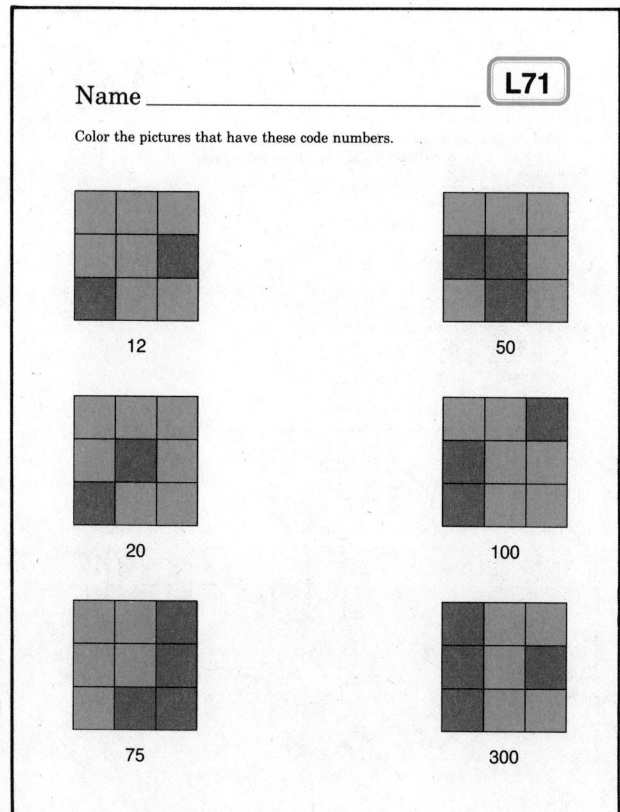
Name
L71
Color the pictures that have these code numbers.
12
50
20
100
75
300

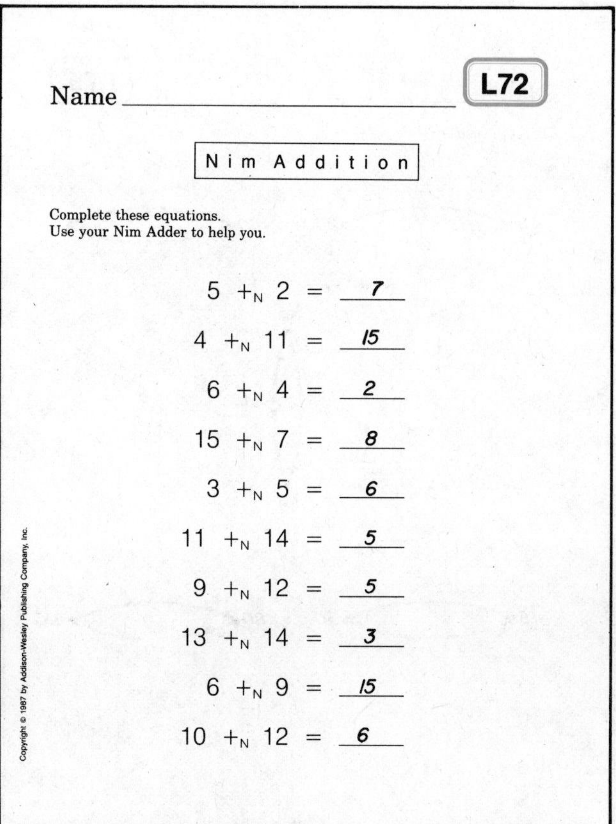
Name
L72
Nim Addition
Complete these equations.
Use your Nim Adder to help you.
5 +N 2 = 7
4 +N 11 = 15
6 +N 4 = 2
15 +N 7 = 8
3 +N 5 = 6
11 +N 14 = 5
9 +N 12 = 5
13 +N 14 = 3
6 +N 9 = 15
10 +N 12 = 6
Copyright © 1987 by Addison-Wesley Publishing Company, Inc.

Name ______________________ **L73**

Complete these equations.

Nim Addition

$12 +_N 7 +_N 5 =$ 14

$6 +_N 5 +_N 4 =$ 7

$12 +_N 14 +_N 2 =$ 0

$14 +_N 11 +_N 5 =$ 0

$3 +_N 15 +_N 9 =$ 5

$13 +_N 7 +_N 10 =$ 0

$9 +_N 8 +_N 7 =$ 6

$13 +_N 4 +_N 9 =$ 0

Four of the Nim additions come from hopeless positions.
Write the hopeless positions here:

12, 14, 2 — 14, 11, 5

13, 7, 10 — 13, 4, 9

Name ______________________ **L74**

Complete the labels of the red arrows.
Then label the dots.

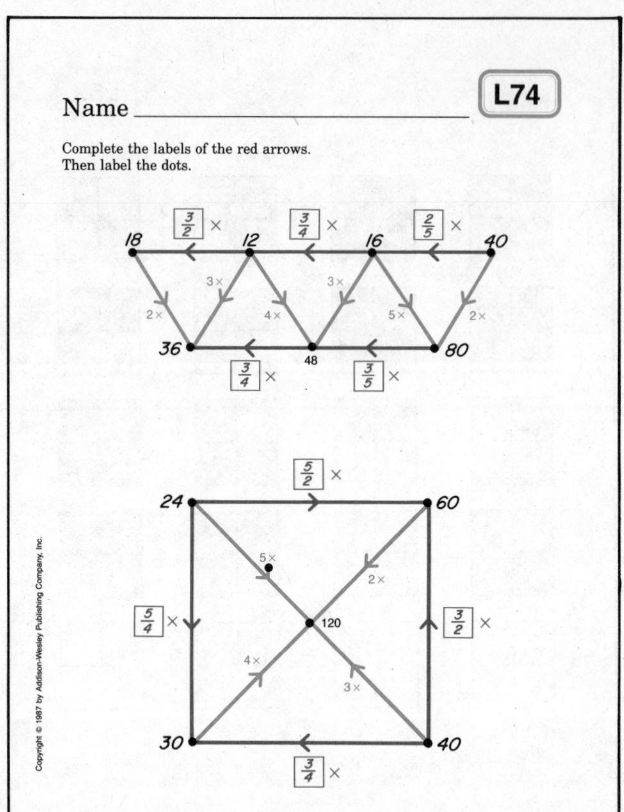

Name ______________________ **L75**

Label the dots.

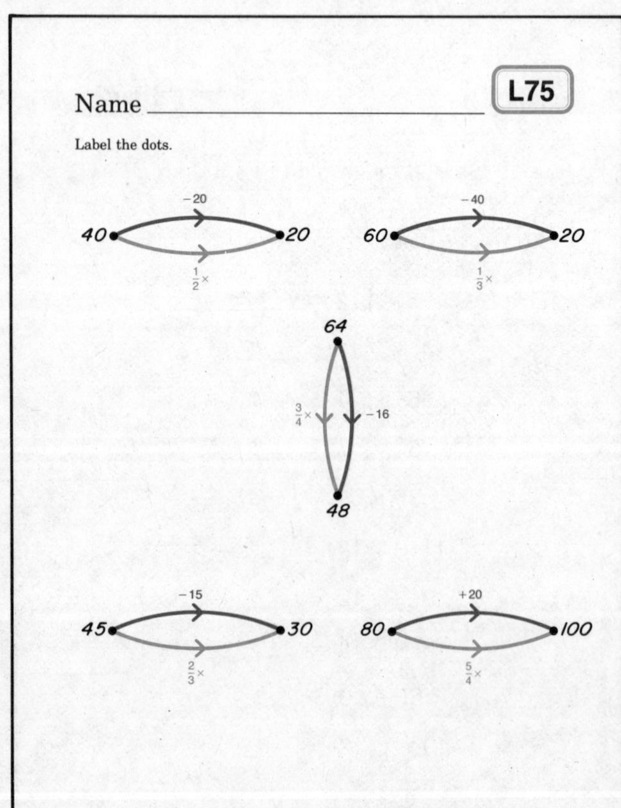

Name ______________________ **L76**

Label the dot and complete the label of the arrow.
Then draw checkers on the blank Minicomputer so that only **one** checker is moved.

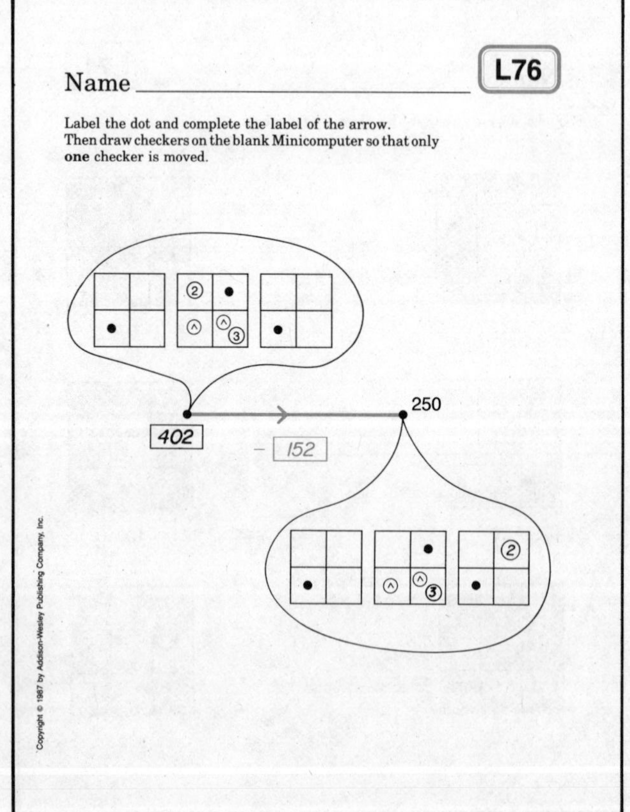

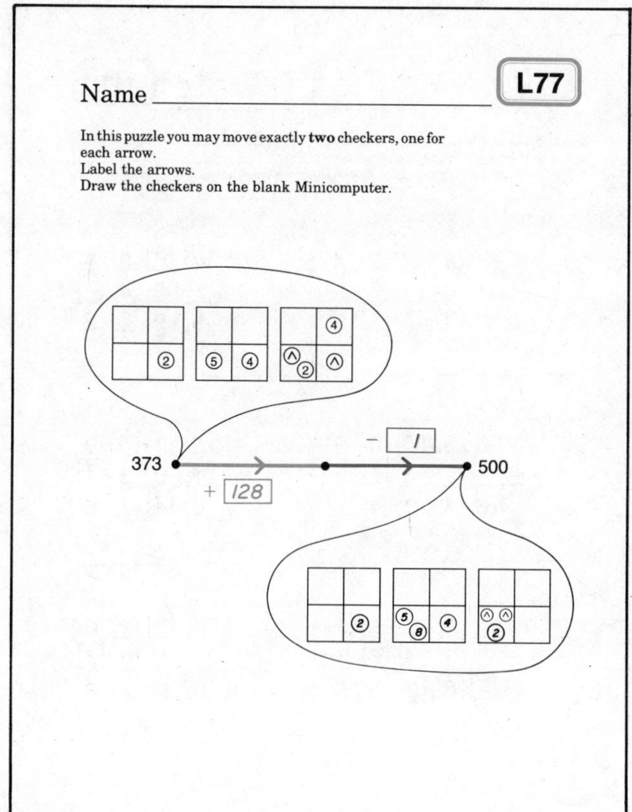

Name ____________________ **L77**

In this puzzle you may move exactly **two** checkers, one for each arrow.
Label the arrows.
Draw the checkers on the blank Minicomputer.

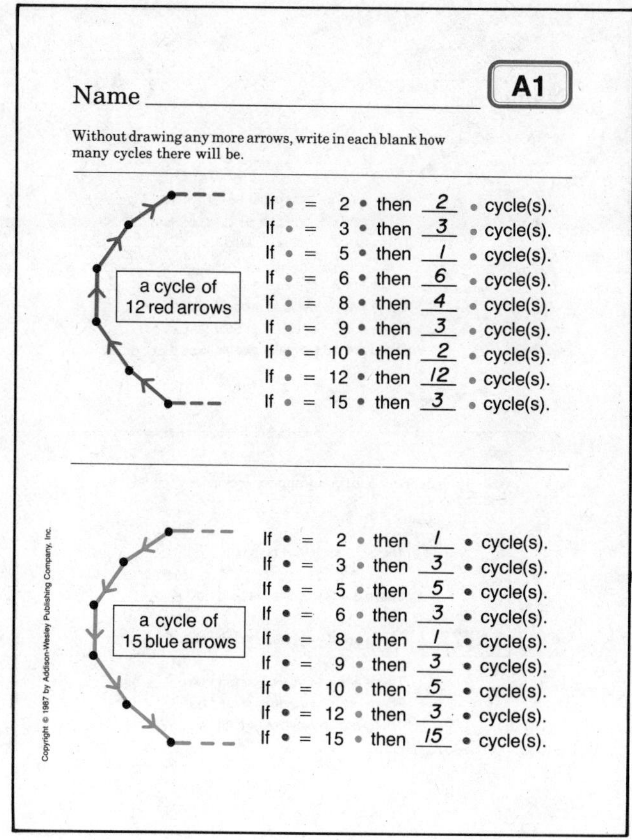

Name ____________________ **A1**

Without drawing any more arrows, write in each blank how many cycles there will be.

If • = 2 • then 2 • cycle(s).
If • = 3 • then 3 • cycle(s).
If • = 5 • then 1 • cycle(s).
If • = 6 • then 6 • cycle(s).
If • = 8 • then 4 • cycle(s).
If • = 9 • then 3 • cycle(s).
If • = 10 • then 2 • cycle(s).
If • = 12 • then 12 • cycle(s).
If • = 15 • then 3 • cycle(s).

If • = 2 • then 1 • cycle(s).
If • = 3 • then 3 • cycle(s).
If • = 5 • then 5 • cycle(s).
If • = 6 • then 3 • cycle(s).
If • = 8 • then 1 • cycle(s).
If • = 9 • then 3 • cycle(s).
If • = 10 • then 5 • cycle(s).
If • = 12 • then 3 • cycle(s).
If • = 15 • then 15 • cycle(s).

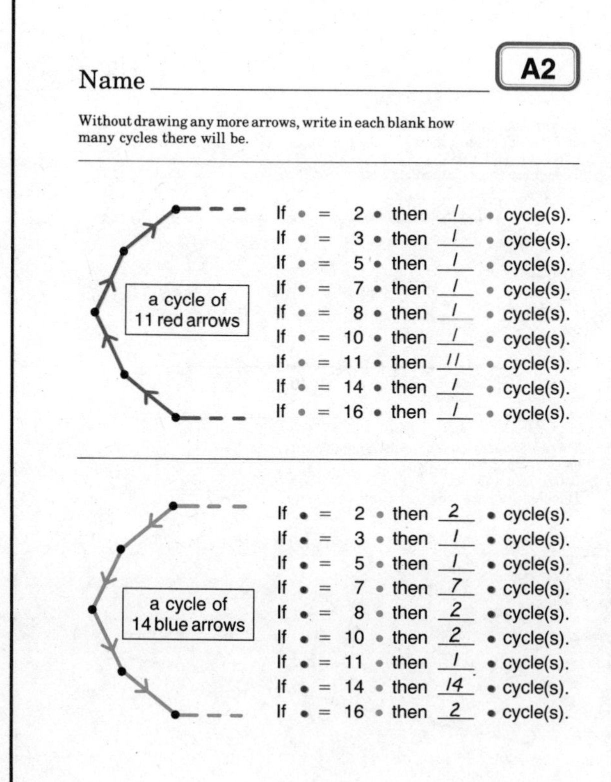

Name ____________________ **A2**

Without drawing any more arrows, write in each blank how many cycles there will be.

If • = 2 • then 1 • cycle(s).
If • = 3 • then 1 • cycle(s).
If • = 5 • then 1 • cycle(s).
If • = 7 • then 1 • cycle(s).
If • = 8 • then 1 • cycle(s).
If • = 10 • then 1 • cycle(s).
If • = 11 • then 11 • cycle(s).
If • = 14 • then 1 • cycle(s).
If • = 16 • then 1 • cycle(s).

If • = 2 • then 2 • cycle(s).
If • = 3 • then 1 • cycle(s).
If • = 5 • then 1 • cycle(s).
If • = 7 • then 7 • cycle(s).
If • = 8 • then 2 • cycle(s).
If • = 10 • then 2 • cycle(s).
If • = 11 • then 1 • cycle(s).
If • = 14 • then 14 • cycle(s).
If • = 16 • then 2 • cycle(s).

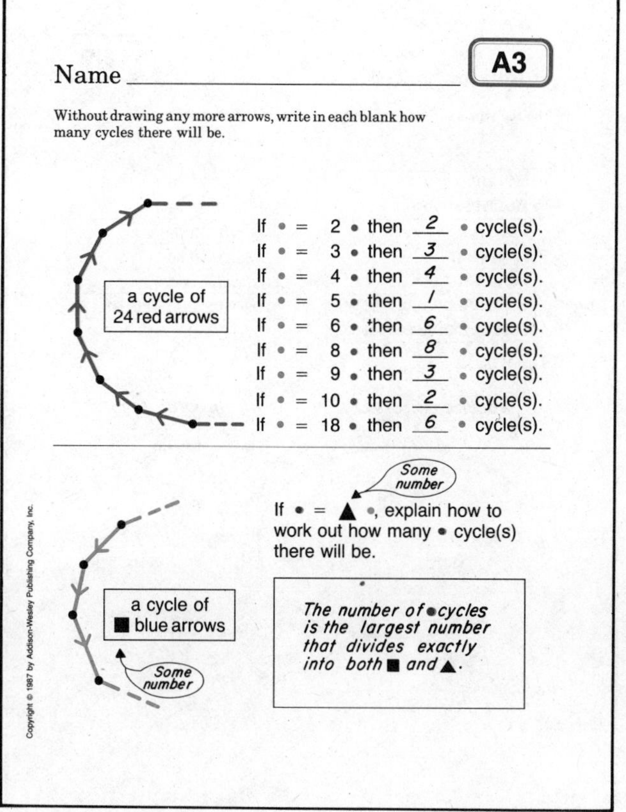

Name ____________________ **A3**

Without drawing any more arrows, write in each blank how many cycles there will be.

If • = 2 • then 2 • cycle(s).
If • = 3 • then 3 • cycle(s).
If • = 4 • then 4 • cycle(s).
If • = 5 • then 1 • cycle(s).
If • = 6 • then 6 • cycle(s).
If • = 8 • then 8 • cycle(s).
If • = 9 • then 3 • cycle(s).
If • = 10 • then 2 • cycle(s).
If • = 18 • then 6 • cycle(s).

If • = ▲ •, explain how to work out how many • cycle(s) there will be.

The number of • cycles is the largest number that divides exactly into both ■ and ▲.

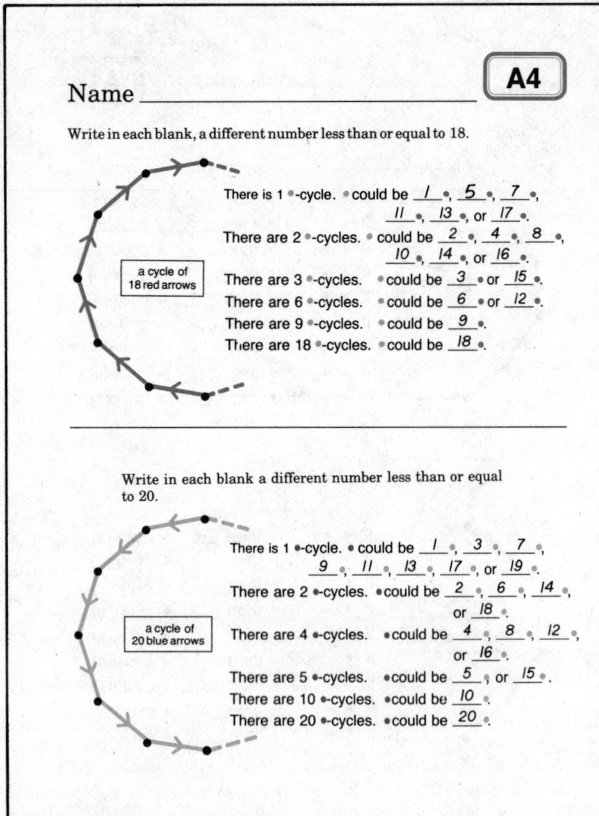

Name ______________ **A4**

Write in each blank, a different number less than or equal to 18.

There is 1 ●-cycle. ● could be 1●, 5●, 7●, 11●, 13●, or 17●.
There are 2 ●-cycles. ● could be 2●, 4●, 8●, 10●, 14●, or 16●.
There are 3 ●-cycles. ● could be 3● or 15●.
There are 6 ●-cycles. ● could be 6● or 12●.
There are 9 ●-cycles. ● could be 9●.
There are 18 ●-cycles. ● could be 18●.

Write in each blank a different number less than or equal to 20.

There is 1 ●-cycle. ● could be 1●, 3●, 7●, 9●, 11●, 13●, 17●, or 19●.
There are 2 ●-cycles. ● could be 2●, 6●, 14●, or 18●.
There are 4 ●-cycles. ● could be 4●, 8●, 12●, or 16●.
There are 5 ●-cycles. ● could be 5● or 15●.
There are 10 ●-cycles. ● could be 10●.
There are 20 ●-cycles. ● could be 20●.

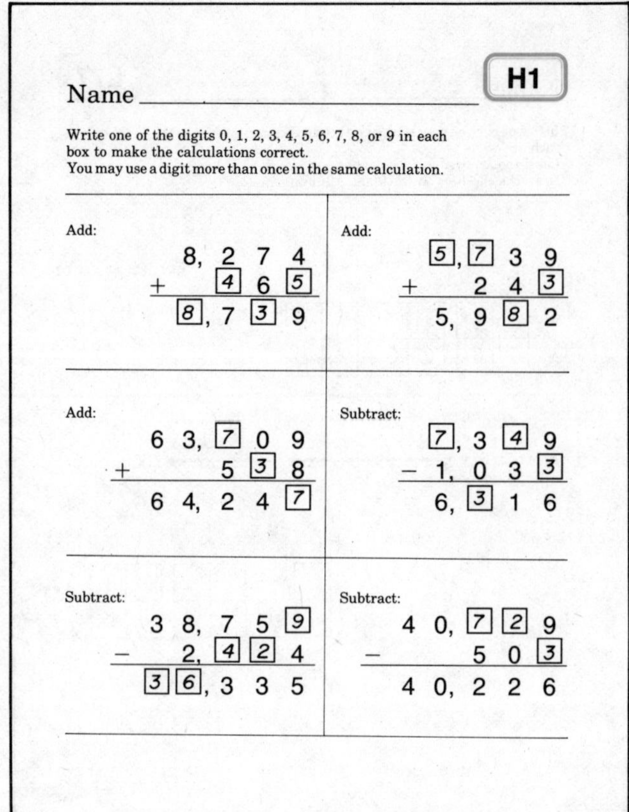

Name ______________ **H1**

Write one of the digits 0, 1, 2, 3, 4, 5, 6, 7, 8, or 9 in each box to make the calculations correct.
You may use a digit more than once in the same calculation.

Add:

$$\begin{array}{r} 8,274 \\ +\ \boxed{4}6\boxed{5} \\ \hline \boxed{8},7\boxed{3}9 \end{array}$$

Add:

$$\begin{array}{r} \boxed{5},\boxed{7}39 \\ +\ 24\boxed{3} \\ \hline 5,9\boxed{8}2 \end{array}$$

Add:

$$\begin{array}{r} 63,\boxed{7}09 \\ +\ 5\boxed{3}8 \\ \hline 64,24\boxed{7} \end{array}$$

Subtract:

$$\begin{array}{r} \boxed{7},3\boxed{4}9 \\ -\ 1,03\boxed{3} \\ \hline 6,\boxed{3}16 \end{array}$$

Subtract:

$$\begin{array}{r} 38,75\boxed{9} \\ -\ 2,\boxed{4}\boxed{2}4 \\ \hline \boxed{3}\boxed{6},335 \end{array}$$

Subtract:

$$\begin{array}{r} 40,\boxed{7}\boxed{2}9 \\ -\ 50\boxed{3} \\ \hline 40,226 \end{array}$$

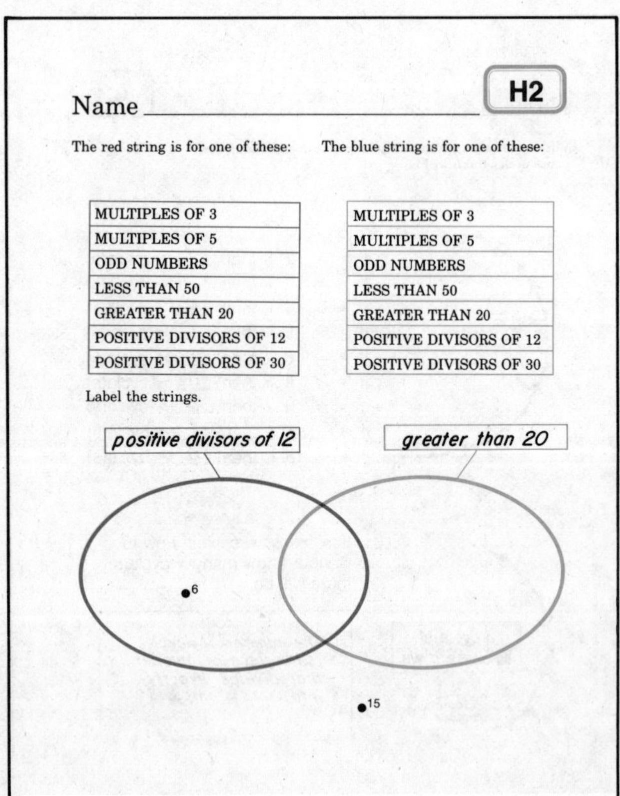

Name ______________ **H2**

The red string is for one of these:

MULTIPLES OF 3
MULTIPLES OF 5
ODD NUMBERS
LESS THAN 50
GREATER THAN 20
POSITIVE DIVISORS OF 12
POSITIVE DIVISORS OF 30

The blue string is for one of these:

MULTIPLES OF 3
MULTIPLES OF 5
ODD NUMBERS
LESS THAN 50
GREATER THAN 20
POSITIVE DIVISORS OF 12
POSITIVE DIVISORS OF 30

Label the strings.

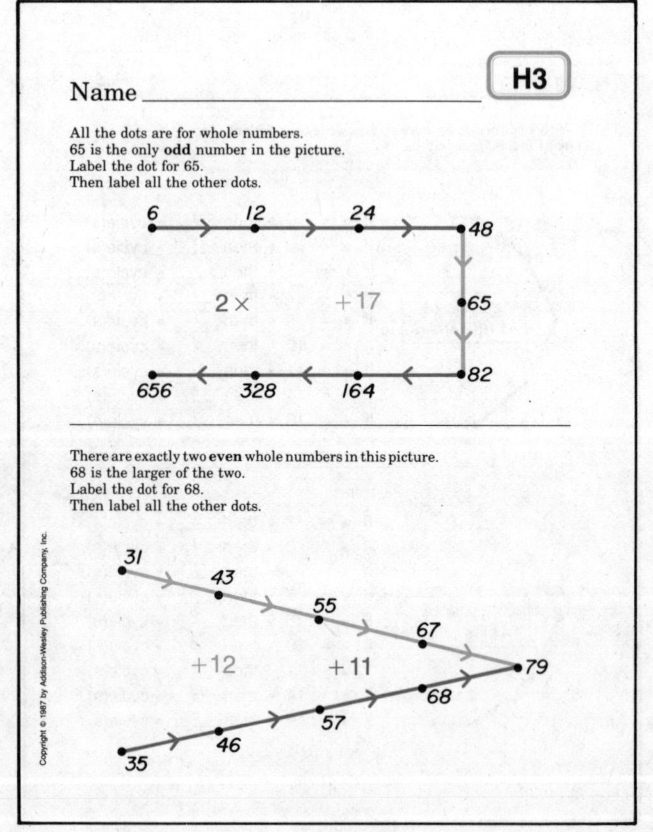

Name ______________ **H3**

All the dots are for whole numbers.
65 is the only **odd** number in the picture.
Label the dot for 65.
Then label all the other dots.

There are exactly two **even** whole numbers in this picture.
68 is the larger of the two.
Label the dot for 68.
Then label all the other dots.

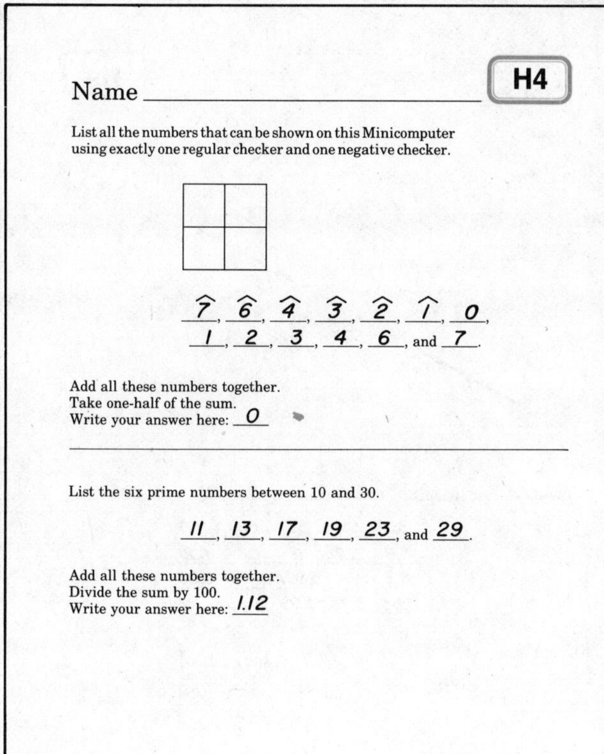
Name
H4
List all the numbers that can be shown on this Minicomputer using exactly one regular checker and one negative checker.
Add all these numbers together.
Take one-half of the sum.
Write your answer here:
List the six prime numbers between 10 and 30.
Add all these numbers together.
Divide the sum by 100.
Write your answer here:

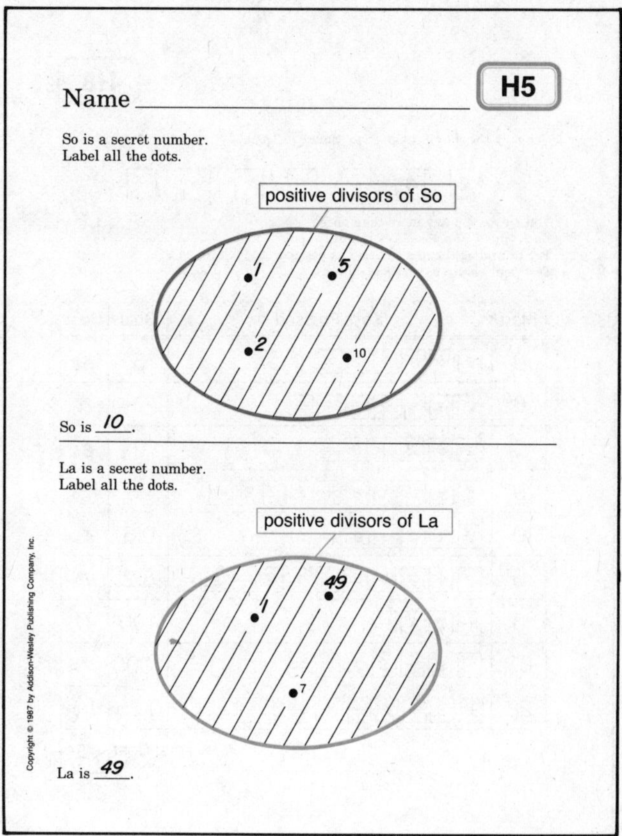
Name
H5
So is a secret number.
Label all the dots.
positive divisors of So
So is
La is a secret number.
Label all the dots.
positive divisors of La
La is
Copyright © 1987 by Addison-Wesley Publishing Company, Inc.

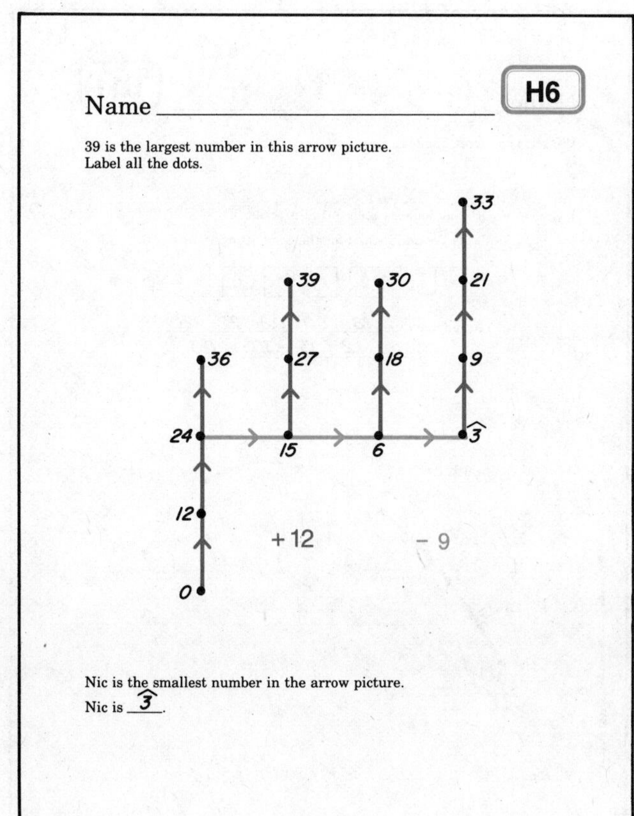
Name
H6
39 is the largest number in this arrow picture.
Label all the dots.
+12
−9
Nic is the smallest number in the arrow picture.
Nic is

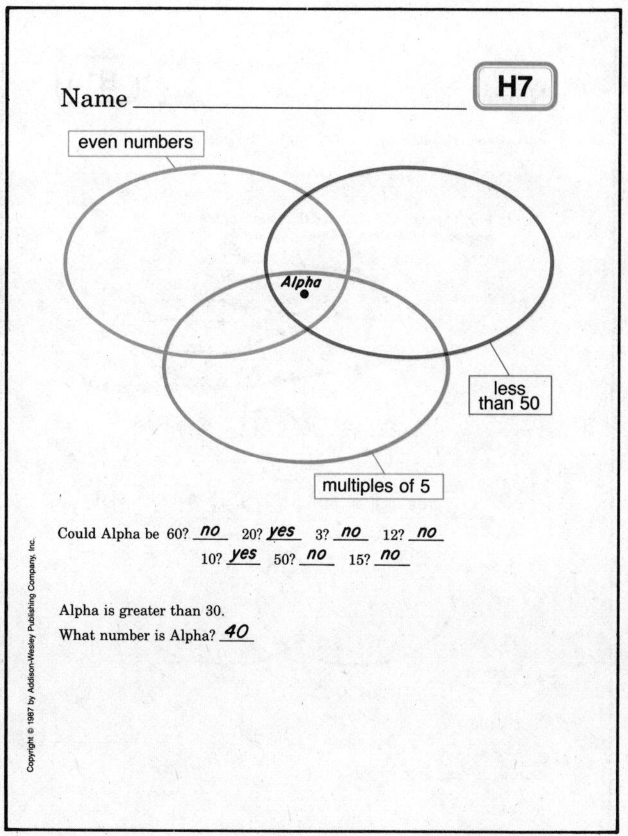
Name
H7
even numbers
less than 50
multiples of 5
Could Alpha be 60? 20? 3? 12?
10? 50? 15?
Alpha is greater than 30.
What number is Alpha?
Copyright © 1987 by Addison-Wesley Publishing Company, Inc.

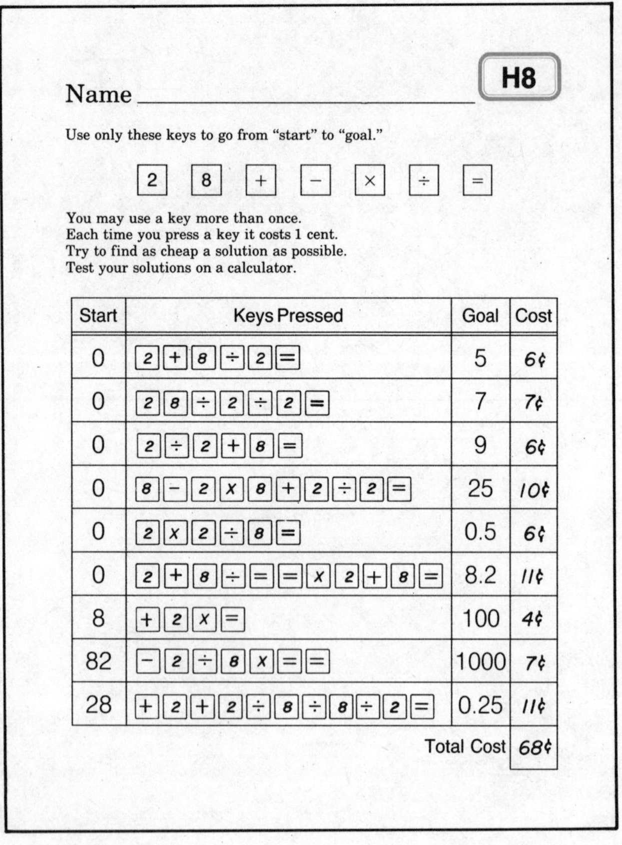

Name ______________________ **H8**

Use only these keys to go from "start" to "goal."

[2] [8] [+] [−] [×] [÷] [=]

You may use a key more than once.
Each time you press a key it costs 1 cent.
Try to find as cheap a solution as possible.
Test your solutions on a calculator.

Start	Keys Pressed	Goal	Cost
0	[2][+][8][÷][2][=]	5	6¢
0	[2][8][÷][2][÷][2][=]	7	7¢
0	[2][÷][2][+][8][=]	9	6¢
0	[8][−][2][×][8][+][2][÷][2][=]	25	10¢
0	[2][×][2][÷][8][=]	0.5	6¢
0	[2][+][8][÷][=][=][×][2][+][8][=]	8.2	11¢
8	[+][2][×][=]	100	4¢
82	[−][2][÷][8][×][=][=]	1000	7¢
28	[+][2][+][2][÷][8][÷][8][÷][2][=]	0.25	11¢
		Total Cost	68¢

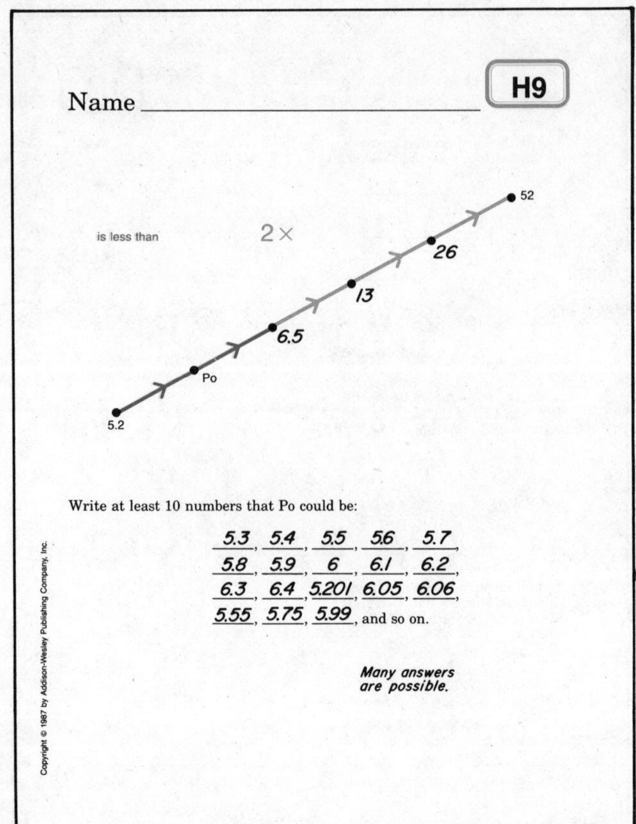

Name ______________________ **H9**

Write at least 10 numbers that Po could be:

5.3, 5.4, 5.5, 5.6, 5.7,
5.8, 5.9, 6, 6.1, 6.2,
6.3, 6.4, 5.201, 6.05, 6.06,
5.55, 5.75, 5.99, and so on.

Many answers are possible.

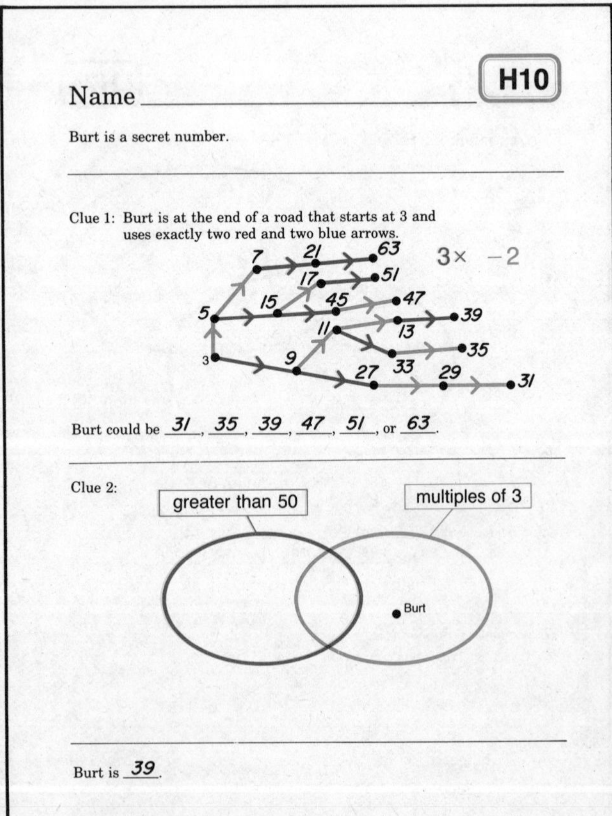

Name ______________________ **H10**

Burt is a secret number.

Clue 1: Burt is at the end of a road that starts at 3 and uses exactly two red and two blue arrows.

Burt could be 31, 35, 39, 47, 51, or 63.

Clue 2:

Burt is 39.

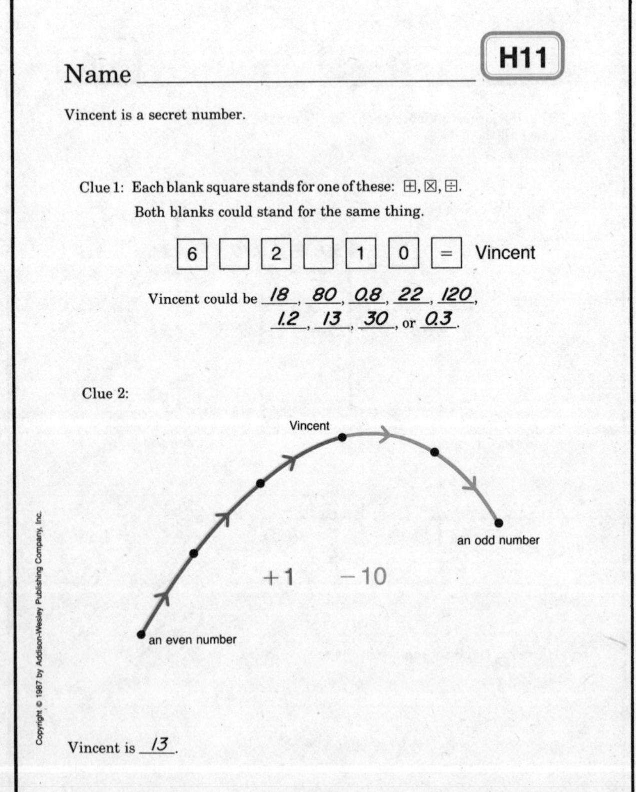

Name ______________________ **H11**

Vincent is a secret number.

Clue 1: Each blank square stands for one of these: [+], [×], [÷].
Both blanks could stand for the same thing.

[6] [ ] [2] [ ] [1] [0] [=] Vincent

Vincent could be 18, 80, 0.8, 22, 120, 1.2, 13, 30, or 0.3.

Clue 2:

Vincent is 13.

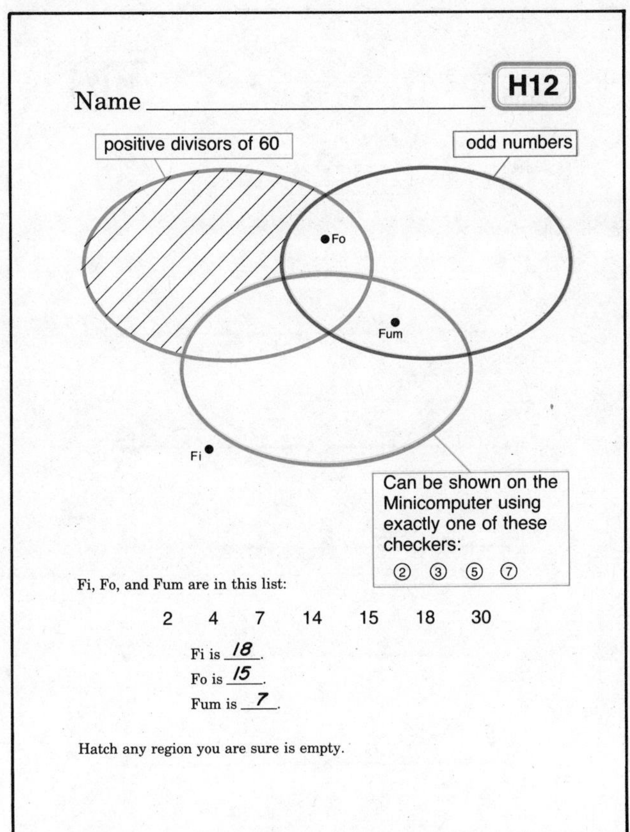

Name ______________________________ **H12**

positive divisors of 60

odd numbers

Fo

Fum

Fi

Can be shown on the Minicomputer using exactly one of these checkers:
② ③ ⑤ ⑦

Fi, Fo, and Fum are in this list:

2 4 7 14 15 18 30

Fi is _18_.
Fo is _15_.
Fum is _7_.

Hatch any region you are sure is empty.

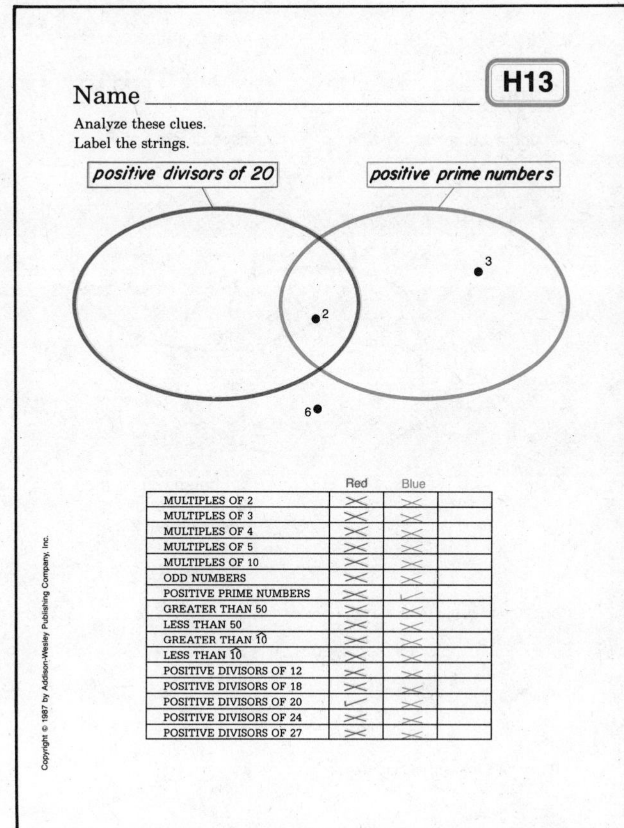

Name ______________________________ **H13**

Analyze these clues.
Label the strings.

positive divisors of 20

positive prime numbers

3
2
6

	Red	Blue	
MULTIPLES OF 2	X	X	
MULTIPLES OF 3	X	X	
MULTIPLES OF 4	X	X	
MULTIPLES OF 5	X	X	
MULTIPLES OF 10	X	X	
ODD NUMBERS	X	X	
POSITIVE PRIME NUMBERS	X	✓	
GREATER THAN 50	X	X	
LESS THAN 50	X	X	
GREATER THAN 10	X	X	
LESS THAN 10	X	X	
POSITIVE DIVISORS OF 12	X	X	
POSITIVE DIVISORS OF 18	X	X	
POSITIVE DIVISORS OF 20	✓	X	
POSITIVE DIVISORS OF 24	X	X	
POSITIVE DIVISORS OF 27	X	X	

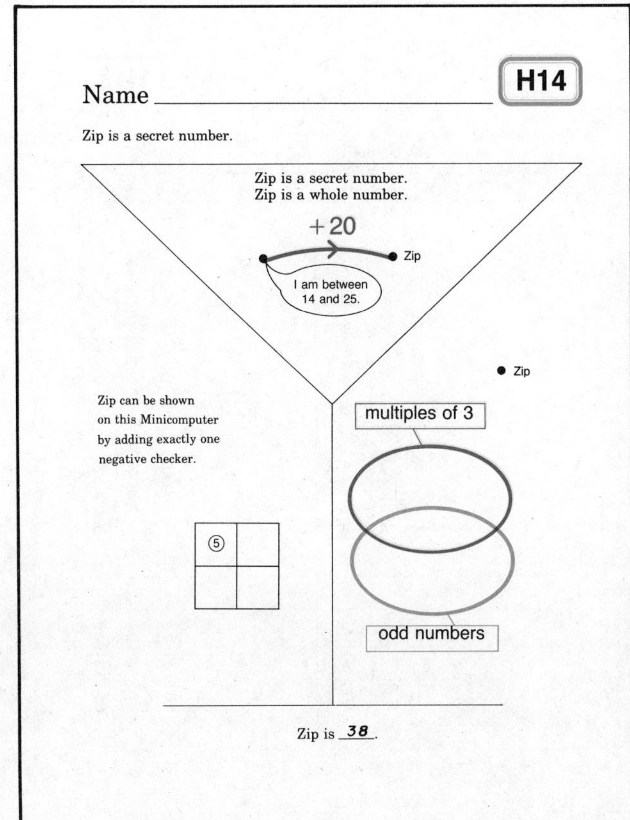

Name ______________________________ **H14**

Zip is a secret number.

Zip is a secret number.
Zip is a whole number.

+20

Zip

I am between 14 and 25.

Zip

Zip can be shown on this Minicomputer by adding exactly one negative checker.

⑤

multiples of 3

odd numbers

Zip is _38_.

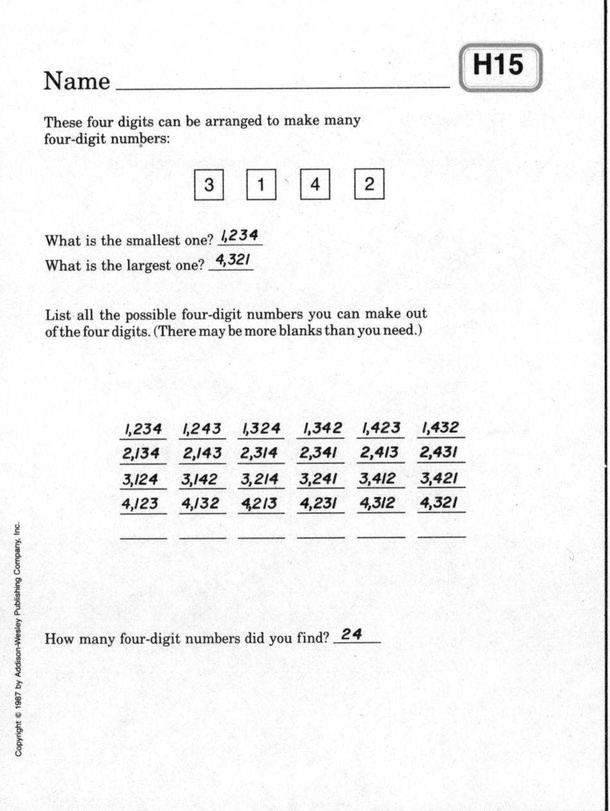

Name ______________________________ **H15**

These four digits can be arranged to make many four-digit numbers:

3 1 4 2

What is the smallest one? _1,234_
What is the largest one? _4,321_

List all the possible four-digit numbers you can make out of the four digits. (There may be more blanks than you need.)

1,234 1,243 1,324 1,342 1,423 1,432
2,134 2,143 2,314 2,341 2,413 2,431
3,124 3,142 3,214 3,241 3,412 3,421
4,123 4,132 4,213 4,231 4,312 4,321

How many four-digit numbers did you find? _24_

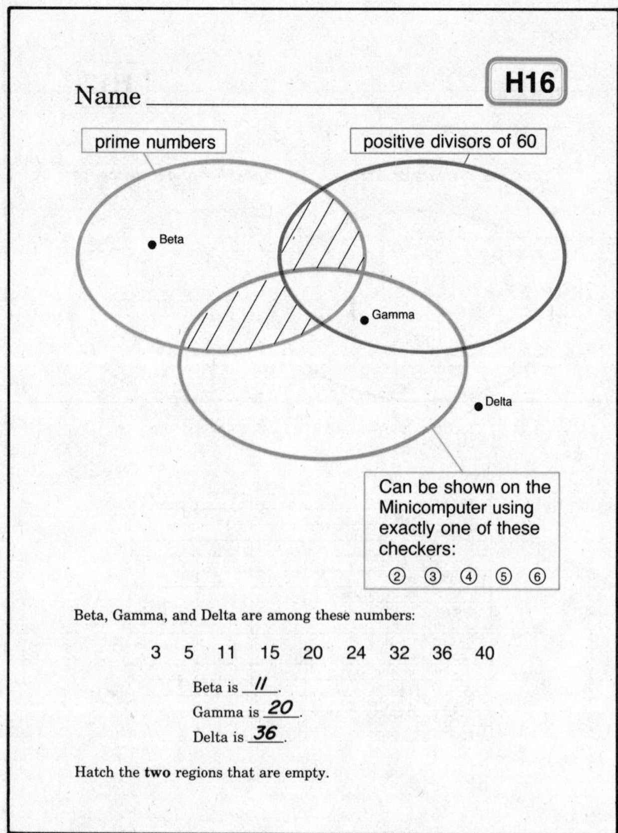
Name
H16
prime numbers
positive divisors of 60
Beta
Gamma
Delta
Can be shown on the Minicomputer using exactly one of these checkers:
② ③ ④ ⑤ ⑥
Beta, Gamma, and Delta are among these numbers:
3 5 11 15 20 24 32 36 40
Beta is 11.
Gamma is 20.
Delta is 36.
Hatch the two regions that are empty.

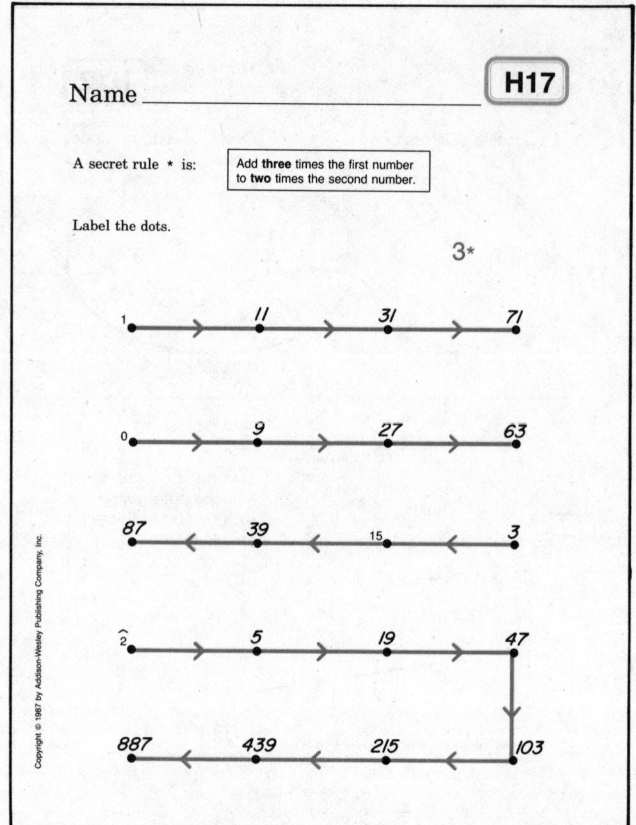
Name
H17
A secret rule * is:
Add three times the first number to two times the second number.
Label the dots.
3*
1 11 31 71
0 9 27 63
87 39 15 3
2 5 19 47
887 439 215 103
Copyright © 1987 by Addison-Wesley Publishing Company, Inc.

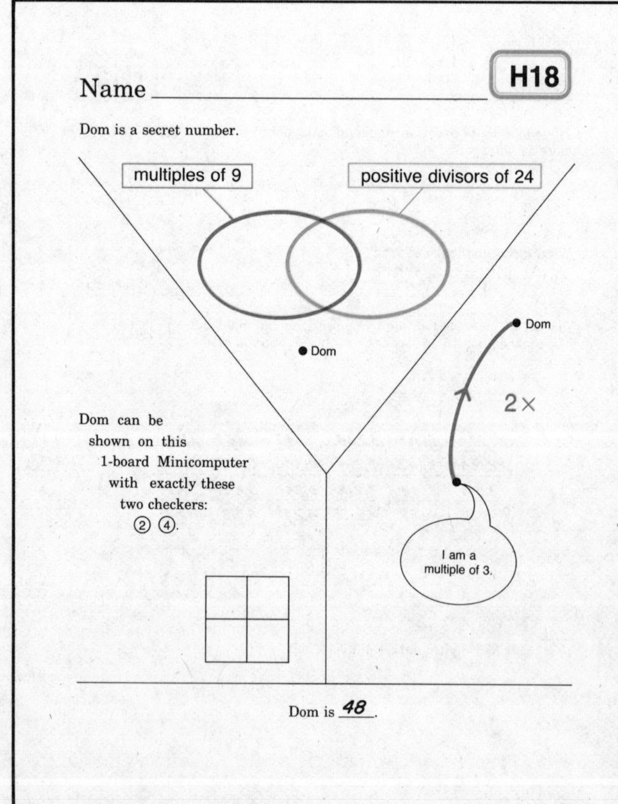
Name
H18
Dom is a secret number.
multiples of 9
positive divisors of 24
Dom
Dom
2×
Dom can be shown on this 1-board Minicomputer with exactly these two checkers:
② ④.
I am a multiple of 3.
Dom is 48.

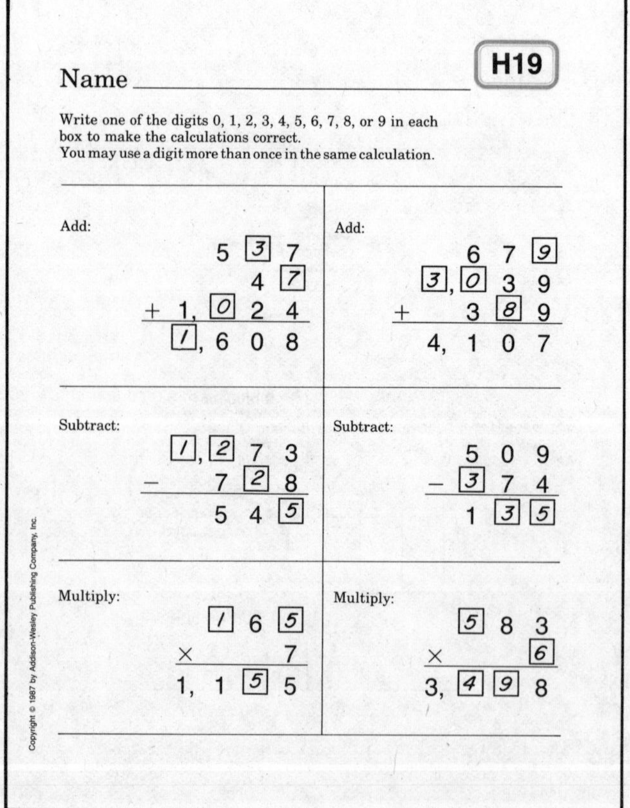
Name
H19
Write one of the digits 0, 1, 2, 3, 4, 5, 6, 7, 8, or 9 in each box to make the calculations correct.
You may use a digit more than once in the same calculation.
Add:
5 3 7
4 7
+ 1, 0 2 4
1, 6 0 8
Add:
6 7 9
3, 0 3 9
+ 3 8 9
4, 1 0 7
Subtract:
1, 2 7 3
− 7 2 8
5 4 5
Subtract:
5 0 9
− 3 7 4
1 3 5
Multiply:
1 6 5
× 7
1, 1 5 5
Multiply:
5 8 3
× 6
3, 4 9 8
Copyright © 1987 by Addison-Wesley Publishing Company, Inc.

H20

Name ______________________

Flo is a secret whole number less than 60.

Clue 1: positive divisors of Flo

Flo could be 6, 15, 21, 27, 33, 39, 51, or 57.

Clue 2: If you subtract 2 from Flo you will get a square number.

Flo could be 6, 27, or 51.

Clue 3: Flo cannot be shown on the Minicomputer with exactly three regular checkers.

Flo is 27.

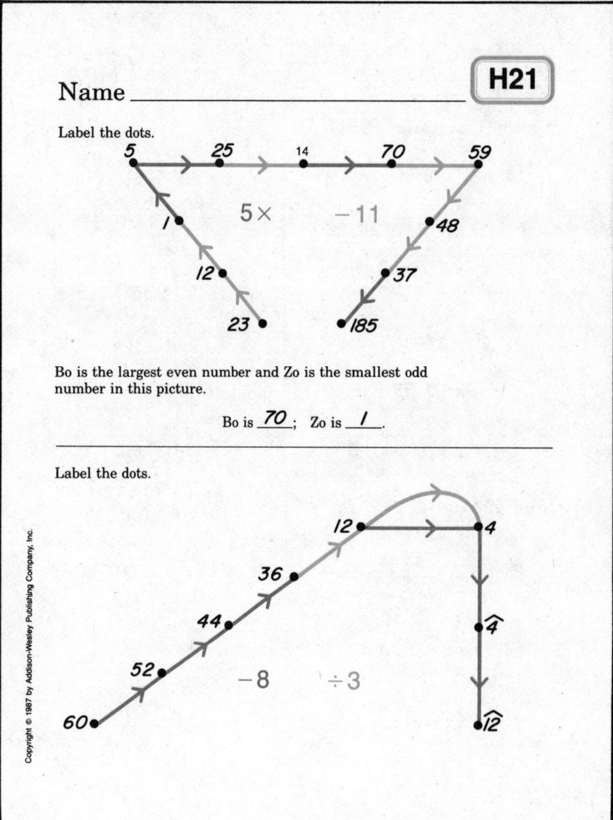

H21

Name ______________________

Label the dots.

Bo is the largest even number and Zo is the smallest odd number in this picture.

Bo is 70; Zo is 1.

Label the dots.

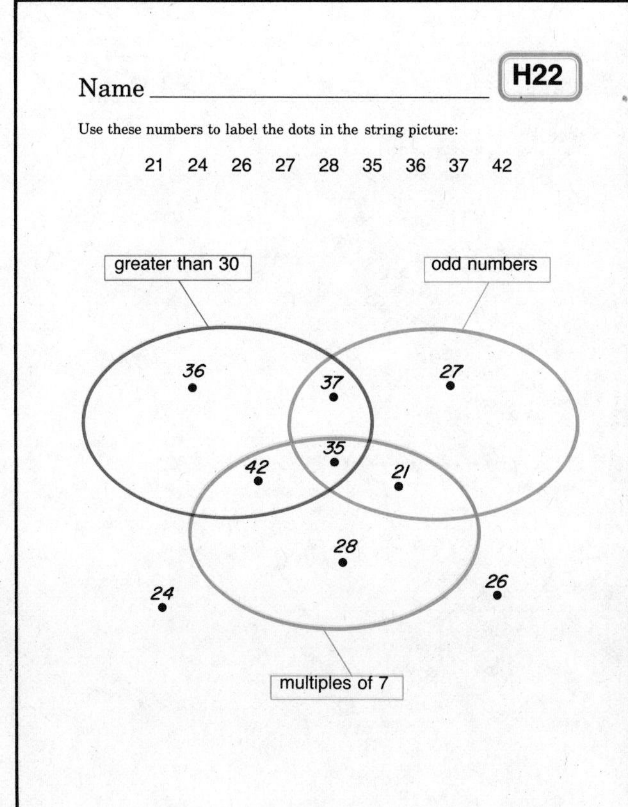

H22

Name ______________________

Use these numbers to label the dots in the string picture:

21 24 26 27 28 35 36 37 42

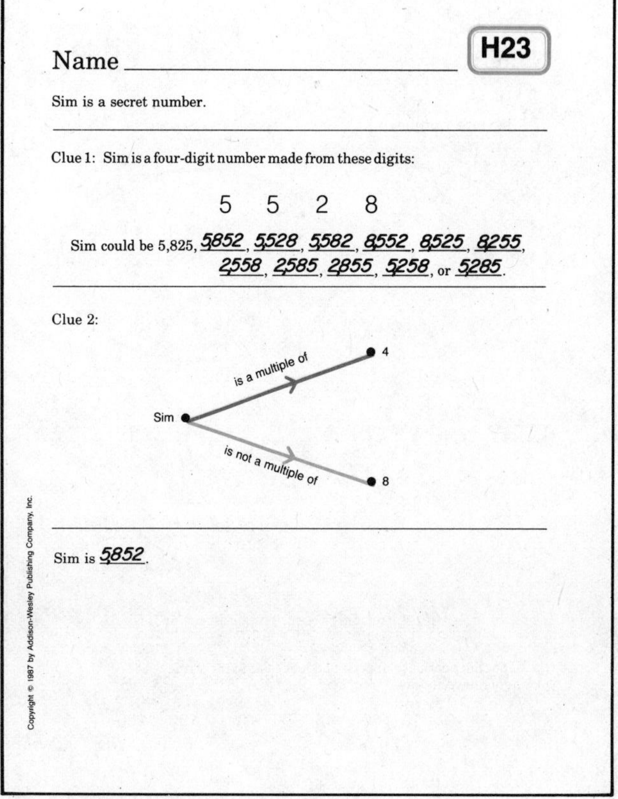

H23

Name ______________________

Sim is a secret number.

Clue 1: Sim is a four-digit number made from these digits:

5 5 2 8

Sim could be 5,825, 5852, 5528, 5582, 8552, 8525, 8255, 2558, 2585, 2855, 5258, or 5285.

Clue 2:

Sim is 5852.

Name ______________________ **H24**

Complete these equations.

$3^2 \times 3^3 = 3^{\boxed{5}} = \boxed{243}$

$3^3 \times 2^3 = \boxed{6}^3 = \boxed{216}$

$5^2 \times 5^4 \times 5^7 = 5^{\boxed{13}}$

$2^3 + 2^2 = \boxed{12}$

$2^5 = \boxed{32}$

$14^5 \times 14^8 \times 14^{11} = 14^{\boxed{24}}$

$8^6 \times 8 \times 8^{12} = 8^{\boxed{19}}$

$6^5 \times 9^5 = \boxed{54}^5$

$3^8 \times 2^8 \times 5^8 = \boxed{30}^8$

$9^4 = 3^{\boxed{8}}$

$3^6 = 9^{\boxed{3}} = 27^{\boxed{2}}$

$5^{\boxed{4}} = 625$

$2^{\boxed{7}} = 128$

$4^{\boxed{4}} = 256$

$3^{\boxed{5}} = 243$

$10^{\boxed{6}} = 1{,}000{,}000$

$100^{\boxed{3}} = 1{,}000{,}000$

$10^4 = 100^{\boxed{2}}$

$100^5 = 10^{\boxed{10}}$

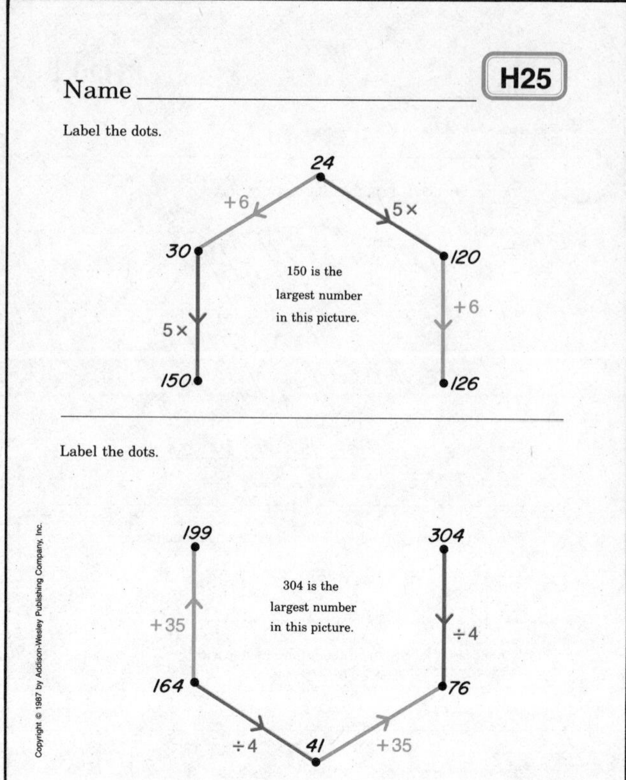

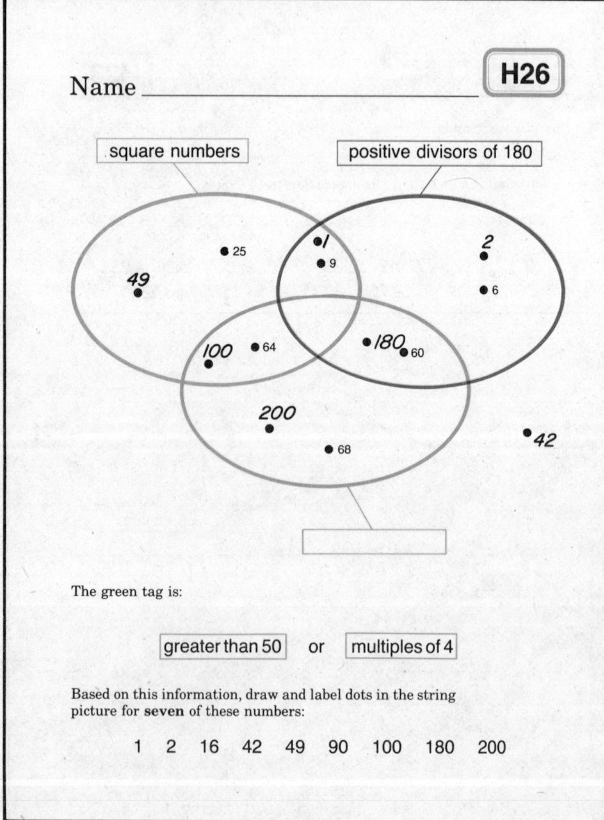

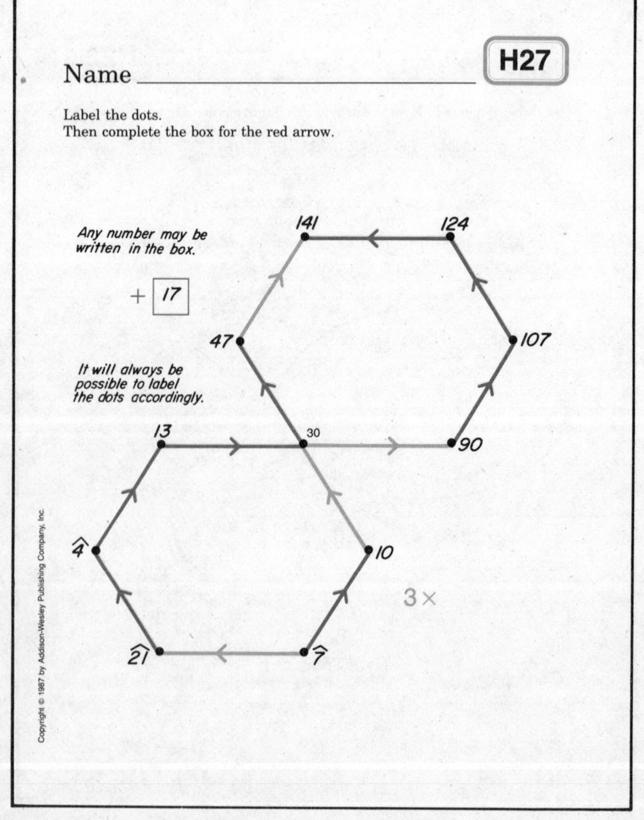

Name ______________ **H28**

Use only these keys to go from "start" to "goal."

[4] [6] [+] [−] [×] [÷] [=]

You may use a key more than once.
Each time you press a key it costs 1 cent.
Try to find as cheap a solution as possible.
Test your solutions on a calculator.

Start	Keys Pressed	Goal	Cost
0	4 × 4 + 4 ÷ 4 =	5	8¢
0	6 × 6 + 6 ÷ 6 =	7	8¢
0	4 6 + 4 6 ÷ 4 =	23	8¢
0	6 6 × 6 ÷ 4 =	99	7¢
0	6 − 4 ÷ 4 =	0.5	6¢
0	4 + 6 ÷ = = = *	0.1	6¢
0	6 × 6 ÷ 4 =	9	6¢
0	6 4 − 4 ÷ 4 =	15	7¢
0	4 + 6 ÷ = = × 6 4 = *	0.64	10¢
68	− 4 4 × 4 + 4 =	100	8¢
100	− 6 4 ÷ 6 ÷ 6 =	1	8¢
		Total Cost	82¢

* (only if your calculator allows constant division)

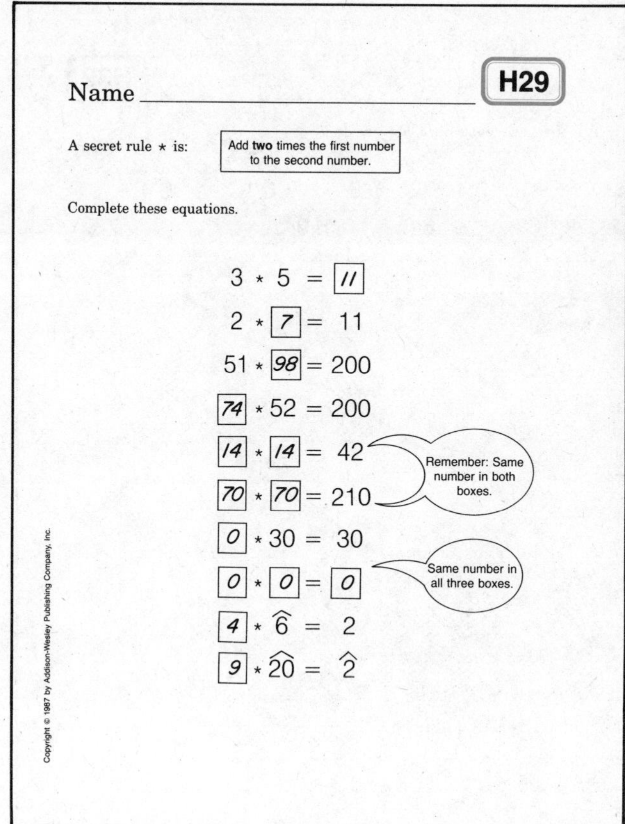
Name ______________ **H29**

A secret rule ⋆ is: Add **two** times the first number to the second number.

Complete these equations.

3 ⋆ 5 = [11]
2 ⋆ [7] = 11
51 ⋆ [98] = 200
[74] ⋆ 52 = 200
[14] ⋆ [14] = 42
[70] ⋆ [70] = 210
[0] ⋆ 30 = 30
[0] ⋆ [0] = [0]
[4] ⋆ 6 = 2
[9] ⋆ 20 = 2

Name ______________ **H30**

Write one of the digits 0, 1, 2, 3, 4, 5, 6, 7, 8, or 9 in each box to make the calculations correct.
You may use a digit more than once in the same calculation.

Add:

```
    5 [5] 2
+ 4, 8 3 [0]
[5],[3] 8 2
```

Add:

```
  [6] 2 6
      [3] 6
+   3 1 6
    9 7 [8]
```

Multiply:

```
  [4] 7 [6]
×         9
4, 2 [8] 4
```

Subtract:

```
   8, [6] 5 2
− [3], 0 [3] 6
   5, 6 1 [6]
```

Subtract:

```
  2 [7], 7 4 4
−    4, [2] 8 [0]
  [2] 3, 4 [6] 4
```

Multiply:

```
  [3] 5 2
×       [8]
2, 8 1 6
```

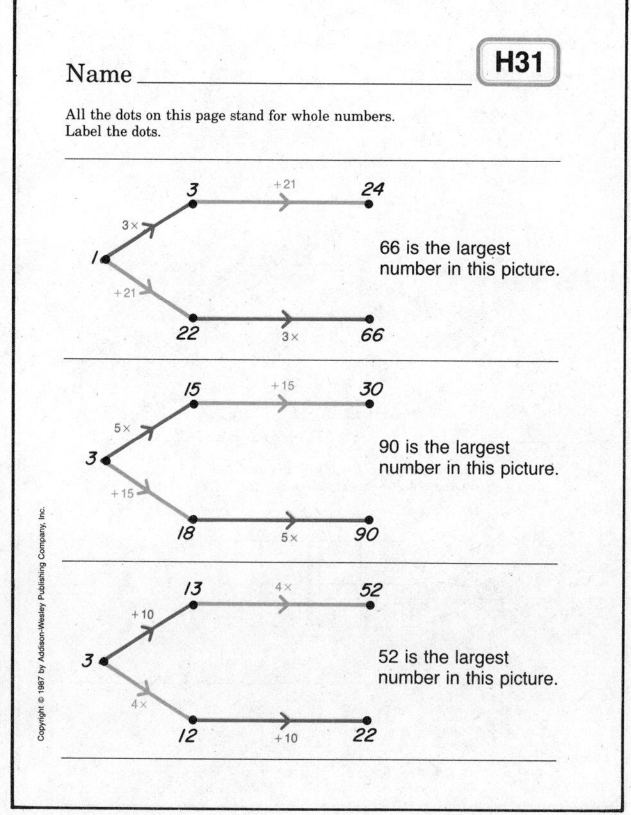
Name ______________ **H31**

All the dots on this page stand for whole numbers.
Label the dots.

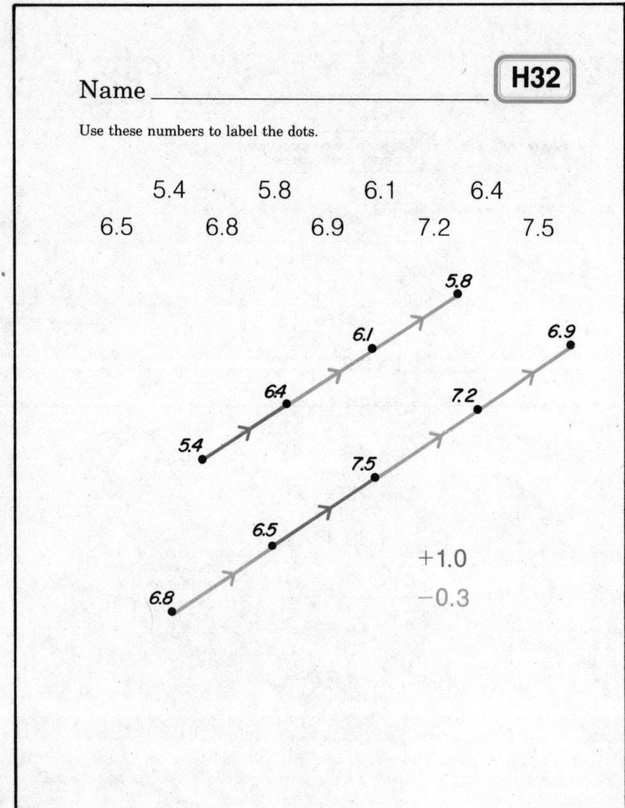
Name
H32
Use these numbers to label the dots.
5.4 5.8 6.1 6.4
6.5 6.8 6.9 7.2 7.5
5.8
6.1
6.9
6.4
7.2
5.4
7.5
6.5
+1.0
6.8
−0.3

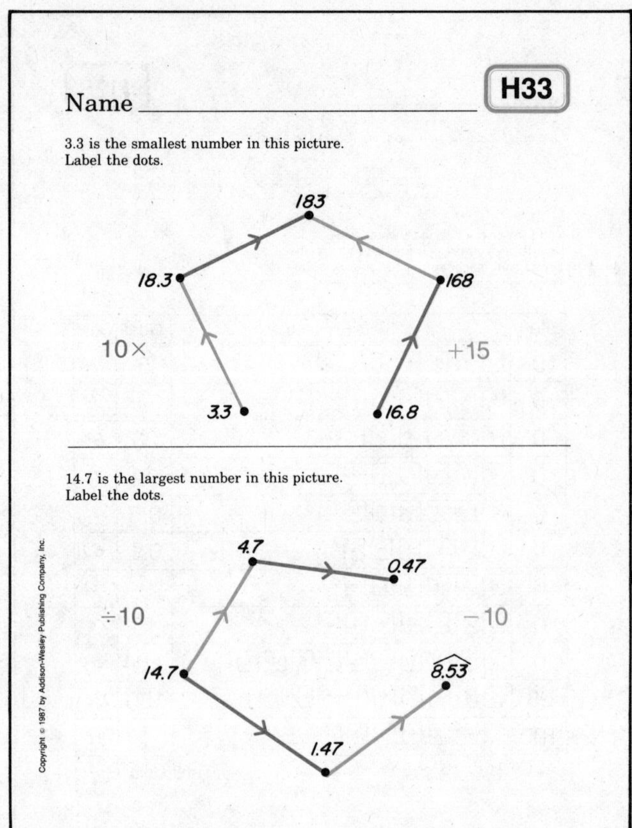
Name
H33
3.3 is the smallest number in this picture.
Label the dots.
183
18.3
168
10×
+15
3.3
16.8
14.7 is the largest number in this picture.
Label the dots.
4.7
0.47
÷10
−10
14.7
8.53
1.47
Copyright © 1987 by Addison-Wesley Publishing Company, Inc.

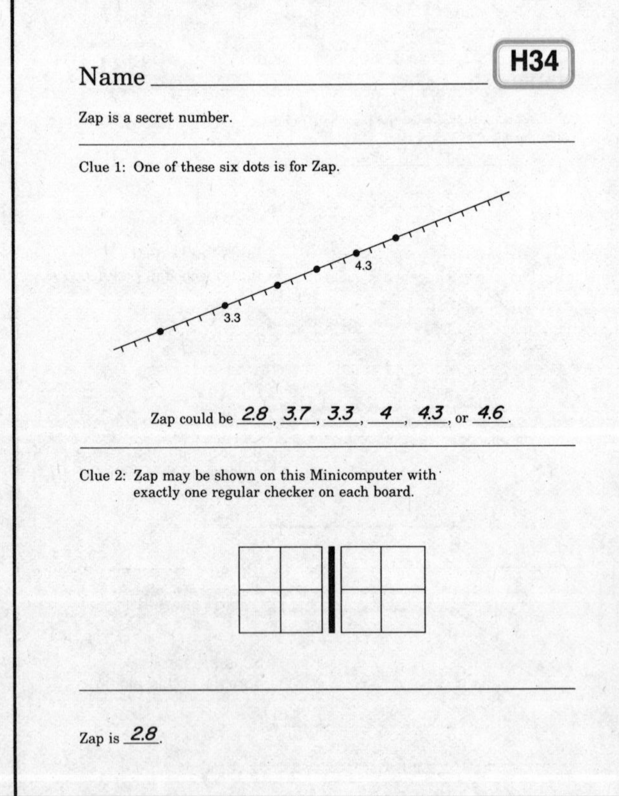
Name
H34
Zap is a secret number.
Clue 1: One of these six dots is for Zap.
4.3
3.3
Zap could be 2.8, 3.7, 3.3, 4, 4.3, or 4.6.
Clue 2: Zap may be shown on this Minicomputer with exactly one regular checker on each board.
Zap is 2.8.

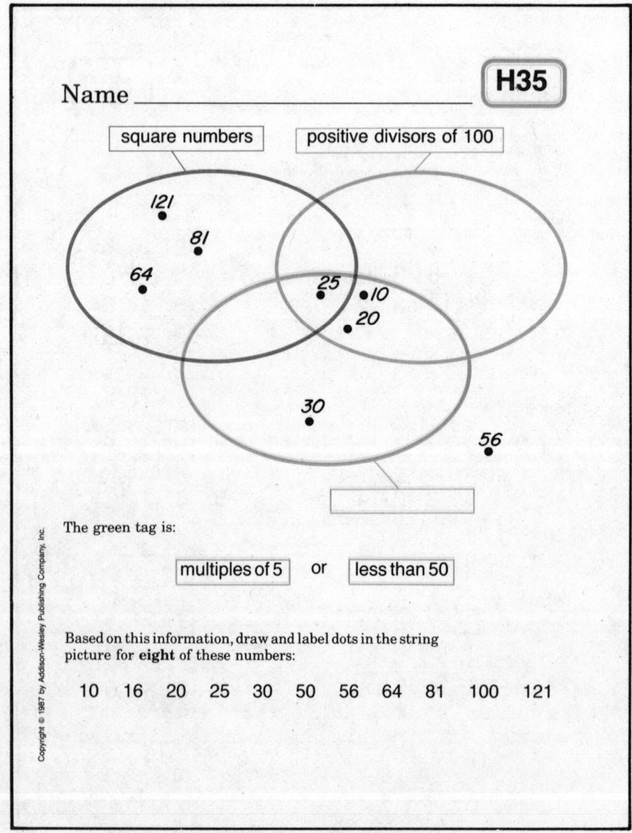
Name
H35
square numbers
positive divisors of 100
121
81
64
25
10
20
30
56
The green tag is:
multiples of 5
or
less than 50
Based on this information, draw and label dots in the string picture for eight of these numbers:
10 16 20 25 30 50 56 64 81 100 121
Copyright © 1987 by Addison-Wesley Publishing Company, Inc.

H36

Name ____________________

Complete these equations.

$8^2 =$ 64	$10^{20} =$ 100,000,000,000,000,000,000
$2^5 =$ 32	$100^2 =$ 10,000
$5^3 =$ 125	$100^3 =$ 1,000,000
$(2 \times 5)^4 =$ 10,000	$1{,}000^2 =$ 1,000,000
$2^3 \times 5^2 =$ 200	$1{,}000^3 =$ 1,000,000,000
$1^{17} =$ 1	$4^1 \times 3^2 =$ 36
$0^{35} =$ 0	$2^2 \times 3^2 =$ 36
$1^{100} \times 3^3 =$ 27	$(2 \times 3)^2 =$ 36
$0^{1,000} \times 75^6 =$ 0	$2^2 \times 3^2 \times 5^1 =$ 180
$10^2 =$ 100	$2^2 \times 4^3 =$ 256
$10^3 =$ 1,000	$2^4 \times 4^2 =$ 256
$10^4 =$ 10,000	$2^6 \times 4^1 =$ 256
$10^5 =$ 100,000	$2^8 =$ 256
$10^{10} =$ 10,000,000,000	

H37

Name ____________________

Label the dots.

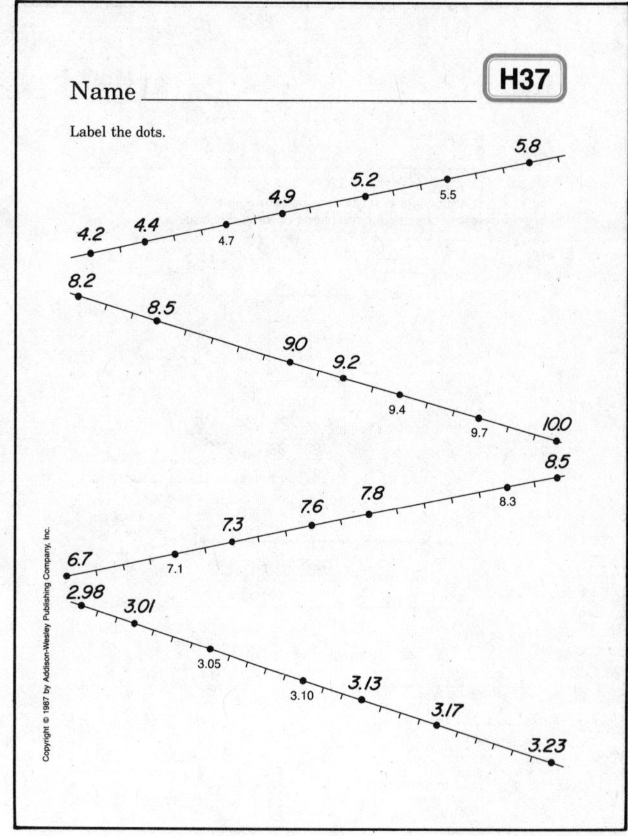

H38

Name ____________________

Pic is a secret number.

Clue 1: Pic is a four-digit number made up of exactly two 4s and exactly two 6s.

Pic could be 4,664, 4,646, 4,466, 6,446, 6,464, or 6,644.

Clue 2:

[+] [4] [=] ···

10 ● ——→ ● Pic

Pic could be 4,646, 4,466, or 6,446.

Clue 3:

Pic is greater than 80^2.

Pic is 6,446.

H39

Name ____________________

Draw exactly one negative checker ⓐ on each Minicomputer.
Get the kind of number asked for in each part.
Then fill in the blanks.

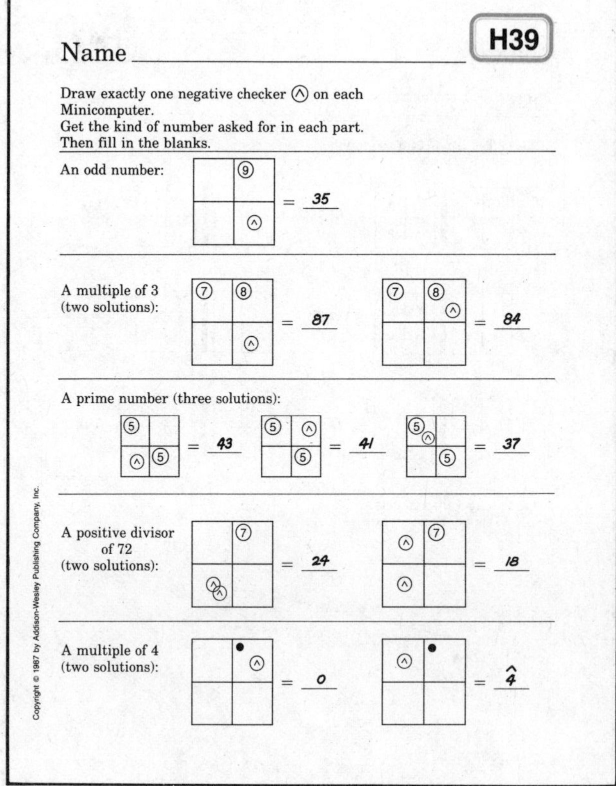

Name ______________________ **H40**

Zip is a secret number.

Clue 1: Zip is a multiple of 6 that can be shown on this Minicomputer using exactly one of these checkers:

② ③ ④ ⑤ ⑥ ⑦ ⑧ ⑨

Zip could be *6*, *12*, *24*, *48*, *18*, *36*, or *72*.

Clue 2: Zip → ×50 → (I am between 800 and 1,900.)

Zip could be *18*, *24*, or *36*.

Clue 3: Zip is 15 more than a prime.

Zip is *18*.

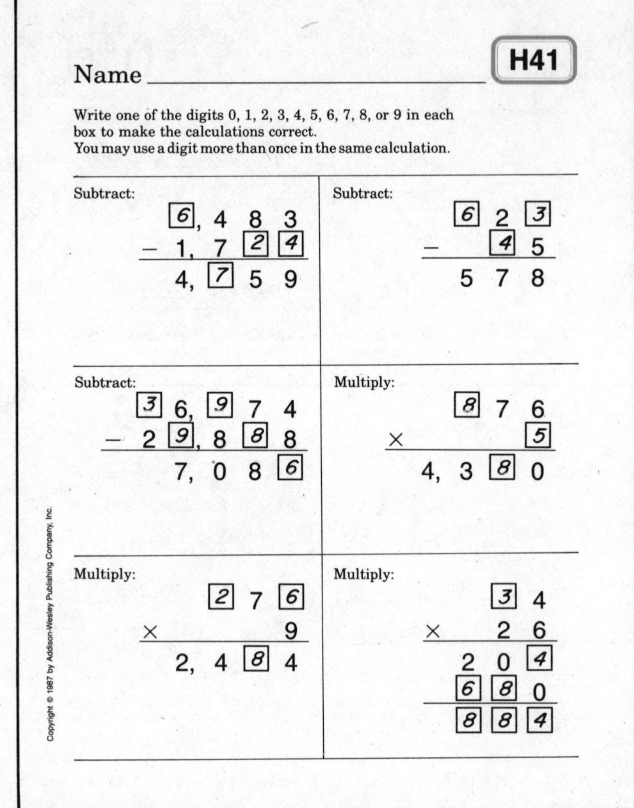

Name
H41
Write one of the digits 0, 1, 2, 3, 4, 5, 6, 7, 8, or 9 in each box to make the calculations correct.
You may use a digit more than once in the same calculation.
Subtract:
6, 4 8 3
− 1, 7 2 4
4, 7 5 9
Subtract:
6 2 3
− 4 5
5 7 8
Subtract:
3 6, 9 7 4
− 2 9, 8 8 8
7, 0 8 6
Multiply:
8 7 6
× 5
4, 3 8 0
Multiply:
2 7 6
× 9
2, 4 8 4
Multiply:
3 4
× 2 6
2 0 4
6 8 0
8 8 4
Copyright © 1987 by Addison-Wesley Publishing Company, Inc.

Name ______________________ **H42**

Tao is a secret number.

Clue 1: Tao is one of these numbers.

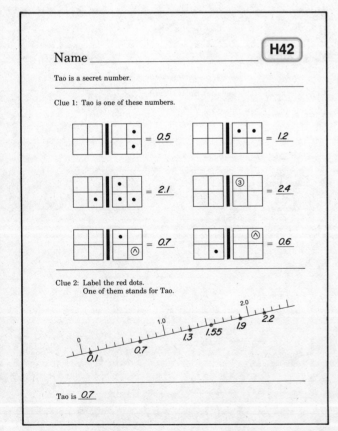

= *0.5*	= *1.2*
= *2.1*	= *2.4*
= *0.7*	= *0.6*

Clue 2: Label the red dots.
One of them stands for Tao.

0, 1.0, 2.0 — *0.1*, *0.7*, *1.3*, *1.55*, *1.9*, *2.2*

Tao is *0.7*

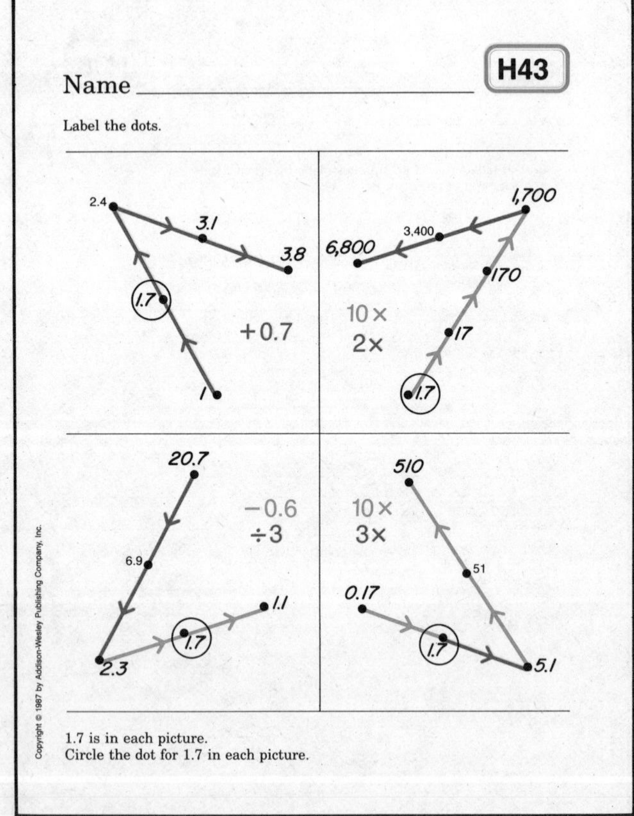

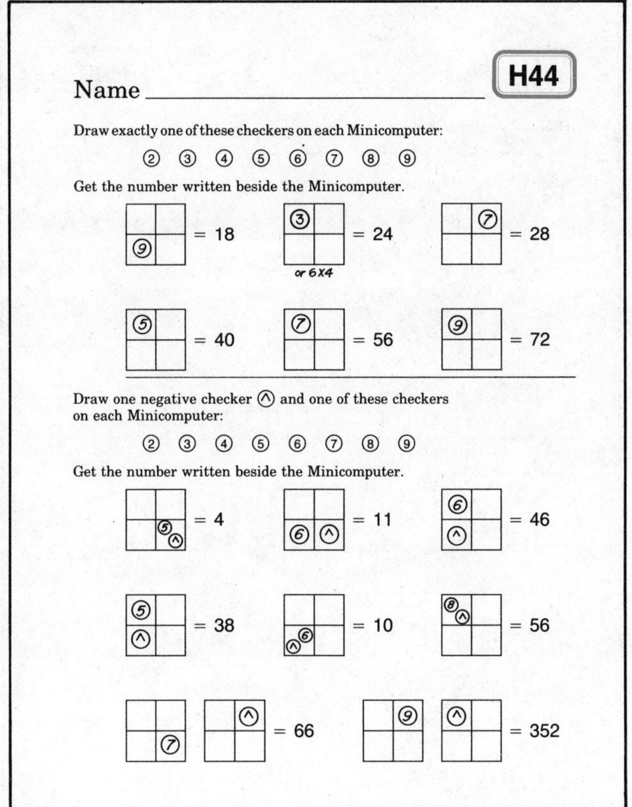

H44

Name ____________________

Draw exactly one of these checkers on each Minicomputer:

② ③ ④ ⑤ ⑥ ⑦ ⑧ ⑨

Get the number written beside the Minicomputer.

= 18 = 24 = 28

or 6X4

= 40 = 56 = 72

Draw one negative checker ^ and one of these checkers on each Minicomputer:

② ③ ④ ⑤ ⑥ ⑦ ⑧ ⑨

Get the number written beside the Minicomputer.

= 4 = 11 = 46

= 38 = 10 = 56

= 66 = 352

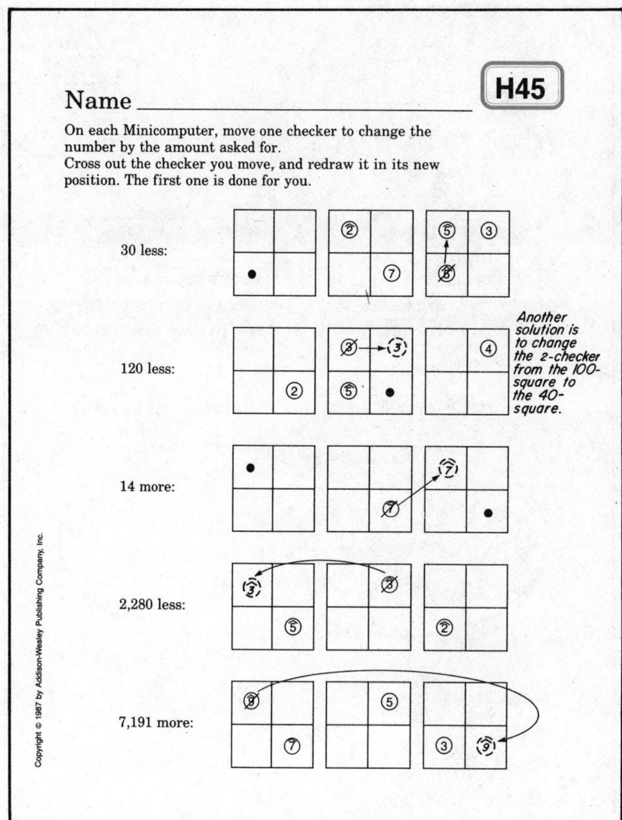

H45

Name ____________________

On each Minicomputer, move one checker to change the number by the amount asked for.
Cross out the checker you move, and redraw it in its new position. The first one is done for you.

30 less:

120 less:

Another solution is to change the 2-checker from the 100-square to the 40-square.

14 more:

2,280 less:

7,191 more:

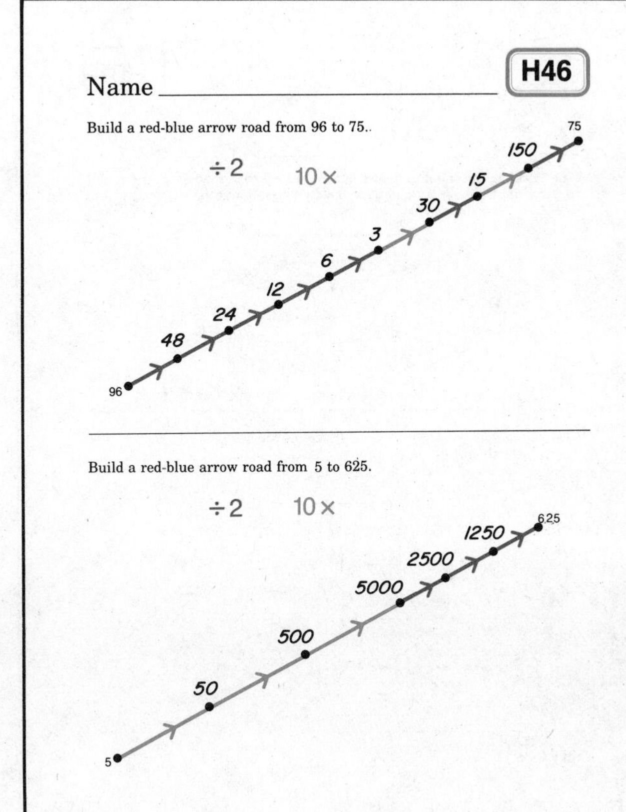

H46

Name ____________________

Build a red-blue arrow road from 96 to 75.

÷2 10×

96, 48, 24, 12, 6, 3, 30, 15, 150, 75

Build a red-blue arrow road from 5 to 625.

÷2 10×

5, 50, 500, 5000, 2500, 1250, 625

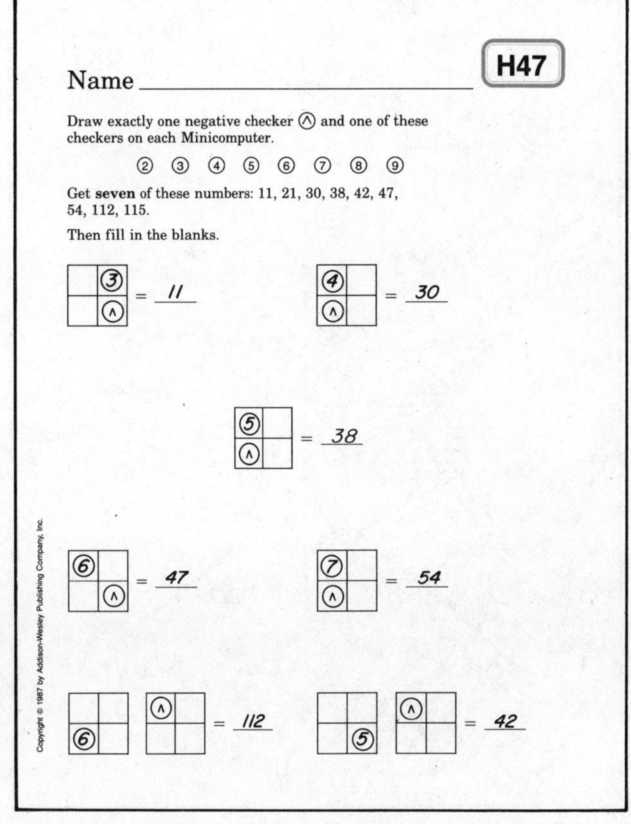

H47

Name ____________________

Draw exactly one negative checker ^ and one of these checkers on each Minicomputer.

② ③ ④ ⑤ ⑥ ⑦ ⑧ ⑨

Get **seven** of these numbers: 11, 21, 30, 38, 42, 47, 54, 112, 115.

Then fill in the blanks.

= 11 = 30

= 38

= 47 = 54

= 112 = 42

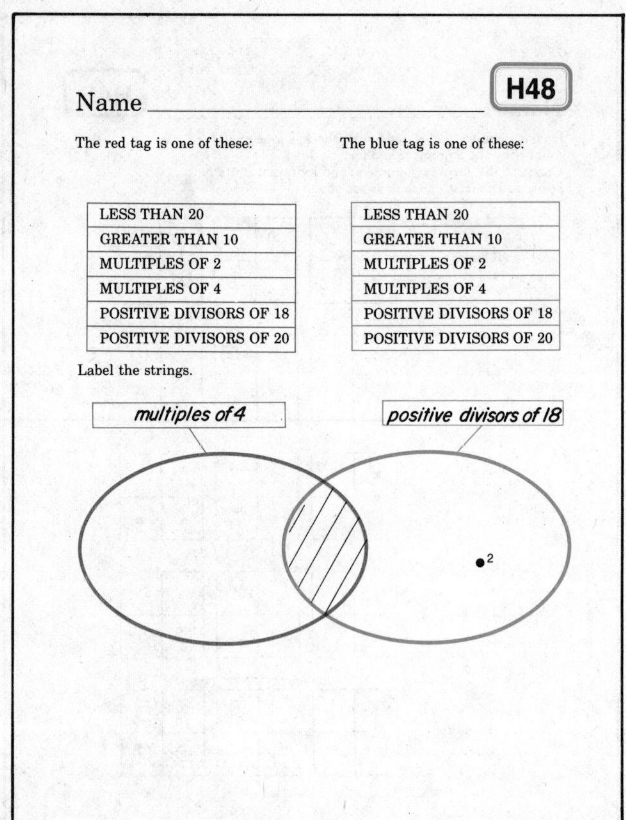
Name ______ **H48**

The red tag is one of these:

LESS THAN 20
GREATER THAN 10
MULTIPLES OF 2
MULTIPLES OF 4
POSITIVE DIVISORS OF 18
POSITIVE DIVISORS OF 20

The blue tag is one of these:

LESS THAN 20
GREATER THAN 10
MULTIPLES OF 2
MULTIPLES OF 4
POSITIVE DIVISORS OF 18
POSITIVE DIVISORS OF 20

Label the strings.

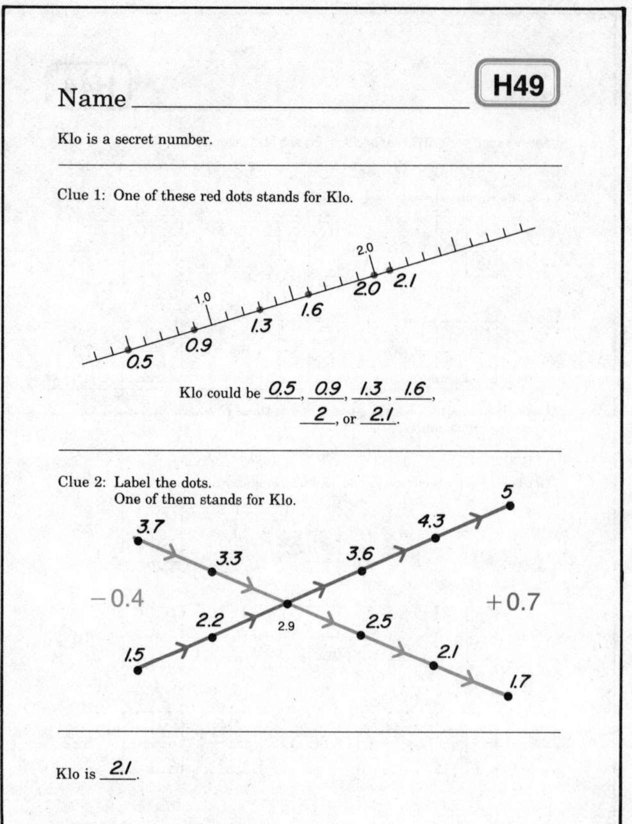
Name ______ **H49**

Klo is a secret number.

Clue 1: One of these red dots stands for Klo.

Klo could be 0.5, 0.9, 1.3, 1.6, 2, or 2.1.

Clue 2: Label the dots.
One of them stands for Klo.

Klo is 2.1.

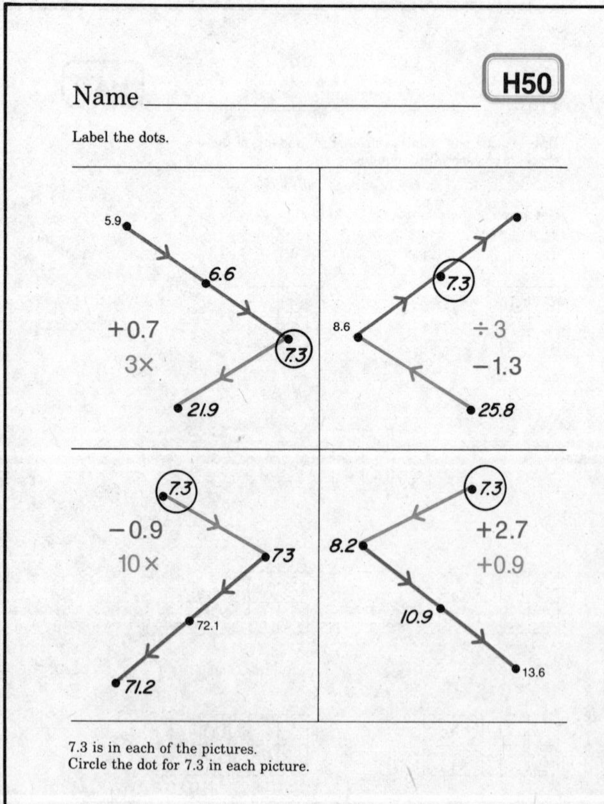
Name ______ **H50**

Label the dots.

7.3 is in each of the pictures.
Circle the dot for 7.3 in each picture.

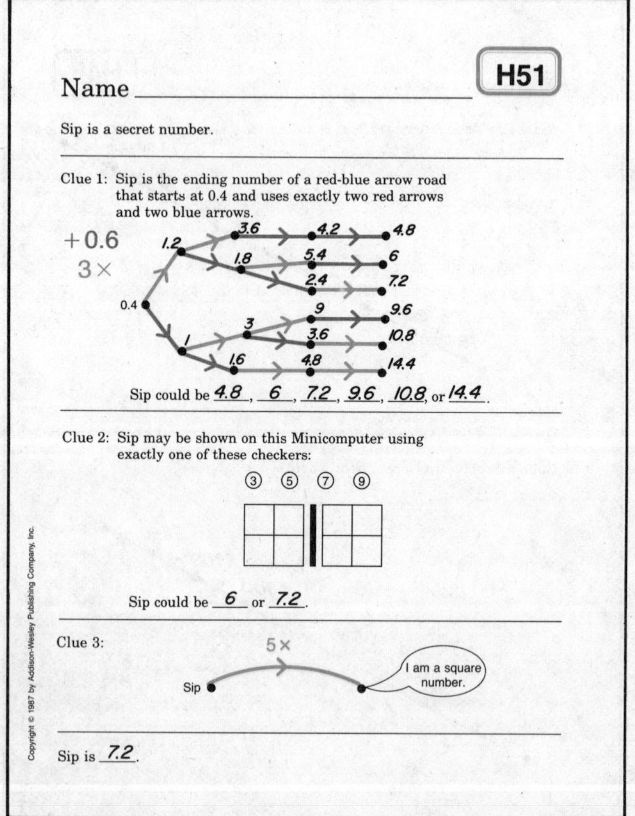
Name ______ **H51**

Sip is a secret number.

Clue 1: Sip is the ending number of a red-blue arrow road that starts at 0.4 and uses exactly two red arrows and two blue arrows.

Sip could be 4.8, 6, 7.2, 9.6, 10.8, or 14.4.

Clue 2: Sip may be shown on this Minicomputer using exactly one of these checkers:

Sip could be 6 or 7.2.

Clue 3:

Sip is 7.2.

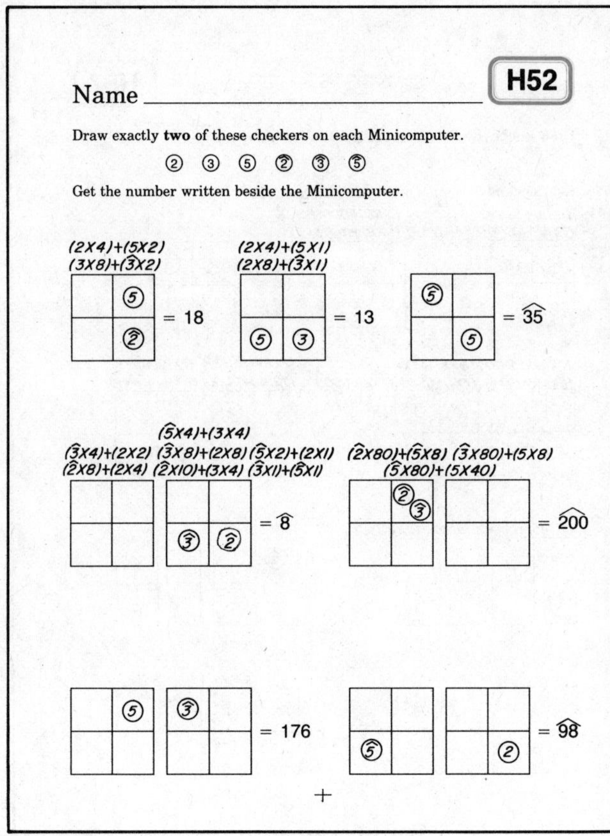
H52
Name
Draw exactly two of these checkers on each Minicomputer.
Get the number written beside the Minicomputer.
= 18
= 13
= 176

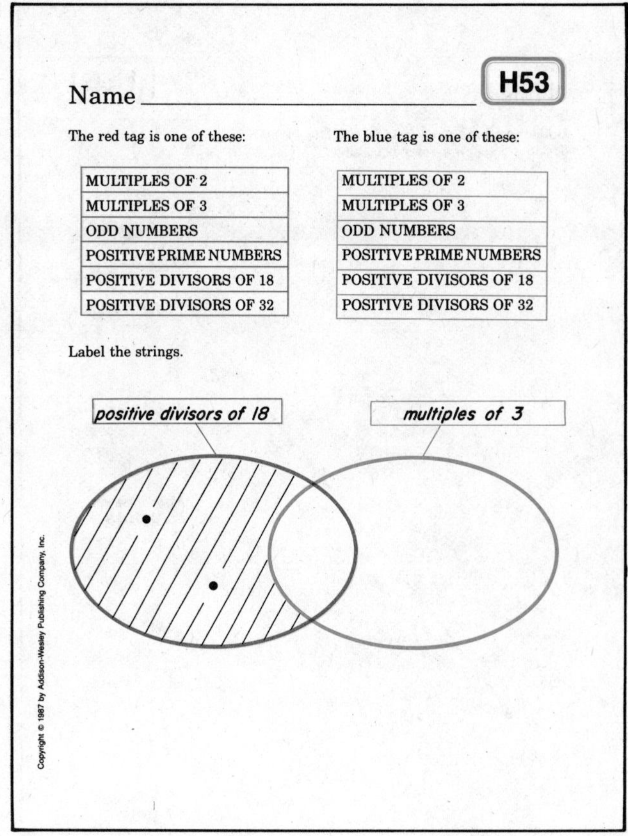
H53
Name
The red tag is one of these:
The blue tag is one of these:
MULTIPLES OF 2
MULTIPLES OF 3
ODD NUMBERS
POSITIVE PRIME NUMBERS
POSITIVE DIVISORS OF 18
POSITIVE DIVISORS OF 32
Label the strings.
positive divisors of 18
multiples of 3

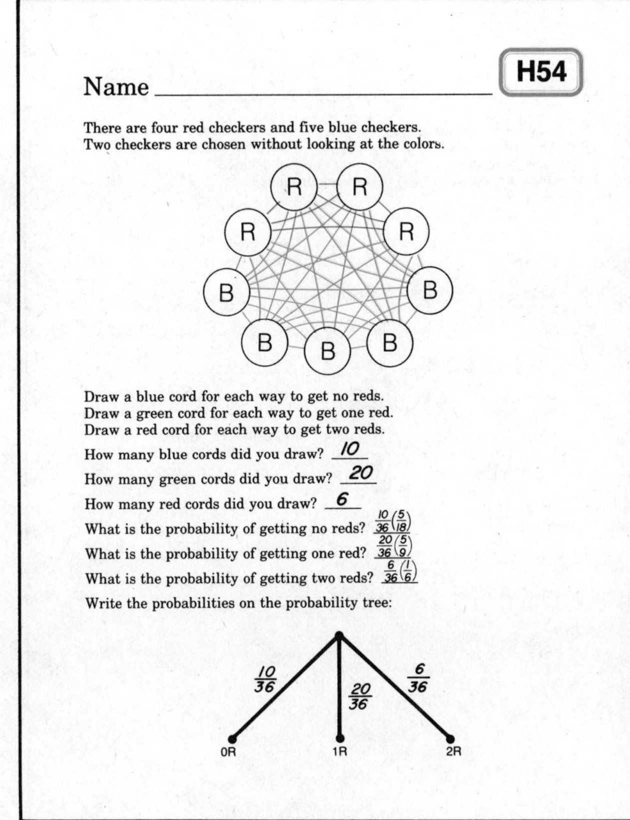
H54
Name
There are four red checkers and five blue checkers.
Two checkers are chosen without looking at the colors.
Draw a blue cord for each way to get no reds.
Draw a green cord for each way to get one red.
Draw a red cord for each way to get two reds.
How many blue cords did you draw? 10
How many green cords did you draw? 20
How many red cords did you draw? 6
What is the probability of getting no reds?
What is the probability of getting one red?
What is the probability of getting two reds?
Write the probabilities on the probability tree:
0R
1R
2R

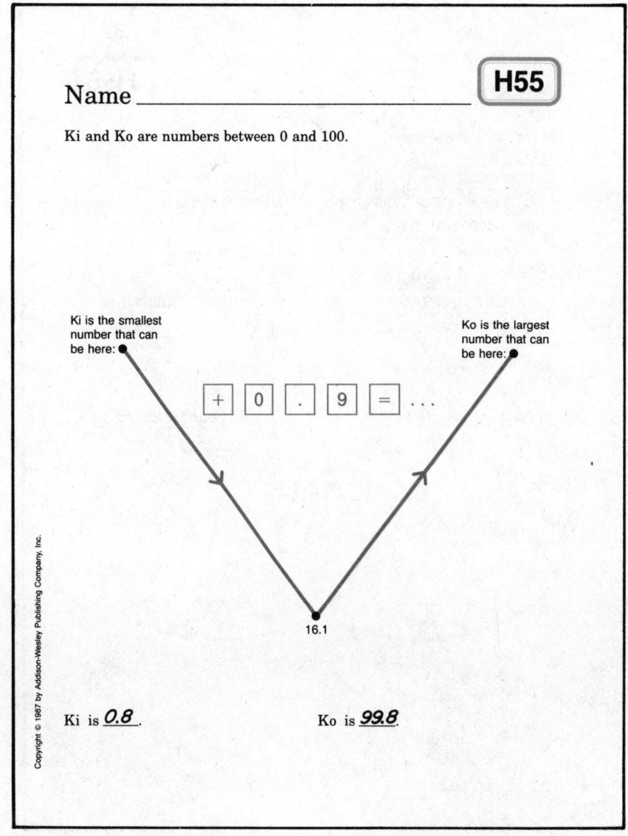
H55
Name
Ki and Ko are numbers between 0 and 100.
Ki is the smallest number that can be here:
Ko is the largest number that can be here:
16.1
Ki is 0.8.
Ko is 99.8

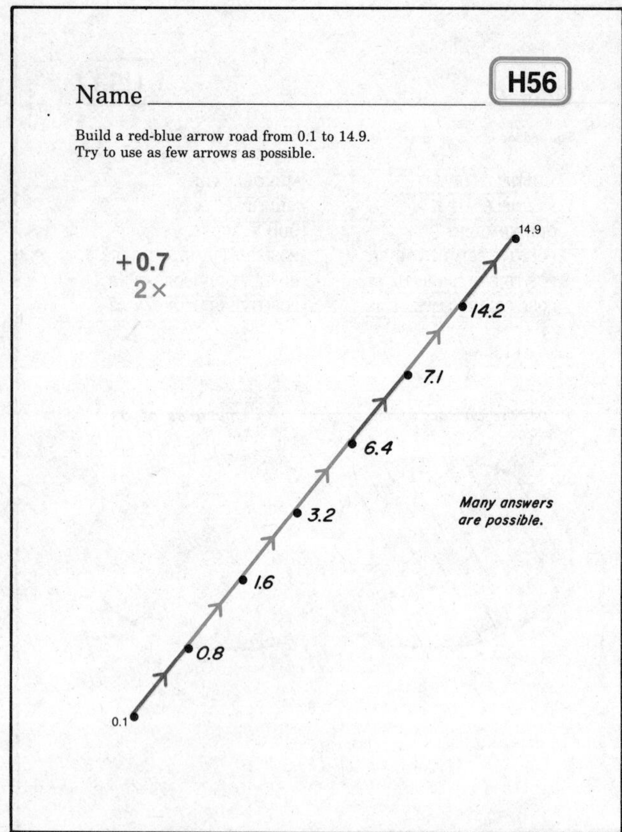

Name ____________ **H56**

Build a red-blue arrow road from 0.1 to 14.9.
Try to use as few arrows as possible.

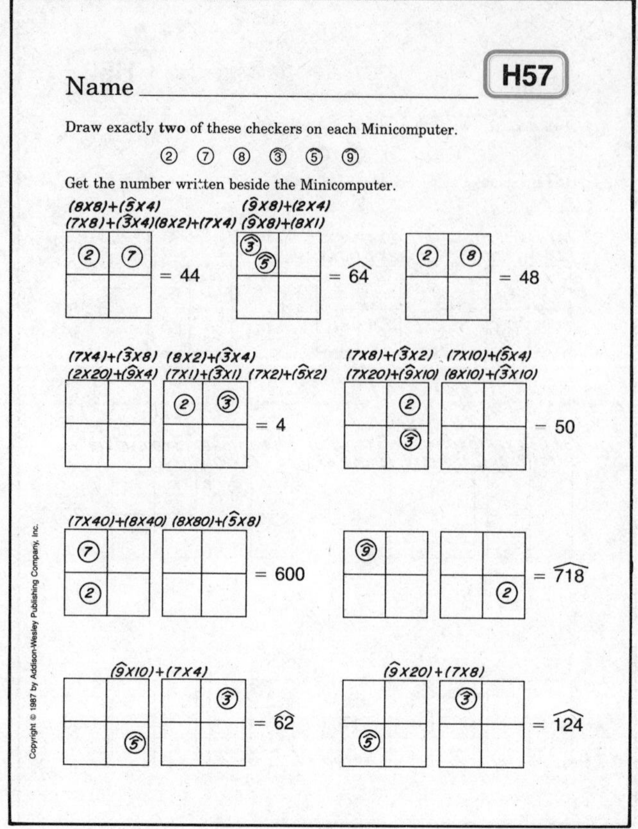

Name ____________ **H57**

Draw exactly **two** of these checkers on each Minicomputer.

② ⑦ ⑧ ③ ⑤ ⑨

Get the number written beside the Minicomputer.

(8X8)+(5̂X4) (7X8)+(3̂X4)(8X2)+(7X4) = 44
(9̂X8)+(2X4) (9̂X8)+(8X1) = 6̂4
= 48
(7X4)+(3̂X8) (8X2)+(3̂X4) (2X20)+(9̂X4) (7X1)+(3̂X1) (7X2)+(5̂X2) = 4
(7X8)+(3̂X2) (7X10)+(5̂X4) (7X20)+(9̂X10) (8X10)+(3̂X10) = 50
(7X40)+(8X40) (8X80)+(5̂X8) = 600
= 7̂18
(9̂X10)+(7X4) = 6̂2
(9̂X20)+(7X8) = 1̂24
Copyright © 1987 by Addison-Wesley Publishing Company, Inc.

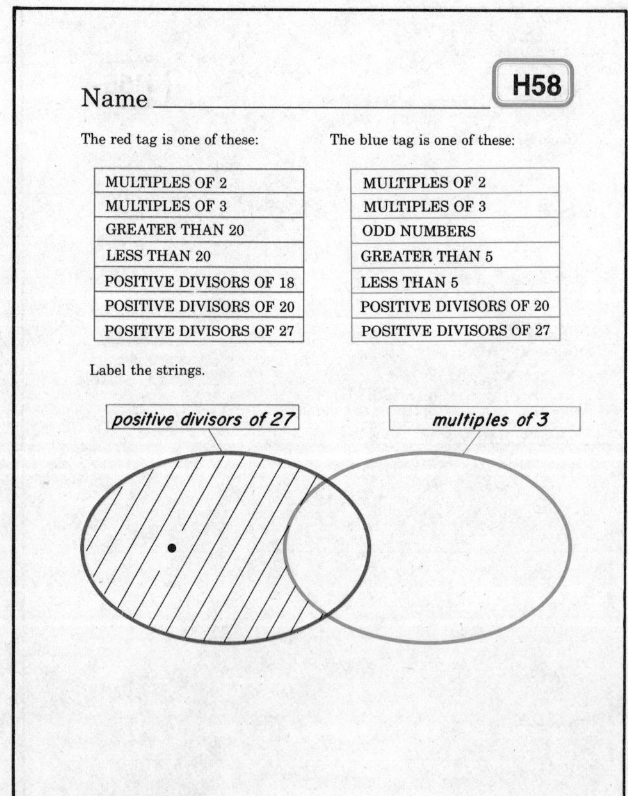

Name ____________ **H58**

The red tag is one of these:

MULTIPLES OF 2
MULTIPLES OF 3
GREATER THAN 20
LESS THAN 20
POSITIVE DIVISORS OF 18
POSITIVE DIVISORS OF 20
POSITIVE DIVISORS OF 27

The blue tag is one of these:

MULTIPLES OF 2
MULTIPLES OF 3
ODD NUMBERS
GREATER THAN 5
LESS THAN 5
POSITIVE DIVISORS OF 20
POSITIVE DIVISORS OF 27

Label the strings.

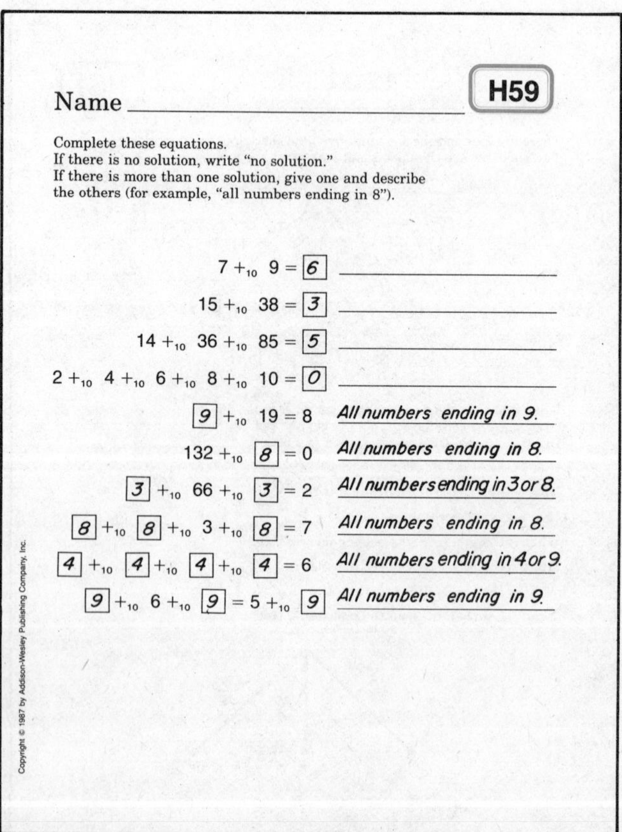

Name ____________ **H59**

Complete these equations.
If there is no solution, write "no solution."
If there is more than one solution, give one and describe the others (for example, "all numbers ending in 8").

$7 +_{10} 9 =$ [6]

$15 +_{10} 38 =$ [3]

$14 +_{10} 36 +_{10} 85 =$ [5]

$2 +_{10} 4 +_{10} 6 +_{10} 8 +_{10} 10 =$ [0]

[9] $+_{10} 19 = 8$ — All numbers ending in 9.

$132 +_{10}$ [8] $= 0$ — All numbers ending in 8.

[3] $+_{10} 66 +_{10}$ [3] $= 2$ — All numbers ending in 3 or 8.

[8] $+_{10}$ [8] $+_{10} 3 +_{10}$ [8] $= 7$ — All numbers ending in 8.

[4] $+_{10}$ [4] $+_{10}$ [4] $+_{10}$ [4] $= 6$ — All numbers ending in 4 or 9.

[9] $+_{10} 6 +_{10}$ [9] $= 5 +_{10}$ [9] — All numbers ending in 9.

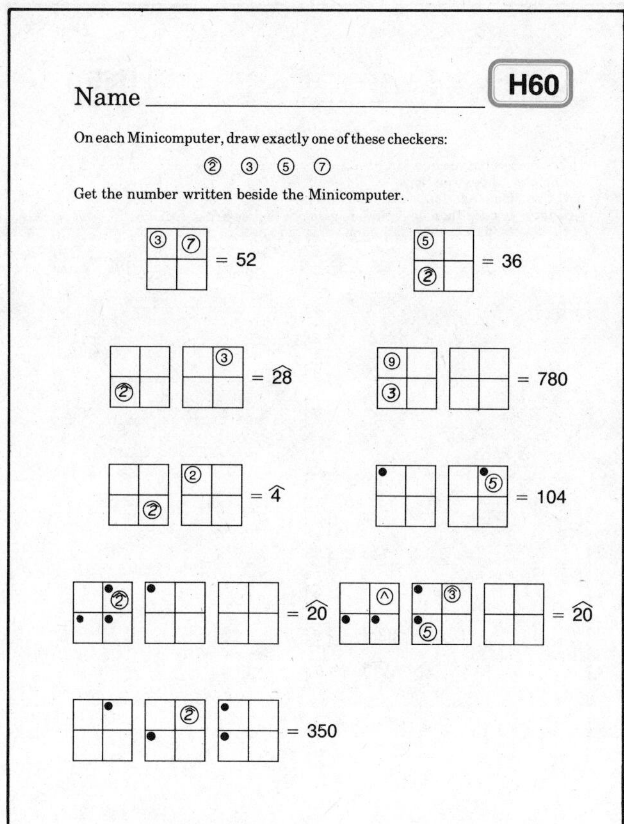

Name ______________________ **H60**

On each Minicomputer, draw exactly one of these checkers:

② ③ ⑤ ⑦

Get the number written beside the Minicomputer.

= 52

= 36

= $\widehat{28}$

= 780

= $\widehat{4}$

= 104

= $\widehat{20}$

= $\widehat{20}$

= 350

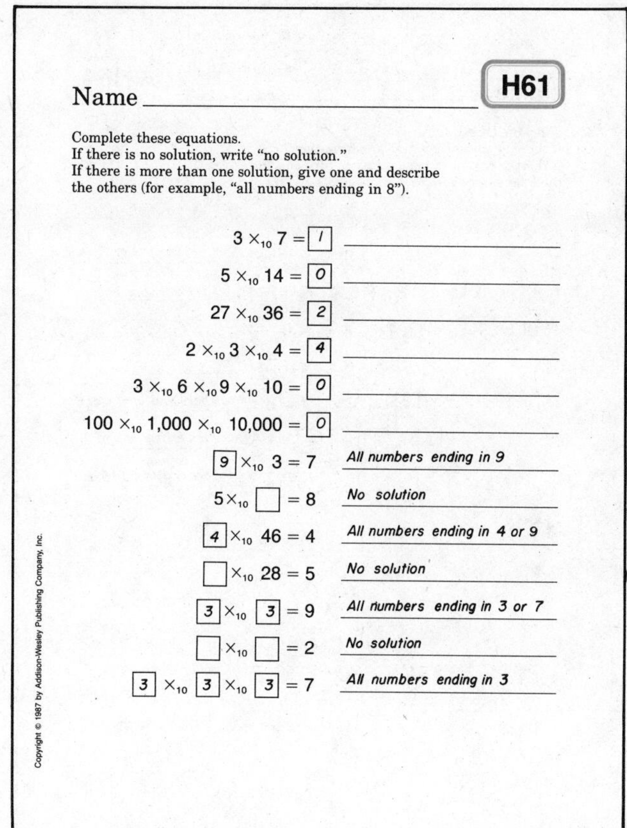

Name ______________________ **H61**

Complete these equations.
If there is no solution, write "no solution."
If there is more than one solution, give one and describe the others (for example, "all numbers ending in 8").

$3 \times_{10} 7 =$ 1

$5 \times_{10} 14 =$ 0

$27 \times_{10} 36 =$ 2

$2 \times_{10} 3 \times_{10} 4 =$ 4

$3 \times_{10} 6 \times_{10} 9 \times_{10} 10 =$ 0

$100 \times_{10} 1{,}000 \times_{10} 10{,}000 =$ 0

9 $\times_{10} 3 = 7$ — All numbers ending in 9

$5 \times_{10}$ ☐ $= 8$ — No solution

4 $\times_{10} 46 = 4$ — All numbers ending in 4 or 9

☐ $\times_{10} 28 = 5$ — No solution

3 $\times_{10}$ 3 $= 9$ — All numbers ending in 3 or 7

☐ $\times_{10}$ ☐ $= 2$ — No solution

3 $\times_{10}$ 3 $\times_{10}$ 3 $= 7$ — All numbers ending in 3

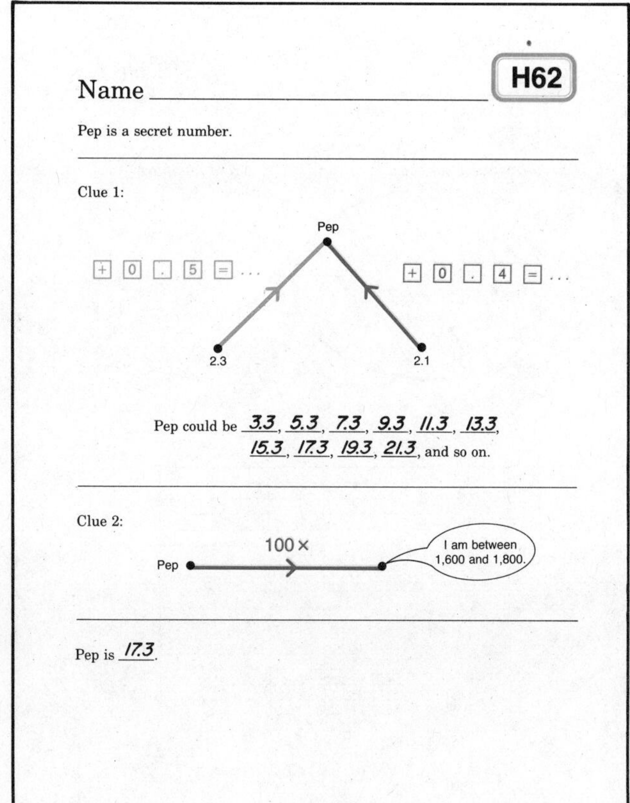

Name ______________________ **H62**

Pep is a secret number.

Clue 1:

Pep could be 3.3, 5.3, 7.3, 9.3, 11.3, 13.3, 15.3, 17.3, 19.3, 21.3, and so on.

Clue 2:

Pep is 17.3.

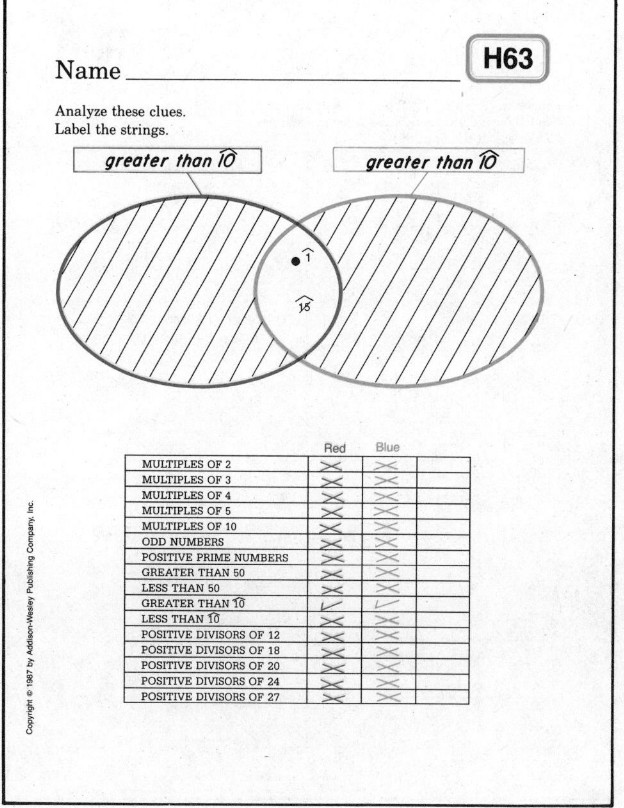

Name ______________________ **H63**

Analyze these clues.
Label the strings.

	Red	Blue	
MULTIPLES OF 2	X	X	
MULTIPLES OF 3	X	X	
MULTIPLES OF 4	X	X	
MULTIPLES OF 5	X	X	
MULTIPLES OF 10	X	X	
ODD NUMBERS	X	X	
POSITIVE PRIME NUMBERS	X	X	
GREATER THAN 50	X	X	
LESS THAN 50	X	X	
GREATER THAN $\widehat{10}$	✓	✓	
LESS THAN $\widehat{10}$	X	X	
POSITIVE DIVISORS OF 12	X	X	
POSITIVE DIVISORS OF 18	X	X	
POSITIVE DIVISORS OF 20	X	X	
POSITIVE DIVISORS OF 24	X	X	
POSITIVE DIVISORS OF 27	X	X	

H64

Name ______________________________

Complete these equations.
If there is no solution, write "no solution."
If there is more than one solution, give one and describe the others (for example, "all numbers ending in 8").

$(3 +_{10} 13) \times_{10} 4 = \boxed{4}$ ____________

$(21 \times_{10} 9) +_{10} (16 \times_{10} 7) = \boxed{1}$ ____________

$4 +_{10} 4 +_{10} 4 +_{10} 4 +_{10} 4 +_{10} 4 = \boxed{4}$ ____________

$6 \times_{10} 4 = \boxed{4}$ ____________

$(\boxed{4} +_{10} 3) \times_{10} 4 = 8$ *All numbers ending in 4 or 9*

$(\boxed{2} \times_{10} \boxed{2}) +_{10} \boxed{2} = 6$ *All numbers ending in 2 or 7*

$(\boxed{1} +_{10} \boxed{1}) \times_{10} \boxed{1} = 2$ *All numbers ending in 1,4,6,or 9*

H65

Name ______________________________

Powers Modulo 10

Remember that, modulo 10, $2^4 = 2 \times_{10} 2 \times_{10} 2 \times_{10} 2 = 6$.
Complete these equations.
If there is no solution, write "no solution."
If there is more than one solution, give one and describe the others (for example, "all numbers ending in 8").

$2^5 = \boxed{2}$ ____________

$2^2 \times_{10} 2^3 = \boxed{2}$ ____________

$2^6 = \boxed{4}$ ____________

$2^7 = \boxed{8}$ ____________

$2^8 = \boxed{6}$ ____________

$2^{100} = \boxed{6}$ ____________

$2^{162} = \boxed{4}$ ____________

$2^{85} \times_{10} 2^{66} = \boxed{8}$ ____________

$32^{19} = \boxed{8}$ ____________

$82^{33} = \boxed{2}$ ____________

$42^{96} \times_{10} 72^{104} = \boxed{6}$ ____________

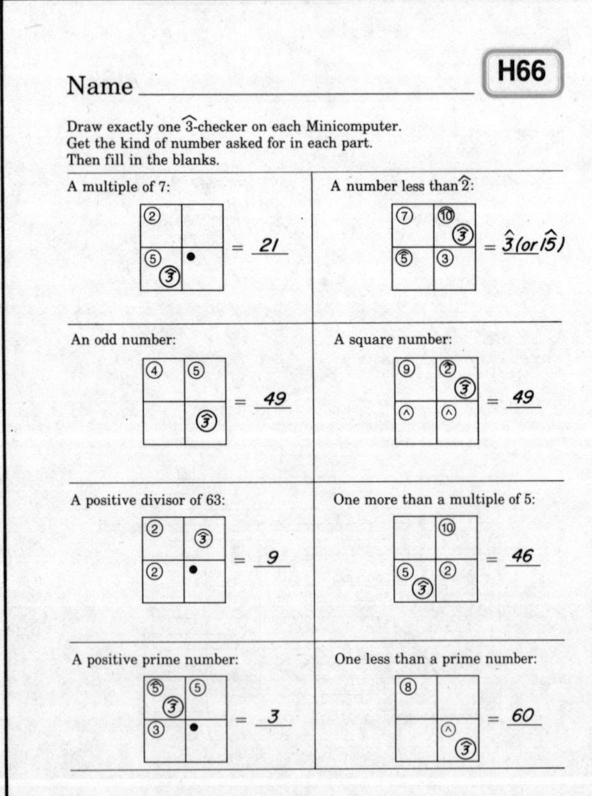

H66
Name
Draw exactly one $\hat{3}$-checker on each Minicomputer.
Get the kind of number asked for in each part.
Then fill in the blanks.
A multiple of 7: = 21
A number less than $\hat{2}$: = $\hat{3}$ (or $\hat{15}$)
An odd number: = 49
A square number: = 49
A positive divisor of 63: = 9
One more than a multiple of 5: = 46
A positive prime number: = 3
One less than a prime number: = 60

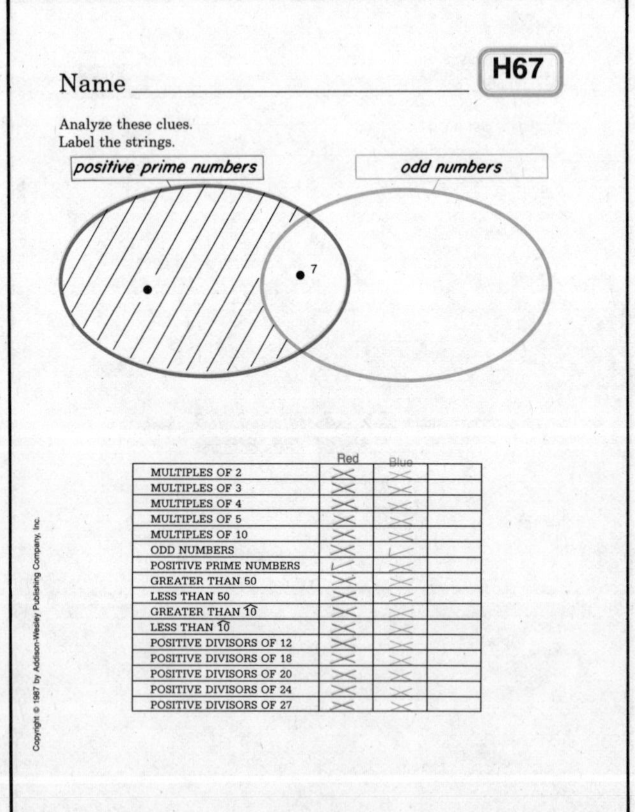

	Red	Blue	
MULTIPLES OF 2	X	X	
MULTIPLES OF 3	X	X	
MULTIPLES OF 4	X	X	
MULTIPLES OF 5	X	X	
MULTIPLES OF 10	X	X	
ODD NUMBERS	X	✓	
POSITIVE PRIME NUMBERS	✓	X	
GREATER THAN 50	X	X	
LESS THAN 50	X	X	
GREATER THAN $\hat{10}$	X	X	
LESS THAN $\hat{10}$	X	X	
POSITIVE DIVISORS OF 12	X	X	
POSITIVE DIVISORS OF 18	X	X	
POSITIVE DIVISORS OF 20	X	X	
POSITIVE DIVISORS OF 24	X	X	
POSITIVE DIVISORS OF 27	X	X	

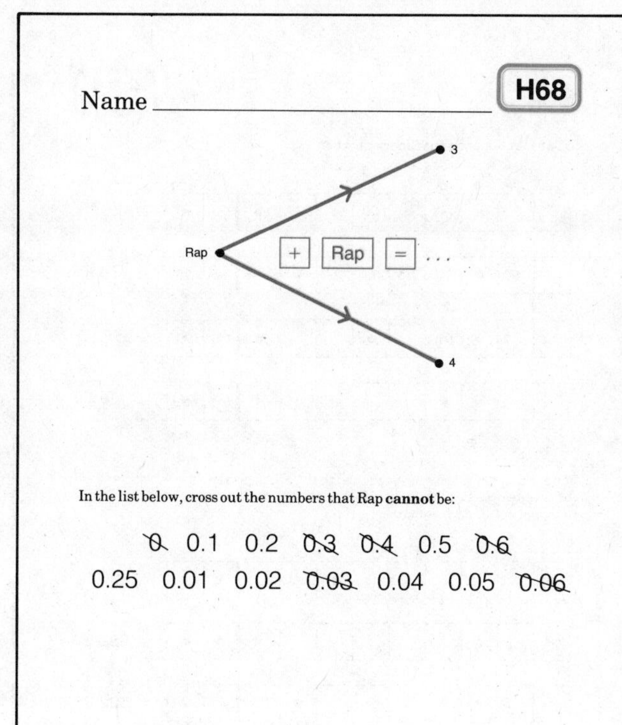

Name ____________ **H68**

In the list below, cross out the numbers that Rap **cannot** be:

~~0~~ 0.1 0.2 ~~0.3~~ ~~0.4~~ 0.5 ~~0.6~~

0.25 0.01 0.02 ~~0.03~~ 0.04 0.05 ~~0.06~~

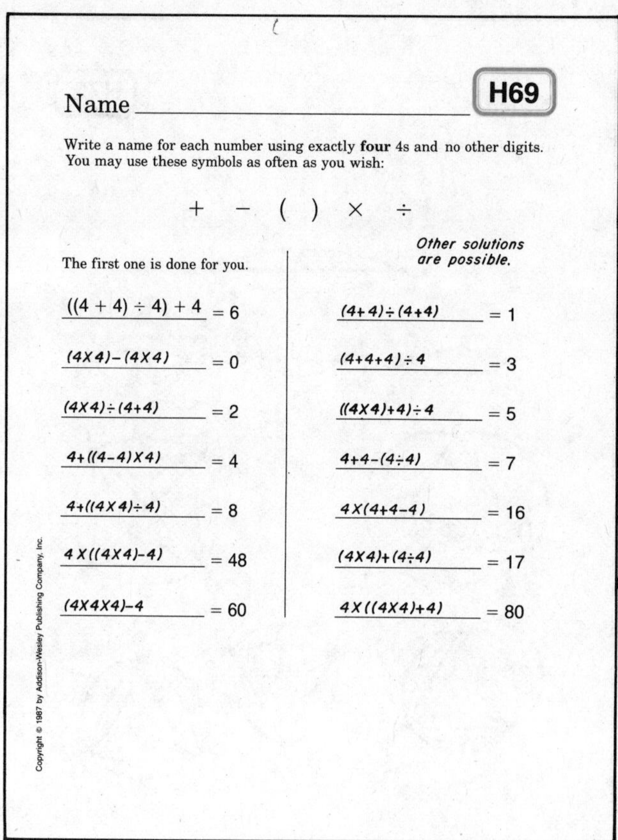

Name ____________ **H69**

Write a name for each number using exactly **four** 4s and no other digits. You may use these symbols as often as you wish:

+ − ( ) × ÷

The first one is done for you.

Other solutions are possible.

((4 + 4) ÷ 4) + 4 = 6	(4+4)÷(4+4) = 1
(4X4)−(4X4) = 0	(4+4+4)÷4 = 3
(4X4)÷(4+4) = 2	((4X4)+4)÷4 = 5
4+((4−4)X4) = 4	4+4−(4÷4) = 7
4+((4X4)÷4) = 8	4X(4+4−4) = 16
4X((4X4)−4) = 48	(4X4)+(4÷4) = 17
(4X4X4)−4 = 60	4X((4X4)+4) = 80

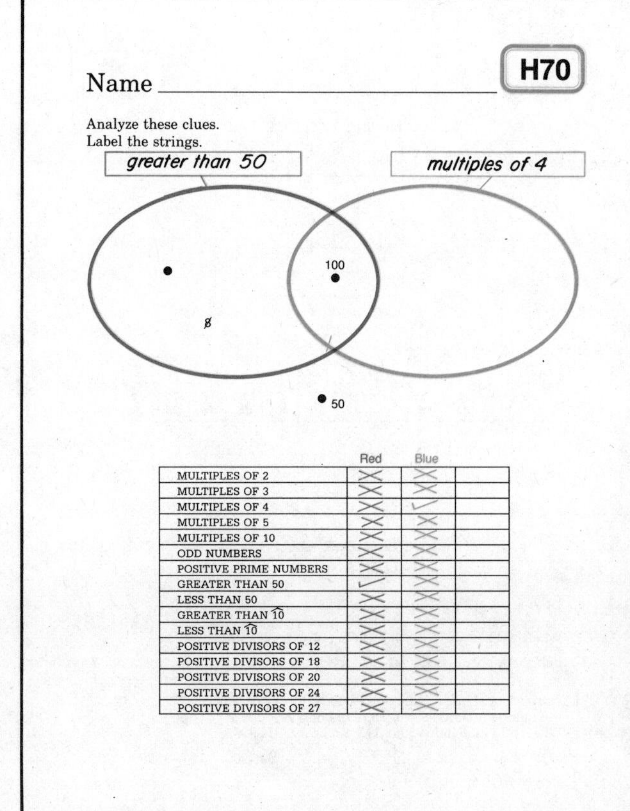

Name ____________ **H70**

Analyze these clues.
Label the strings.

	Red	Blue	
MULTIPLES OF 2	X	X	
MULTIPLES OF 3	X	X	
MULTIPLES OF 4	X	✓	
MULTIPLES OF 5	X	X	
MULTIPLES OF 10	X	X	
ODD NUMBERS	X	X	
POSITIVE PRIME NUMBERS	X	X	
GREATER THAN 50	✓	X	
LESS THAN 50	X	X	
GREATER THAN 10	X	X	
LESS THAN 10	X	X	
POSITIVE DIVISORS OF 12	X	X	
POSITIVE DIVISORS OF 18	X	X	
POSITIVE DIVISORS OF 20	X	X	
POSITIVE DIVISORS OF 24	X	X	
POSITIVE DIVISORS OF 27	X	X	

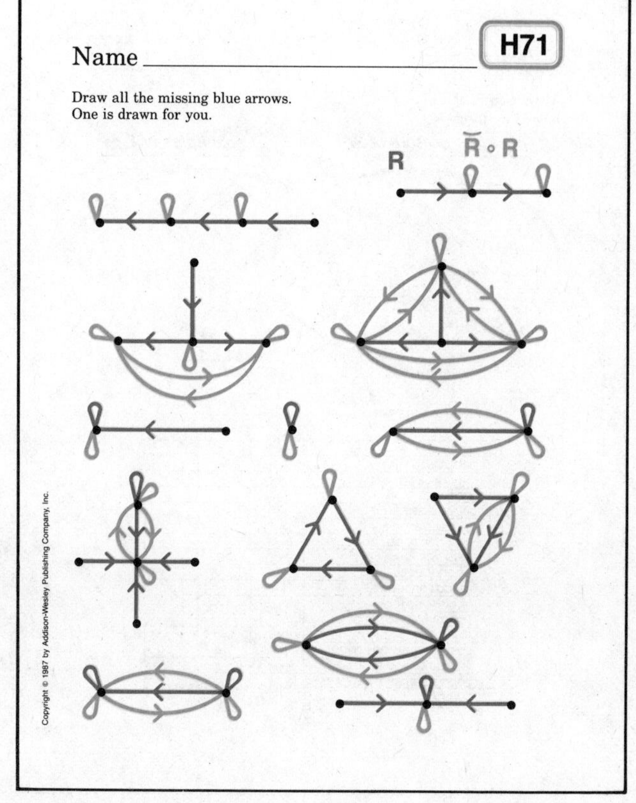

Name ____________ **H71**

Draw all the missing blue arrows.
One is drawn for you.

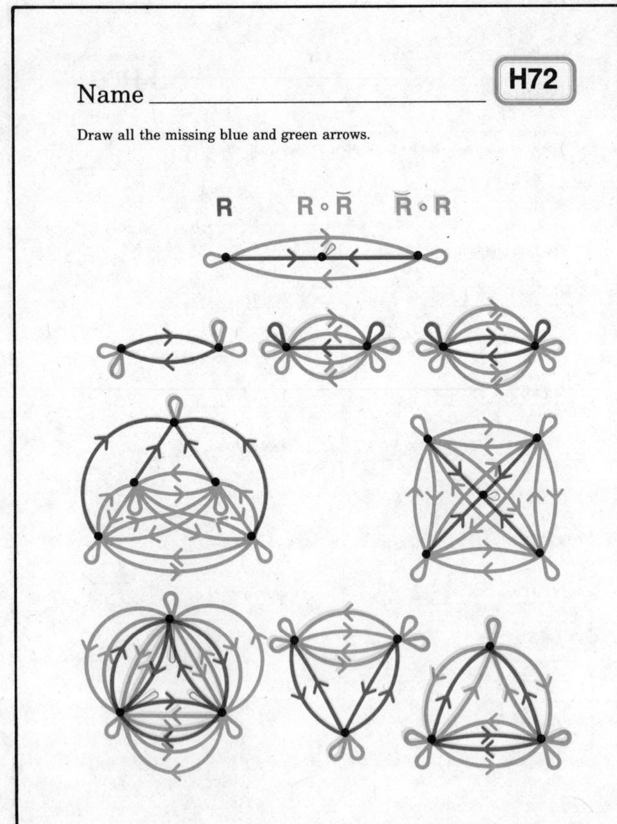

Name ______________________ **H72**

Draw all the missing blue and green arrows.

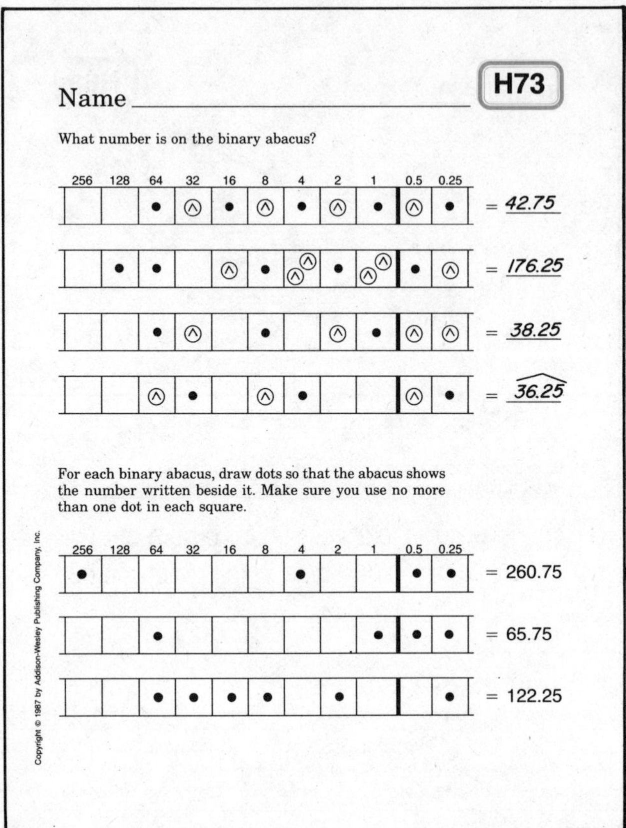

Name ______________________ **H73**

What number is on the binary abacus?

256	128	64	32	16	8	4	2	1	0.5	0.25	
		•	^	•	^	•	^	•	^	•	= *42.75*
	•	•		^	•	^^	•	^^	•	^	= *176.25*
		•	^		•		^	•	^	^	= *38.25*
		^	•		^	•			^	•	= *36.25*

For each binary abacus, draw dots so that the abacus shows the number written beside it. Make sure you use no more than one dot in each square.

256	128	64	32	16	8	4	2	1	0.5	0.25	
•						•			•	•	= 260.75
		•						•	•	•	= 65.75
		•	•	•	•		•			•	= 122.25

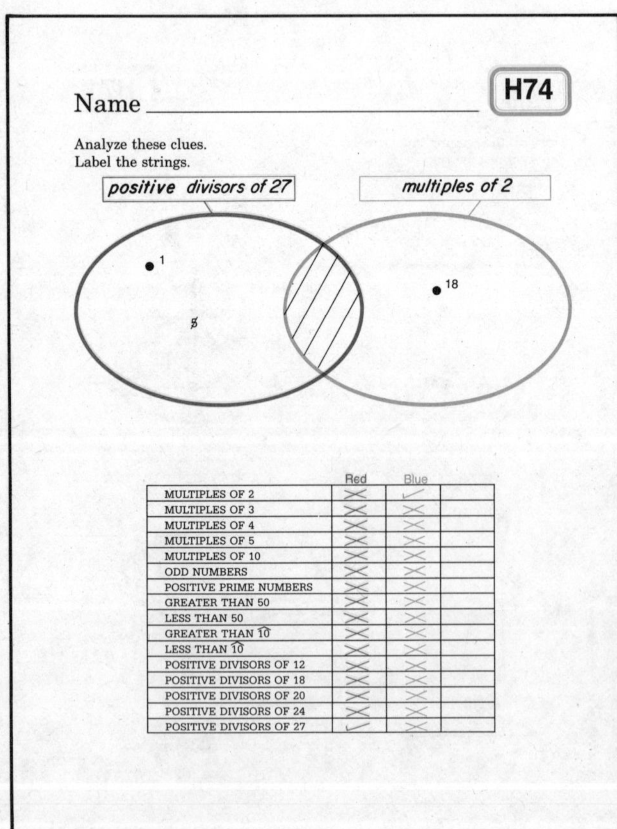

Name ______________________ **H74**

Analyze these clues.
Label the strings.

	Red	Blue
MULTIPLES OF 2	X	✓
MULTIPLES OF 3	X	X
MULTIPLES OF 4	X	X
MULTIPLES OF 5	X	X
MULTIPLES OF 10	X	X
ODD NUMBERS	X	X
POSITIVE PRIME NUMBERS	X	X
GREATER THAN 50	X	X
LESS THAN 50	X	X
GREATER THAN 10	X	X
LESS THAN 10	X	X
POSITIVE DIVISORS OF 12	X	X
POSITIVE DIVISORS OF 18	X	X
POSITIVE DIVISORS OF 20	X	X
POSITIVE DIVISORS OF 24	X	X
POSITIVE DIVISORS OF 27	✓	X

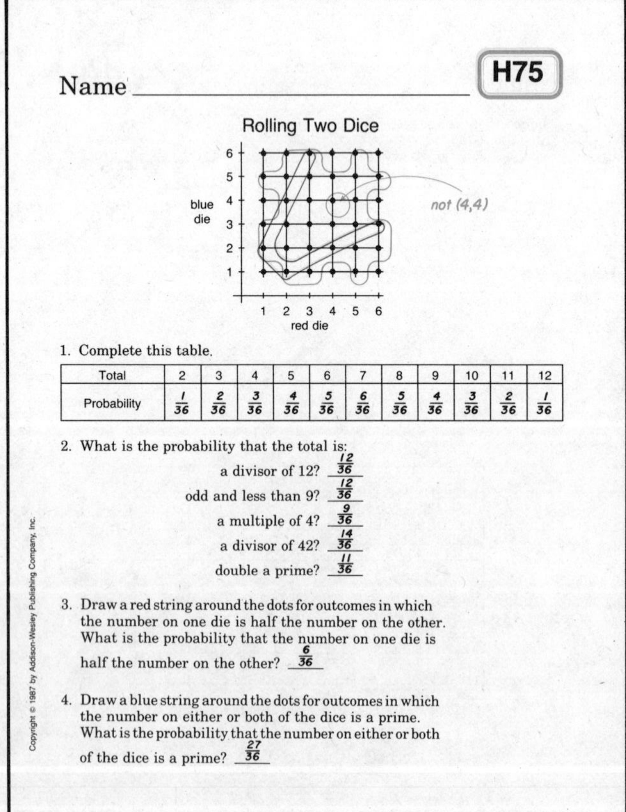

Name ______________________ **H75**

Rolling Two Dice

1. Complete this table.

Total	2	3	4	5	6	7	8	9	10	11	12
Probability	*1/36*	*2/36*	*3/36*	*4/36*	*5/36*	*6/36*	*5/36*	*4/36*	*3/36*	*2/36*	*1/36*

2. What is the probability that the total is:
   - a divisor of 12? *12/36*
   - odd and less than 9? *12/36*
   - a multiple of 4? *9/36*
   - a divisor of 42? *14/36*
   - double a prime? *11/36*

3. Draw a red string around the dots for outcomes in which the number on one die is half the number on the other. What is the probability that the number on one die is half the number on the other? *6/36*

4. Draw a blue string around the dots for outcomes in which the number on either or both of the dice is a prime. What is the probability that the number on either or both of the dice is a prime? *27/36*

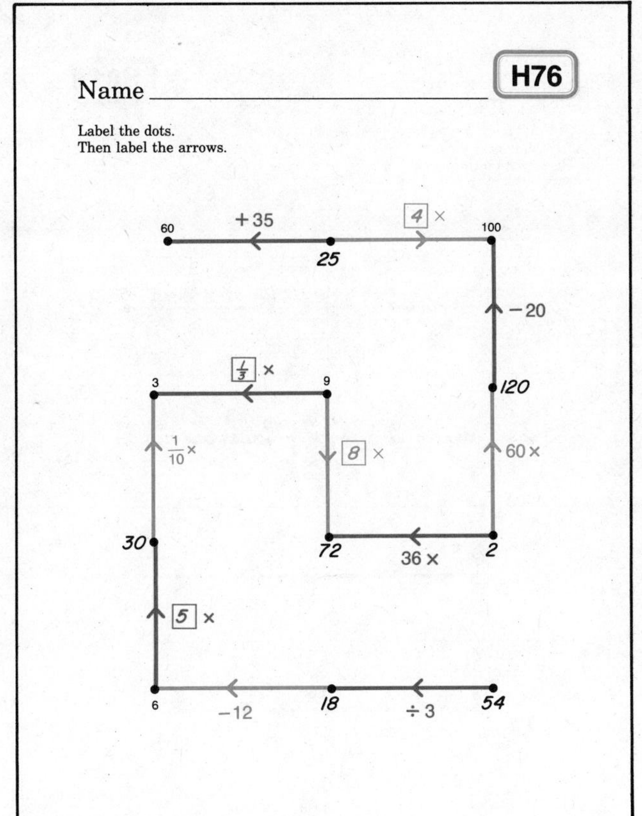

H76

Name ______________________

Label the dots.
Then label the arrows.

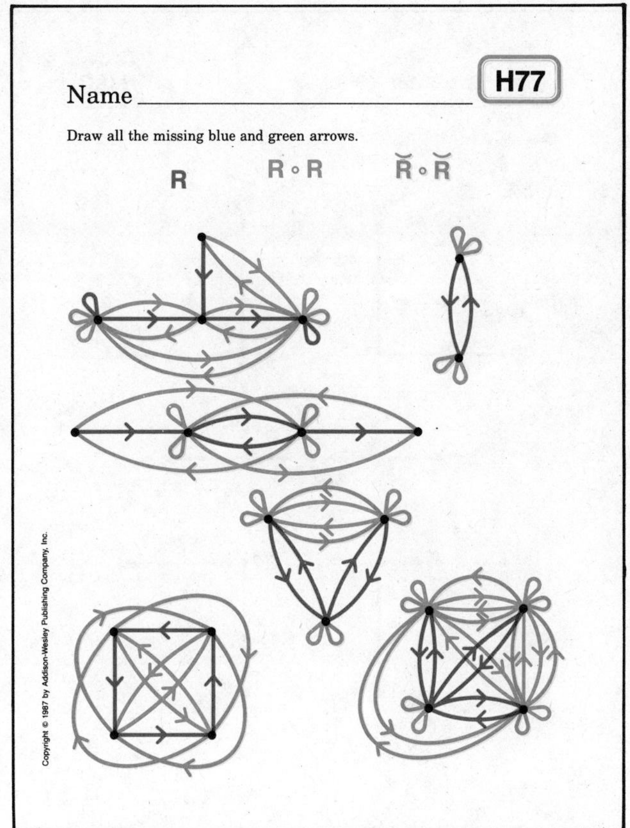

H77

Name ______________________

Draw all the missing blue and green arrows.

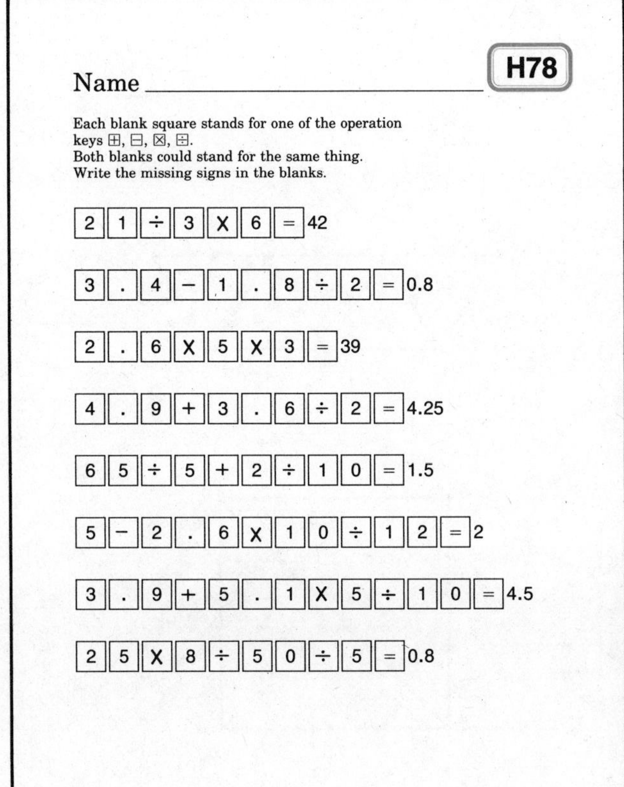

H78

Name ______________________

Each blank square stands for one of the operation keys ⊞, ⊟, ⊠, ⊡.
Both blanks could stand for the same thing.
Write the missing signs in the blanks.

2 1 ÷ 3 X 6 = 42

3 . 4 − 1 . 8 ÷ 2 = 0.8

2 . 6 X 5 X 3 = 39

4 . 9 + 3 . 6 ÷ 2 = 4.25

6 5 ÷ 5 + 2 ÷ 1 0 = 1.5

5 − 2 . 6 X 1 0 ÷ 1 2 = 2

3 . 9 + 5 . 1 X 5 ÷ 1 0 = 4.5

2 5 X 8 ÷ 5 0 ÷ 5 = 0.8

H79

Name ______________________

Each blank square stands for one of the operation keys ⊞, ⊟, ⊠, ⊡.
Both blanks could stand for the same thing.

7 . 2 ☐ 1 ☐ 2 = Mu

What is the largest number that Mu could be? *16.4 (+ ×)*

What is the smallest number that Mu could be? *3.1 (− ÷)*

0 . 7 2 ☐ 1 ☐ 2 = Ma

What is the largest number that Ma could be? *3.72 (+ +)*

What is the smallest number that Ma could be? *2.28 (− −)*

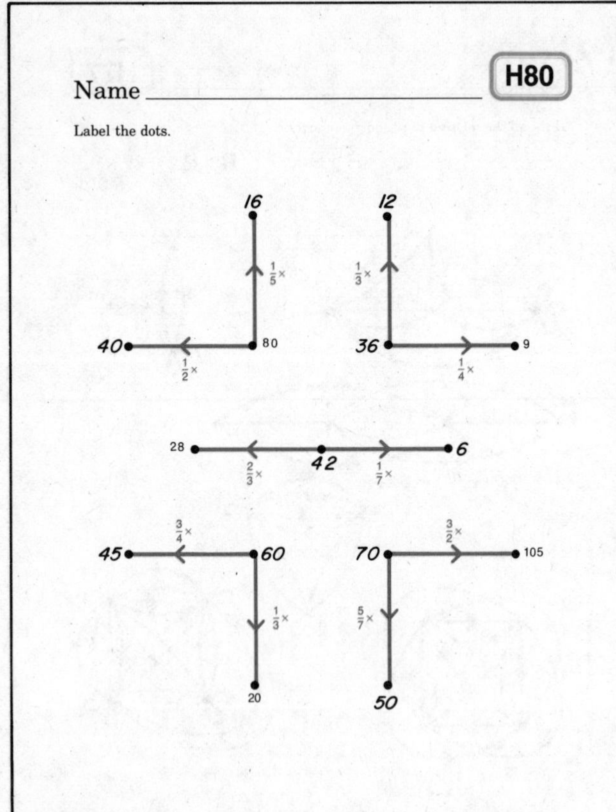
Name
H80
Label the dots.
16
$\frac{1}{5}\times$
12
$\frac{1}{3}\times$
40
80
$\frac{1}{2}\times$
36
9
$\frac{1}{4}\times$
28
42
6
$\frac{2}{3}\times$
$\frac{1}{7}\times$
$\frac{3}{4}\times$
45
60
$\frac{1}{3}\times$
20
$\frac{3}{2}\times$
70
105
$\frac{5}{7}\times$
50

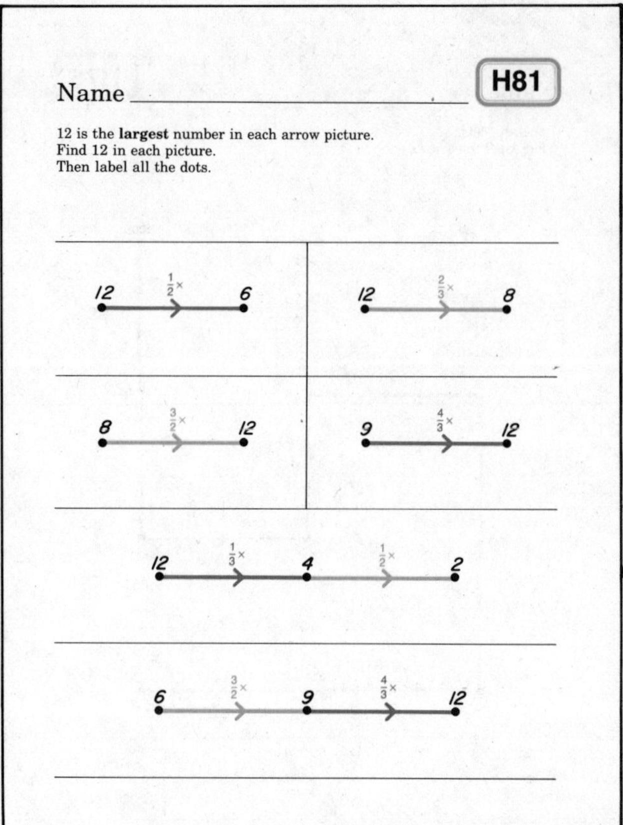
Name
H81
12 is the **largest** number in each arrow picture.
Find 12 in each picture.
Then label all the dots.
12
$\frac{1}{2}\times$
6
12
$\frac{2}{3}\times$
8
8
$\frac{3}{2}\times$
12
9
$\frac{4}{3}\times$
12
12
$\frac{1}{3}\times$
4
$\frac{1}{2}\times$
2
6
$\frac{3}{2}\times$
9
$\frac{4}{3}\times$
12

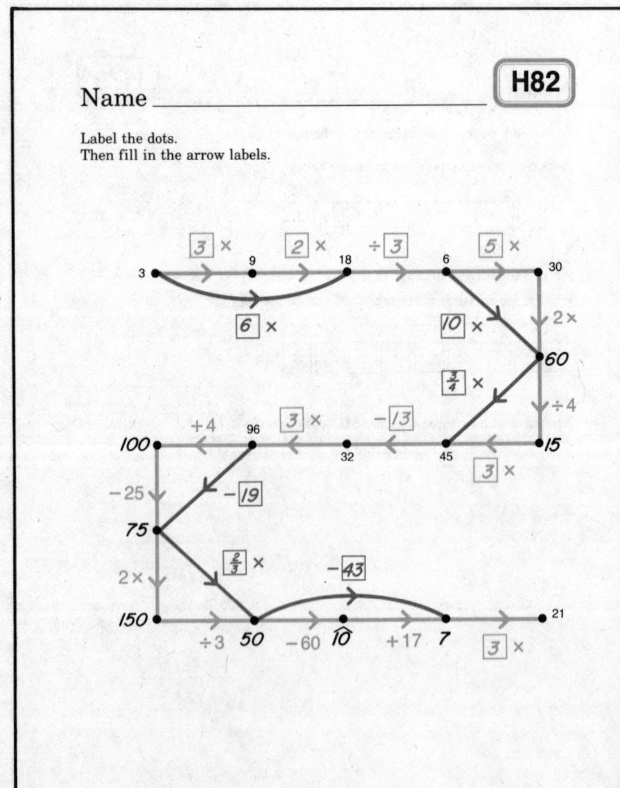
Name
H82
Label the dots.
Then fill in the arrow labels.
3 ×
2 ×
÷ 3
5 ×
3
9
18
6
30
6 ×
10 ×
2 ×
60
$\frac{3}{4}\times$
÷ 4
+4
96
3 ×
−13
100
32
45
15
3 ×
−25
−19
75
$\frac{2}{3}\times$
−43
2 ×
150
50
10
7
21
÷ 3
−60
+17
3 ×

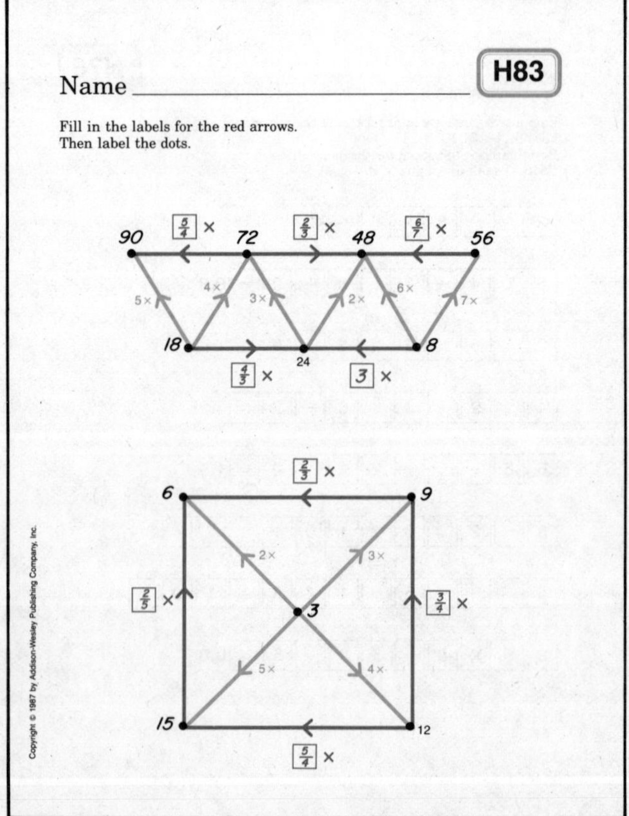
Name
H83
Fill in the labels for the red arrows.
Then label the dots.
$\frac{5}{4}\times$
$\frac{2}{3}\times$
$\frac{6}{7}\times$
90
72
48
56
5×
4×
3×
2×
6×
7×
18
24
8
$\frac{4}{3}\times$
3 ×
$\frac{2}{3}\times$
6
9
2×
3×
$\frac{2}{5}\times$
3
$\frac{3}{4}\times$
5×
4×
15
12
$\frac{5}{4}\times$

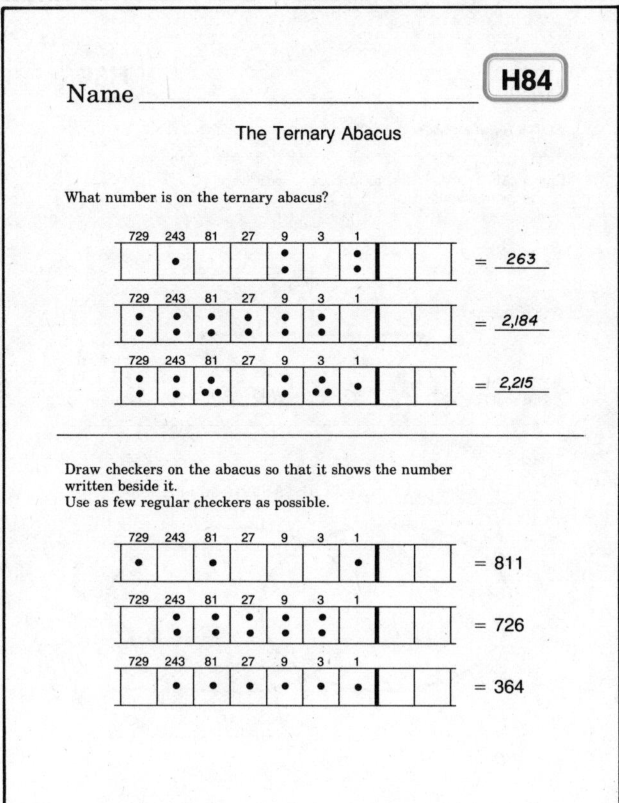
Name
H84
The Ternary Abacus
What number is on the ternary abacus?
729 243 81 27 9 3 1
= 263
= 2,184
= 2,215
Draw checkers on the abacus so that it shows the number written beside it.
Use as few regular checkers as possible.
= 811
= 726
= 364

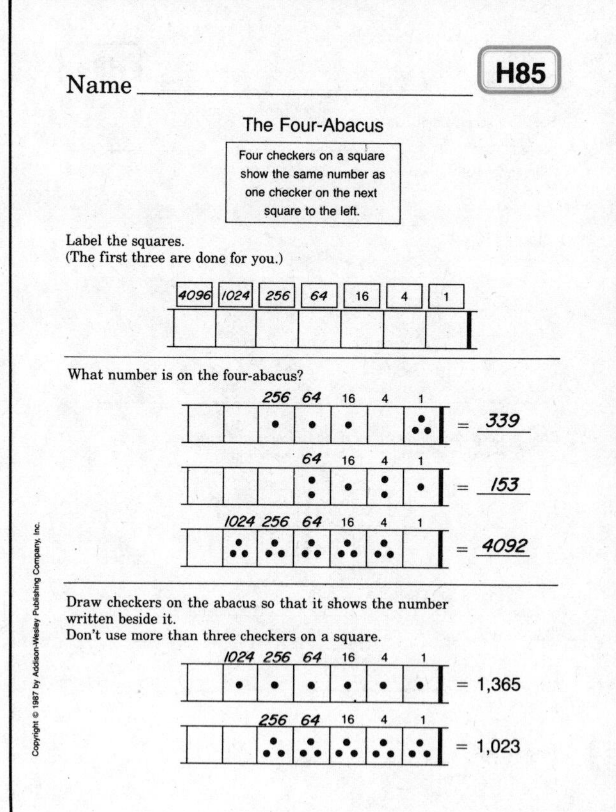
Name
H85
The Four-Abacus
Four checkers on a square show the same number as one checker on the next square to the left.
Label the squares.
(The first three are done for you.)
4096 1024 256 64 16 4 1
What number is on the four-abacus?
= 339
= 153
= 4092
Draw checkers on the abacus so that it shows the number written beside it.
Don't use more than three checkers on a square.
= 1,365
= 1,023
Copyright © 1987 by Addison-Wesley Publishing Company, Inc.

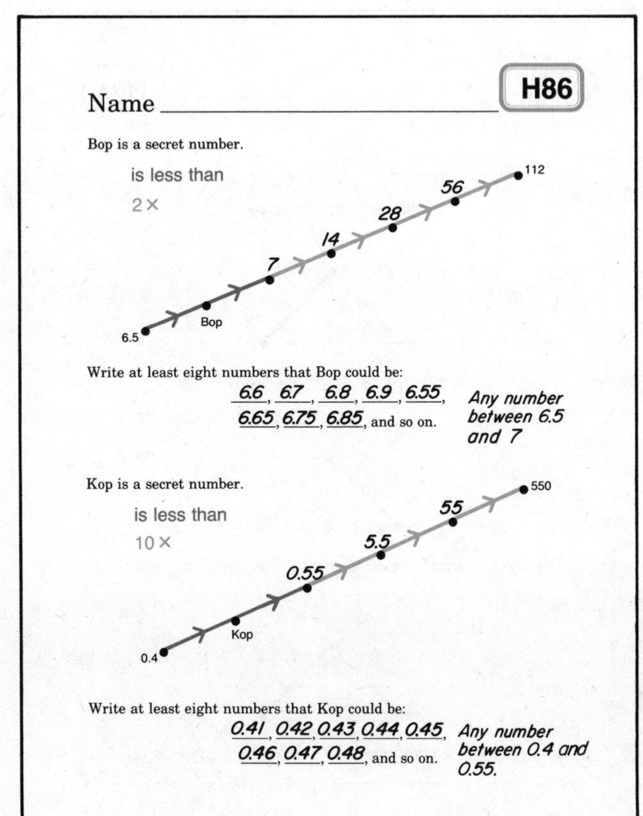
Name
H86
Bop is a secret number.
is less than
2×
6.5
Bop
7
14
28
56
112
Write at least eight numbers that Bop could be:
6.6, 6.7, 6.8, 6.9, 6.55, 6.65, 6.75, 6.85, and so on.
Any number between 6.5 and 7
Kop is a secret number.
is less than
10×
0.4
Kop
0.55
5.5
55
550
Write at least eight numbers that Kop could be:
0.41, 0.42, 0.43, 0.44, 0.45, 0.46, 0.47, 0.48, and so on.
Any number between 0.4 and 0.55.

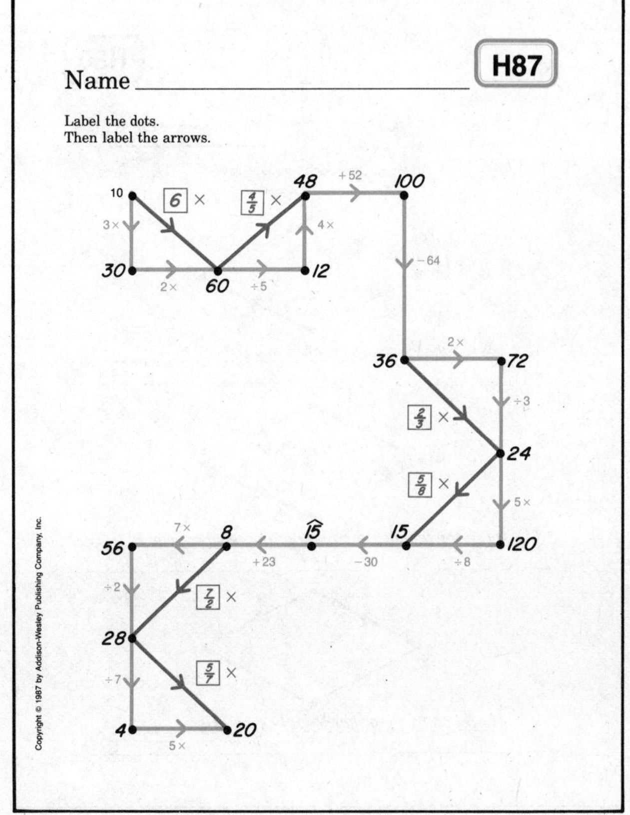
Name
H87
Label the dots.
Then label the arrows.
10
30
60
12
48
100
36
72
24
120
15
8
56
28
4
20
Copyright © 1987 by Addison-Wesley Publishing Company, Inc.

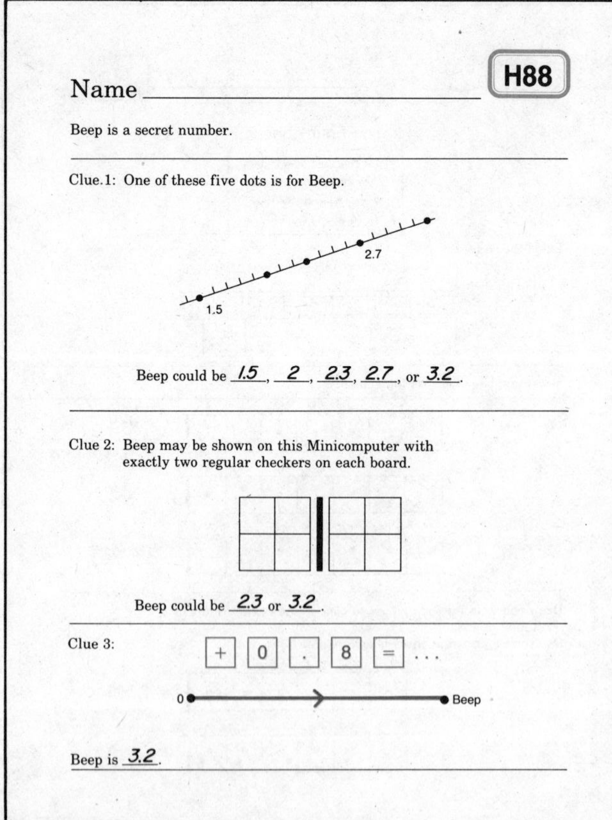

Name ______________ **H88**

Beep is a secret number.

Clue 1: One of these five dots is for Beep.

Beep could be *1.5*, *2*, *2.3*, *2.7*, or *3.2*.

Clue 2: Beep may be shown on this Minicomputer with exactly two regular checkers on each board.

Beep could be *2.3* or *3.2*.

Clue 3:

Beep is *3.2*.

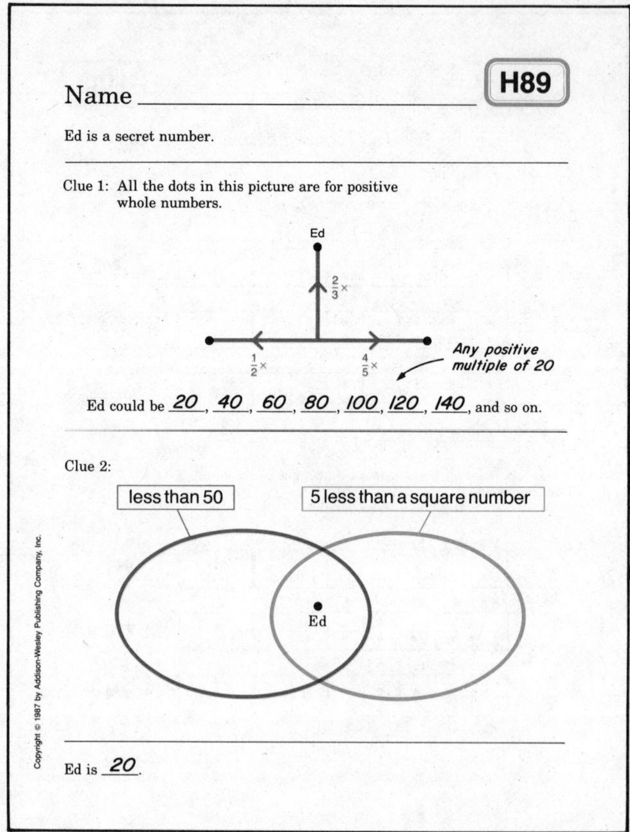

Name ______________ **H89**

Ed is a secret number.

Clue 1: All the dots in this picture are for positive whole numbers.

Ed could be *20*, *40*, *60*, *80*, *100*, *120*, *140*, and so on.

Clue 2:

Ed is *20*.

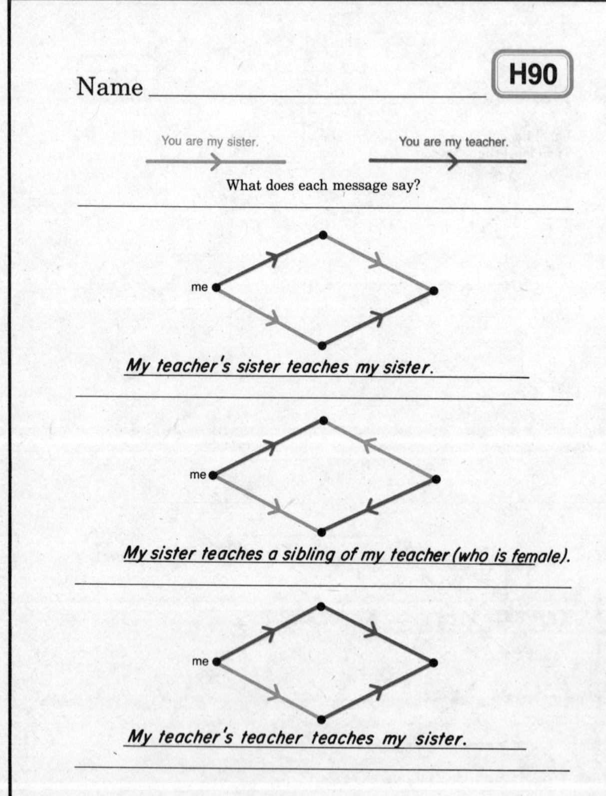

Name ______________ **H90**

What does each message say?

My teacher's sister teaches my sister.

My sister teaches a sibling of my teacher (who is female).

My teacher's teacher teaches my sister.

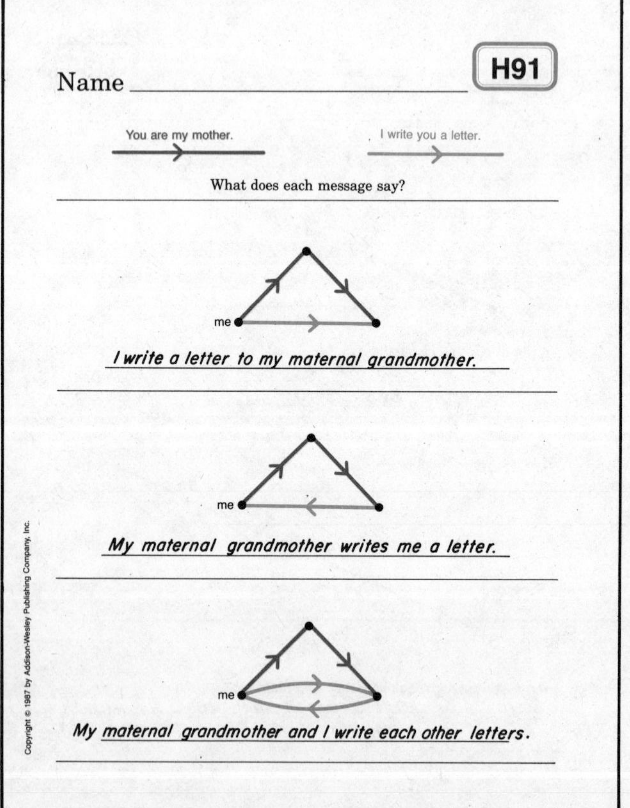

Name ______________ **H91**

What does each message say?

I write a letter to my maternal grandmother.

My maternal grandmother writes me a letter.

My maternal grandmother and I write each other letters.

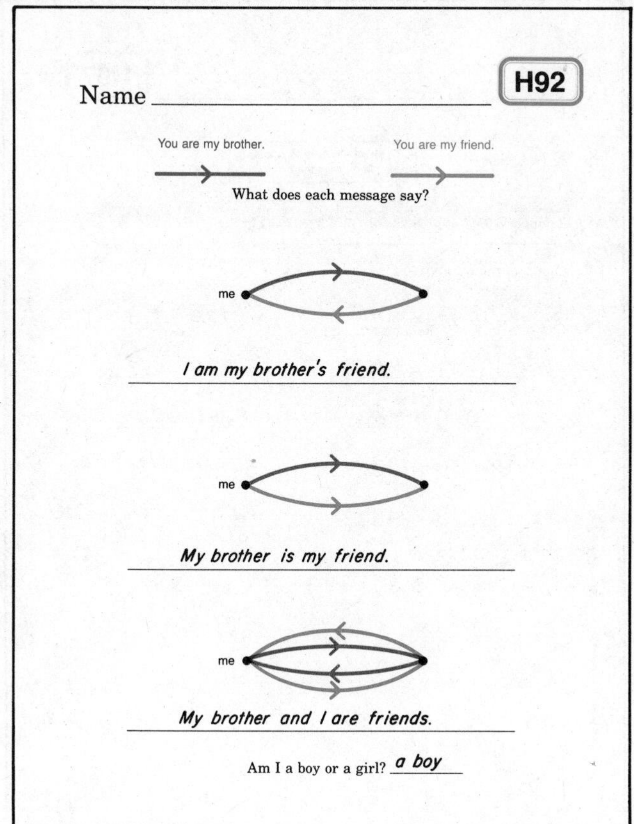

Name ______________________ **H92**

You are my brother. You are my friend.

What does each message say?

me

I am my brother's friend.

me

My brother is my friend.

me

My brother and I are friends.

Am I a boy or a girl? *a boy*

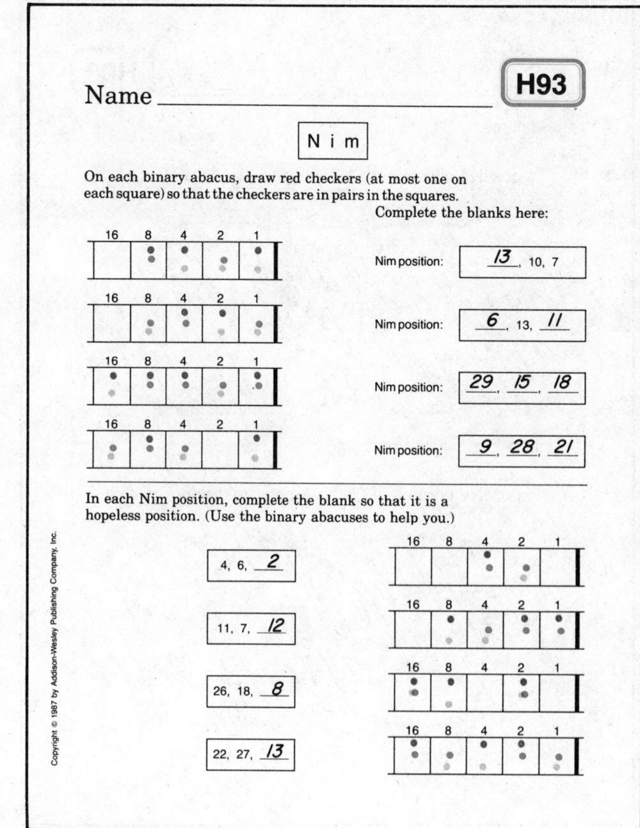

Name ______________________ **H93**

Nim

On each binary abacus, draw red checkers (at most one on each square) so that the checkers are in pairs in the squares.

Complete the blanks here:

16	8	4	2	1	Nim position:
					13, 10, 7
					6, 13, *11*
					29, *15*, *18*
					9, *28*, *21*

In each Nim position, complete the blank so that it is a hopeless position. (Use the binary abacuses to help you.)

4, 6, *2*

11, 7, *12*

26, 18, *8*

22, 27, *13*

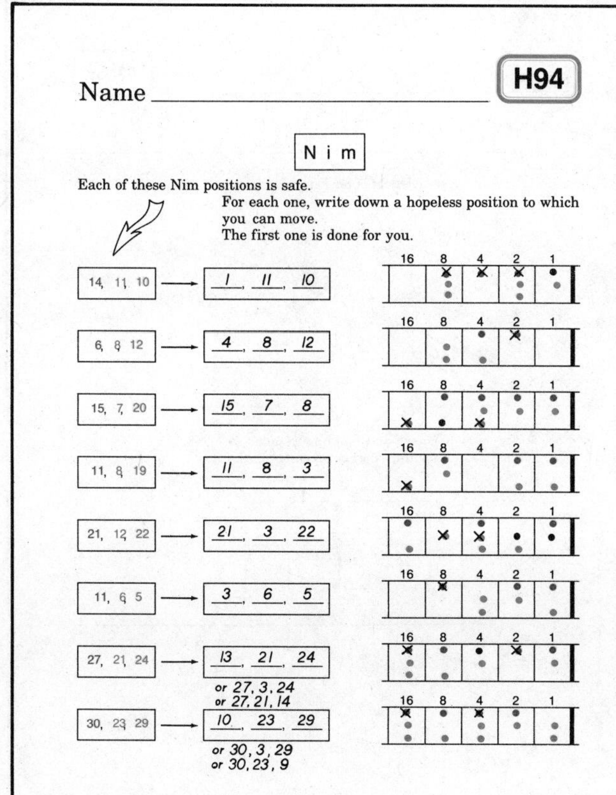

Name ______________________ **H94**

Nim

Each of these Nim positions is safe.

For each one, write down a hopeless position to which you can move.

The first one is done for you.

Safe position	Hopeless position
14, 11, 10	*1, 11, 10*
6, 8, 12	*4, 8, 12*
15, 7, 20	*15, 7, 8*
11, 8, 19	*11, 8, 3*
21, 12, 22	*21, 3, 22*
11, 6, 5	*3, 6, 5*
27, 21, 24	*13, 21, 24* or *27, 3, 24* or *27, 21, 14*
30, 23, 29	*10, 23, 29* or *30, 3, 29* or *30, 23, 9*

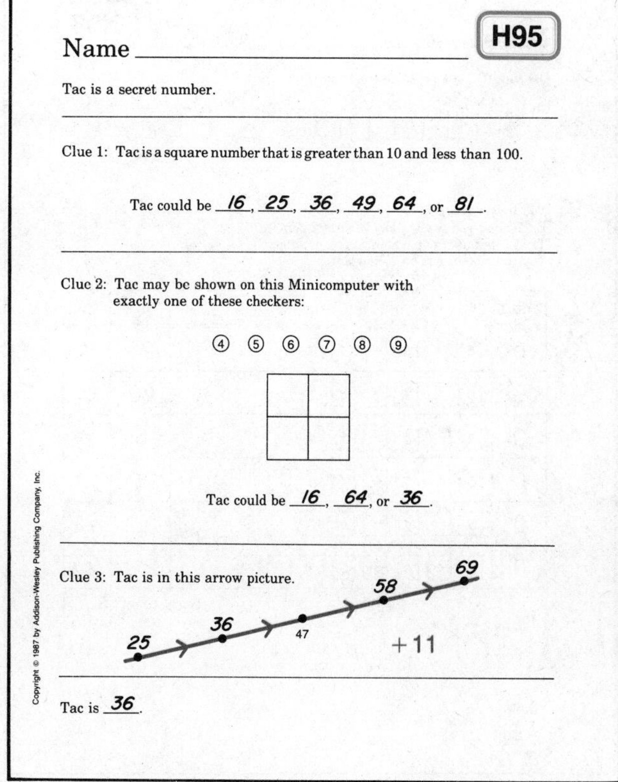

Name ______________________ **H95**

Tac is a secret number.

Clue 1: Tac is a square number that is greater than 10 and less than 100.

Tac could be *16*, *25*, *36*, *49*, *64*, or *81*.

Clue 2: Tac may be shown on this Minicomputer with exactly one of these checkers:

④ ⑤ ⑥ ⑦ ⑧ ⑨

Tac could be *16*, *64*, or *36*.

Clue 3: Tac is in this arrow picture.

Tac is *36*.

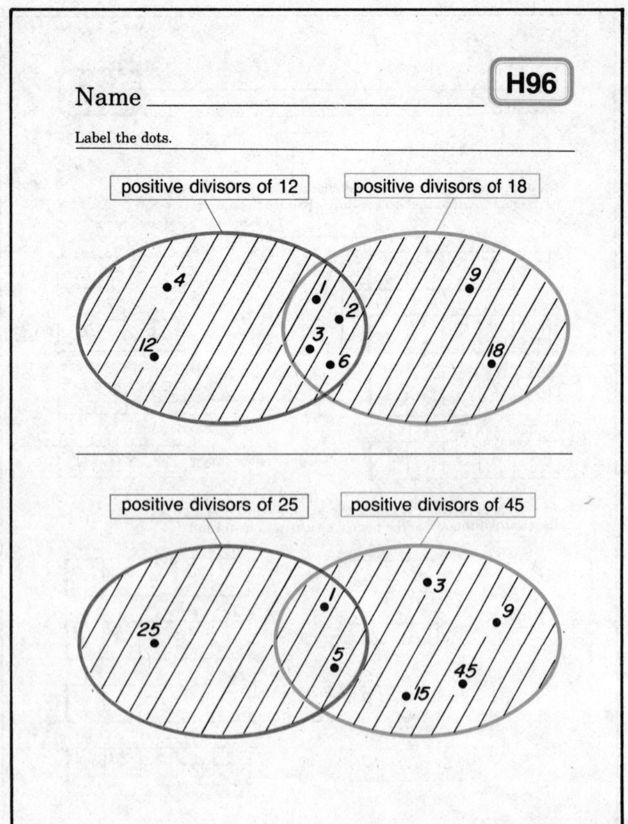

Name ____________ **H96**

Label the dots.

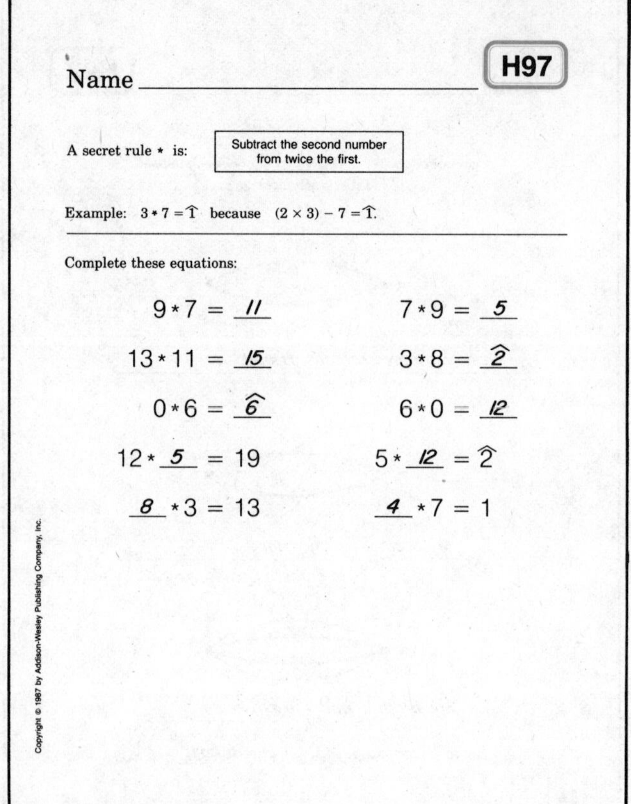

Name ____________ **H97**

A secret rule * is: Subtract the second number from twice the first.

Example: $3 * 7 = \hat{1}$ because $(2 \times 3) - 7 = \hat{1}$.

Complete these equations:

$9 * 7 = 11$ $7 * 9 = 5$

$13 * 11 = 15$ $3 * 8 = \hat{2}$

$0 * 6 = \hat{6}$ $6 * 0 = 12$

$12 * 5 = 19$ $5 * 12 = \hat{2}$

$8 * 3 = 13$ $4 * 7 = 1$

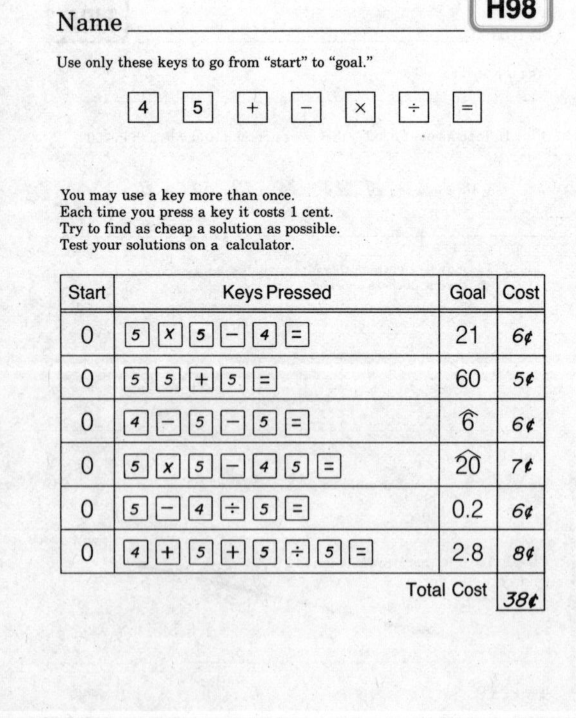

Name ____________ **H98**

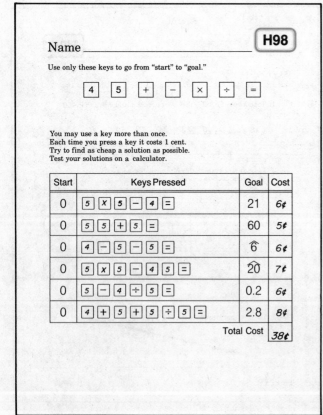

Use only these keys to go from "start" to "goal."

[4] [5] [+] [−] [×] [÷] [=]

You may use a key more than once.
Each time you press a key it costs 1 cent.
Try to find as cheap a solution as possible.
Test your solutions on a calculator.

Start	Keys Pressed	Goal	Cost
0	[5] [×] [5] [−] [4] [=]	21	6¢
0	[5] [5] [+] [5] [=]	60	5¢
0	[4] [−] [5] [−] [5] [=]	$\hat{6}$	6¢
0	[5] [×] [5] [−] [4] [5] [=]	$\hat{20}$	7¢
0	[5] [−] [4] [÷] [5] [=]	0.2	6¢
0	[4] [+] [5] [+] [5] [÷] [5] [=]	2.8	8¢
		Total Cost	38¢

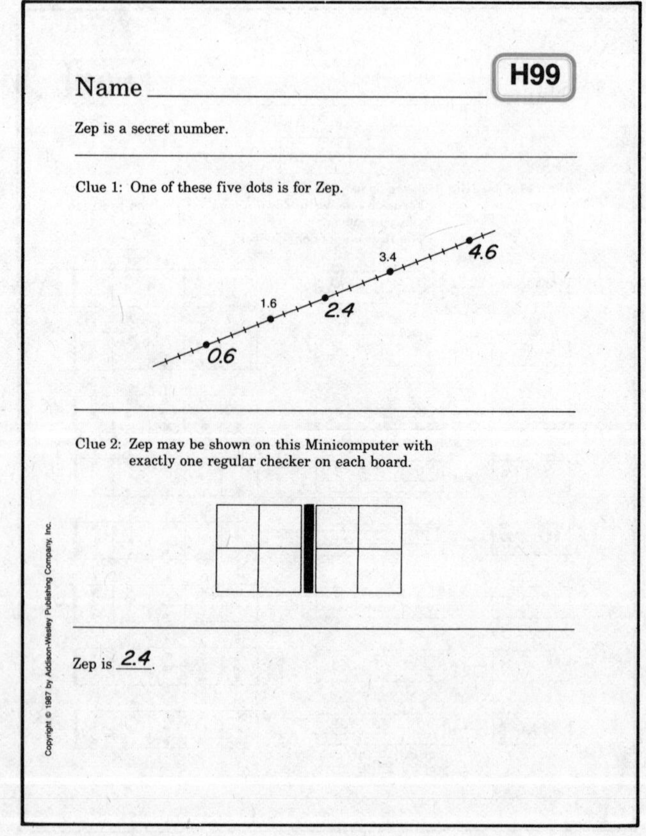

Name ____________ **H99**

Zep is a secret number.

Clue 1: One of these five dots is for Zep.

Clue 2: Zep may be shown on this Minicomputer with exactly one regular checker on each board.

Zep is 2.4

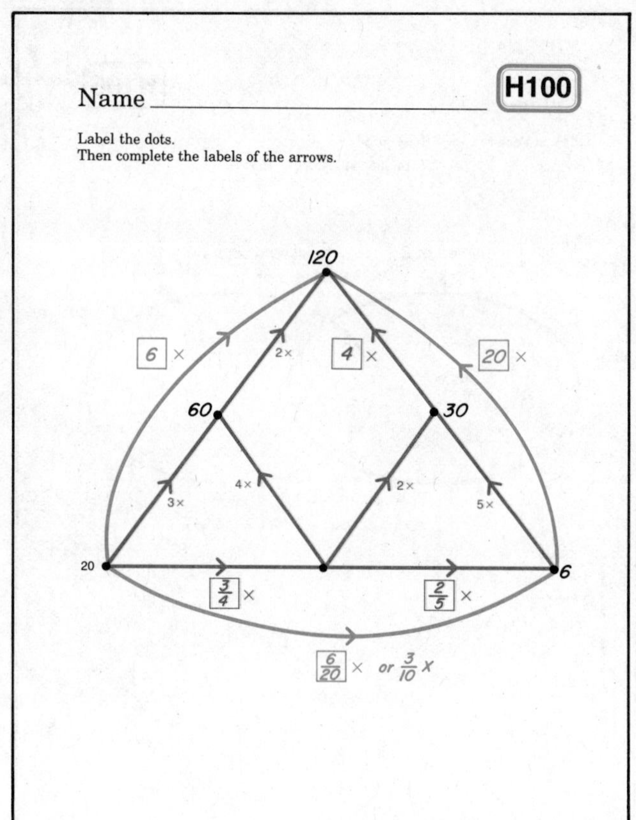

Name
H100
Label the dots.
Then complete the labels of the arrows.
120
6 ×
2×
4 ×
20 ×
60
30
3×
4×
2×
5×
20
6
3/4 ×
2/5 ×
6/20 × or 3/10 ×

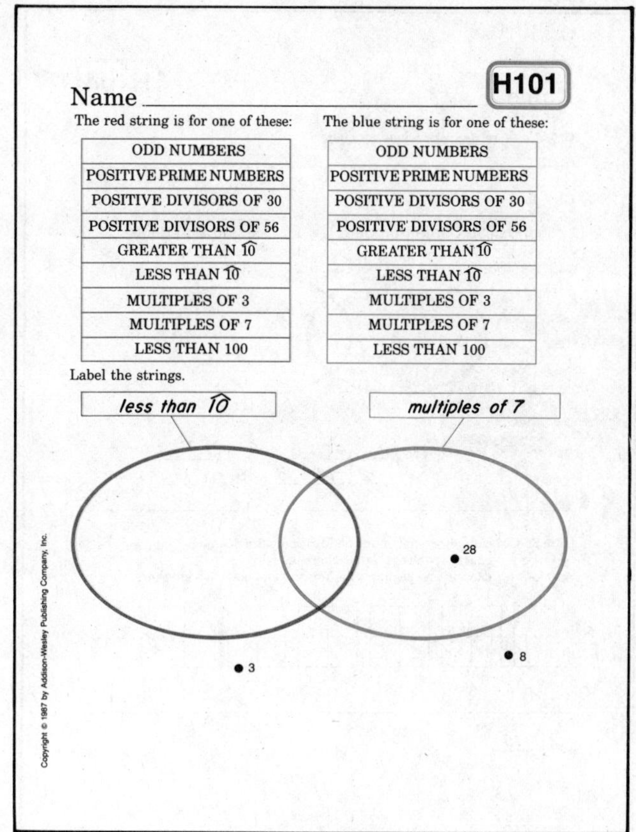

Name
H101
The red string is for one of these:
ODD NUMBERS
POSITIVE PRIME NUMBERS
POSITIVE DIVISORS OF 30
POSITIVE DIVISORS OF 56
GREATER THAN 10
LESS THAN 10
MULTIPLES OF 3
MULTIPLES OF 7
LESS THAN 100
The blue string is for one of these:
ODD NUMBERS
POSITIVE PRIME NUMBERS
POSITIVE DIVISORS OF 30
POSITIVE DIVISORS OF 56
GREATER THAN 10
LESS THAN 10
MULTIPLES OF 3
MULTIPLES OF 7
LESS THAN 100
Label the strings.
less than 10
multiples of 7
28
3
8
Copyright © 1987 by Addison-Wesley Publishing Company, Inc.

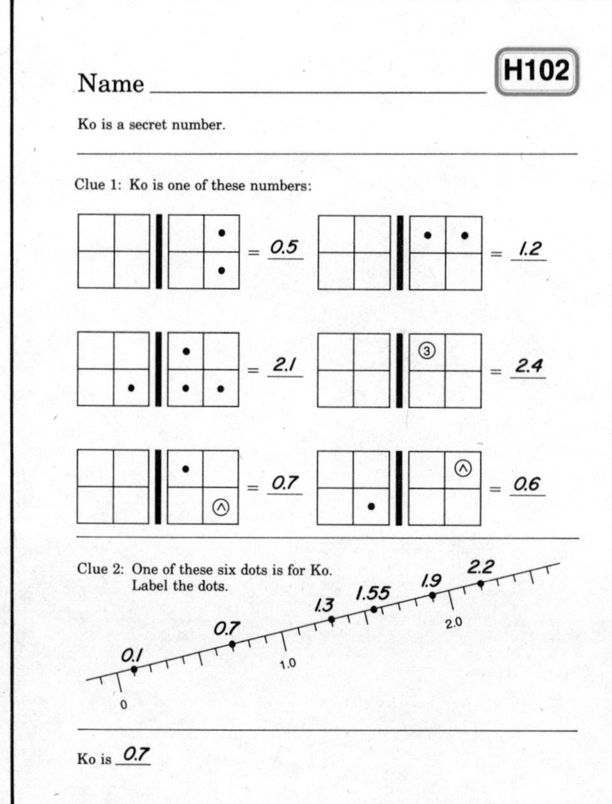

Name
H102
Ko is a secret number.
Clue 1: Ko is one of these numbers:
= 0.5
= 1.2
= 2.1
= 2.4
= 0.7
= 0.6
Clue 2: One of these six dots is for Ko.
Label the dots.
0.1
0.7
1.3
1.55
1.9
2.2
0
1.0
2.0
Ko is 0.7

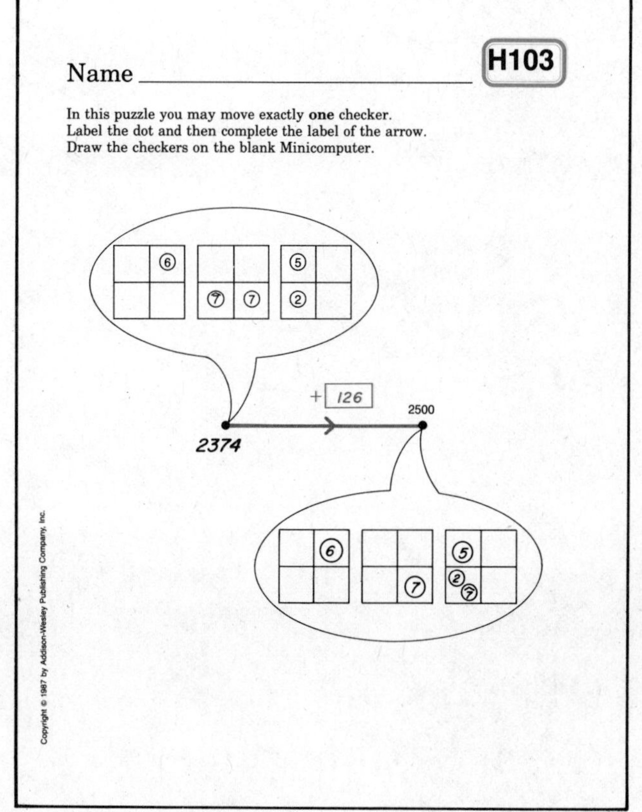

Name
H103
In this puzzle you may move exactly one checker.
Label the dot and then complete the label of the arrow.
Draw the checkers on the blank Minicomputer.
+ 126
2374
2500
Copyright © 1987 by Addison-Wesley Publishing Company, Inc.

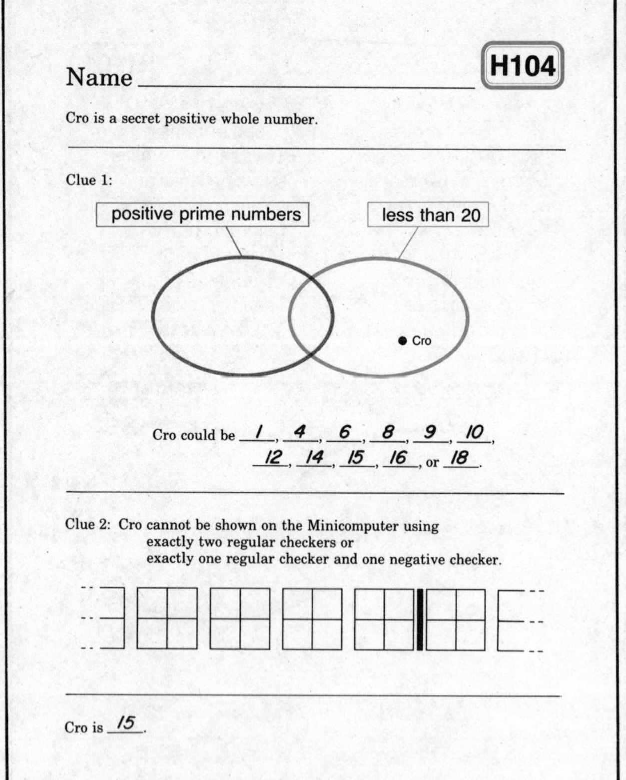
Name
H104
Cro is a secret positive whole number.
Clue 1:
positive prime numbers
less than 20
Cro
Cro could be 1, 4, 6, 8, 9, 10, 12, 14, 15, 16, or 18.
Clue 2: Cro cannot be shown on the Minicomputer using exactly two regular checkers or exactly one regular checker and one negative checker.
Cro is 15.

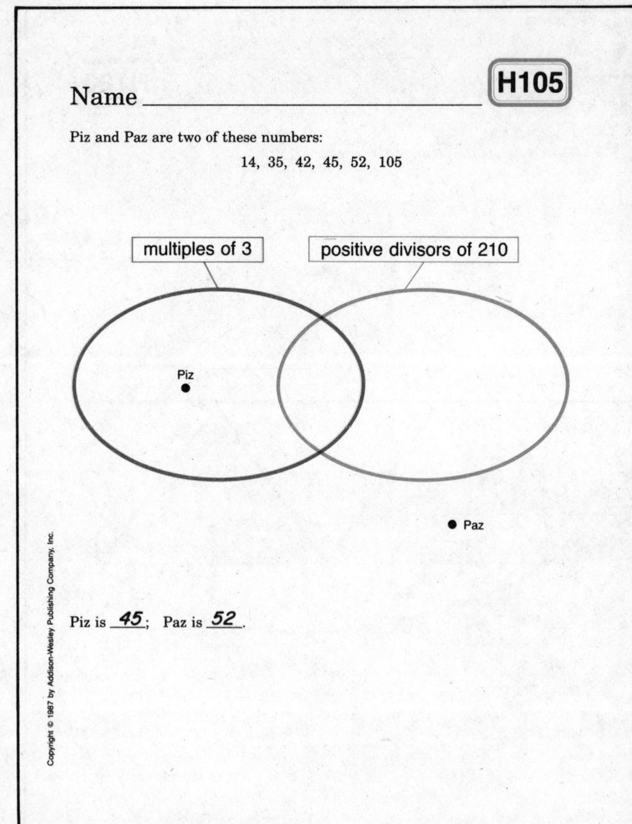
Name
H105
Piz and Paz are two of these numbers:
14, 35, 42, 45, 52, 105
multiples of 3
positive divisors of 210
Piz
Paz
Piz is 45; Paz is 52.
Copyright © 1987 by Addison-Wesley Publishing Company, Inc.